FIFTY YEARS OF BOTANY

FIFTY YEARS
OF BOTANY

Golden Jubilee Volume of the Botanical Society of America

Edited by

WILLIAM CAMPBELL STEERE

Director of the New York Botanical Garden

McGraw-Hill Book Company, Inc.

NEW YORK   TORONTO   LONDON

1958

FIFTY YEARS OF BOTANY

LIST OF AUTHORS' AFFILIATIONS

1. *Oswald Tippo,* Eaton Professor and Chairman, Department of Botany, Yale University, New Haven, Connecticut
2. *Bernard S. Meyer,* Professor and Chairman, Department of Botany and Plant Pathology, Ohio State University, Columbus, Ohio
3. *Kenneth B. Raper,* Professor of Bacteriology and Botany, Department of Bacteriology, University of Wisconsin, Madison, Wisconsin
4. *James G. Horsfall,* Director, Connecticut Agricultural Experiment Station, New Haven, Connecticut
5. *Elvin C. Stakman,* Professor Emeritus, University of Minnesota, St. Paul, Minnesota, and Special Consultant in Agriculture, Rockefeller Foundation
6. *Katherine Esau,* Professor of Botany, University of California, Davis, California
7. *Vernon I. Cheadle,* Professor and Chairman, Department of Botany, University of California, Davis, California
8. *Edmund W. Sinnott,* Professor Emeritus, Department of Botany, and Dean Emeritus of the Graduate School, Yale University, New Haven, Connecticut
9. *Ralph E. Cleland,* Professor and Chairman, Department of Botany, and Dean of the Graduate School, Indiana University, Bloomington, Indiana
10. *O. J. Eigsti,* Professor, Department of Natural Sciences, Chicago Teachers College, Chicago, Illinois
11. *G. Ledyard Stebbins,* Professor of Genetics, University of California, Davis, California
12. *Reed C. Rollins,* Asa Gray Professor of Systematic Botany, and Director, Gray Herbarium, Harvard University, Cambridge, Massachusetts
13. *Bassett Maguire,* Curator and Coordinator of Tropical Research, New York Botanical Garden, New York, N.Y.
14. *Edgar Anderson,* Missouri Botanical Garden, St. Louis, Missouri
15. *Stanley A. Cain,* Professor and Chairman, Department of Conservation, University of Michigan, Ann Arbor, Michigan
    Gustavus M. de Oliveira Castro, Instituto Oswaldo Cruz, Rio de Janeiro, Brazil
    J. Murça Pires, Instituto Agronômico do Norte, Belém, Brazil
    Nilo Tomás da Silva, Instituto Agronômico do Norte, Belém, Brazil
16. *E. Lucy Braun,* Professor Emeritus of Plant Ecology, University of Cincinnati, Cincinnati, Ohio
17. *R. H. Whittaker,* Department of Biology, Brooklyn College, Brooklyn, New York
18. *Paul B. Sears,* Chairman, Conservation Program, and Professor of Botany, Yale University, New Haven, Connecticut
19. *A. G. Norman,* Professor of Botany, and Director, Botanical Gardens, University of Michigan, Ann Arbor, Michigan
20. *William J. Robbins,* Director Emeritus, New York Botanical Garden, and Professor of Botany, Columbia University, New York, N.Y.

21. *Kenneth V. Thimann,* Professor of Plant Physiology, Harvard University, Cambridge, Massachusetts
22. *A. S. Crafts,* Professor of Botany, University of California, Davis, California
23. *H. B. Tukey,* Professor and Head, Department of Horticulture, Michigan State University, East Lansing, Michigan
24. *H. W. Youngken, Jr.,* Dean, College of Pharmacy, University of Rhode Island, Kingston, Rhode Island
25. *Donald Culross Peattie,* 2784 Glendessary Lane, Santa Barbara, California (Author with no affiliation.)
26. *Andrew Denny Rodgers III,* 37 South Dawson Avenue, Bexley, Columbus, Ohio (Author with no affiliation.)
27. *Gilbert M. Smith,* Professor Emeritus, Stanford University, Stanford, California
28. *Hiden T. Cox,* Executive Director, American Institute of Biological Sciences, Washington, D.C.
    John A. Behnke, Vice President and Science Editor, The Ronald Press Company, New York, N.Y.
29. *Harry J. Fuller,* Professor of Botany, University of Illinois, Urbana, Illinois
30. *Clarence J. Hylander,* Lakeview Farm, Brookville, Maine (Author with no affiliation.)
31. *W. H. Hodge,* Head, Department of Education and Research, Longwood Gardens, Kennett Square, Pennsylvania
32. *Edmund H. Fulling,* Editor and Publisher of "Botanical Review," New York Botanical Garden, New York, N.Y.
33. *George S. Avery, Jr.,* Director, Brooklyn Botanic Garden, Brooklyn, New York
34. *R. J. Seibert,* Director, Longwood Gardens, Kennett Square, Pennsylvania
35. *George F. Papenfuss,* Professor of Botany, University of California, Berkeley, California
36. *William H. Weston,* Professor Emeritus of Cryptogamic Botany, Harvard University, Cambridge, Massachusetts
37. *Lincoln Constance,* Professor and Curator of Seed Plants, Department of Botany, and Dean, College of Letters and Science, University of California, Berkeley, California
38. *Theodor Just,* Chief Curator, Department of Botany, Chicago Natural History Museum, Chicago, Illinois
39. *Arthur J. Eames,* Professor Emeritus, Department of Botany, Cornell University, Ithaca, New York
40. *F. W. Went,* Professor of Plant Physiology, California Institute of Technology, Pasadena, California

Introduction preceding Paper 35: *James E. Canright,* Associate Professor of Botany, Indiana University, Bloomington, Indiana

To the twenty-five charter members
of the original Botanical Society of America
who strove for a greater unification
of the plant sciences

PREFACE

This book has resulted from the cooperative efforts of many different individuals. In September, 1955, the Council of the Botanical Society of America and the members present at the annual business meeting voted to celebrate the fiftieth anniversary of the Society in 1956 by the publication of a Golden Jubilee Volume of the *American Journal of Botany.* It was also decided that special invitational papers of broad and general interest should be included in as many issues as possible and that these invited contributions should be brought together and published as a separate, bound, repaged volume. The 1956 volume (43) of the *American Journal of Botany* was officially designated as the Golden Jubilee Volume, and each issue was unmistakably identified by a special caption and by a golden cover. Most of the forty papers that compose this book appeared as Special Papers in Volumes 43 and 44 of the *American Journal of Botany.*

The Golden Jubilee Volume Committee of the Botanical Society of America was appointed in November, 1955, and charged by the President of the Society, Professor Oswald Tippo, with the responsibility of selecting authors to represent the various fields of plant science and of inviting them to present contributions on the major advances or important developments in botany during the past fifty years, with emphasis on present trends and future problems and on the contribution of plant science to mankind and to his civilization. The Committee, consisting of George Beadle, John Behnke, Vernon I. Cheadle, Edmund H. Fulling, David Goddard, C. J. Hylander, Oswald Tippo, and William C. Steere, Chairman, hopes that in addition to its value and interest to plant scientists, this volume will enable intelligent nonbotanists to understand and to appreciate what botany is and what botanists are doing.

Reminiscent of the facetious definition of a camel as "an animal that looks like something designed by a committee," a book written by forty authors—and designed by a committee—very naturally tends to lack uniformity of style and treatment. The papers included in this volume differ as widely as the nature of the authors themselves and vary from rather general surveys to the presentation of the results of original research. The coverage of the whole field of plant science is not as complete as the Committee had planned

ix

and would have liked—but this is unavoidable. Some potential authors of central importance in their fields refused an invitation to contribute to this volume for lack of time or because their field had too recently been reviewed elsewhere; others accepted the invitation but did not produce the papers. Still other authors developed new and unexpected interests and wrote with enthusiasm on topics quite different from the one they had been invited to cover. When all these circumstances are considered, the coverage is better than might have been predicted, especially since a surprisingly high proportion of the authors who promised papers actually produced them.

Grateful acknowledgment is due to the authors who contributed papers, to the members of the Golden Jubilee Committee, to friends and colleagues who nominated potential authors, and to many others who helped in the planning and the preparation of this volume.

William Campbell Steere

CONTENTS

1

THE EARLY HISTORY OF THE BOTANICAL SOCIETY OF AMERICA

Oswald Tippo [1,2]

Although 1956 has been designated the Golden Jubilee year for the Botanical Society of America, the Society may claim, with some validity, to be at least 63 years old rather than 50. The facts are that the original Botanical Society of America was founded in 1893 and this original Botanical Society is a direct outgrowth of the Botanical Club of the American Association for the Advancement of Science. In 1906 the earlier Botanical Society of America merged with the Society for Plant Morphology and Physiology (founded in 1896) and with the American Mycological Society (founded in 1903) to form the present Botanical Society of America. Thus, in reality, in this year of 1956, we are celebrating a wedding anniversary rather than a birthday.

With this brief outline before us, let us turn to some of the events which led to the founding of the original Botanical Society and to its eventual fusion with the other plant-science organizations. The botanists present at the 1883 Minneapolis meetings of the American Association for the Advancement of Science (formally organized in 1848) formed the American Botanical Club as an association of botanists who were members of the A.A.A.S.[3] Later, the Botanical Club became Section G of the American Association.

The original Botanical Society of America had its inception at a meeting of the Botanical Club of the A.A.A.S. held in Rochester, New York, on August 22, 1892.[4] Professor L. H. Bailey (Rodgers, 1949, p. 178–180)

[1] Dr. Tippo also deserves much credit for bringing together the collection of fifty portraits of distinguished botanists that accompanies Article 2.—Editor.

[2] Address of the retiring president of the Botanical Society of America, delivered at the Golden Jubilee Banquet, August 29, 1956, at Storrs, Connecticut.

[3] *Bot. Gaz.* 8:291–295. 1883.

[4] *Bot. Gaz.* 17:285–290. 1892.

suggested that a new society of botanists be established to unify and subserve the botanical interests of the country. There seems to have been general agreement that such a society was desirable, although some doubts were expressed about the advisability of establishing a society at that particular time. In any case, the following resolution was adopted: "That a committee of nine members be appointed by the chairman to consider the formation of an American Botanical Society, after obtaining the views of the botanists of America on the proposition, and report thereon at the next meeting of the Club." [5] Professor Bailey was named chairman of this committee.

On August 22, 1893, the Botanical Club, meeting with the American Association at Madison, Wisconsin, considered the report of this committee. "A letter from Mr. L. H. Bailey, chairman of the committee, was read, as virtually the report of the majority in favor of abandoning the attempt for the present. Eight of the Committee thought its organization by the Club impracticable; one favored the organization but offered no plan of procedure." [6] C. R. Barnes, the remaining member, submitted the following report: "As a member of the committee appointed last year to report on the feasibility of forming an American botanical society I find myself unable to agree with the majority in reporting that such organization through the initiative of the Botanical Club is not feasible at present. . . . At the time the plan was broached for the formation of a national botanical society I was not in favor of it, believing that the time was not yet ripe for such an organization. On thinking over the matter during the year past I have become convinced not only that the time is opportune, but that the Botanical Club, an open association of the loosest possible organization, can establish a restricted society without friction, and with great benefit to the science of botany. I therefore submit the following suggestions in lieu of the majority report. I recommend:

1. That the Botanical Club approve the formation of an American botanical society whose membership shall be restricted to those who have published worthy work and are actively engaged in botanical investigation.

2. That to this end the Botanical Club proceed to elect ten men who beyond all question should belong to a society so restricted.

3. That these ten be directed to select fifteen additional members who in their judgment fall well within the limits suggested.

4. That the twenty-five persons so chosen be invited to become the charter members of the botanical society, to proceed to organize the same, and to provide for the election of additional members by such methods and on

[5] Brief historical sketch of the Society. *Bot. Soc. Amer. Pub.* No. 11. Ithaca, N.Y. 1899.

[6] *Bot. Gaz.* 18:342–349. 1893.

such terms (not incompatible with the intent of recommendation 1) as they see fit." [7]

The Barnes' minority report was adopted by a two-thirds majority of the Club, and the Club then elected ten charter members. This committee of ten met the next day, August 23, and elected by ballot fifteen additional members. The following are the names of the twenty-five charter members: J. C. Arthur, G. F. Atkinson, L. H. Bailey, C. R. Barnes, C. E. Bessey, N. L. Britton, E. G. Britton, D. H. Campbell, J. M. Coulter, F. V. Coville, D. C. Eaton, W. G. Farlow, E. L. Greene, B. D. Halsted, A. Hollick, C. Mac-Millan, B. L. Robinson, C. S. Sargent, F. L. Scribner, J. Donnell Smith, R. Thaxter, W. Trelease, L. F. Ward, W. P. Wilson, and L. M. Underwood.[8] Invitations were issued to the designated twenty-five to become charter members of the new Botanical Society. All accepted except for Eaton, Ward, Campbell, and Farlow. Later (in 1898) Bailey and Thaxter resigned. Several informal meetings of those selected were held after the election, and a committee was appointed to prepare a preliminary draft of the constitution to be submitted at the next annual meeting of the Association. William Trelease, chairman of the committee to draft the constitution, sent the following communication on November 1, 1893, to all charter members: "The aim of the society was stated to be the promotion of botanical research, and it was thought best that the limits of membership should be very rigidly drawn. It will, I think, be evident that the original list of twenty-five members contains the names of no persons not entitled to membership on the basis of creditable published work. . . . The object being the promotion of research, it was thought best not to make membership, at least in the charter list, complimentary to distinguished botanists who are no longer engaged in the performance of active work, hence, the omission of certain honored names which must suggest themselves to every American botanist. For the same reason, it was the sense of the members present that continued membership in the society should depend upon the continued activity of members and a continued interest in the realization of this principal aim of the society; and it was thought that a provision should be included in the constitution providing that failure to attend the meetings, or to present papers at the meetings, for a period of three years, should work forfeiture of membership. . . . The feeling of the members present was, that the Society might ultimately find it necessary to assume the expense of publishing papers presented by members; and to this end, and also to check application for membership from persons who were not really in sympathy with the objects of the society, it was decided that the admission fee should be $25.00, and the annual dues $10.00. . . . It was thought best for the present that only one meeting should be held each year, that meeting to be held in close con-

[7] *Ibid.*   [8] *Bot. Gaz.* 18:368. 1893.

nection with the annual meeting of the American Association for the Advancement of Science, either preceding or following it, to avoid conflict. . . . In order that the high character which is hoped for in the society may be attained, it is desirable that the intention of rigid scrutiny in admitting members should be adhered to, and it is also necessary that each member of the society shall feel that it is worthy of his best effort in research." [9]

The drafted constitution contained the above provisions, and in addition, it was stated that "Its object is the advancement of botanical knowledge. Only American botanists engaged in research, who have published work of recognized merit, shall be eligible to active membership." [10]

On August 15, 1894, ten of the charter members met in Brooklyn, New York (Rodgers, 1944b, p. 319). The constitution was adopted, and William Trelease was elected the first president of the Botanical Society of America.[11]

On August 27–28, 1895, the newly organized Botanical Society held its first annual meeting at Springfield, Massachusetts, with thirteen members present. Nine scientific papers were presented, including one by N. L. Britton on the New York Botanical Garden and one on the Laboulbeniaceae by Roland Thaxter. The minutes of that meeting carry the following item: "A book having already been presented to the Society, the Council recommends that all books and pamphlets sent to the Society be deposited in the library of the Missouri Botanical Garden, subject to the order of the Council, and that a list of the annual additions be reported to the Society at each annual meeting." [12] Charles E. Bessey was elected president for the next year.

The second annual meeting was held in Buffalo in August, 1896, with twenty-five members present. John M. Coulter was elected president. William Trelease delivered the first presidential address of the Society on the topic "Botanical Opportunity." It appears that the Society was early plagued with mishaps in arrangements, for the minutes of the meeting contain this notation: "The Secretary announced that the failure of the Local Committee to furnish a projecting lantern, tho' repeatedly promised, would prevent the reading of Atkinson's paper and seriously interfere with MacMillan's. The latter, however, consented to present the chief facts without the aid of the slides." [13] The Council received and accepted declination of membership from D. H. Campbell, W. R. Dudley, and W. A. Setchell, "based upon the extreme distance from meeting places of the Society." [14] "Britton asked that the Society consider the relations of the proposed botanical society to meet in connection with the Eastern Naturalists Society and its effect upon the

[9] *Bot. Soc. Amer. Pub.* No. 2. 1893.
[10] *Bot. Soc. Amer. Pub.* No. 3.
[11] *Bot. Gaz.* 19:388. 1894.
[12] *Bot. Soc. Amer. Minutes,* 1894–1926, p. 10.
[13] *Ibid.,* p. 20.
[14] *Ibid.,* p. 15.

Botanical Society of America. The matter was generally discussed, in connection with the possibility of a winter meeting of the Society." [15] The new Botanical Society of America, hardly established, was already being subjected to criticism, especially by certain eastern botanists who favored winter meetings over summer meetings (a difference of opinion continuing to the present day, it might be added). Many botanists objected to the high annual dues and admission fee. Some preferred to meet with the American Society of Naturalists, rather than the A.A.A.S. (another dichotomy which has persisted to the present day). The sharpest criticism, however, was leveled at the exclusive nature of the Botanical Society, for many felt that membership should be open to anyone interested in Botany.

On December, 1895, at the Philadelphia meetings of the American Society of Naturalists, a group of botanists met to consider the question of the formation of a botanical organization to meet with the American Society of Naturalists. A committee of five, including L. H. Bailey and C. E. Bessey, was appointed to canvass the situation. The committee explained, "This movement has originated in the feeling that the winter meetings are quite as valuable as any in the year. . . . Since no existing organization attempts to occupy the field here open, it has been suggested that a simple form of association to afford a centre of attraction to botanists might be planned without antagonism to the older bodies. The restriction of the winter meetings to the eastern seaboard would in some degree limit the active membership of the proposed organization. . . ." [16] At the December 30, 1896, Boston meeting of the American Society of Naturalists, this committee, augmented by other botanists in attendance, gave further consideration to the formation of a Botanical Society. The group decided that there were a sufficient number of botanists interested in such an organization to make a winter meeting possible. It was stated: "Eight or ten members would suffice; more would be better." [17] Further, "Membership in the new Society should accord geographically with that of the American Society of Naturalists; residence in the Eastern States should not be essential to membership, but conditions of time and distance are such that practically only those within that range are likely to attend, and for the present year no botanists outside of the Eastern States shall be invited to cooperate." [18] Finally, a committee on the organization of the Society for Vegetable Morphology and Physiology was organized with instructions to report to the next annual meeting of the group. On December 20, 1897, this committee met at Sage College, Ithaca, New York. The committee decided that it would establish a Society for Plant Morphol-

---

[15] *Ibid.,* p. 16.

[16] *Soc. for Plant Morphology and Physiology, Records and Accounts,* 1897–1906, p. 59.

[17] *Ibid.,* p. 63.

[18] *Ibid.,* p. 64.

ogy and Physiology with the general understanding that it would meet with the American Society of Naturalists. It was further "resolved that the geographical range for meetings of this Society be limited to the region of 'Eastern Standard Time' as far south as Washington." [19] W. G. Farlow was elected president of the new organization. One of the actions taken was the following: "Resolved that this Society recognizes the metric system as a standard of measurement to be employed in its work, and members are requested to observe this rule in the preparation of papers." [20] Thus was established a competing society to the Botanical Society of America, and the two groups met separately for a number of years. By 1903 the Society for Plant Morphology and Physiology had 72 members; many botanists, of course, were members of both organizations.

Returning to the account of the subsequent history of the Botanical Society of America, it may be reported that the Society met in Toronto in 1897 with N. L. Britton as president. It is not my intention to give an exhaustive history of the various meetings which occurred in subsequent years, but I shall note a few events which may be of interest. The present members of the Society will be interested in the fact that the announcement of the Boston meetings of 1898 carries the statement that hotel rates were to be from $1 to $2 per day. It should also be recalled that in that happier era the Botanical Society enjoyed special rates on the railways of the country, namely, a provision of one and one-third fare for a round trip to the meetings. The Society apparently was plagued by attendance difficulties, because the minutes of the meeting carry this report: "The president then stated the difficulty of proceeding with any business matters owing to the absence of the secretary, the treasurer, and the secretary's records, also to the lack of a quorum at the Council meeting which had been called at 1:30." [21] In the evening the Society met at the appointed hour to hear the address of the retiring president. However, President Britton announced that the address would be postponed until the following day because the retiring president, J. M. Coulter, had not arrived. On the next day Coulter again failed to appear, and so B. M. Davis read Coulter's address.

The membership of the Society continued to be small—in 1899, 18 charter members remained in the organization, augmented by 15 others, making a total of 33 members. By 1902 there were 57 members.

At the 1902 Pittsburgh meetings of the Society, the organization approved a plan for making grants-in-aid for investigations by its members in good standing, providing that not more than $500 be used for this purpose in the next year. At the 9th annual meeting held in Washington in December, 1902,

[19] *Ibid.*, p. 1.
[20] *Ibid.*, p. 6.
[21] *Bot. Soc. Amer. Minutes,* 1894–1926, p. 31.

J. C. Arthur was granted $90 to further his investigations of plant rusts, Arthur Hollick was given $150 to continue his study of the fossil flora of the Atlantic coastal plains, and Dr. D. S. Johnson was awarded $200 to carry on field study of the Piperaceae and Chloranthaceae. A special committee was appointed to define a "bud." A committee which had been named at the Pittsburgh meetings on the relationship of the Botanical Society of America to other similar organizations made its report. It was pointed out that "a union of interests of the various botanical organizations of the country would be advantageous to all concerned." [22] A committee of three members was appointed to consider the matter and to confer with other committees from similar societies. After this meeting, C. R. Barnes (Rodgers, 1944a, p. 222–223) wrote to Bessey as follows: "At the Washington meeting a committee with Underwood, Barnes and Bessey as members was appointed to confer with similar committees from other societies regarding cooperative action. I have long cherished the hope that we might avoid the organization and maintenance of multifarious botanical societies, and that all professional botanists of the country of high standing should unite in one society. When the B.S.A. was founded, it was with that idea, as I believe. Misconception partly, and partly the high fees imposed, together with the limitations of distance strongly felt by eastern colleagues led to the foundation of the Society for Plant Morphology and Physiology. I understand the arrangements are now completed for the organization of a mycological society. Recently the central botanists organized. The membership of these four societies is more or less identical. Around the nucleus of identical membership there is a fringe of local membership. I believe it should be the policy of the Botanical Society of America to make itself a dominant force so far as organized botanical activity is concerned, and I believe it can only do this by uniting all." Bessey (Rodgers, 1944a, p. 222–223) replied with these words: "My feeling is that in general it is not a good thing to have too many societies, but this multiplication of societies which we are now witnessing is merely a phase of the development of botanical knowledge in this country. Now we cannot stop the formation of many societies. Let them be formed by the men who are interested in them. Let us not discourage them, while on the other hand we need not give a boisterous encouragement. When these many societies are having meetings, let us avoid conflicts as far as possible. In this way we may have for a time a 'struggle for existence,' resulting in the 'survival of the fittest.'" At the 10th annual meeting of the Society, held in St. Louis in December, 1903, B. T. Galloway gave the retiring presidential address on the subject "The Twentieth Century Botany." He concluded his address with the following words: "No question is raised as to the value and necessity of other botanical organizations. We do not believe that there are too many of them, but that

[22] *Bot. Soc. Amer. Minutes of Council*, 1895–1923, p. 43.

there is a woeful lack of proper unification and coordination were shown at the last Washington meeting, where the number of papers presented was so great that it was impossible for visiting botanists to take anything like advantage of them. [Forty papers were given at the Washington meeting.] In the future it is hoped and believed that existing botanical organizations can be continued and their integrity and independence maintained, but at the same time it would seem highly important that some steps be taken toward unification. There would seem no reason why the Botanical Society of America should not be the medium for bringing this about, and why, through its efforts, there should not be effected an organization representing the various botanical societies throughout the country which would affiliate with the Society and assist in shaping a general policy on all matters affecting the welfare of the science. The time seems ripe for bringing about this result. Never was Botany more prosperous, never more aggressive. On the threshold of the twentieth century we stand, knowing our strength and only needing to weld it into harmonious action to make it vital and lasting. Let us join hands and do our best to bring this about." [23]

At the 11th annual meeting held in Philadelphia in December, 1904, the committee on relations reported that it had conferred with committees appointed by the Society for Plant Morphology and Physiology and by the American Mycological Society. As a result of these conferences and a canvass of botanists in the country, the committee recommended that the Botanical Society merge with the other two societies, under the name of the Botanical Society of America. The Council adopted the committee report and named another committee to negotiate with the other two societies. At the next annual meeting, the 12th, held in New Orleans, January, 1906, the committee on the federation of botanical societies recommended that the Botanical Society merge with the Society for Plant Morphology and Physiology and the American Mycological Society. A new constitution was presented. The report and constitution were approved by the Society. The official union of the three societies, the Botanical Society of America (founded in 1893), the Society for Plant Morphology and Physiology (founded in 1896), and the American Mycological Society (founded in 1903), occurred in New York City, December 27, 1906,[24] at the meetings of the American Association for the Advancement of Science. Some sixty members from the three societies were present, and thirty botanical papers were given. The three societies combined their membership lists, making a total of 119 members. They also merged their funds. The Botanical Society provided $3,566, the Society for Plant Morphology and Physiology furnished $64.38, and the American Mycological Society contributed $38.45. And so the present Botanical Society of America came into being fifty years ago.

[23] *Bot. Soc. Amer. Pub.* No. 23, p. 11–12.
[24] *Bot. Soc. Amer. Minutes,* 1894–1926, p. 95.

It is not my purpose to give a complete history of the Botanical Society of America, but I do want to mention a few significant actions and events which took place in the next twenty years. At the 1908 meeting in Baltimore the Society approved an honorarium of $50 to be paid the secretary for each annual meeting which he attends. Although this action was taken almost fifty years ago, it is of interest that the Society has never seen fit to raise the magnitude of the honorarium, although the work of the secretary's office has increased tenfold and there has been a marked inflation. The Society also approved $250 for research grants for the following year.

At the 1909 meetings of the Society in Boston a committee was appointed on Botanical Publication, and for the first time a symposium on botanical teaching was held. At the 1911 meeting in Washington, the Publication Committee pointed out that annually some 300 or more pages of American botanical production were sent abroad for publication and that the delays before publication amount to about one year. It was estimated that a journal publishing 400 to 600 pages annually could be published at a cost of $2500. It was pointed out that after a few years the journal might expect to have as many as 400 subscribers. However, in view of the large annual outlay demanded, the Committee recommended that action be delayed until some source of funds could be found. The committee on the relation of other botanists to the Botanical Society of America urged that the Botanical Society invite the Society of Phytopathologists, the Society of Bacteriologists, the Sullivant Moss Chapter (as it was then called), and the American Fern Club to appoint committees "to confer with a similar committee from the Botanical Society with the possibility of establishing closer relations among these various organizations in order to bring about an effective union of all who are engaged in botanical work in this country." [25] At the 1912 meeting of the Society a committee of five under the chairmanship of Professor Newcombe was empowered to establish a journal as the official organ of the Botanical Society of America. The Society authorized expenditures up to $500 to aid in this enterprise. At the next meeting—the 1913 conclave—the Committee reported that it had reached an agreement with the Brooklyn Botanic Garden which offered to cooperate in publishing and to share the expenses of the new journal, the *American Journal of Botany*. At the December, 1914, meetings at Philadelphia, an editorial committee of the new journal was named as follows: F. C. Newcombe, L. R. Jones, A. S. Hitchcock, and I. W. Bailey. Later, Newcombe was named editor-in-chief. Some nineteen years before (on August 18, 1895) F. C. Newcombe (Rodgers, 1952, p. 284) had written to Erwin F. Smith: "that another journal might not come amiss, I would like to see pushed. In the whole English language we have no journal like the *Botanische Zeitung* or *B. Centralblatt*. The *Annals* is good for extensive articles, but gives us no reviews. The *Gazette* gives us

[25] *Ibid.*, p. 138.

neither. *Science* does part of the work; but I should like to see a journal combining both extensive articles and numerous reviews. You have observed probably that Americans furnish one-third or more of the copy for the *Annals*. I do not believe in multiplying unnecessarily the journals; but do we not need an American journal of Botany? The number of real botanists is increasing in this country year by year. You can count twelve to twenty now in this country who will be sure to publish year after year. I think I said the same to you last summer. I would like to see Farlow take hold of the matter and put some of his cash into it for a few years." It has become a tradition in our society to reward members who make suggestions with the task of initiating and executing these suggestions.

The year 1915 appears to have been a noteworthy one, because in that period 146 new members were elected to the Society. In 1916 J. Pierpont Morgan was elected a patron of the Society "by unanimous rising vote." [26] At the 1921 meeting of the Society there occurred an event which unfortunately has not established a precedent in the organization. Dr. N. L. Britton, the retiring president, was unable to give his presidential address but instead sent the following communication to the Society: "I regret that administrative duties prevent my attending the annual meeting of the Society, at which I will, however, be represented by my colleague, Dr. Marshall Avery Howe, who has kindly consented to bring you this communication and my accompanying check for $1000 to be applied to any part of the work of the Society as it may be deemed most necessary or desirable. With best wishes for a wholly successful meeting, I am, yours very truly, N. L. Britton." [27]

The 1925 meetings authorized the appointment of a committee to consider the inauguration of a monthly leaflet of botanical notes and news which would be of benefit to teachers, amateurs, and others. This suggestion remained fallow for thirty years but finally came to fruition in January, 1955, when the Society's *Plant Science Bulletin* appeared for the first time.

I do not propose to give an account of the history of the Society after 1925, but shall leave this period for some other retiring president. I am sure it will be understood that this has been a very sketchy historical account and that many important actions and developments have been slighted. Among these are the Society's activities with respect to the National Herbarium, the National Arboretum, the defense of the *Journal of Agricultural Research,* the formation of the National Research Council, and various steps taken to aid the war effort during the First World War. Incidentally, during the early years of the Society, it was customary to present resolutions upon the death of its members, and these resolutions appear in the records of the Society. In recent decades this practice has been discontinued.

[26] *Ibid.,* p. 177.   [27] *Ibid.,* p. 237.

On this, our Fiftieth Anniversary (or our Sixty-third Anniversary, if you prefer), we may well ask what have been the accomplishments of the Botanical Society of America. I would list the following:

1. The establishment and the publication of forty-three volumes of the *American Journal of Botany*. This is certainly an accomplishment of which we all can be proud. The *Journal's* high standards are praised by all botanists, and our *Journal* has come to be recognized as one of the leading botanical journals in the world. Our Society has been most fortunate in its appointment of outstanding and devoted editors [28]—F. C. Newcombe, C. E. Allen, E. W. Sinnott, S. F. Trelease, R. E. Cleland, B. S. Meyer, and the present incumbent, W. C. Steere. And we should not forget the business managers who have administered the finances of the *Journal*, and the innumerable authors and reviewers who have made the *Journal* what it is today.

2. We may also point with pride to our successful annual meetings with their galaxies of scientific papers, symposia, addresses, panels, etc.

3. Our membership has grown by leaps and bounds, especially during the last few decades. You will recall that in 1893 the Society began with 21 charter members, while at the time of the fusion of the three societies in 1906 there were 119 members. In 1956 we have nearly 2000 members.

4. On this festive occasion we can take considerable satisfaction in the role that the Society and its representatives have played in the affairs of the National Research Council, the American Association for the Advancement of Science, and, more recently, the American Institute of Biological Sciences.

5. One of the more significant developments of the past few years has been the work of the Committee on the Role of Botany (or the Greenfield Committee, as it has come to be called). The provocative reports that have come from this Committee have done much to open the eyes of Society members to the status of Botany in the colleges and universities. It has led to much discussion, considerable thought, and, we hope, eventual results.

6. A year and a half ago the *Plant Science Bulletin* appeared. Although it is still a struggling seedling, we hope that it will eventually become as sturdy and respected as the *American Journal of Botany*.

7. This summer the Botanical Society of America cosponsored, with Cornell University, the National Science Foundation–financed Summer Institute of Botany at Ithaca, New York. We hope that this will be the first of many such institutes to be held throughout the country in future years.

8. After several years' work on the part of a special committee, the Botanical Society is ready to publish a career-guidance pamphlet.

9. To celebrate the Golden Jubilee year, the Society has invited some forty of its members to prepare special articles summarizing developments

---

[28] EDITOR'S NOTE—The author has himself been for several years a member of this group, as Editor-in-chief, but modestly does not list his own name.

during the last five decades in the field of Plant Science, or papers relating Botany to human affairs. These articles, which promise to be of great general interest, will appear in subsequent issues of the *American Journal of Botany* and then will be published in book form as the Jubilee Volume.

10. Finally, the Society has decided on this occasion of its fiftieth anniversary to honor fifty living botanists by awarding certificates of merit for their outstanding contributions to Botany and Plant Science. The plan is to award one or more certificates each year at our future annual meetings.

An occasion of this kind is not only an occasion for taking stock, but also a time for looking toward the future. One of the regrettable features of contemporary Botany is its fragmented nature. There is no *one* botanical society to which all botanists belong; instead we have a dozen or more small organizations representing special professional areas. In the past (namely, 1906) our botanical forebears decided it was the path of wisdom to merge the separate Botanical Society, the Society for Plant Morphology and Physiology, and the American Mycological Society. Perhaps in the future we may expect the emergence of a single Botanical Society in which all botanists—all plant scientists—will hold membership. If this happy event does not come to pass, perhaps we may be able to persuade all plant scientists as a matter of principle and professional obligation to belong to the Botanical Society as well as to hold membership in special plant-science groups. At least this is one of the important problems facing the Council and the membership of the Society as a whole. Two committees are working in this area. One is the Committee on Relationships of the Society to Other Plant Science Organizations, which hopes through representation from all areas of plant science to explore ways and means of achieving some sort of unity among plant scientists. The other is the Membership Committee, which is constantly striving to convince botanists of all persuasions that they should affiliate with the Botanical Society as well as with their special groups.

Eventually our Society may become sufficiently mature professionally to tackle the important and complex problem of the best type of organization of botanical work in colleges and universities. Should it be organized in separate botanical departments or in biology departments? What about the wisdom of siphoning off special segments of botanical work into separate departments of microbiology, genetics, plant pathology, plant physiology, etc.? What is the best type, if there is a best type, of beginning course? Should it be a botany course, or a biology course?

Eventually we may want to come to grips with the problem which is of great concern to all botanists in the colleges and universities—how can we attract *more,* and *more competent,* botanical majors? At the present time, ten to fifteen majors seem to be the maximum for even the largest universities. We must devise ways and means of attracting our fair share of undergraduate majors. It is a strange paradox that in this day and age when there is such widespread interest in plants and in gardening there is so little interest in Botany, at least in Botany as a profession. We may well devote our next fifty years to this and allied problems.

LITERATURE CITED

RODGERS, A. D., III. 1944a. John Merle Coulter, Missionary in science. Princeton Univ. Press. Princeton, N.J.

————. 1944b. American botany, 1873–1892, Decades of transition. Princeton Univ. Press. Princeton, N.J.

————. 1949. Liberty Hyde Bailey, A story of American plant sciences. Princeton Univ. Press. Princeton, N.J.

————. 1952. Erwin Frink Smith, A story of North American plant pathology. Amer. Philosophical Soc. Philadelphia, Pa.

2

AWARDS OF CERTIFICATES OF MERIT AT THE FIFTIETH ANNIVERSARY MEETING

Bernard S. Meyer

As one feature of the celebration of the fiftieth anniversary of the founding of the Botanical Society of America, the Society authorized the awarding of Certificates of Merit to fifty persons who were judged to have made outstanding contributions in botanical science. A committee was appointed by past-president Tippo in December of 1955 to handle this matter. In addition to the writer, who served as chairman, the following persons were members of this committee: Ronald Bamford, University of Maryland; Norman Boke, University of Oklahoma; Pierre Dansereau, University of Montreal; James Jensen, Iowa State College; Rogers McVaugh, University of Michigan; and Donald Rogers, New York Botanical Garden. Nominations for these awards were solicited not only from members of the committee itself, but also from members and friends of the Society. A notice requesting the submission of such nominations was published in the April issue of the *Plant Science Bulletin,* where it was assumed that it would come generally to the attention of members of the Society. Nearly two hundred persons were nominated for these awards; most of the nominations were accompanied by a statement of the qualifications of the nominee for such a distinction. From among these nominees the fifty recipients of the awards were selected by group judgment of the entire committee as expressed through a series of ballots. An appropriate citation was also prepared by members of the committee for each recipient.

The committee also had the responsibility of designing and having printed a suitable certificate to be presented to each of the recipients. In this matter we were greatly assisted by the advice and counsel of Savoie Lottinville of the University of Oklahoma Press and James Hendrickson of William E. Rudge's Sons of New York City.

Announcement of the awards, together with a reading of the appropriate citations, was made a prominent feature of the program at the annual banquet of the Society held at the University of Connecticut on August 29, 1956. All recipients had been notified in advance of their selection, and it was gratifying that approximately half of them could be present on this occasion to receive the award in person.

In concluding this brief account, it may be appropriate to add that the committee is under no illusion that it has selected *the* fifty outstanding botanists of this continent. This would be a task beyond human capabilities. In the committee's judgment, however, all recipients are highly deserving of the recognition which has been given them. Since it is the intention of the Society that the practice of making such awards, on a smaller scale, will be continued for future meetings, other botanists deserving such a distinction will undoubtedly be so recognized in the years to come.

Following is the list of the recipients [1] of these awards and the accompanying citations:

HARRY ARDELL ALLARD, for his pioneer investigations of photoperiodism in plants and for his long-continued contributions to our knowledge of this phenomenon and to other areas of botanical science.

EDGAR ANDERSON, for his extensive contributions to the general problems of evolution, including the species problem, self-sterility, and particularly his sponsorship of the idea of introgressive hybridization.

DIXON LLOYD BAILEY, discerning analyst and interpreter of the concepts of plant pathology, enriching influence in the lives of his associates, and outstanding contributor to the vigor of scientific study in Canada.

IRVING WIDMER BAILEY, plant anatomist and inspiring teacher, for his outstanding contributions on the structure of the cell wall and the histology of the cambium and for his application of anatomy and morphology to problems of evolution of angiosperms.

HARLEY HARRIS BARTLETT, for his unflagging support and encouragement of the whole field of botany and its students and for his diverse contributions to paleobotany, enthnobotany, ecology, and systematics.

GEORGE WELLS BEADLE, for his long list of contributions to the cytogenetics of *Zea mays* and *Drosophila* and the tremendous impetus he has lately given to the field of physiological and chemical genetics, particularly in *Neurospora*.

ERNST ATHEARN BESSEY, who with an undeviating zeal for accuracy has fashioned our generation's magisterial presentation of the science of mycology.

[1] Dr. Oswald Tippo deserves much credit for his accomplishment of a difficult task, namely, of bringing together into one collection portraits of the fifty distinguished recipients of Certificates of Merit, to accompany their citations.

SIDNEY FAY BLAKE, for his scholarly contributions to the taxonomy of the Compositae and other vascular plants and to our knowledge of the floras of the world.

EMMA LUCY BRAUN, for her contribution to our knowledge of the origin and structure of the Eastern American deciduous forest. Her critical evaluation of the works of others, her capacity to observe correctly in the field and to interpret forcefully have given biogeographers a new point of departure.

STANLEY ADAIR CAIN, whose sensitive perception of complex environmental problems and intimate understanding of conflicting points of view have provided us with many new insights. His courage in opening up new areas has made him an outstanding interpreter and a leader of men.

RALPH WORKS CHANEY, for his notable achievements in paleobotany, which have so greatly enriched our knowledge of the Tertiary floras.

AGNES CHASE, one of the world's outstanding agrostologists and preeminent among American students in this field.

JENS CHRISTIAN CLAUSEN, for his work toward the improvement of our understanding of the nature and origin of plant species.

RALPH ERSKINE CLELAND, for his extensive researches into the species relationships and segmental-interchange problems in *Oenothera* and also for his statesmanship in representing plant science at the national level.

HENRY SHOEMAKER CONARD, taxonomist, morphologist, mycologist, ecologist, bryologist, shining proof that versatility may serve only to multiply excellences, and above all a beloved teacher.

WILLIAM SKINNER COOPER, one of the creators of an American tradition in ecology. His deep feeling for the relatedness and parallel developments of geology, physiology, taxonomy, and vegetation science has been a guiding light to a whole generation.

JOHN NATHANIEL COUCH, whose studies of the small, the intricate, and the odd among fungi and their relatives have come to fructification in the vivid, the significant, and the delectable.

BERNARD OGILVIE DODGE, whose perceptive researches into the taxonomy, evolution, and pathological relations of the fungi have not been surpassed, but only overshadowed, by his discovery and exploitation of *Neurospora* as a principal source of genetical truth.

BENJAMIN MINGE DUGGAR, for his outstanding researches in plant physiology, plant pathology, and mycology for over half a century and for his wise and patient counseling to many students for whom he provided inspiration, imagination, and high standards of scholarship.

ARTHUR JOHNSON EAMES, plant anatomist and morphologist, for his sustained researches on the morphology and anatomy of vascular plants and for his noteworthy contributions to our knowledge of floral development and evolution.

KATHERINE ESAU, plant anatomist and histologist, for her numerous contributions on tissue development of vascular plants and in particular for her outstanding studies on the structure, development, and evolution of phloem.

ALEXANDER WILLIAM EVANS, who to a fruitful life as the honored master of hepaticology has added a second as profitably devoted to the disentangling of the noble genus *Cladonia*.

HENRY ALLAN GLEASON, for his work on tropical and temperate floras of America and for the ideas and inspiration which he has supplied to the field of systematic botany.

THOMAS HENRY KEARNEY, for his early theoretical contributions to plant geography, his work in cotton breeding, his systematic studies in the Malvaceae, and his part in the preparation of the "Flora of Arizona."

GEORGE WANNAMAKER KEITT, for his many contributions to plant pathology, and in particular for his excellent researches on fruit-tree diseases, for his leadership in plant-pathology administration, and for his patience and kindness in counseling many students for whom he provided by illustrative example the life of a true gentleman.

PAUL JACKSON KRAMER, for productive investigations in various branches of plant physiology, and especially for significant contributions to our knowledge of plant-water relations and tree physiology.

LOUIS OTTO KUNKEL, for his researches and indefatigable efforts in experimentation, for his wise counseling of associates and students, for experimental techniques and publications, and for his productive studies on the nature of plant viruses.

DANIEL TREMBLY MACDOUGAL, for numerous contributions over many years to our knowledge of various phases of plant physiology and plant ecology, and especially for advances in our understanding of growth and physiology of tree species.

GEORGE WILLARD MARTIN, courageous investigator, teacher, editor, and philosopher, who has brought to the elucidation of the classification of the fungi field familiarity, laboratory exactness, and a critical intelligence that neither claims nor acknowledges authority.

MAXIMINO MARTÍNEZ, for his many technical and semipopular books and articles on the plants of Mexico. His works have made him a recognized authority on the Mexican flora and on the use of plants by man.

FREDERICK WILSON POPENOE, for his efforts toward the improvement and increased utilization of horticultural crops in tropical America.

WILLIAM JACOB ROBBINS, a physiologist whose studies have enlarged our knowledge of the growth and nutrition of plants, and an administrator the breadth of whose labors has notably contributed to the growth and nutrition of all phases of botany.

ANDREW DENNY RODGERS III, a unique figure on the American literary scene. His biographies of well-known botanists and histories of phases of the development of botanical science are readable, scholarly, and authentic.

JACQUES ROUSSEAU, whose explorations of the unknown North have provided an important contribution to Pleistocene biogeography. His sympathetic interest in Indian and Eskimo folklore and ways of life and his encyclopedic knowledge of the history of Canadian exploration have yielded a rich harvest of ethnobotanical studies.

KARL SAX, for his classical studies on the chromosomes of wheat, his continued interest in the chromosomes of the ornamental woody plants, and his extensive contributions about the effect of irradiation on chromosome breakage and chromosome structure.

PAUL BIGELOW SEARS, whose pioneering efforts in pollen analysis and continued interest in geochronological problems have made him the leader of all in this field, on our continent. The keenness of his mind, the warmth of his personality, the quality of his writing, and his capacity to relate all scientific problems to man have earned for him the distinction of an exemplary figure in American science.

HOMER LEROY SHANTZ, plant physiologist, plant ecologist, and administrator of note. His contributions to the understanding of drought resistance in plants, to the ecology of grasslands, and to world-wide plant geography have been laudable achievements in botanical science.

EDMUND WARE SINNOTT, morphologist, anatomist, geneticist, and botanical statesman, for his numerous, varied, and sustained contributions to plant anatomy, histology, evolution, and botanical theory.

FOLKE KARL SKOOG, for outstanding contributions to knowledge in various subdivisions of plant physiology, especially tissue culture, hormonal regulation of plant growth, and algal physiology.

GILBERT MORGAN SMITH, morphologist, for his numerous contributions to cryptogamic botany, and in particular for his study of life histories of marine and fresh-water algae.

ELVIN CHARLES STAKMAN, for his illustrious international leadership in science, for his recognized world leadership in researches on the pathogens of cereal smuts and rusts, and for his genius in inspiring students and workers to labor untiringly to provide food for mankind.

GEORGE LEDYARD STEBBINS, for his specific contributions to the cytogenetics of parthenogenesis, hybridization, and polyploidy, particularly in Guayule, Kok-saghyz, and the forage grasses, and for his outstanding review of the whole problem of evolution in plants.

JOHN ALBERT STEVENSON, whose encyclopedic knowledge of the fungi of the world and the diseases they induce has with generosity and humility been placed at the service of a generation of botanists.

KENNETH VIVIAN THIMANN, for his extensive and preeminent contributions to the biochemical physiology of green and nongreen plants and to the physiology of plant growth.

EDGAR NELSON TRANSEAU, for his lifetime of support and encouragement of botanical science in its broadest sense, both in its educational and scientific aspects. He has made substantial contributions to plant ecology, algology, and to botanical education at all levels, from high school to graduate school.

CORNELIS BERNARDUS VAN NIEL, whose studies in the realm where kingdoms and classes scarcely exist have provided illumination for syntheses of diverse phases of biology.

JOHN ERNST WEAVER, for his lifetime of researches on the ecology of grasslands. His investigations have contributed to the understanding of the dynamics of vegetation and have helped provide a necessary background for new policies in range management.

FRITS WARMOLT WENT, for his breadth of constructive interest in botanical science and especially for his contributions in the fields of plant physiology and ecology. The first botanist to put the assay of auxins on a quantitative basis, he subsequently has added substantially to our knowledge of the hormonal relations of plants. He has also been an outstanding investigator of the growth of plants under controlled environmental conditions.

RALPH HARTLEY WETMORE, plant anatomist and student of morphogenesis, for his numerous investigations of the developmental anatomy of vascular plants and for his studies on morphogenesis of vascular cryptogams.

TRUMAN GEORGE YUNCKER, for his lifetime of effective teaching at the undergraduate level, which has resulted in launching many able young scholars into careers in botany, and for effective contributions in taxonomy, especially of the Piperaceae.

HARRY ARDELL ALLARD

EDGAR ANDERSON

DIXON LLOYD BAILEY

IRVING WIDMER BAILEY

HARLEY HARRIS BARTLETT

GEORGE WELLS BEADLE

ERNST ATHEARN BESSEY

SIDNEY FAY BLAKE

EMMA LUCY BRAUN

STANLEY ADAIR CAIN

RALPH WORKS CHANEY

AGNES CHASE

JENS CHRISTIAN CLAUSEN

RALPH ERSKINE CLELAND

HENRY SHOEMAKER CONARD

WILLIAM SKINNER COOPER

JOHN NATHANIEL COUCH

BERNARD OGILVIE DODGE

BENJAMIN MINGE DUGGAR

ARTHUR JOHNSON EAMES

KATHERINE ESAU

ALEXANDER WILLIAM EVANS

HENRY ALLAN GLEASON

THOMAS HENRY KEARNEY

GEORGE WANNAMAKER KEITT

PAUL JACKSON KRAMER

LOUIS OTTO KUNKEL

DANIEL TREMBLY MacDOUGAL

GEORGE WILLARD MARTIN

MAXIMINO MARTÍNEZ

FREDERICK WILSON POPENOE

WILLIAM JACOB ROBBINS

ANDREW DENNY RODGERS III

JACQUES ROUSSEAU

KARL SAX

PAUL BIGELOW SEARS

HOMER LEROY SHANTZ

EDMUND WARE SINNOTT

FOLKE KARL SKOOG

GILBERT MORGAN SMITH

ELVIN CHARLES STAKMAN

GEORGE LEDYARD STEBBINS

JOHN ALBERT STEVENSON

KENNETH VIVIAN THIMANN

Edgar Nelson Transeau

Cornelis Bernardus Van Niel

John Ernst Weaver

Frits Warmolt Went

RALPH HARTLEY WETMORE   TRUMAN GEORGE YUNCKER

3

MICROBES—MAN'S MIGHTY MIDGETS

Kenneth B. Raper

In no other area of botanical science have greater advances been made during the past half century than in applied microbiology, advances that have come about largely through man's ability to isolate microscopic organisms in pure culture and to grow these under defined conditions of nutrition and environment. Whereas thousands of new species and hundreds of new genera have been described within this 50-year period, few additional major groups of microorganisms have been revealed. It has been rather a period marked by penetrating study and, not infrequently, re-evaluation. Much has been revealed concerning their morphology, life cycles, genetical behavior, and metabolism—and it is this newer knowledge of their vital processes that has enabled man to enlist their aid so successfully in many and diverse ways.

In the early 1900's and for many years thereafter, attention was directed largely along three often interrelated paths, namely (1) the collection, description, and categorization of the myriad types of microscopic life encountered on every hand; (2) the demonstration that certain of these microorganisms were the diminutive antagonists in many types of disease; and (3) the recognition that the ever-present microbes were the miscreants responsible for the spoilage of foods and feed supplies. There was of course some comprehension of the beneficent activities of some of them, and there was the beginning of a general belief that many microbes were man's true and helpful friends. It was of course known that yeasts played an all-important role in the leavening of bread, and their definitive role in the alcoholic fermentation had been known since the pioneering work of Pasteur. The conversion of ethyl alcohol to acetic acid by bacteria was well established for the vinegar fermentation, as was the role of other bacteria in the manufacture of hard cheeses. The fixation of atmospheric nitrogen by bacteria growing symbiotically in the roots of leguminous plants had been demonstrated, and the responsible role played by microorganisms in the decomposition of most types of organic materials was widely if incompletely recognized. The capacity of anaerobic bacteria to produce solvents had been reported, and the retting of plant tissues by related microorganisms to release valuable fibers was reasonably well understood. In the Orient, certain molds in association with yeasts and bacteria were propagated empirically for the production of soy sauce and other fermented foods.

Nevertheless, the primary emphasis in microbiology, particularly with reference to the bacteria, had been directed principally toward isolating them and elucidating their roles in the disease processes of man, his domestic animals, and his cultivated plants. Thus germs, as they had come to be known, were generally regarded as vicious, if miniscule, enemies to be combated at all costs. There was, of course, ample cause for such concern. Whereas this phase of microbiology has not become less important during the past fifty years and continued efforts and the application of techniques then unknown must be used unrelentingly to hold disease-producing microbes in check, there has developed parallel with it a broad and expanding area of research and technological application directed toward the utilization of microorganisms for constructive ends. I shall direct my attention to this latter development. It is not possible in a brief paper to encompass the whole field of present-day applied microbiology, and I must seek the reader's indulgence as I select, somewhat arbitrarily, certain areas for consideration.

THE PRODUCTION OF ORGANIC ACIDS

The microbiological production of organic acids represents one of the older and one of the more productive of these areas—productive not only for the variety of acids that can now be manufactured biosynthetically, but equally important for the background of accumulated information that made possible the large-scale production of antibiotics and other microbial products of more recent date. As early as 1867 the French mycologist van Tieghem demonstrated that the tannin contained in gall nuts was converted to gallic acid by the action of a common saprophytic mold *Sterigmatocystis nigra* (*Aspergillus niger*). By present standards, the fermentation as conducted was quite empirical, for it consisted merely of piling the substrate into mounds and periodically turning these inside out to provide aeration and thus facilitate the growth of the fungus, following which the acid was recovered by leaching. It is interesting to note that this acid is still produced by mold fermentation, although other tannin-rich materials are now utilized as substrates and the responsible enzyme, tannase, is often freed from the mold prior to being used as the converting agent. The current production of this acid is not large, but it finds important industrial uses in the manufacture of inks and dyes and in the formulation of pharmaceuticals for the treatment of burns. It commands a price of ca. $2.00 per pound.

The mycological production of citric acid represents the next oldest and still the most important mold fermentation aside from the production of penicillin. The production of citric acid by a mold was first discovered by the German mycologist Wehmer, in 1893. He was investigating the metabolic products of species of *Penicillium,* and being cognizant of the potential importance of his discovery, he obtained patents covering this. The operation of a factory for the manufacture of citric acid was attempted, but his molds were not highly productive, contamination was a recurrent problem, and technical difficulties of such magnitude were encountered that the operation was soon abandoned. Two decades later Charles Thom, who had become much interested in molds belonging to the genera *Penicillium* and *Aspergillus* as the result of his cheese investigations, was joined by J. N. Currie in an investigation on the production of oxalic acid by different strains of *Aspergillus niger.* They detected the presence of a considerable amount of acidity additional to oxalic and identified this as citric acid. By careful attention to the composition of the nutrient solutions and to the selection of the strains of *A. niger* employed for the fermentation, he and Currie soon found it possible to produce very substantial yields of citric acid from sugar solutions (1916–1917). The only source of citric acid then available was to recover it from citrus fruits and fruit wastes. Italy supplied about 90 per cent of the world's supply, exporting this in the form of calcium citrate. Within a few years after publication of their researches a large factory was operating in New York City, and by 1927 the United States had become virtually self-sufficient with regard to this important chemical. Today, production in the United States and its territories ranges in the neighborhood of 65 million pounds per year, and of this amount ca. 90 per cent represents citric acid of microbiological origin. The current price is in the neighborhood of 28 to 30 cents per pound. Citric acid, particularly in the form of the calcium salt, is used in the preparation of pharmaceuticals, while the uncombined acid is used in carbonated beverages, fruit-flavored extracts, and confections. It also finds important uses in the manufacture of engraving inks and certain textile dyes and as a plasticizer of synthetic resins.

The conversion of glucose to gluconic acid by bacteria was reported as early as 1880. However, the success of the citric fermentation was required to stimulate further investigations leading to a practical production process. Molliard in 1922 found that molds, including *Sterigmatocystis nigra,* could effect this oxidation. Soon thereafter a team of researchers, consisting of mycologists and chemists in the Department of Agriculture, and including Herrick, May, Moyer, and Wells, evolved a mycological method for the production of gluconic acid from glucose. Molds were also employed in their investigations, and early work was concentrated upon species of *Penicillium,* including *Penicillium chrysogenum,* the species that is now universally used for the production of the antibiotic penicillin. Later, they determined that selected strains of *Aspergillus niger* produced even higher yields and were less subject to serious contamination. The gluconic acid fermentation is important because it provides a rapid and economic process for producing this acid; it is probably of even greater importance because it represented the first mold fermentation conducted on a large scale where the fungus was grown not as a felt on the surface of thin layers of substrate but as a submerged mycelium in large tanks with rapid agitation and strong aeration. Today, gluconic acid is produced in an amount estimated at about 10 million pounds per annum. Some of this, in the form of its various salts, is used for the preparation of pharmaceuticals used in the treatment of calcium and other mineral deficiencies in man, and a considerable amount as calcium gluconate is used for treatment of milk fever in cattle. The free acid is used in a variety of industrial operations, and very recently in the form of its sodium salt it has found an important application as a sequestering agent for the removal of calcium and other metallic ions in the washing of glassware, including milk bottles and other containers of this type.

Fumaric acid is also produced by a fermentation process. The molds employed in this case are selected strains of *Rhizopus oryzae* and *R. nigricans,* belonging to the Mucorales. Interestingly enough, the first report of the mycological production of fumaric acid was by Wehmer, in 1918, who utilized a special strain of *A. niger,* reported as *A. fumaricus.* Exhaustive studies by Foster and Ward have shown conclusively that the aforementioned phycomycetous fungi carry out this fermentation most effectively. Fumaric acid is produced in fairly large amounts and finds its greatest applications as a mordant in the dyeing of textiles and in the plastics industry, but in the latter field it must now compete with maleic anhydride, which is produced from benzene by synthetic processes. By altering the conditions of culture and by the selection of other strains of *R. oryzae,* D-lactic acid can be produced with reasonable efficiency. However, the mold product in this case must compete with cheaper lactic acid resulting from bacterial fermentations which can be operated more rapidly and with less attention to problems of contamination; hence the mold is little used. Lactic acid production amounts to several million pounds per year, of which almost half is of edible grade and is used primarily in foods and in food processing. The remaining product, representing technical grade, finds a variety of industrial applications.

Itaconic acid represents yet another product of mold fermentation which can be produced in good yield. The earliest report of its production (1931) was by a Japanese investigator, Kinoshita, who identified it as a metabolic product of *A. itaconicus,* a mold possessing osmophilic growth requirements which precluded its economic exploitation. Subsequent studies by Professor Harold Rastrick and his associates (1939) in London revealed that this acid was produced in varying amounts by strains of the common soil mold, *A. terreus.* Starting from this point, Lockwood, Moyer, and other investigators at the Northern Regional Laboratory developed during the 1940's a process for its efficient and economical production. Their success hinged upon comparative studies of different mold strains together with unprecedented attention to nutrient composition and environmental conditions. This acid is now available commercially. It represents a most attractive ingredient for the production of crystal-clear plastics.

The production of acids other than lactic and acetic by bacteria has been amply demonstrated, and for some of these, efficient production methods have been worked out by Lockwood, Stodola, and others. Included among these are the following: 5-keto gluconic acid, produced by *Acetobacter suboxydans;* 2-keto gluconic acid, produced by *Pseudomonas fluorescens;* α-keto glutaric acid, produced by *P. fluorescens* when the fermentation is allowed to proceed beyond the 2-keto stage; maltobionic and lactobionic acids, produced from maltose and lactose through the oxidation of these sugars by *P. graveolens;* and pentonic acids, produced by the oxidation of various pentose sugars by species of *Pseudomonas.*

VITAMIN BIOSYNTHESIS

Another area of important microbial biosynthesis is found in the production of vitamins. Almost twenty years ago two French microbiologists, Raffy and Fontaine, reported riboflavin, or vitamin B_2, to be produced by a fungus, *Eremothecium ashbyii,* which was responsible for serious boll diseases of cotton, particularly in Egypt and Sudan. Much interest was shown in this discovery, for the essentiality of riboflavin in the nutrition of animals had been clearly demonstrated. At that time, however, there was no known means of producing it. Unfortunately, also, this discovery had been revealed in Europe shortly before the beginning of World War II and no accessible culture of *Eremothecium* had been received in this country at the time communications with most of Europe were cut off. A closely related organism, *Ashbya gossypii,* however, was known from Guillermond's work to produce limited amounts of this vitamin, and a culture of this fungus was contained in some of the collections in the United States. William J. Robbins, at the New York Botanical Garden, had employed this latter fungus for the assay of biotin in his basic and highly important studies on the nutrition of many fungi and other microorganisms. The fungus in question had been variously classified as a yeast and as a mold. For this reason it was of special interest to L. J. Wickerham, zymologist of the Northern Regional Laboratory, who obtained a culture from Robbins. Subsequent to this, Wickerham noted a yellow sector in one of his cultures, and upon re-isolation and examination of this pigmented growth he observed the presence of striking yellow crystals within the mycelium of the fungus. This proved to be riboflavin. Careful attention by Wickerham and his associates to the composition of substrates and the conditions under which the fungus was propagated led to the development of a process for the production of this needed vitamin in substantial yield. Today, riboflavin is produced in large amounts by the fermentation industry. It is manufactured by the use of either *Ashbya* or *Eremothecium,* which became available after the war. Concurrent with these developments a process was worked out for the production of riboflavin by purely chemical synthesis. However, the microorganisms can effect its production with such efficiency and economy that the bulk of the current production stems from the microbiological process. For many purposes the latter method of manufacture possesses a distinct advantage, for if the vitamin is to be used in animal feeds, it can be recovered as a crude concentrate which is used in proportion to its vitamin content. The annual production of riboflavin today amounts to nearly 300,000 pounds (expressed as pure riboflavin) with a current sales price in the neighborhood of $40.00 per pound for U.S.P. grade, whereas that of feed grade is about $30.00 per pound of riboflavin contained in approximately 115 pounds of vitamin-rich supplement. Riboflavin is also produced by species of the genus *Clostridium,* anaerobic bacteria used for the microbial production of acetone and butyl alcohol. In this case the vitamin-rich fermentation residue is dried and sold as a feed supplement.

The microbiological production of cyanocobalamin, or vitamin B_{12}, is equally important, and processes for its manufacture arose from a singularly interesting sequence of events. For many years it had been known that pernicious anemia could be held in check by the administration of liver extracts. In 1947, Shorb found that the effectiveness of these extracts in controlling this disease could be correlated with their ability to support the growth of certain fastidious bacteria belonging to the genus *Lactobacillus.* The following year research investigators at Merck and Company discovered that the extracts contained a highly active principle, which in a pure state represented a red crystalline compound. This substance was nutritionally essential for the *Lactobacilli,* and significantly, the amount of their growth was proportional to its content in the liver extracts. Soon thereafter they demonstrated that the compound showed positive hematological activity when administered to patients suffering from Addisonian pernicious anemia. Identity with the anti-anemia factor in liver was established, and it was reported as vitamin B_{12}. Later it was found that this vitamin could be extracted also from the residues of the streptomycin fermentation, and subsequently, that it could be obtained in even greater yield from the residues of the Aureomycin fermentation. In fact, it was disclosed that many of the Actinomycetes produced this substance, and it was logically suspected that a determined search might reveal a species or strain which would produce it in even greater amount. Harlow H. Hall of the Northern Regional Laboratory conducted such a search, and his efforts were rewarded by the discovery that a particular strain of *Streptomyces olivaceus* when grown under appropriate conditions could produce this vitamin in yields that warranted the conduct of fermentations in which it was the primary product. Today, vitamin B_{12} is regularly recovered in crystalline form and marketed for pharmaceutical use. Much greater quantities are sold as vitamin-rich concentrates, which, as in the case of riboflavin, are used for the supplementation of poultry and animal feeds. In the latter case the product is sold upon the basis of its vitamin content, and it may represent a product recovered from the residues of one of the *Streptomyces* antibiotic fermentations, or it may have its origin in special fermentations designed to yield maximum vitamin concentrations. Vitamin B_{12} is an exceedingly active compound biologically, and it is commonly used at levels of only 1.5 to 2.0 μg. per pound of feed. This being true, it is fabulously expensive on a weight basis, the U.S.P. crystalline compound being priced at about \$250 per gram. The wholesale value of vitamin B_{12} currently produced in the United States is estimated at \$20 to \$25 million per year.

Vitamin D is regularly produced by the irradiation of ergosterol, which is generally obtained from yeast, but which can be recovered from the mycelia of a variety of other fungi, including that used for the penicillin fermentation.

MICROBIAL ENZYMES

Enzymes of microbial origin have been used for centuries in the Orient for the conversion of starch and the degradation of certain plant proteins, but it is only within the past half century that significant information concerning their nature or activities has become known. Prior to that time, selected "kojis," consisting of some type of farinaceous materials seeded with appropriate microorganisms, were used to effect the breakdown of starch preparatory to alcoholic fermentation or the partial decomposition of proteins (e.g., those of soybeans) for the manufacture of soy sauce and other fermented foods and condiments. The kojis were perpetuated empirically by the implantation to new substrates of fragments from previously grown kojis of proven activity and their incubation under environmental conditions which favored the desired microorganisms. Thus by trial and error, regimens for such enrichment cultures were evolved which ensured their effectiveness with reasonable reproducibility. Kojis wherein different types of microorganisms predominated were used for different purposes; e.g., in the manufacture of soy sauce two separate kojis were employed: a mold koji that effected both a conversion of the starch in rice and parched wheat and brought about a partial breakdown of the bean proteins, and a second koji in which yeasts and lactobacilli predominated that was used for the secondary brine fermentation.

The first serious attempts to utilize the responsible enzymes per se were made by a Japanese investigator, Takamine, around the turn of the century.

It was then known that the molds responsible for the desired hydrolytic processes represented, in the main, strains of *Aspergillus oryzae* and closely related species, and Takamine obtained patents covering processes for the propagation of such molds and the recovery from them of preparations rich in amylolytic enzymes. He subsequently established a factory in New Jersey for the manufacture of diastatic and proteolytic enzymes of mold origin.

Other microbiologists in other laboratories extended his investigations and at the same time broadened their researches to include other microbial enzymes. Much has been accomplished, and today a great number and diversity of products with varied properties derived from molds, yeasts, and bacteria are commercially available. It is not possible to cover all these, but I shall briefly discuss the more important products and their applications.

Much attention has been directed toward the production of amylolytic enzymes. Normally there are substantial outlets for these, and in periods of national emergency such need is greatly increased because of the necessity of conserving grain supplies, including the barley from which malt is derived. Substantial progress toward the development of a mold-bran process for the production of amylolytic enzymes was made during World War I and in the years that followed, and during World War II a large mechanized factory was constructed and operated. The product in this case is the enzyme-rich dried bran upon which a selected strain of *A. oryzae* has been propagated, and it is used by direct addition to grain mashes in lieu of malt. Concentrated enzyme preparations can be produced as needed by aqueous extraction and evaporation, and crystalline products can be obtained by precipitation with ethyl alcohol. Of recent date, H. M. Tsuchiya and other investigators at the Northern Regional Laboratory have developed a process for the production of fungal amylase in submerged culture using selected strains of *A. niger*. As with mold bran, the whole culture is used as a converting agent, this substituting either largely or entirely for malt. In addition to their somewhat intermittent use in the alcoholic fermentations (depending largely upon economic considerations), microbial amylases find important uses in other industries. Those obtained from molds find a limited outlet in certain pharmaceuticals and substantially larger uses in the food and baking industries, the products being more or less tailor-made for particular applications. Amylolytic enzymes are likewise produced by bacteria, and the amylase of *Bacillus subtilis* is now manufactured on a large scale. This can be produced by growing the bacillus on bran, as a surface pellicle on the surface of shallow layers of a liquid substrate, or in submerged culture with aeration and agitation. It is of special value in the textile industry since it retains its activity at 95°C.; because of this property it has permitted revolutionary changes in the desizing operations of the textile industry.

Proteolytic enzymes can be produced by molds of the same species, *Asper-*

gillus oryzae, as that used for amylase manufacture by the mold-bran process. However, other strains must be employed since high amylase producers are seldom optimal for protease production, and vice versa. Products of such origin find their greatest application in the preparation of chill-proofing agents used in the manufacture of beer and ale. Proteases of bacterial origin are of much greater importance, industrially. These are produced also by selected strains of *Bacillus subtilis* and the processes of manufacture duplicate, in the main, those employed for the production of bacterial amylase, except that different substrates and operating conditions favoring maximum protease production are employed. Bacterial proteases find important industrial applications in the degumming of silk, the baiting of hides, the digestion of fish livers to release oil, and in the recovery of silver from photographic plates. Their largest use is for the preparation of spot removers (in combination with other enzymes) for the dry-cleaning industry, an outlet which exceeds $1 million annually.

There is an increasing market for the pectin-hydrolyzing enzymes in the food industries. Whereas many microorganisms produce such enzymes, species of *Penicillium* (e.g., *P. frequentans*) are generally employed for their manufacture. This can be accomplished either by a shallow-tray or deep-tank operation. Best yields are obtained in the presence of pectin-rich substrates such as fruit wastes and beet cossets, a by-product of the beet-sugar industry. A variety of pectic enzymes are produced, and to some degree the commercial products are fashioned to meet specific applications. They are used primarily for the clarification of fruit juices, wines, jellies, and syrups and to prevent fruit-juice concentrates from jelling.

Invertase, an intracellular enzyme, is obtained commercially from the yeast *Saccharomyces cerevisiae,* although it is produced in substantial amounts by certain molds and bacteria. The yeast is grown in the presence of sucrose under conditions which favor heavy cell growth. The yeast cells are then recovered, and allowed to undergo autolysis under toluene, after which the cell debris is removed and the enzyme is precipitated with ethyl alcohol. The product is commonly marketed as a 60 per cent concentrate dissolved in glycerol. It finds its chief use in the manufacture of invert sugar, and possibly its most striking application is in the production of soft- or liquid-center candies, e.g., chocolate-covered cherries.

Some additional enzymes of microbial origin are produced commercially that have important, if more limited, applications, including: catalase, produced in submerged cultures of *Aspergillus niger,* is used in the manufacture of surgical gut, in the bleaching of furs, and for the perpetuation of platinum blondes; glucose oxidase, similarly produced by *A. niger,* finds applications in the desugaring of eggs, and in the processing of foods where residual glucose must be oxidized to preclude enzymatic browning; penicillinase, produced in deep tanks by *Bacillus cereus* or *B. subtilis,* is used to in-activate the antibiotic penicillin in order to test the sterility of the packaged drug; and streptokinase and streptodornase, products of virulent hemolytic streptococci, are used for the debridement of pus and necrotic tissue in wounds and burns. These enzymes are often used in conjunction with or precedent to antibiotic therapy.

ANTIBIOTICS

In no other area of human affairs have microorganisms contributed so importantly as they have in modern medicine. Many diseases which formerly claimed thousands of lives annually are today practically non-existent, and many others are effectively held in check by a new class of therapeutic agents, the antibiotics. Whereas man's awareness of such substances goes back many years, realization of their singular curative properties dates only from 1940. Alexander Fleming had in 1929 reported the production of a powerful antibacterial substance by a chance mold contaminant (fig. 1), and he named the elusive substance penicillin after the generic name of the fungus, *Penicillium*, that produced it. He was aware of its potentialities in medicine and actually projected these with amazing prescience (fig. 2), but he was not in position to produce and isolate the substance he had revealed. This was done a decade later by Florey, Chain, Heatley, and their associates at Oxford University. This story has been so often retold that to repeat it here would be superfluous. Equally pointless would be a recounting of the momentous events that led to the large-scale production of this antibiotic by the end of World War II (see "Decade of Antibiotics in America," *Mycologia* 44:1–59, 1952).

There are, however, certain aspects of this development which are germane to this presentation. The mold isolated by Fleming was subsequently identified, at the request of Harold Rastrick, by Charles Thom as *Penicillium notatum*, a cosmopolitan fungus found in soil and on decaying vegetation of many kinds. Experience with other fermentations suggested that strains more productive than the original isolate probably could be found, and Thom's diagnosis gave decisive direction to such a search. Not unexpectedly, almost all strains of *P. notatum* and of the closely related species *P. chrysogenum* were found to produce penicillin, and some of the newer isolates produced substantially more than the Fleming strain, particularly when these were grown submerged in large fermenters with strong aeration and agitation. This method of manufacture proved a tremendous boon to large-scale production, but in itself it could never have provided the quantities of penicillin required by the emergency. Two other developments contributed equally to the success of the program, namely (1) formulation of the lactose–corn steep–liquor medium by Moyer that has so greatly enhanced penicillin production, and (2) the development of a long series of increasingly productive

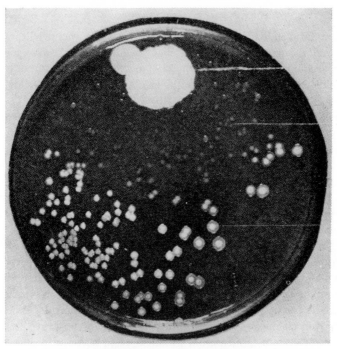

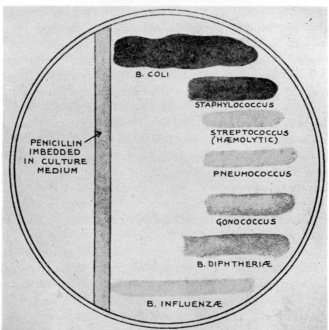

B. COLI

STAPHYLOCOCCUS

STREPTOCOCCUS
(HÆMOLYTIC)

PENICILLIN
IMBEDDED
IN CULTURE
MEDIUM

PNEUMOCOCCUS

GONOCOCCUS

B. DIPHTHERIÆ

B. INFLUENZÆ

Fig. 1–2.—Fig. 1. (*Upper.*) Photograph of a culture plate showing the dissolution of staphylococcal colonies in the neighborhood of a *Penicillium* colony.—Fig. 2. A spectrum plate showing the inhibition of a variety of bacteria by penicillin. (*Fig. 1 and 2 from Fleming's original paper in British Jour. Exp. Path.* 10:229, 1929.)

induced mutations. To this latter endeavor the writer was privileged to contribute, and the end result of researches so initiated and subsequently carried forward most effectively by Backus and Stauffer was to increase penicillin yields from ca. 80 to 3500 units per milliliter in the decade between 1943 and 1953.

From a purely business point of view this tremendously increased productivity proved not to be an unmixed blessing, as illustrated by the following production and valuation (wholesale) figures: Total production of the drug in 1943 amounted to 29 pounds, valued at $3 million ($200 per million units); production in 1945 had risen to 14,000 pounds valued at $70 million; in 1951, 636,000 pounds were produced valued at $137 million; and in 1954, production amounted to 860,000 pounds valued at $63 million ($0.09 to $0.10 per million units). The precipitous decline in the wholesale value of the drug over the past twelve years has placed manufacturers in the awkward position of receiving less and less for more and more. Viewed from a more humanitarian point of view, however, it has meant wholly adequate supplies of the drug for all the manifold uses where it has proved beneficial, including the use of very large quantities as feed supplements. Whereas new and improved chemical syntheses tend constantly to supplant the microbial production of certain fermentation products (e.g., acetic acid and ethyl and butyl alcohols), industrial manufacture by such means has never challenged the microbial production of penicillin, although a synthesis of the drug was reported as early as 1945. Its adoption today would be utterly inconceivable.

The tremendous contributions of penicillin to world health need not be recounted. It is sufficient to say that it was the first of a lengthening list of antibiotic drugs, and even now it is the least toxic of these. It was and is the drug of choice for combating virtually all infections caused by gram-positive bacteria. Yet it is not and never was a cure-all. The pathogenic gram-negative bacteria are relatively insensitive to it; it is ineffective against the rickettsiae and viruses; and with its continued use penicillin-resistant strains have developed among those bacterial pathogens against which it was initially most effective, e.g., the staphylococci and streptococci. Additional wonder drugs were and are urgently needed. There are still no adequate chemotherapeutic agents for the control of virus diseases, and cancer in its many forms still resists all forms of medication.

Spurred on by the singular therapeutic properties of penicillin and by the success that attended the researches which led to its large-scale manufacture, investigators in many laboratories embarked upon a vast campaign of discovery. Out of this unprecedented search has come more than a dozen additional antibiotics which together with penicillin have extended man's life expectancy by several years. These newer drugs are of course obtained from different microorganisms, but without exception they are produced by modifications of the basic techniques developed for the manufacture of penicillin.

The second major antibiotic was discovered by S. A. Waksman and represented the first of a lengthening list of drugs derived from the Actinomycetes, a group of soil microorganisms superficially intermediate between the bacteria and the mold fungi but with true bacterial affinities. Streptomycin is produced commercially by selected strains of *Streptomyces griseus* and has been available to physicians since 1946. Like penicillin, it is currently manufactured in large quantities. The annual production of the drug is in the neighborhood of 450,000 pounds, with a wholesale valuation of approximately $36 million in 1955. It finds important uses in combating diseases caused by gram-negative bacteria that are unaffected by penicillin; its greatest application is in the treatment of tuberculosis. However, nerve and kidney toxicity limit its usefulness somewhat, and even more than penicillin, it tends to promote the development of drug-resistant pathogens. In common with penicillin, it is ineffective against the rickettsiae and viruses, hence it narrows but does not remove the area of uncontrolled infections.

Following the discovery of streptomycin, particular attention was centered upon the actinomycetes as possible sources of additional new and valuable antibiotics. Five new drugs of major importance have been discovered. Whereas these have different characteristics which often commend them for specific applications, they possess to a considerable degree common curative properties. All of them are active against both gram-positive and gram-negative bacteria and, in addition, have proved quite effective in combating diseases caused by the rickettsiae (e.g., typhus fever and Rocky Mountain spotted fever). They are referred to as broad-spectrum antibiotics because of the wide range of microorganisms that they inhibit.

The first of these newer drugs, chloromycetin (chloramphenicol) was discovered independently by two research teams in 1947. It was developed and is now manufactured in quantity by Parke, Davis and Company. It has particular merit in the treatment of typhoid fever, bacillary dysentery, and other intestinal diseases. A chemical synthesis was early achieved for this drug, and it can be produced alternatively by synthetic processes or by fermentation. The actinomycete used for its production by fermentation processes is *S. venezuelae*.

The second antibiotic of this series, aureomycin (chlortetracycline) was discovered in 1948 by B. M. Duggar of the Lederle Laboratories. It is interesting to recall that this was accomplished after the retirement of this eminent mycologist and plant physiologist from his academic position at the University of Wisconsin. Aureomycin is produced by the actinomycete *S. aureofaciens*. It is manufactured in large amounts and finds important applications in the treatment of a wide range of different diseases caused by gram-negative and gram-positive bacteria, rickettsiae and the larger viruses, and the parasitic amoebae. It is generally less toxic than chloromycetin, and it possesses great penetrating powers which commend it for use in deep tissue infections.

The third of the broad-spectrum antibiotics, terramycin (oxytetracycline), was discovered by a team of research microbiologists at the Charles Pfizer Company in 1950, and it is manufactured on a large scale by that pharmaceutical firm. In general, terramycin is used for the same types of therapy as aureomycin. Like that drug, it is used in the treatment of amoebic dysentery, and it is reported to be effective in the treatment of African sleeping sickness, caused by another type of protozoa, the trypanosomes. Terramycin is obtained from *S. rimosus*.

The fourth broad-spectrum antibiotic, ilotycin (erythromycin), was discovered by J. M. McGuire and coworkers in the Research Laboratories of the Eli Lilly Company and is derived from *S. erythreus*. This antibiotic is currently produced in substantial amounts by this firm and by two additional ones, who market the drug under different trade names. Erythromycin finds its greatest usefulness in combating infections caused by gram-positive pathogens that have developed resistance to the earlier-discovered antibiotics.

The fifth broad-spectrum antibiotic, tetracycline, is very closely related to aureomycin and terramycin, differing from these in the absence of a chlorine atom and an OH group, respectively. This antibiotic can be produced by chemical means wherein the chlorine is removed from aureomycin by simultaneous dechlorination and hydrogenation, or it can be produced by conducting a primary fermentation using a strain of *Streptomyces* different from those employed to produce aureomycin or terramycin. The drug is now being produced in large amounts by each of these processes. Tetracycline seems to be generally the most useful and the least toxic of the five broad-spectrum drugs. It possesses curative properties equal to aureomycin and terramycin coupled with fewer disagreeable side reactions, hence is preferred for many types of therapy. It is currently produced in amounts almost equal to that of the other four broad-spectrum drugs combined. The total production of all broad-spectrum antibiotics in 1955 was somewhat in excess of 450,000 pounds. The net value of these drugs (produced and marketed by single companies, except for tetracycline and erythromycin) in the same year amounted to approximately $195 million. The tetracycline produced in that year alone was marketed for $95 million.

Additional to these major drugs obtained from species of *Streptomyces,* two additional antibiotics of actinomycetous origin should be mentioned. Neomycin, produced by *S. fradiae* and discovered by Waksman, finds important uses in the preparation of ointments for topical use and as a preoperative drug in surgery. It is often combined with other antibiotics. The other, nystatin, discovered by Hazen and Brown and produced by *S. noursei,* exhibits much desired fungistatic properties. One of the drawbacks of the broad-spectrum drugs has been their capacity to remove effectively the bacterial flora from the intestinal tracts of patients undergoing treatment. In consequence, the yeasts, species of *Candida,* which are generally present in small numbers, may flourish in the absence of competing microorganisms, thus giving rise to a secondary disease, monilasis, of serious proportion. Nystatin offers promise in the alleviation of this condition and in other disease processes caused by pathogenic fungi.

In addition to penicillin and the actinomycetous antibiotics, there are a few drugs of this class produced by bacteria. None of these have wide applications, and they are not manufactured on a large scale, but they possess invaluable therapeutic properties. The oldest of these, tyrothrycin, produced by *Bacillus brevis* and discovered by DuBos, is widely used in the preparation of medicated bandages and in troches and sprays for respiratory infections. The second, bacitracin, produced by *B. licheniformis,* is also used in medicinals for topical application and is commonly employed as a preoperative drug. It is an effective medicant in amebiasis. The third, polymyxin, produced by *B. polymyxa,* is especially useful in combating infections of the blue-pus type caused by *Pseudomonas aeruginosus.* Like neomycin, it is often used in combination with other antibiotics. The total sales of any one of these minor antibiotics is not great, but in the aggregate, together with three or four others unmentioned here, they amounted to approximately $20 million in 1955.

Following the discovery that vitamin B_{12} stimulated the growth of chickens and other meat animals, it was found that minute amounts of aureomycin, and subsequently penicillin and other antibiotics, would produce a marked growth stimulation in chickens, turkeys, pigs, and many other animals. The net result of this has been to provide an additional market for antibiotics which, on a weight basis, approaches for some of these the quantities used as drugs. Whereas all the antibiotics exhibit this property in some measure, those which have proved most useful as feed supplements are penicillin, aureomycin, and bacitracin. It is not necessary that the antibiotics be highly purified for use as feed supplements, although this is commonly done to enhance product stability and to obviate the necessity of dual manufacturing processes. For the year 1954 the value of antibiotics used for feed supplementation alone exceeded $25 million.

Two additional uses for antibiotics of enlarging proportions are their application in the control of certain plant diseases and for extending the marketable life of meats and other perishable foods. Of the antibiotics used against plant diseases at the present time, streptomycin leads the field by a wide margin, whereas aureomycin is the principal antibiotic currently employed for food preservation. This latter type of application includes the storage of fish in ice containing low concentrations of the antibiotic, and also a recently approved process whereby eviscerated poultry is dipped in a bath containing 7 p.p.m. of this drug before entering distribution channels. The further use of antibiotics for food preservation undoubtedly offers an increasingly important outlet for the future.

MICROBIAL CONVERSIONS

One of the newest and most exciting industrial applications of microorganisms is in the area, still poorly defined, that is oftentimes referred to as microbial conversions. This has stemmed naturally from a growing appreciation of the biosynthetic potentialities of microorganisms, and from the equally important fact that almost any microbial cell can be propagated in tank culture if sufficient attention is given to its nutrition, oxygen requirements, incubation temperature, pH, etc. Probing investigations are in progress on many frontiers, and there can be little doubt that some of these explorations will in time open new horizons wherein microorganisms can contribute handsomely to man's further progress. Already there is one very striking and singularly successful example. This relates not to the production of a specific end product as in most fermentations, but rather to the utilization of microorganisms to effect a series of intricate, costly, and time-consuming chemical steps in the synthesis of cortisone. In this development, Durey H. Peterson and his associates at the Upjohn Laboratories have played a leading role. Starting with meager clues that microorganisms could possibly effect a series of necessary modifications in the molecule of progesterone, many microorganisms were surveyed. The bread mold, *Rhizopus arrhizus,* was found to do the job, and to do it in a manner that permitted a commercially feasible fermentation process. Three pharmaceutical firms now use microorganisms to effect steroid transformations. The market value of cortical hormones in 1955 amounted to $75 million, of which production three-quarters was based upon microbial conversions.

As one would expect, this is currently an area of intense research activity and in it cortisone occupies the position that penicillin did in the antibiotic field in the mid-forties. No one can predict where the next "breakthrough" will come, but microbiologists are confident that the future for microbial conversions is indeed bright. The microorganisms with which they work are subtle and profound, and they are withal amazingly diverse in the biosynthetic capabilities they have already demonstrated.

If I have seemed to emphasize the economic aspects of microorganisms in their service to man, let us not conclude that these, important as they are, represent the truest measure of their contributions. Of infinitely greater importance has been their roles in providing the agents for the alleviation of disease and the improvement of human and animal nutrition. To appreciate these facts one need only contemplate the rare incidence of many diseases such as pneumonia, scarlet fever, and many others, the lessening ravages of tuberculosis and syphilis and the debilitating effects of prolonged fevers, the advances of surgery made possible by the almost complete control of secondary infections, and the increased productivity of our population which stems in substantial measure from improvements in our national health and nutrition.

The foregoing account represents in no wise a complete picture of the contributions of microorganisms to man's progress during the past half century. We have said nothing about the many ways in which microorganisms have contributed to our basic knowledge of vital processes such as cellular metabolism and heredity. We have not included, except indirectly, their vast contributions to agriculture. Our coverage of industrial application has been incomplete, for we have not included the alcoholic fermentation, the oldest and largest application of all. We have said nothing about the possible use of microbial cells as a source of protein for human and animal feed. But what has been said, I believe, will provide a basis for a truer appreciation of their increasing contributions to our economy and well-being. Considered as individuals the microorganisms are midgets in the extreme; considered collectively these smallest plants constitute a mighty and often unbelievably ingenuous labor force for us to enlist and direct. As we learn more and more about the hidden secrets of their life processes and the diversity of the reactions they can perform, it is inevitable that they should become used on an ever-widening scale. We have hardly crossed the threshold of the microbiological age.

LITERATURE CITED

BEESCH, S. C., AND G. M. SHULL. 1955. Fermentation. Ind. & Eng. Chem. 47:1857–1875.

FLEMING, ALEXANDER. 1946. Penicillin and its practical application. pp. 1–380. Blakiston. New York.

LOCKWOOD, L. B. 1952. Industrial enzymes—Production and use. Trans. N.Y. Acad. Sci. Ser. II, 15:2–5.

RAPER, KENNETH B. 1952. A decade of antibiotics in America. Mycologia 44:1–59.

STODOLA, F. H., AND R. W. JACKSON. 1950–51. Fermentation acids in industry. pp. 84–92, in Yearbook of Agriculture (Crops in peace and war).

UNDERKOFLER, L. A., AND R. J. HICKEY (Eds.). 1954. Industrial fermentations. Vol. 1, pp. 1–565; Vol. 2, pp. 1–578. Chemical Publishing Co. New York.

U.S. TARIFF COMMISSION. 1955. Synthetic organic chemicals—U.S. production and sales, 1954. Report No. 196, 2d series, pp. 1–184.

WAKSMAN, S. A. 1949. Streptomycin. pp. 1–618. Williams & Wilkins. Baltimore, Md.

4

THE FIGHT WITH THE FUNGI

The Rusts and Rots That Rob Us, the Blasts and the Blights That Beset Us

James G. Horsfall

The title of this article sounds as if the roof were about to fall in on us—as if we have lost or are about to lose the fight with the fungi. Say not so! We have only begun to fight, but fight we must.

We may easily forget that fungi feed at the same table with us. This is so because they have a ticket to the first sitting. They consume our food in the farmer's field, on the trains and trucks that bring it to us, and in the grocer's store. If this fight go not forward to success, we may one day not be able to smile at the "naïveté" of Mr. Malthus who thought that we would soon eat ourselves out of our own food supply.

Fungi have been on this planet longer than we. They have developed some fantastically efficient devices that serve them in their fight with us. They are well able to search out our food plants so that they also may eat, drink, and be merry.

It has been fun to help a little in the research to develop the counter measures that we use in our fight with them. Before we come to the counter measures, however, I should like to discuss some of the famous plant diseases of antiquity and how some of them have altered the course of history.

Three plant diseases of modern times are known to almost everyone. Perhaps the best known is the chestnut blight that swept every chestnut tree from the hills from Maine to Georgia. The second is the Dutch elm disease that is marching down the streets of cities and killing the elms from Montreal to Denver. And the third is oak wilt. It is scaring the wits out of the people who produce the oak flooring for our houses and the kegs for our beer.

These diseases latch onto our consciousness because they are new and they strike down handsome big trees. These are some of the blasts and blights that beset us, but what really rob us are such diseases as wheat rust and potato rot.

Wheat rust is perhaps the most famous disease of antiquity, and it is still with us. Wheat rust robs us of our bread, the very staff of life. Those of us who went through both World Wars remember the "wheatless days" of World War I. We had wheatless days in that war because 1917 was one of those years when wheat rust swept the plains and consumed the grains like a prairie fire. The wheat rust fungus ate most of our bread at the first sitting. We had to settle for rice and corn bread.

We were lucky during World War II. Wheat rust did not stage another such ruinous raid, and we did not have wheatless days. Of course, scientific research had also been at work in the meantime and had won part of the fight with that fungus.

Wheat rust was known to the Israelites, who talked about it in Genesis. It was known to the Romans. And it was known in Colonial America. On this last point, there hangs a tale of the impact of a plant disease on civilization. This is the tale of how wheat rust altered the eating habits of a group of people.

When the English colonists came to America, some settled in New England, and others in tidewater Virginia, Plymouth and Jamestown being settled within a few years of each other. Undoubtedly, both groups of immigrants brought wheat with them, and they both found the Indians growing corn. The wheat rust disease, however, acted differently on the wheats in the two colonies, just as it does today.

WHEAT RUST ALTERS EATING HABITS

Wheat rust is a much more serious disease in a warm than in a cool climate. It was to be expected, therefore, that wheat rust proved much more damaging to the Colonial crops of wheat in warm Virginia than in cool New England. It is probable that the settlers of Virginia found wheat a difficult crop on account of rust, whereas the settlers of New England found wheat a good crop, as it had been in England itself.

It seems to me quite likely that wheat rust explains today's difference between the carbohydrate diets of the southern and the northern United States. Bread, we say, is the "staff of life." In the South bread means corn bread. In the North bread means wheat bread.

I submit that wheat rust was so destructive in the South that the colonists, perforce, had to eat corn bread, grits, and hominy. Difficult as food habits are to change, the southern colonists had to change from wheat to corn. Wheat bread was so rarely obtainable in the South that it came to have its own name, light, or white, bread.

Wheat grew well enough in the North, so that wheat bread remained the "staff of life."

Now you may be thinking that wheat can be and is grown in some of the warm parts of the United States—in Texas and Oklahoma. The explanation for this is that wheat rust is severe only when warmth is accompanied by moisture. In Oklahoma and Texas there is much less moisture during the wheat-growing season than in the more humid areas of the eastern part of the South. Hence, wheat rust does not make the crop unprofitable in the dry Southwest as it does in the humid Southeast.

The relation of moisture and warmth to wheat rust has also resulted in some interesting dietary habits in Europe, and in turn in the development of a scourge known as St. Anthony's fire.

A MEDIEVAL SCOURGE

The same pattern of food habits applies in Europe as in America. Wheat grows well in England, which, like New England, is moist enough for wheat rust but a little too cool. Therefore, in England, bread is wheat bread. Wheat also grows well in Italy, which, like Oklahoma, is warm enough for wheat rust but a little too dry. Therefore, in Italy also bread is wheat bread—and spaghetti and macaroni are wheaten also.

Wheat grows relatively poorly, however, in central Europe, which, like Virginia, is warm and moist in the wheat season. This makes wheat rust bad there. In turn this makes bread in central Europe rye bread. Central Europe is a rye-eating area.

Let us see how St. Anthony's fire was related to this interesting distribution of staple food plants brought on by the action of wheat rust. St. Anthony's fire was a strange malady that afflicted the people in the Middle Ages. The characteristic of the disease was the raging fever that gave the disease its name—St. Anthony's fire. In the Middle Ages it was supposed that the disease could be cured by the intercession of St. Anthony.

The fever led to mental failure and often to death. The victims suffered initially with nerve tingling in the feet and hands. They might lose the sense of touch. Then gangrene would set in, and the extremities might have to be amputated.

Like the plague, it struck down large numbers of people, but, unlike the plague, it was not catching.

This peculiar disease occurred mainly in central Europe, seldom in Italy or England. In other words, the disease was coexistent with the occurrence of rye. It occurred where wheat could not be grown on account of rust.

It is not surprising, then, that as early as 1630 the French physician Thullier recognized that St. Anthony's fire was caused from eating rye kernels infected with another plant disease called ergot. Ergot, like wheat rust, liked the warm humid climate of central Europe. It did not attack rye seriously enough to curtail the yield disastrously, but it did produce enough diseased kernels to contaminate the flour for bread.

Of course the disease was most serious in those years when the rye crop was the shortest. In those years it was sometimes difficult to get rye that did not contain ergot, and the people, especially the poor, had to eat it. These were the years when St. Anthony's fire scourged the population. If wheat rust had not been so serious in the warm, humid areas of central and southern Europe, St. Anthony's fire might never have reached such gigantic proportions and caused so much suffering and sorrow as it did during the Middle Ages.

St. Anthony's fire began to decline in the eighteenth century and was only occasionally serious in the nineteenth century. This decline in severity of St. Anthony's fire was due to the rise of the potato as a source of carbohydrate in Europe. People began to eat potatoes and reduce their use of rye. This had a salubrious effect on St. Anthony's fire, but it led inevitably to one of the most devastating famines of modern times, for which a plant disease was again the cause.

THE IRISH FAMINE

Sir Walter Raleigh, visiting in Virginia in the early part of the seventeenth century, discovered the Indians cultivating a plant, the name of which he transliterated as *potato*. He took it to Europe where it remained a botanical curiosity for a while. Eventually, the people began to eat it in some volume and the crop spread rapidly across Europe. The peasant farmer of Europe soon discovered that the potato would produce more carbohydrate per acre than either rye or wheat. Slowly in some areas, rapidly in others, the potato replaced the cereals which had been the staple diet of the white men since the dawn of history. Lush fields of green potatoes began to appear all over Europe, instead of the nodding waves of wheat and rye. The potato was adapted to as wide an area as any cereal, in fact, far wider than wheat. This shift from cereals to potatoes was particularly prominent in Ireland; that's the reason why we often refer to a potato as the Irish potato. Ireland was so densely populated in the early part of the nineteenth century that the potato was a godsend to them. The first thing anybody knew, Ireland had almost ceased to grow cereal of any kind and was depending almost exclusively on the potato.

Just about one hundred years ago a new disease of potato appeared in central Europe. It had never been seen before. It was a nasty disease; it made the leaves suddenly turn water-soaked, slimy, rotten, and black. That wasn't such a bad symptom except that the fungus that caused the disease spread from the leaves into the tubers and caused them to decay with a very curious and unusual sort of hard rot. The disease, which we now know as late blight, spread with lightning rapidity over Europe and appeared in Ireland in 1844. We might describe its catastrophic attack on Ireland in the words of an eye witness, Father Matthew, who says, "On July 27th I passed from Cork to Dublin, and the doomed plant bloomed in all the luxuriance of an abundant harvest. Returning on August 3rd, I beheld with sorrow mere wastes of putrefying vegetation."

In the seven days mentioned by Father Matthew, the stage was set for a famine in which a quarter of a million people actually starved to death from slow malnutrition and a million and a half emigrated, many of them to the United States. Essentially the entire potato crop of Ireland was wiped out. The people who had been dependent upon potatoes to pay the rent and to carry them through the winter suddenly found themselves without any potatoes, and they knew that they faced a dreadful winter. A few feeble efforts at public relief were undertaken, partly by the Church and partly by the State, but they were inadequate and probably could never have been adequate to feed the whole population of Ireland. The best they could do was to stave off the evil day for a few people. The starvation showed first as dull headaches and bloated bellies; finally, the sufferer came under the spell of hallucinations and died. He did not seem to be in any great pain but died from weakness. Terror and panic were common throughout the land, and the ships sailing westward to the United States were packed to the gunwales with people rushing away from the famine that had encompassed their homeland.

So much for a couple of plant diseases that altered history.

WHAT CAUSES DISEASE

In the fight with the fungi, we had to find out first that it was fungi that we were fighting. We had somehow to discover what it was that caused plant disease. This was not so easy. The ancient man knew some of the causes of food destruction. He could see the locusts that ate his wheat in the field and the rats that ate his wheat in the granary. But he could not see the fungus that was stealing the starch from the grains and causing them to shrivel and shrink.

We very glibly say these modern days that plant diseases are caused chiefly by fungi, and we all pretty well understand that a fungus is a small, chlorophyll-free thread that we can see quite easily under the microscope. How did we arrive at this simple-sounding conclusion?

First of all, what is a disease? Is disease a condition? Some people would say that it is. In that case, would you say that fever is a disease? Well, most of us would say that fever is not a disease. Fever is a condition. When our temperature goes up, we have the condition called fever. Is a leaf spot on a plant a disease? No, that is like fever, that is a condition—a *symptom* of disease. We see that it is not the disease but it is a symptom of a diseased plant, the same as fever is a symptom of a diseased human.

A characteristic of disease is that it is continuous. If we cut our finger, we don't say that it is diseased—it's abnormal but it's not diseased, because we know that it is a transient and temporary thing, and so we distinguish an injury like that from a disease. Similarly a lawn mower does not produce disease in the grass; it cuts the grass off, producing some injury, but we don't say the grass is diseased. We can, therefore, help to distinguish disease from injury by saying that disease is a continuously acting process, not a transient, temporary one such as the bite of a dog or the cut of a lawn mower in the grass. So, in simple language, we can say that disease is an abnormal and deleterious process caused by something which acts more or less continuously.

The crux of this matter of plant disease lies in that term *caused by*. Cause is not a very difficult concept. We have seen that reckless driving causes accidents, and we say that eating a green apple causes a stomach-ache. But what causes plant diseases?

The cause of plant disease remained enigmatic for a long time because for many centuries we could not see the fungus involved.

We could not see it or feel it or otherwise experience it with one or more of our five senses.

The Israelites were told (Deuteronomy 28:22) that God was responsible for wheat rust, that the Lord would smite them with blasting and mildew if they didn't obey the commandments of Jehovah. There must have been some doubters about this point, however, because four or five hundred years later the prophet, Haggai, says, "I smote you with blasting and mildew and with hail and yet ye turned not to me, saith the Lord." It is not recorded in the Bible what the people thought caused wheat rust, but they must have doubted that the Lord did or Haggai would never have said that in spite of the blast and mildew they still did not obey the Lord.

The writer of Genesis (41:23), however, must have been somewhat more of a naturalist than the writer of Deuteronomy because he referred to the east wind as the cause of the blasting. This, however, undoubtedly meant the drying east wind coming off the desert which would blast the blossoms if it hit them at the proper time.

There is, however, some element of truth in this east wind business even for rust. In the United States, at least, many of our storms come in on the east wind which brings water with it. Of course, moisture itself does not bring on wheat rust. The wheat rust fungus is the true cause; but the fungus likes moisture, grows best in moisture, grows more prolifically in moisture. Hence, we can say that moisture encourages wheat rust and to that degree is a cause of the disease.

Wheat rust swept on down through the ages, and nobody learned what caused it because nobody could yet see it. The year 1726 marks a significant step forward in our understanding of *causation* of disease. *And this was recorded in a law book.*

DISEASE CHANGES THE LAW

The colony of Connecticut in 1726 passed a law specifying that barberries must be eradicated in the vicinity of wheat fields, and the General Court (legislature) set a fine of 20 shillings for failure to kill out the barberries and a further fine of 10 shillings per month until the barberries were eradicated. The law says, "Whereas the abounding of barberries is thought to be very hurtful, it being by plentiful experience found that, where they are in large quantities, they do *occasion or at least increase the blast* on all sorts of English grain." Looking back on the situation from the vantage point of 1956, it is an amazing thing that the Legislature of Connecticut would pass a law eradicating the barberry plant in order to control a disease on another plant. This must have sounded fantastic to the lawyers of that day. In fact, you can hear a little bit of skepticism in the statement, "Whereas the abounding of barberries is *thought* to be very hurtful." The effect of the barberries on the wheat was scoffed at by the botanists of the day, but the practical wheat grower was very insistent that the barberries produced the blast. It was not until 150 years later that the great German plant pathologist De Bary discovered that the wheat rust fungus spends part of its life on the barberry plant. Without the barberry plant to support it during part of the year, the wheat rust would have died in Colonial Connecticut. This indicates the remarkable perspicacity and keen observation of the practical wheat grower of long ago. They said in effect, "Barberries cause wheat rust." Barberries they could see.

In passing we might note that the Connecticut law led eventually to barberry-eradication laws in most of the wheat-growing areas of the world. Actually barberry eradication has not worked well in America as a method of controlling wheat rust. The fungus winters in Mexico, and the microscopic spores ride north on the spring storms. Hence, the fungus does not now need the barberry to get it through the year. Nevertheless, the barberry law initially promulgated here in Connecticut in 1726 might in some ways be considered as altering the course of history. As far as I know, it was the grandfather of all laws specifying that it is the duty of the State to protect people from the consequences of pestilence. It was the first quarantine law.

Jethro Tull, the famous English writer on agricultural subjects, in his well-known book *Horse-hoeing Husbandry*, published in 1733, decided that insects were the cause of wheat rust because he thought that the spots on the leaves were caused by excreta from insects. He could see the insects and was inclined to ascribe the disease to this visible cause.

SEEING IS BELIEVING

It so happens that a Dutch lens grinder named Leeuwenhoek had invented the microscope the latter part of the seventeenth century and now we could see. Leeuwenhoek was a few years ahead of Jethro Tull, but not far enough ahead so that Tull knew much of anything about a microscope. Some hundred years after Leeuwenhoek described his microscope, an Italian, Fontana, in 1766, looked through it at diseased wheat leaves and found the microscopic fungus which we today call *Puccinia graminis*. Fontana, however, did not conceive that these microscopic bodies that he saw were the cause of wheat rust. He got himself embroiled in another mix-up in causation. He decided that the fungus bodies he saw were excrescences growing out of the diseased tissue. Fontana thought that the rust disease was the cause of the fungus rather than that fungus was the cause of the rust disease. This is a curious inversion of reasoning as we look back on it from here, but it was not so strange to Fontana.

Ten years later, Tillet, the master of the French mint, who was an amateur plant pathologist on the side, was working with another ancient disease of wheat called smut. Tillet looked through Leeuwenhoek's microscope and discovered the fungus of the wheat smut, but he also tended to look upon the fungus as the result of the smut rather than the cause thereof. Later, however, he changed his mind because he was actually able to take the small spores of the fungus and mix them up with healthy wheat seed. Wheat so inoculated came down with the disease. This is probably the earliest experimental production of any disease, plant or animal, on record. We might pause for just a second to note that this was almost an even one hundred years ahead of Pasteur and his famous demonstration of anthrax in sheep, normally recorded as the first demonstration of the germ causation of disease. Tillet's work, however, did not convince very many people; more people were inclined to consider the fungus as an excrescence from diseased tissue rather than the cause of disease.

In 1844 when the potato blight was devastating the potato crops of Ireland, Dr. Lindley, the well-known editor of the *Gardener's Chronicle* in London, was writing that the fungus that he could find with his microscope on the leaves of the diseased plants was an excrescence from diseased tissue and not the cause thereof. Thereby, Dr. Lindley did a great disservice to the Irish. If he had truly sensed the nature of the fungus that he found on the diseased tissue, he might very well have solved the potato blight problem right then and there. But enough of that for now.

EXPERIMENTAL DISEASE

The critical consideration in deciding about the cause of a plant disease is whether or not one can produce the disease experimentally. This is the hard core of the science of plant pathology. Can we, in any given disease, dig out the cause, bring the suspected cause to bear on healthy plants, produce the disease, and isolate the cause again? In the case of the potato blight that devastated the potatoes in Ireland, it is technically possible, although not easy, to find the fungus that is suspected to cause the disease. One can grow it free and clear of all other fungi in test tubes in the laboratory, examine its characteristics and its nature, inoculate it into living healthy plants that are separated from other plants, and produce the typical disease. One can then re-isolate the fungus clear and free back in the test tube again. If the disease agrees with the disease normally found in the field, and the fungus that is taken out of the artificially infected plants looks like the fungus that was put in, then we say that we have fulfilled the basic postulates to prove causation of any given plant disease.

The interesting point to note here is that we didn't discover the true cause of plant disease until the invention of the microscope. We would probably still be speculating as to what causes plant diseases and still not have any very good methods of controlling them, if it were not for Mr. Leeuwenhoek's invention, which made it possible to see fungi and demonstrate their association with plant diseases.

With a brief digression, one might say, however, that several plant diseases are now known which are caused, not by fungi, but by bacteria which are too small to be seen with Mr. Leeuwenhoek's microscope. The discovery of bacteria had to await the arrival of an improvement in the microscope, called the oil-immersion lens. As soon as the oil-immersion lens was invented, we could find bacteria in the diseased tissues. Once observed, the bacteria could be isolated like the fungi, grown in pure culture, inoculated into plants, re-isolated, and compared with the original, thereby proving that bacteria produce plant disease.

Once the importance of bacteria was settled there was still a residue of diseases which were catching like other diseases but which were not caused by either bacteria or fungi. Techniques had been devised by then for inoculation and experimental production of disease, and it could be shown that the disease could be transferred from plant to plant but no "causal organism" could be found. It was suspected then that the causal organism was ultra-microscopic, and it was labeled by the old term, virus, which originally meant poison. But virus has now come to mean a cause for disease that cannot be seen with a microscope. In the middle of the 1930's, the Radio Corporation of America invented a new kind of microscope depending upon a beam of electrons, not light. With this machine, viruses can now be seen; we know about how big they are and can make out something of their characteristics and structure.

CHEMICAL WARFARE

Once the role of fungi in causing disease was established, control measures became feasible. Much of the modern control of plant disease is accomplished with fungicides that search out the fungus and kill it.

In the last ten years, more has been learned about chemical control of fungi than in the whole course of history before. Chemical killers of fungi are called fungicides. These are the substances that will help to keep the roof from falling in. They are the substances that will help in the fight with the fungi. They comprise nowadays a vast armamentarium to assure farmers of the means to protect food from fungi so that people may have it to eat.

These compounds also were the end of a long and toilsome road.

We have mentioned Dr. Lindley and his misconception of the role of the fungus in producing the rot of the Irish potato in the famine year 1844. In the very same year, an amateur plant pathologist, Judge Cheever of the Court in New York City, came mighty close to providing the Irish with an answer to their blight problem. Judge Cheever had read some of the agricultural literature and remembered that a Frenchman, Prévost, had killed the fungus of wheat smut with copper sulfate and thus had been able to control the disease. Prévost worked in 1807, almost forty years ahead of the Irish famine. The control of wheat smut by treating the seed with copper sulfate to kill the fungus had become almost standard practice by the time of the famine in 1844.

Judge Cheever, knowing this control of the wheat smut, had suggested that copper sulfate be applied to the potato plant for the control of blight. As far as I can find, there is no record that Judge Cheever ever tried this experimentally, but I suspect that he did try it and it failed, because the copper sulfate burned up his plants just as badly as the blight and was, therefore, not practical. Copper sulfate does not burn wheat seed for numerous technical reasons, but it does burn foliage and therefore could have been of no use in the control of potato blight.

The same year a Belgian amateur named Morren actually did put together a safe mixture of copper sulfate. He mixed copper sulfate with lime and table salt and applied it for the control of potato blight. The only trouble with Morren's method was that he poured the mixture on the ground where the fungus was not and he did not pour it on the foliage where it was. Morren missed the significance of the fungus on the leaf. He thought that the disease came from a miasma arising from wet soil. Hence, he poured his mixture on the ground, where it was worthless, rather than on the foliage, where it would have solved the Irish famine.

In 1882, almost forty years after the Irish famine, Morren's mixture, minus the salt, was rediscovered in the province of Bordeaux in France by Professor Millardet. Thus was born Bordeaux mixture, the most famous fungicide of all time. If Judge Cheever, who recognized the fungus, had used the lime with his copper, or if Morren, who used lime, had recognized the fungus, we would probably have fewer Irishmen in Boston today than we do.

5

PROBLEMS IN PREVENTING PLANT-DISEASE EPIDEMICS

E. C. Stakman [1]

Plant disease epidemics, outbreaks of insect pests, bad weather, and human ignorance are the greatest obstacles to assured food supplies for the peoples of the world. Throughout recorded history, and probably before that, man has been confronted at certain times and in certain places with the specters of hunger and famine because of devastating plant diseases, destructive insects, droughts and floods, searing heat, and killing cold. This is evident from legends of the remote past, from historical records, and from recent experiences.

When man progressed from a food gatherer to a food producer, he alleviated some problems of human subsistence but he also created many new ones. He not only transformed rice, wheat, barley, maize, and millet from grass to grain but he also transformed the lands on which they were grown. He removed the natural vegetation by clearing forests, ploughing grasslands, draining swamps, and irrigating deserts. And he planted one kind of plant in dense stands on lands where there had been sparser populations of many kinds of native plants. This concentration of homogeneous plant populations created the same kind of problems as the concentration of human populations in cities; it tended to aggravate the problems of diseases and pests. Plant public health became a problem, just as human public health became a problem when people crowded together in cities.

Man had to become a botanist in order to become civilized. As M. D. C. Crawford said, "Civilization is, as it were, a second flowering of barley, wheat, rice, and Indian corn." Although the concept of civilization usually includes more than the improvement and cultivation of plants, there could be no civilization without them, because man could not exist without them.

[1] The writer is indebted to Laura M. Hamilton for assistance in the preparation of the material on epidemiology of stem rust.

Man is completely dependent on plants for subsistence. Important as animals are, it is almost literally true that all flesh is grass. Important as is modern industry, it cannot produce the basic foods needed for human subsistence. Basically, man's existence on earth is dependent on plants, and the degree to which he can develop a biotechnology based on science is an important factor in determining how and how many people can live in the world.

Agriculture, then, is the most basic of all industries, and in the last analysis agriculture is applied botany. The course of evolution of agriculture is traced by the history of the improvement, the adaptation, the nutrition, and the protection of plants that man utilizes directly or indirectly for foods, feeds, and fibers. As plant foods are converted by animals, various branches of zoology become important also, but animals are essentially transformers rather than primary producers of human food. We still are dependent on the process of photosynthesis, which is carried on only by plants; and the problem is to develop a biotechnology that provides the most efficient kinds of plants and then helps them to function as efficiently as possible. Efficient plants must be well bred and well fed, and they must be protected against the debilitating and devastating diseases that continually menace them.

There are thousands of kinds of plant diseases that attack the thousands of kinds of wild and cultivated plants of gardens, fields, and forests. They cause spots and blotches, rots and cankers, blights and wilts, rusts and mildews, smuts and sooty molds, galls and witches'-brooms. There are more than three thousand kinds of plant rusts that attack grains and grasses, trees and shrubs, the most beautiful flowers of the gardens, and the ugliest weeds of the fields. And there are more than fifteen hundred kinds of powdery mildews that attack oaks and willows, roses and lilacs, wheat and barley, and hundreds of other kinds of plants.

Disease is universal among all our cultivated plants and most of our wild ones. Some kinds of disease attack many kinds of plants; others attack only a few. Some diseases cause relatively little damage; others are ruthless killers. Some spread slowly; others can spread with frightening rapidity and cause widespread destruction in a short time; they have the ability to become devastatingly epidemic when weather and other conditions favor their development.

Most epidemic diseases are caused by viruses, bacteria, or fungi that can multiply with amazing rapidity and that can be quickly disseminated far and wide by insects or by the wind. The rusts of wheat and certain other cereal grains have periodically caused catastrophic epidemics for more than two thousand years, and they still continue their destructive careers despite man's best efforts to control them. They are among the most typically epidemic diseases.

Three of the more than three thousand kinds of plant rusts are among the oldest-known enemies of wheat. There is evidence from many statements in the Bible that one or more of them plagued the farmers of the Holy Land, as there are warnings in Deuteronomy and other books that the Lord would curse the land with blasting and with mildew if His commandments were not obeyed. In I Kings, Chapter 8, famine and pestilence, blasting and mildew, locust and caterpillar are mentioned in the same verse with ". . . if their enemy besiege them in the land of their cities." Plant diseases and insect pests evidently were included among the major menaces to national welfare. The ancient Hebrews obviously feared plant diseases but did not understand them and therefore attributed their occurrence to the wrath of God because of the transgressions of the people. In Amos, Chapter 4, it appears that punishment actually was inflicted, for it is said "I have smitten you with blasting and mildew . . . yet have ye not returned unto me saith the Lord."

That rusts of wheat and barley were major factors in the production of these crops in ancient Greece and Rome is clear from the writings of Theophrastus, the "Father of Botany," in the Fourth Century B.C. and those of Pliny, the great Roman compiler of natural history, in the First Century A.D., who called the rust of wheat and barley the greatest pest of crops. Like the Hebrews, the Greeks and Romans attributed epidemics to supernatural causes and besought various of their gods to protect the crops against them. "Stern Robigo, spare the herbage of the cereals; withhold, we pray, thy roughening hand . . ." was the opening of a prayer to the Roman rust god, Robigo, or Robigus, who reputedly came into existence about 700 B.C. and whom the Romans tried to placate in the annual festival of the Robigalia from that time until well into the Christian era. The Greeks and Romans mixed their superstition with naturalism, as they attributed rust epidemics to multiple causes: the gods, the position of the moon and stars, and to certain kinds of weather. They observed differences in varietal susceptibility and in the effect of location on rust, correctly stating that rust was likely to be most abundant in low-lying fields.

In *King Lear*, 1605, Shakespeare says that ". . . the foul fiend Flibbertigibbet . . . mildews the white wheat. . . ." From this time onward several writers on agricultural subjects in England complained that no remedies were known for the destructive rusts and smuts of wheat, and Parliament asked for a report on the situation.

There was much speculation about plant diseases, but Rouen, France, took action by passing a law, ca. 1660, requiring the destruction of barberry bushes because of the observed fact that rust was most severe near them. This was two hundred years before it was known how barberry affected the development of rust on wheat. Indeed, it was long before it was even known that stem rust was caused by a microscopic fungus. The legislators of Rouen deserve much credit for realizing that there was a dangerous alliance between barberry and stem rust and for trying to break it, even though they did not know how it operated. There must have been good observers among them. Barberry-eradication laws were passed also in colonial Connecticut, Massachusetts, and Rhode Island a century or longer before the true nature of stem rust was finally revealed by the researches of De Bary, about 1865, during the period when Pasteur, Koch, and others were proving that germs could cause diseases of man and other animals.

Man's ignorance about devastating plant diseases drove him to super-natural or speculative explanations about their nature and to many irra-tional and some effective empirical procedures in attempting to control them. Attempts by philosophers and scientists to understand the nature of diseases were balked for almost two thousand years because there was no compound microscope to reveal the invisible world of microorganisms that cause most of the destructive plant diseases and many of the diseases of human beings and of domestic animals. The development of the microscope by Janssen, in 1590, finally made it possible to see bacteria, fungus spores, and other microorganisms, but it was almost a hundred years more before Leeuwenhoek actually saw them, and still another hundred and fifty years before it was learned what they can do.

De Bary is generally credited with the discovery, about a hundred years ago, that fungi can cause plant disease; and it was discovered even more recently that bacteria and viruses can cause them also. There had long been curiosity about the nature and cause of plant diseases, and many attempts had been made to control them because of the extensive and sometimes ter-rific damage that they caused. A powerful impetus was given to more inten-sive study by the ravages of potato blight in Western Europe, which cul-minated in the catastrophic epidemic of 1845. This epidemic was vastly destructive and became a national calamity in Ireland, where the Irish potato was almost literally the staff of life for most of the people. Every potato field was virtually ruined; the foliage was suddenly killed to the ground, and the tubers rotted in the ground. And man, even the wisest botanist, was pathetically helpless because no one knew whence or why the blight came. It was as if a curse had descended upon the land. Commissions of inquiry and relief were established, but the price of scientific ignorance was terrible: a million deaths from starvation, hunger, or disease in Ireland within a decade and a half, the direct and indirect results of a plant disease that was as mysterious in origin as tragic in effect.

How can plant diseases spread so fast and so far and cause such complete destruction in so short a time? And why, after a hundred years of scientific study, do some of them still defy complete and permanent control? The stem rust of wheat is a good illustrative example.

Every one who has ever studied botany knows that stem rust of wheat, oats, barley, rye, and many wild grasses is caused by a microscopic fungus, *Puccinia graminis,* which is still classed as an obligate parasite because it has not yet been propagated on anything except living plants. It also is generally known that stem rust is heteroecious; like many other rusts it requires two distinct kinds of plants to complete its full life cycle. Like other fungi, stem rust multiplies and reproduces by means of microscopic spores, one one-thousandth of an inch or less in size. Stem rust produces two kinds of spores on wheat, the urediospores, or summer spores, of the red stage, and the teliospores, or winter spores, of the black stage. The urediospores can germinate immediately after they are formed; they can infect wheat and produce successive generations about once a week on growing plants. As the wheat begins to ripen, however, teliospores, or winter spores, are formed. They require exposure to cold weather, especially alternate freezing and thawing, before they will germinate. They therefore survive severe winters and germinate in the spring. On germination, the teliospore sends out one or two germ tubes, each of which produces four sporidia, a third kind of spore. The sporidia are forcibly shot off from the tubes, or promycelia, on which they are formed, are disseminated by wind, and can infect only certain kinds of barberry, on which a fourth and fifth kind of spore are produced, the pycniospores and the aeciospores, or cluster-cup spores. The pycniospores are restricted to a sexual function, but the aeciospores are forcibly shot out from the cups, in which they are formed in long, closely packed chains. The aeciospores are disseminated by the wind and can infect only wheat or certain other wild or cultivated grasses, resulting in the formation of the uredial stage. It is only the uredial stage, then, that can produce successive generations of spores on wheat and that enables the rust to spread rapidly from wheat to wheat.

The basic reason why stem rust can become quickly and widely epidemic is that it can multiply so rapidly from small beginnings. A urediospore may germinate in less than an hour, send out a germ tube that grows along the epidermal surface of wheat, enters through a stoma, and is inside of the plant within six hours or even less. The rust tubes, or hyphae, then branch and grow parasitically between the plant cells, form an extensive network, or mycelium, about 5 mm. in extent, which then produces a new crop of 50 thousand to 450 thousand urediospores within a week or ten days. Each of the new spores can then repeat the process, and this can go on and on as long as wheat is green and growing. On a single barberry bush in northern United States there may be about 70 billion aeciospores by the middle of May. If only 1 per cent caused infection and produced small uredial pustules on wheat, the progeny would be 70 thousand billion urediospores. On an acre of moderately rusted wheat there are about 50 thousand billion urediospores, each one capable of surviving a long air journey and starting infection many miles from the place where it was produced.

The astronomically large numbers of rust spores can be quickly disseminated far and wide by the wind. Only the teliospores and pycniospores are not adapted to wind dissemination. The aeciospores and sporidia are shot forcibly into the air, and the urediospores are produced in powdery pustules so that the slightest air movement can carry them away. The urediospores, the largest of the three kinds mentioned, are so small and light that they fall only at the rate of about 10 mm. per second in perfectly still air. If a rust pustule is attached to the bottom of a cork inserted in a vertical glass cylinder illuminated by a beam of light, clouds of spores can be seen falling as minute, bright-colored, dust-like particles. But the slightest rise in temperature from the beam of light sets up convection currents that quickly carry the spores back upward. In nature, convection currents, whirlwinds, and other air movements may carry the spores upward several thousand feet. Large numbers have been caught on petroleum-jelly-covered microscope slides exposed from airplanes flying at altitudes of 7 to 10 thousand feet, and some have been caught at more than 16 thousand feet. Horizontal air currents can carry them hundreds or even thousands of miles; they literally move with the speed of wind until brought down to earth again by air currents or rain. Urediospores are often deposited at the level of growing grain at a daily rate of a few thousand to a million per square foot of surface, far from the area where they were produced. And so, astronomically large numbers of rust spores can be carried on the wings of the wind, spreading the red scourge over millions of acres of wheat with dramatic and catastrophic suddenness. This is not mere theory; it is fact, as can be shown by several examples.

In 1925, when little was known about the long-distance dissemination of cereal rusts, stem rust left a clear and unmistakable record of a sudden mass migration. By June 1 rust had extended from central Texas to central Kansas, but none could be found anywhere farther north. Then southerly winds blew northward for several days in succession at average velocities of 17 to 26 miles an hour. Spores were caught on spore traps exposed at various places north of the rusted area, rains or dews permitted the spores to germinate and cause infection, and within ten days rust broke out on wheat over an area of a quarter of a million square miles. The wind had carried spores 600 miles northward, from central Kansas to the Canadian border, over a front more than 400 miles wide. As another example, in early June, 1953, it was calculated that there were 4,000 tons of urediospores, with about 150 billion spores per pound, on 4 million acres of wheat in northern Oklahoma and south-central Kansas. Winds carried spores northward from this area into the Dakotas and Minnesota, where they were deposited at the rate of 3.5 million an acre in an area comprising 40 thousand square miles.

In order to develop most rapidly and become epidemic, stem rust must have favorable weather. In general, it is most destructive in warm, moist seasons, although there are so many combinations of conditions and patterns of development in North America that they cannot be discussed in detail here. The extent and severity of epidemics varies greatly with the region and the season. In general, epidemics are a function of wind and weather wherever there are extensive areas of susceptible host plants.

The history of attempts to control stem rust in the United States and Canada coincides closely in time with the history of the Botanical Society of America. Wheat has been protected fairly well against widespread and destructive attacks of stem rust in twenty of the past fifty years. The question naturally arises as to why it could not have been protected all the time. A general answer is that there was not enough basic research to furnish the information needed for the most effective procedures; there was too much scientific ignorance. Consequently many of the efforts to solve the problem, at least in the early years, were not made on a broad enough front and on a sufficiently extensive scale. Scientific concepts and technologic efforts simply were not commensurate with the complexity of the problem. Another possible reason could be that the problem is not completely soluble, but only future research will determine whether this is true.

Practical necessity forced attempts to control stem rust in North America. From colonial times onward, rust was destructive at some times and in some places, but the problem was aggravated when wheat growing was extended to the vast area of the Mississippi Basin and into the prairie provinces of Canada, where wind and weather are often at their destructive worst in spreading infection. A widespread and destructive epidemic in the Upper Mississippi Valley in 1904 stimulated efforts to control the rust. But how was it to be controlled?

Three possible methods of rust control were considered: (1) spraying or dusting the wheat with protective fungicides; (2) eradicating barberries to interrupt the life cycle of the rust; and (3) selecting or breeding rust-resistant varieties. The results of early spraying experiments were not promising, and experimentation on chemical control therefore languished for a number of years. There was evidence, however, that barberry eradication had alleviated the rust situation in Denmark. But the eradication of barberries in a large country like the United States seemed like a fantastic undertaking to plant scientists not yet accustomed to extensive plant public-health measures. The development of resistant varieties seemed the most feasible method of attack. Some varieties of the durum and emmer groups of *Triticum*—wheats in the broad sense—appeared to be highly resistant, but they were not bread wheats. Shortly after the epidemic of 1904, therefore, breeding was started in an attempt to combine the rust resistance of the durums, emmers, and certain apparently resistant common wheats with the desired quality of the bread wheats.

The terrific epidemic of 1916, which destroyed approximately 300 million bushels of wheat in the United States and Canada, was so ruinous in its direct and indirect effects that plant scientists took another look at the situation. They concluded that much more information was needed about the epidemiology of the rust, that the breeding work should be intensified, and that barberry eradication should be undertaken on a national scale.

A state-wide barberry-eradication campaign was begun under state law in North Dakota in 1917, and a national campaign was begun early in 1918 as a war emergency measure to increase food production. Thirteen of the principal wheat-growing states of northern United States were first included in the eradication area, and several were added subsequently. Except at high elevations, barberries seldom rust south of the 38th parallel of latitude, because the teliospores do not survive the long, hot summers. Eradication was restricted, therefore, to the more northern states, where it was known that rust appeared earlier near barberries than away from them and that epidemics might extend a number of miles from the bushes. It soon became apparent that there were unexpectedly large numbers of bushes and that they had escaped extensively from cultivation in unexpected areas. Nevertheless the campaign was prosecuted vigorously, and 296 million bushes had been destroyed on 126 thousand properties by 1941.

It had been realized before this that barberry eradication alone would not prevent epidemics entirely because there usually was an abundant source of rust in Mexico and Texas in the early spring. In Mexico the uredial stage of rust can persist throughout the year, so it is always a potential source of inoculum. Although the uredial stage does not survive the long hot summers of Texas because there is no wheat during that time, fall-sown wheat usually becomes infected in the fall by wind-blown spores from the north or later by spores blown in from Mexico. The uredial stage often persists in some fields during the winter, may increase early in the spring, and constitute a menace for wheat farther north. The wind then can carry countless numbers of spores northward in successive waves, so that wheat is always in jeopardy of infection.

There are, then, two possible sources of rust in the spring. In northeastern United States, in certain inter-mountain areas of western United States, and in certain European countries, the persistence of stem rust is almost completely dependent on barberries. In other areas, however, such as central Mexico where wheat is grown throughout the year at varying elevations, rust can persist in the uredial stage independently of the barberry. In the great inter-mountain area of the United States and the prairies of Canada, however, rust cannot persist throughout the year without the aid of the barberry, but so much rust can be blown into this area from Mexico or Texas in the early summer that widespread epidemics can develop from a source 1,500–2,000 miles away. The wheat-growing area extending from central Mexico for about 2,500 miles northward through the United States and into Canada, then, is a vast wind-swept area in which countless billions of spores may be blown from south to north in the spring and from north to south in the fall. Consequently there is always the danger of epidemics when winds and weather are favorable.

Despite the fact that barberry eradication did not prevent epidemics entirely in the United States, there were several very valuable results. On the assumption that each bush that was destroyed would have produced less than half of maximum infection, the destruction of 296 million bushes prevented the annual production of 9×10^{18}, or 9 quintillion, aeciospores. This would have been enough to inoculate every acre of wheat in the United States and Mexico with more than 100 billion spores an acre. Barberry eradication also controlled rust on rye, because there is little rye in the southern States and in Mexico to furnish inoculum for the North; hence stem rust of rye was largely dependent for its existence on barberry bushes. The eradication also eliminated thousands of early-infection centers on wheat; it prevented many local epidemics and some extensive ones; it reduced the danger of general epidemics; and it resulted in practical control of rust in certain areas outside of the south-to-north sweep of the winds.

Barberry eradication is still one of the major weapons against stem rust because the barberry is the breeding ground for new kinds of rust. It has long been known that the sexual stage of stem rust is on the barberry, and it was therefore suspected that new kinds of rust might result from sexual recombinations. The discovery of the sexual function of the pycnia by Craigie in 1927 facilitated experiments that confirmed the hypothesis that new parasitic races resulted from sexual recombination on the barberry.

The species *Puccinia graminis*, stem rust, is complex in composition. It comprises at least six varieties that differ in minor morphological characters but especially in the kinds of plants that they can attack. Thus the variety *tritici* can attack wheat, barley, and more than a hundred kinds of wild grasses; it can also infect rye to some extent but not oats and certain wild grasses. The variety *avenae* infects oats and a number of wild grasses but not wheat, barley, and rye. The *secalis* variety develops well on rye, barley, and a number of wild grasses but not on wheat and oats. There are three other varieties that develop principally on timothy, Kentucky bluegrass and closely related species, and redtop and other species of *Agrostis*, respectively. But the specialization goes still farther. Within the *tritici* variety there are at least 275 known physiologic races that look alike but differ in their ability to attack certain varieties of wheat. A single variety, therefore, may be immune from certain races, highly resistant to others, and completely susceptible to still others. It is now known that new races are produced very commonly as a result of hybridization between existing races on the barberry, although some are produced by mutation and by nuclear rearrangement in the uredial stage also.

During the early attempts to develop resistant varieties, nothing was known about physiologic races within varieties of stem rust. When physiologic races of wheat stem rust were discovered, in 1916, attempts were made to determine their number, geographic distribution, and parasitic effects.

A system was devised for identifying races by their parasitic effects on a standard set of twelve varieties that seemed to be representative of the principal types of wheat. The races are designated by number. Each year, races are identified from about a thousand collections of rusted wheat from the principal wheat-growing areas of the United States and Mexico. Similar studies are made in Canada, so that the geographic distribution and population trends of the principal races in North America during the past thirty-five years are fairly well known. What has been their record?

Following the terrible epidemic of 1916, rust-resistant durum wheats, from which macaroni is made, were substituted extensively for bread wheats in the spring-wheat region of the United States, but within a few years rust races appeared to which they were completely susceptible. Kanred, a good winter wheat selected in Kansas, appeared to be immune from rust, but almost as soon as it was distributed rust races were found to which it is completely susceptible. In 1926 the rust-resistant hybrid variety Ceres, a good spring wheat, was distributed and soon became by far the most popular variety in the spring-wheat region of Minnesota, the Dakotas, eastern Montana, and adjacent Canada. Ceres seemed to have solved the stem rust problem in spring wheat. But in 1935 it was suddenly and tragically ruined in a terrific epidemic caused principally by race 56 of stem rust. This race had first been isolated from barberry in Iowa in 1928, two years after Ceres was first distributed, and by 1934 it was the most prevalent race in the United States. In 1935 race 56 almost literally exploded and virtually ended the career of Ceres wheat. Many other varieties, however, had been in the making, among them Thatcher, which resulted from crosses involving three parents. It had been severely tested against all known races of stem rust prior to its first distribution in 1934. It came unscathed through the epidemic of 1935 and another severe epidemic in 1937. It was extremely susceptible to orange leaf rust and to Fusarial head blight, however, so that it could not be grown successfully in the more humid parts of the spring-wheat area where these diseases are most prevalent and destructive. It persisted, however, in the drier areas of western Canada, where it still produces well on millions of acres.

Another series of varieties were soon released that had the "Hope type" of resistance. The variety Hope resulted from a cross between Jaroslav emmer, which had no virtues except rust resistance, and Marquis wheat, which had all the virtues except rust resistance. Hope did not have the qualities needed in a commercial bread wheat, but it was widely and successfully hybridized with good bread wheats. Similarly, highly resistant durums had been produced by crossing good macaroni varieties with Vernal emmer. Thus the era of "Hope resistance" began. Again it looked as if stem rust was under control in the spring wheat area.

From 1938 to 1949, inclusive, there were no epidemics of stem rust in the spring-wheat area of the United States and Canada. As barberry eradication progressed, the number of prevalent rust races decreased. Only four were prevalent enough to be important during this period, and the varieties grown were resistant to all of them. But many different races were being found on barberries in eastern United States. Among them was the very virulent race 15B, to which all the resistant varieties of bread wheat and durum then grown were susceptible. The question as to whether this very dangerous race would ever become widespread and prevalent was answered suddenly and dramatically in 1950. An unusual sequence of wind and weather conditions enabled the improbable to happen: race 15B spread over most of North America in a single season. A few spores apparently were blown into the Gulf States early in the spring, then 15B appeared sparingly in Texas and gradually spread northward, gathering momentum as it went onward to southern Canada. A very late crop season and a late and wet fall in the north enabled the rust to produce countless billions of spores on the very late wheat and on wild grasses, especially wild barley. Now the question arose as to whether winter would descend on the rust and freeze it to death before favorable winds could carry spores to the far south, where they could establish the rust for the winter. Winds did their worst; they carried a heavy cargo of spores far southward into Mexico, where the rust became established, survived the winter, and was ready to reinfect wheat fields to the northward in the spring. Thus the most virulent race of wheat stem rust ever found in North America spread over most of the continent and became independent of barberry in a single year. The consequences were tragic. Race 15B ruined thousands of acres of the most resistant wheat that had been laboriously developed in Mexico, it caused heavy local damage to all resistant varieties in northern United States and Canada, and in 1953 and 1954 it ruined the durum wheat crop of the United States and caused extensive damage to hitherto resistant bread wheats.

Preliminary attempts had been made to develop varieties resistant to race 15B shortly after it was first discovered on barberries in Iowa in 1939, even though it was subsequently found only in barberry areas of eastern United States. Certain Kenya wheats seemed to be highly resistant, but it was soon found that some of them were resistant only at moderate temperatures and completely susceptible at higher temperatures, when resistance is most needed. It is, of course, hard to breed against something that is not yet in existence, and there is good evidence that race 15B not only increased in quantity but also in diversity in 1950, for it soon became apparent that it comprised many biotypes or sub-races that differ in virulence on certain new, and some old, wheat varieties. It is a confederation of an indefinite number of biotypes. Other new races have appeared since 1950, and some almost forgotten ones have returned. It is impossible to say how many rust races there are, but the number certainly is many times greater than the approxi-

mately 275 that are now recognized. The problem is to find wheat varieties
that reveal the differences. As new combinations of genes are made in varieties
of wheat, additional differences become apparent between and within rust
races.

It is of course impossible to predict the outcome of the long fight against
wheat stem rust until we find out the maximum genic potentiality for virulence in the rust and the maximum genic potential for resistance in wheat.
This obviously requires extensive and basic studies of the genetics of the
rust, of the genes for resistance in wheat, and of the nature and variability of
resistance. It is known, of course, that resistance may be due to physiologic
and to structural characters. Nothing is known about the real nature of
physiologic resistance, but there are several morphological characters, such
as thick epidermis and woody stems, that contribute to resistance. Physiologic resistance varies widely with temperature and light in some rust-race–
wheat-variety combinations but not in others. Morphologic resistance seems
more constant. Can a universally resistant variety be built by combining all
known characters for resistance in a single variety? The answer may be
available in the centenary year of the Botanical Society, but it is hoped
that it may be sooner. A world-wide search must be made among the score
of thousands of wheat varieties, those that appear to have desirable characters
must be thoroughly studied and tested under an adequate sample of environmental conditions, and the problem still remains of combining all needed
characters. If the desired combinations of characters cannot be found or
made, there is still the possibility that gene changes can be induced by
chemicals or by irradiation. And this possibility should be investigated
thoroughly.

Researches on the virulence of the rust fungus, on the resistance of wheat,
and on the interaction between the parasite and its host will require very
intensive studies on the physiology of parasitic relations and on the effect of
environmental factors on the processes involved. There must be far more
extensive ecological investigations on a world-wide scale and much more
intensive investigation of the intimate relationships between host and parasite. We now know something about what happens, but too little about how
and why it happens.

The title of this paper imposes the obligation to discuss problems in the
control of epidemics; it may seem that problems have been magnified and
progress minimized. In reality, of course, great progress has been made.
Considering the nature of the problem, a record of protecting spring wheat
twenty years in fifty is not bad. Moreover, the spring bread wheats now
grown are 25 to 50 per cent more resistant than those of fifty years ago.
It is true that they can be ruined by rust, but fewer races can ruin them, and
it takes a longer time and more favorable conditions for even the most virulent North American race to ruin them.

Nevertheless it is pertinent to ask whether the large investment in time, effort, and monies spent in trying to control one epidemic disease has paid dividends. The answer is a categorical and emphatic yes. The breeding of wheats primarily to control stem rust was not restricted to that one objective. There were many very valuable by-products. Earliness, potential productivity, quality, and resistance to other diseases have also been attained for considerable periods of time for some characters, and permanently for others. The necessity of breeding against stem rust was a powerful stimulus to breeding generally, with the result that the wheats of today, although far from perfect, are far better than those of fifty years ago. Finally, the value of an effort can sometimes be measured by assuming that it had not been made. If the approximately half a billion barberry bushes had not been destroyed during the past four decades but had been permitted to multiply and escape from cultivation, there would now be a local source of early rust near almost every wheat field north of central Kansas and the physiologic race problem would have been far more complex. Barberry eradication was started just in time; had it been delayed until the present it probably would have been impossible and probably unnecessary, because it is doubtful if wheat growing could have continued. It is almost certain that it would now be impossible to grow wheat successfully in the Upper Mississippi Valley if breeding for resistance and barberry eradication had not been undertaken.

Stem rust of wheat has been taken as an example because it is the most complex plant-disease problem in many of the wheat-growing areas of the world. Nevertheless there are similar problems with respect to the prevention of epidemics of other rusts, such as the orange leaf rust of wheat, the yellow stripe rust of wheat, the stem rust and crown rusts of oats, and flax rust. All these rusts can become widely and destructively epidemic in a short time. Although their life histories differ from that of stem rust of wheat, all of them are alike in their prolificacy, spreading power, and potential destructiveness. All of them are disseminated by the wind, and all of them comprise physiologic races, thus increasing the difficulty of producing and maintaining resistant varieties.

Some diseases tend to be perennially epidemic because the causal organisms accumulate and persist in the soil. As one example, flax was long a migratory crop in the United States, moving continually westward to new lands, because it could not long be grown successfully in the same soil or even in the same locality. Prior to 1900, the explanation was that the soil became "flax-sick," but nobody knew why until 1900, when it was shown that the trouble was due to *Fusarium*, a fungus that accumulated and persisted in the soil after having been introduced with flax seed. Under appropriate conditions, the fungus then killed the plants and often ruined the crop. Fortunately, however, a few plants usually survived. Seed from the survivors was then sown back on "sick soil," and the survivors again propagated. In this way several wilt-resistant varieties were produced about fifty years ago. But the varieties apparently lost their resistance after a few years in farmers' fields. The discovery that the flax wilt fungus comprises many physiologic races gave the clue to a method of permanent control. Permanent flax wilt plots were established in which the soil is inoculated with all known races of the wilt fungus and with other infective materials from many sources. All potentially new varieties must survive this severe test, and by such continual testing and selecting, flax wilt has been kept under control by a continual succession of varieties. There are several reasons why this procedure has been effective: first, there are a few resistant plants in most varieties; second, the wilt fungus selects rigidly, usually killing susceptible plants outright and leaving only the most resistant; third, the fungus is not disseminated widely by the wind. Fortunately there have been enough resistant individuals in flax to checkmate the activities of the pathogen in producing new races. This continuous effort has made it possible to save the flax crop of the United States and to maintain its productivity during the past fifty years.

A somewhat similar disease of cabbage has been kept under control for the past thirty-five years by means of resistant varieties. The cabbage yellows, also caused by a species of *Fusarium* which accumulates and persists in the soil, was so destructive in many cabbage-growing areas about 1910 that cabbage growing had to be abandoned. Fortunately, however, there are resistant strains within most of the commercial types of cabbage. By selecting and crossing it has been possible to keep the disease under control. In this case, physiologic races have not complicated the problem.

The virus curly top of sugar beets, which is disseminated by leaf hoppers, became epidemic so often as to threaten the sugar-beet industry in certain areas of western United States a few years ago. Strains of sugar beet have been selected that are sufficiently resistant to the disease to yield satisfactorily when non-resistant selections are virtually ruined by the disease. Immunity has not been found, however, in the cultivated sugar beet, but it is known that certain wild beets are immune. As it has not yet been possible to obtain satisfactory crosses between the wild and the cultivated beets, the problem is to devise ways of obtaining fertile hybrids between the two. There often are, of course, many barriers to the transfer of genes from one kind of plant to another. If wide crosses could be made at will, many problems would be simplified. Possibly ways may be devised to combine genes that now seem to be non-combinable.

Some epidemic diseases can be controlled by spraying or dusting with fungicides, but usually at heavy expense. Thus, the Sigatoka disease of banana, which became epidemic and ruined many banana plantations in certain banana-growing districts of tropical America about twenty-five years ago, is kept in check by spraying the plants from seven to fifteen times during the season with bordeaux mixture. The cost, however, is extremely high. It is estimated that spraying to control this disease and certain insects constitutes as much as 50 per cent of the operating costs in banana production in some areas. But bananas could not be grown successfully without the spraying.

The late blight of potatoes also is reasonably well controlled by spraying. But it is necessary to spray the plants from four to twenty times in order to control the disease. The cost in certain potato-growing areas is at least $35 an acre; consequently attempts have been made to develop resistant varieties that do not require spraying. But there are many physiologic races of the late-blight fungus, and most varieties have therefore been only temporarily resistant. The problem here, as with stem rust of wheat, is to produce a variety that resists all physiologic races under all conditions. Many crosses have been made between wild potatoes that are resistant but otherwise of no value and cultivated potatoes that yield well in the absence of blight. Whether it will be possible to control blight permanently by means of resistant varieties alone remains to be seen. Every increment of resistance that can be incorporated into potatoes, however, will help to reduce the cost of spraying.

Theoretically, plant-disease epidemics could annihilate certain species of plants entirely unless man intervened. The danger is particularly great when new disease organisms are introduced into an area where they have not previously existed, because neither nature nor man has selected for resistance against them. The chestnut blight fungus, which is a native of the Orient, was unwittingly introduced into the United States on ornamental chestnuts about 1904. It rapidly spread from New York, where it was first found, throughout the range of the very valuable American chestnut. Desperate attempts were made to check its spread by cutting barrier zones in which all chestnuts were cut down, but it was a losing fight, because birds and other agents of spore dissemination ignored the barriers. The chestnut forests of the United States have been annihilated. Most of the species of Oriental chestnuts, on which the blight has long existed, have at least sufficient resistance to enable them to grow successfully; but the American chestnut was so susceptible that it quickly succumbed, and there seems to be no chance that the forests will be regenerated because there appears to be no resistance within the species.

Even if the permanent epidemic development of introduced pathogens can be checked, there is always the problem of cost. The bacterium that causes citrus canker was introduced into Florida several decades ago and threatened the existence of the industry. The disease has been brought under control, but only by literally burning the disease out by actually putting a flaming torch to all infected trees and reducing them to charcoal. It was a long and expensive campaign, but it was successful. The white pine blister rust and the Dutch elm disease also are importations from abroad and have become epidemic in certain areas, have gradually extended their range, and are a menace to a group of our best forest trees and one of our best shade trees, respectively. The white pine blister rust fortunately does not spread from pine to pine but only from pine to currants and gooseberries, from which it spreads back to white pine. The disease has been kept in check in certain areas of the United States, therefore, by destroying susceptible currants and gooseberries in the vicinity of valuable stands of white pine. This would be virtually impossible if the rust spread directly from pine to pine, for the difficulty of controlling the disease in forests is obvious. The so-called Dutch elm disease has destroyed large numbers of the most beautiful elms in certain localities in northeastern United States. The only known method of preventing its spread is to find and destroy infected trees. No cure has been found, so that it is a matter of sacrificing some trees in the hope of protecting others. What the final outcome will be no one knows. Oak wilt, probably a native of the United States, has killed large numbers of oaks during the past few years, and the final outcome of its ravages cannot be predicted.

Obviously there are plant public-health problems in connection with the prevention of epidemics of forest, shade, and orchard trees and many other kinds of plants, because individual effort alone often is ineffective. We still need to learn far more about the pathogens of wild and cultivated plants because many of them are equally at home on both but undetected on the wild. We need to learn far more about the world-wide distribution of pathogens and their parasitic races in order that we may know where danger lurks and try to avert it by quarantines, eradication campaigns, and other appropriate control measures. We still pay a high price for permitting man to distribute pathogens from one part of the world to another.

Even after a half century of fairly intelligent effort to control them, plant diseases still cost the people of the United States upwards of 3 billion dollars a year, and this includes principally diseases in the traditional sense, those caused by fungi, bacteria, nematodes, viruses, and a few parasitic seed plants. Many diseases still cannot be controlled at all, some are controlled very imperfectly, and some are controlled only by expensive procedures that add greatly to the cost of production.

Most major diseases of cultivated crops can become epidemic under favorable conditions, and it is a continual fight to keep them within bounds. The first problem is to understand them and their potentialities. This is not always easy because most diseases are caused by insidious and shifty microscopic organisms, or by ultramicroscopic viruses, each species usually comprising hundreds or thousands of parasitic strains, usually designated as physiologic races. To find and identify these innumerable races and to determine their effects on thousands of varieties of economic plants is a herculean task in itself, especially since new races are continually being produced and are being disseminated by wind, insects, and man. As none of these agents of dissemination are noteworthy for respecting international boundaries, epidemics often sweep across several countries and therefore require international cooperation in studying and controlling them. International cooperation is not only desirable but essential in controlling many epidemic diseases.

What are the prospects for more complete and economical control of epidemic diseases? Obviously, the ideal way of controlling all diseases would be by means of resistant varieties, but this has not always been feasible in the past. Progress would be much more rapid in many cases if islands could be made available where a world collection of presumably resistant varieties could be tested against a world collection of races of their principal pathogens, without danger of contaminating agricultural areas. The alternative is to make tests in many places of the world in the hope of providing an adequate sample of existing pathogens. Much more needs to be learned about the nature and variability of resistance and about the possibility of inducing it by nutritional or other procedures. Much more needs to be learned about the genetics, the physiology, and the ecology of pathogens; much more needs to be learned about the physiology of parasitism and about mutual relations between pathogens and other microorganisms, especially to find out whether antibiotic organisms can be used to help man in his fight against plant diseases.

What are the possibilities of revolutionizing chemical control? Most chemicals now used are essentially protective rather than therapeutic in their action, and most of them must be applied to growing plants frequently and in relatively large quantities. Many epidemic diseases that attack aboveground parts of plants could be prevented by chemical dusts or sprays if the plants were grown in small gardens instead of extensive fields. Even the cereal rusts can be controlled in this way. But what would be the expense of dusting 50 million acres of wheat in the United States, with 2.5 million culms on each acre, with sulfur or other dusts several times each season? Disease control could be revolutionized if chemicals could be applied once a season in homeopathic doses. Chemicals are urgently needed that can be applied in small quantities and that have permanent and systemic effects, a sort of chemical immunization.

Epidemic diseases of plants are tremendously important, and it is therefore tremendously important to understand and control them. To attain deeper and broader understanding and to devise more efficient and economical control measures will require the services of highly competent research scientists, very skilled technologists, and far more adequate facilities. Scientific competence and physical facilities must be commensurate with the complexity and magnitude of the problems. The improvement and protection of plants is basically of paramount importance to peoples everywhere. And the services of all branches of botanical science, pure and applied, are needed to preserve past gains and to assure future progress.

6

AN ANATOMIST'S VIEW
OF VIRUS DISEASES

Katherine Esau

Anatomic studies of plants affected with viral diseases have taught us much about the behavior of viruses in their host plants and, at the same time, have added to our store of information on reactions of plant cells and tissues to internal injuries. Interest in the anatomy of plants having disorders induced by diseases and other agencies may be traced back to the early days of anatomical research. This parallel development of the inquiries into the normal and the abnormal structures is only natural, for plants are constantly exposed to agents and conditions that interfere with their development. In fact, our usual division into normal and abnormal structures is rather arbitrary. When we say "normal" we simply mean that something is true in the majority of instances. Some would object even to this broad definition of normal since, actually, the peculiar changes in diseased and otherwise disturbed plants are normal reactions to the injurious or merely modifying effects. The difficulty of defining normality is further compounded by the fact that whatever criteria we may choose for distinguishing between normal and abnormal, be it with reference to structures or to reactions, the normal and the abnormal intergrade with one another so that a clear delimitation between the two is not to be found.

We need terms and categories, however, for recording our observations and for conveying their meaning to others. The important thing is not the term or category itself, but that the sense in which they are used be made perfectly clear. For the present purpose we may agree that normal is something we have chosen—somewhat arbitrarily, to be sure—to set up as a norm; with reference to plants, this norm may be a structure or activity usually encountered in plants that grow in conditions most appropriate for them, free of diseases or other disturbances. The opposite is abnormal, that is, something that deviates from that which we established as a norm.

Considering the history of the anatomy of disturbed or deranged plants, the so-called pathological anatomy, we find that pertinent information was compiled in 1909 by Sorauer, then, more comprehensively, in 1925 by Küster, both German botanists. Küster's work was a milestone in that it not only assembled the information in orderly fashion but also crystallized the terminology with regard to the pathological anatomy of plants. There is, as a result, a rather general agreement on such terms as hypertrophy and hyperplasia, referring to phenomena of abnormally intensified growth and differentiation, and hypoplasia, denoting inhibition of growth and differentiation. Commonly hypertrophy is used to designate an excessive enlargement of a cell or a part of it; hyperplasia, an excessive multiplication of cells. In contrast, we use only one term, hypoplasia, to denote inhibition of development, be it expressed in too small a size of cells or cell parts, or too small a number of cells or cell parts, or nondevelopment of some features that are normally expected to be present in the cell or tissue at the particular stage of their development. Death of cells and tissues is referred to as necrosis, with necrotic as the adjectival form.

A review in the English language of some of the general aspects of pathological anatomy—or morbid anatomy, as the author called it—was written by Butler in 1930. He paid particular attention to the fungal and bacterial diseases. Otherwise the information on the anatomic effects of fungi and bacteria must be sought in various compendia and special articles dealing with the diseases induced by these causal agents. A considerable volume of literature in pathological anatomy deals with the very interesting and highly complex plant galls, mainly those induced by insect stimulation.

Viruses were recognized later than fungi and bacteria as causal agents of plant diseases, and the first comprehensive review on the structural effects of the viruses upon plants appeared in 1938 (Esau, 1938). Workers of various countries have studied virus diseases and, incidentally, described the internal symptoms, but mostly those in plants in which the disease had become well established. The ontogenetic, or developmental, approach to the studies of the anatomy of virus-diseased plants and the extensive inquiry into the biologic relation between viruses and the tissues of the host are developments that resulted in a large measure from work in the United States (see Bennett, 1940b, 1956; Esau, 1938, 1948b).

ANATOMIC CHANGES INDUCED BY PLANT VIRUSES. Plants react with certain fundamental changes in structure in response to a variety of injurious or noninjurious stimuli. In this respect, reactions to viruses are not exceptional, and we find, in virus-diseased plants, such basic pathologic symptoms as hypertrophy, hyperplasia, hypoplasia, and necrosis, often in combinations of two or more. An enlightening aspect of viral effects is that the symptoms induced by different viruses differ with regard to their distribution in the plant. Anatomic studies have proved to be particularly useful for the recognition of viruses limited to certain tissues of the host in distinction to those not so limited.

The typical abnormalities of mosaic-diseased plants—the disease is called mosaic because of the mosaic combination of yellow and green patches on leaves (fig. 1)—the underdevelopment and the breakdown of chloroplasts

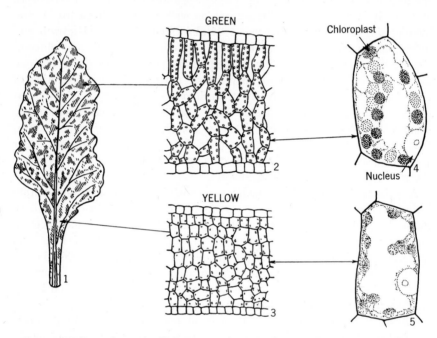

FIG. 1–5. Effect of mosaic disease upon the sugar-beet leaf.—FIG. 1. Mosaic pattern on leaf. Green areas are shaded, yellow areas are left blank.—FIG. 2. Mesophyll from a green area. It shows a loose arrangement of cells and numerous chloroplasts.—FIG. 3. Mesophyll from a yellow area. It shows compact arrangement of cells like a young leaf. This underdevelopment is one of the expressions of hyperplasia. The chloroplasts are few. The deficiency in chloroplasts makes the tissue appear yellow.—FIG. 4. Cell from green mesophyll with numerous chloroplasts.—FIG. 5. Cell from yellow mesophyll. The chloroplasts have become partly or completely disorganized.

are detected in chloroplast-containing tissues, mainly the mesophyll of the leaves (fig. 2–5; see also Esau, 1944). Commonly, mosaics are associated also with the development of peculiar structures in the protoplasts of the affected cells, the so-called inclusion bodies (fig. 6). These may be found in all kinds of living tissues of the host, including the tissues specialized for long-distance conduction of food and water, that is, the phloem and the xylem, respectively. In other words, the distribution of the internal symptoms clearly indicates that the effect of a mosaic virus is not localized in any specific tissue. Tests for infectivity of different parts of diseased plants show that not only the symptoms but the virus itself is thus ubiquitously distributed within the plant. Indeed, some mosaics invade the tissue from which seeds develop and are thus transmitted to a new plant through the seed (see Bennett, 1956). Why some mosaics are transmitted through the seed and others are not is an intriguing problem that is yet to be solved. Some authors think that certain viruses are unable to invade the generative cells, others suggest that viruses are inactivated in the floral parts long before the seeds are formed (see Esau, 1948b).

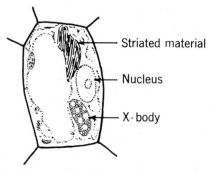

Striated material

Nucleus

X-body

FIG. 6. Cell with inclusion bodies characteristic of tobacco mosaic. The bodies are of two kinds: an amoeboid x-body and a body of crystalline striated material. The relative size of the bodies may be judged from their comparison with the nucleus.

In contrast to the mosaic viruses, those of the yellows group—viruses inducing one or more of such symptoms as dwarfing, general yellowing, and leaf curling—do not appear to be so indiscriminately dispersed in the plant. For example, the viruses of the curly top disease (first described as a disease causing a curling of the leaves, the top, in the sugar beet) and aster yellows disease (first recognized as a disease causing a yellowing of foliage in asters) induce primary pathologic changes in the phloem tissue (Artschwager and Starrett, 1936; Esau, 1933, 1941; Girolami, 1955). Some derangements may occur in other tissues as well, but these abnormalities are obviously secondary and can be explained as resulting from the initial disturbance in the food-conducting tissue, the phloem. The high degree of localization of the curly top virus in the phloem tissue has been clearly demonstrated by the high concentration of the virus in the phloem exudate and the relative freedom from the virus of tissues other than the phloem (Bennett and Esau, 1936).

Thus, with the help of anatomical studies, we have learned to discern between the phloem-limited viruses of the yellows group and the mosaic viruses that occur in all or almost all living tissues of a given host plant. Relatively recently a third possibility was recognized: the close association between the virus and the water-conducting tissue, the xylem. The virus that induces the

Pierce's disease in the grapevine and the dwarf disease in the alfalfa affects primarily the xylem tissue (Esau, 1948a). The water-conducting cells are occluded by products of disintegration of cell contents (gums) and balloon-like cellular outgrowths (tyloses), both derived from adjacent parenchyma cells. The primary nature of these symptoms has been graphically demonstrated by inoculating the virus into grape seedlings, each plant through a single leaf, and checking the kind, location, and time of appearance of symptoms. The first discernible symptoms were tylose development and gummosis in the water-conducting cells; and their location and spread were related to the place of inoculation.

Since viruses show differences in their specific relation to the tissues of the host, the recognition of the primary internal symptoms should prove useful in assigning the viruses to the appropriate groups. In other words, the internal symptoms may be utilized in the classification of viruses, at least with reference to the larger groupings of them. As was just elaborated, some viruses induce the primary symptoms in the phloem, others in the xylem, and still others throughout the plant. In addition, the primary symptoms themselves may vary in details of their development. Among the phloem-limited viruses some induce a collapse and death of phloem cells that pass through an apparently normal course of development (potato leaf roll, cereal yellow dwarf); others bring about abnormal growth phenomena and a profound disturbance of the pattern of differentiation of the phloem before necrosis occurs (curly top, aster yellows). Thus one should be able to separate the phloem-limited viruses into smaller groups by using the character of degeneration of the phloem tissue. We need, however, many more data on anatomic symptoms of viral diseases before their value for classifying viruses may be properly estimated.

The growth changes in the phloem of plants affected by curly top and aster yellows, just alluded to, involve hyperplasia that results in the development of a large number of abnormal sieve elements (fig. 7–10). As is well known, sieve elements are regarded as the principal conducting cells in the phloem, and their protoplasts and walls show certain peculiar characteristics. The abnormal sieve elements develop most, though not necessarily all, of the features found in the normal sieve elements of a given plant; and they may be associated with companion cells. However, their size and shape are abnormal, their arrangement unorderly (fig. 10), and they soon degenerate and collapse (Esau, 1941; Girolami, 1955). The overproduction of sieve elements suggests a disturbance of a fundamental process of differentiation, a process that determines the position and relative numbers of xylem and phloem cells in a given position in the plant. The degree to which this process may be upset is strikingly illustrated by the observations that the abnormal sieve elements may differentiate within the xylem in curly top–diseased plants. This abnormality indicates that, if biochemical gradients are associated with the divergent paths of cellular differentiation in the xylem and the phloem, viruses may profoundly disturb such gradients.

An interesting problem is presented by the pathologic accumulation of

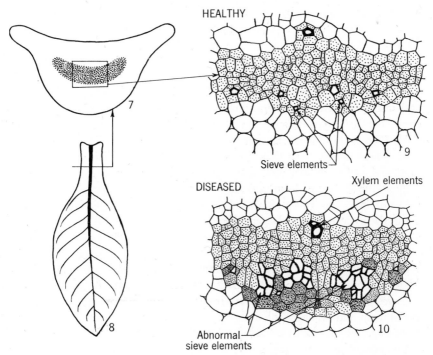

FIG. 7–10. Effect of the curly top disease upon the tobacco leaf.—FIG. 7. Cross section of a petiole with the vascular bundle indicated by the stippling. The rectangular area locates the position of sections like those depicted in fig. 9 and 10.—FIG. 8. Leaf, with the horizontal line indicating the position of the cross section of the petiole shown in fig. 7.—FIG. 9. Part of a cross section of a vascular bundle from a healthy plant. Six sieve elements are mature. Above in the figure, one xylem element is discernible.—FIG. 10. Part of a cross section of a vascular bundle from a diseased plant. In addition to a few small normal sieve elements many large abnormal sieve elements are present. In this figure and in fig. 9 the vascular-bundle cells, except the mature sieve elements, are stippled; the adjacent parenchyma cells are left blank. The densely stippled cells in fig. 10 were those with various signs of disorganization in their protoplasts. (*Fig. 9 and* 10 *adapted from Hilgardia Vol.* 11, *No.* 8, 1938, *and Vol.* 13, *No.* 8, 1941, *respectively.*)

starch in leaves of plants affected by various viral diseases. These may be mosaic diseases, diseases induced by phloem-limited viruses, or by those associated with the xylem. It is likely that the excessive accumulation of starch is a secondary effect that may be related to degenerative changes in tissues concerned with photosynthesis or with the movement of water or food. The viruses may, for example, delay starch removal from leaves or affect the enzymes concerned with carbohydrate metabolism. However, viruses may also prevent or delay starch accumulation. The recognition of the primary symptoms of a virus disease by microscopic observations should be helpful in revealing the significance of the biochemical disturbances caused by a given disease.

Anatomic studies of virus-diseased plants give us some clues to the possible causes of the external symptoms. The breakdown of the food-conducting tissue in curly top, aster yellows, and other diseases in the yellows group is, no doubt, related to the general stunting of the plant and its frequently premature death. The gum deposition and the closing of xylem vessels by tyloses in the Pierce's disease of the grapevine are evidences of a disturbance in the water-conducting system; this disturbance, in its turn, explains such external symptoms as the sudden wilting of vigorously growing young vines and the scalding and drying of leaves on vines of different ages. The translucency of leaf veins in young leaves of plants affected with curly top finds its explanation in the hypertrophic enlargement of parenchyma cells and the obliteration of intercellular spaces by the crowding of the enlarging cells along the veins. Continued hypertrophy of these cells and the hyperplasia that follows result in an excessive thickening and distortion of the vein ribs, a symptom common in later stages of development of the disease (Esau, 1933). The yellow patches on leaves of mosaic-diseased plants are areas of the most pronounced underdevelopment and degeneration of the carriers of the green pigment, the chloroplasts (fig. 3 and 5). These are some of the examples of how an anatomic study may serve as a background for the interpretation of the symptoms visible to the naked eye.

ANATOMIC ASPECTS OF VIRUS TRANSLOCATION IN PLANTS. The specificity of the virus-host relation is revealed not only by the nature and location of the primary symptoms in the tissues of the host, but also—perhaps even more convincingly—by the manner in which the virus is introduced into and transported within the plant.

The viruses of the mosaic group, which induce symptoms generally throughout the plant, are readily introduced into the host by mechanical means, for example, by rubbing the leaf surface with an object previously contaminated with juice from an infected plant. The virus apparently first comes in contact with the cytoplasm of the surface cells, mostly those of the epidermal hairs, that are broken by the rubbing. It then moves into the uninjured surface cells, which may be other hair cells or epidermal cells, and farther into the inner tissues. This is a cell-to-cell progression, and it causes a disturbance in the protoplasts successively invaded by the virus (Zech, 1952).

The movement of the virus from cell to cell, that is, across the walls separating the adjacent cells, is not completely understood. Commonly the plasmodesmata, that is, the cytoplasmic strands supposedly interconnecting the protoplasts of adjacent cells across the dividing walls, are suggested as the pathways (Bennett, 1956). We are not yet sure, however, that plasmodesmata are actually continuous structures from protoplast to protoplast. They may be only processes or extensions of single protoplasts independent of those derived from adjacent protoplasts (Lambertz, 1954). Furthermore, even if the plasmodesmata were continuous from cell to cell, the virus particles seen with the electron microscope usually appear to be much too large for passing through these strands. One plausible suggestion is that viruses move not as complete particles but as fractions of these, fractions that are capable of forming complete particles in the presence of the host cytoplasm in a newly invaded cell (Zech, 1952).

The cell-to-cell movement is relatively slow, 2 to 4 mm. a day (Bennett, 1956; Zech, 1952). When the virus, which is introduced into the leaf through the epidermis, reaches the elongated parenchyma cells located along the vascular bundles, its rate of movement suddenly increases to as much as 8 mm. per hour (Zech, 1952). The virus enters the vascular bundles of the inoculated leaf, reaches the stem, then, usually, moves toward the root and upward again into the youngest, growing parts of the shoot. The movement toward the root may be even more rapid than along the vascular bundles in the leaf. During this downward movement the virus appears to be confined to the vascular bundles. Later it issues from the vascular bundles and spreads in the surrounding parenchyma tissue. The so-called systemic infection is thus accomplished.

The direction and rate of virus spread during the systemic invasion clearly relate this movement to the translocation of food materials in the phloem (Bennett, 1940a, 1956). The interesting experiments designed to test whether mosaic viruses move with the water in the xylem are too many to review here (see Bennett, 1940b; Esau, 1938). Suffice it to say that most workers now agree that the rapid long-distance transport of mosaic viruses occurs in the phloem; and that this rapid movement is combined with a slow spread from cell to cell in parenchyma tissues. This combination assures a thorough invasion of the host tissues by the virus.

If we agree that the rapid phase of virus movement occurs in the phloem, the question is still to be answered regarding what particular phloem cells are concerned with this movement. Students of translocation in the phloem generally assume that the rapid transfer of food materials occurs in the sieve elements because of the specialized characteristics of these cells. The same assumption is made regarding the transport of viruses. However, the mechanism that could make possible a rapid movement of materials in the sieve elements has not yet been revealed (Currier and coworkers, 1955). The problem involves the relation between the cytoplasm and vacuole in the sieve elements, the possible significance of the enucleate state of the elements, and finally the nature of the interconnections between the elements. These connections resemble plasmodesmata but are usually wider.

Curiously enough, inclusion bodies that may be found in all kinds of living cells in tobacco affected with mosaic have not been found in the sieve elements (Esau, 1941; Zech, 1952). Since the sieve elements lack nuclei, they are perhaps incapable of reacting to virus infection or of forming complete virus particles from their precursors.

In contrast to the mosaic viruses, those inducing yellows and leaf curl diseases are more highly specialized with regard to agencies and methods of transmission and transport in the plant. Usually only one or few species of insects are able to transmit such viruses. Furthermore, the phloem-limited viruses, as far as they have been studied in this respect, must be introduced by the insect into the phloem tissue itself before an infection results. Microscopic preparations of plant parts containing feeding punctures of the insect carrier of the curly top virus, the sugar-beet leafhopper, showed that the insect was making every effort to reach the phloem tissue with its mouth parts (Lackey, 1953). It has been shown also that, if the insect fails to reach the phloem, infection is not likely to result (Fife and Frampton, 1936).

As to the movement of the curly top virus in the plant, the data accumulated by Bennett (see Bennett, 1940b) strongly suggest that the movement of the virus and that of the food materials transported in the phloem are closely correlated. A good example is furnished by experiments with triple-crowned sugar-beet plants obtained by splitting each plant longitudinally in three parts but leaving the lowermost part of the fleshy root intact (Bennett, 1937). After a while each of the three parts developed a new crown of leaves. The curly top virus was introduced into one of the three crowns (crown I in fig. 11). Another crown was either defoliated or protected from light for 5 days after the first crown was inoculated with the virus (crown II in fig. 11). The third crown was left untreated (crown III in fig. 11). The inoculated crown developed symptoms of the disease. Shortly thereafter the shaded (or defoliated) crown developed the symptoms also, but the untreated one remained free of symptoms for 3 months or more. When, instead of waiting for the symptoms to appear, Bennett tested the experimental plants for the presence of virus, he found that the virus had moved into the darkened or defoliated crown in 24 to 48 hours after the first crown was inoculated. The most convincing explanation of these results is that the darkened or defoliated crown was dependent on the other parts of the plant for the supply of carbohydrates since without light or leaves it could not form its own photosynthates. In receiving the carbohydrates from the common root part it was also supplied with the virus that moved toward the storage root with the carbohydrates from the inoculated crown (fig. 11). The untreated crown was, of course, forming carbohydrates which moved toward the root. It could receive the virus eventually through possible changes in the prevailing direction of food movement.

Bennett (1934) has furnished also a clear-cut evidence that the phloem

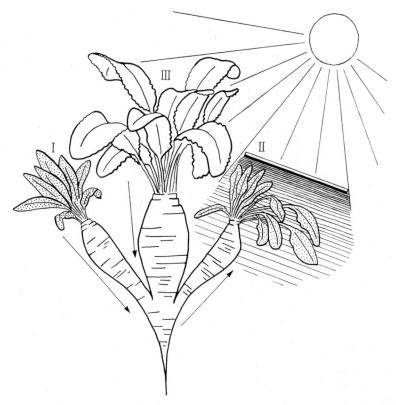

FIG. 11. Translocation of curly top virus in a sugar-beet plant with three crowns. Crown I was inoculated with the virus and developed symptoms. Crown II was shaded but not inoculated. It also developed symptoms. In the absence of light it did not form food and received its supply of food from the root. Virus appeared to have entered crown II from the root. Crown III was not treated in any way. It remained free of symptoms during the experiment. Arrows indicate prevailing direction of movement of food. (*From an original by Milton Shenkofsky.*)

tissue is actually concerned with the transport of the curly top virus. A particularly instructive experiment was carried out with tobacco plants. *Nicotiana glauca,* a species of tobacco that upon inoculation with the curly top virus does not develop the symptoms of the disease (a symptomless carrier), was used as a stock for two scions of *N. tabacum,* a species highly susceptible to curly top. One scion was placed below, the other above on the stock (fig. 12

and 13). In the stem of *N. glauca* intervening between the two scions the phloem and the associated tissues were removed; that is, the stem was "ringed" (fig. 12). (The rather woody stem of *N. glauca* lends itself nicely for this operation.) Since *Nicotiana* has internal as well as external phloem (fig. 16), it was necessary to remove the tissues outside and inside the xylem. Thus the water-conducting tissue alone remained as a connection between the two grafts (fig. 14). The virus was introduced into the upper scion and induced the development of symptoms here. None appeared on the lower scion because the virus failed to pass the xylem bridge (fig. 12). For further checking, a small strip of phloem was left associated with the xylem in another experiment (fig. 15). The virus moved through this strip and caused an infection of the lower scion (fig. 13).

If in contrast to the curly top virus a mosaic virus can easily move through parenchyma cells, the ringing of the stem should form no barrier to the passage of a mosaic virus. The latter could utilize the connected system of parenchyma cells present in the xylem. Indeed, in most experiments involving mosaic viruses and ringed stems, the viruses succeeded in passing the xylem bridge, although they were noticeably delayed in their progress (Bennett, 1940a). The delay must have resulted from the absence of phloem in the ringed part of the stem—an additional evidence that the rapid transport of a mosaic virus occurs in this particular tissue.

Virus-plant relations have been explored also by utilizing the intimate association between the host and one of its plant parasites, the dodder (Bennett, 1944). Viruses were transmitted from one plant to another by inducing the same dodder plant to attach itself to two host plants, one diseased and the other healthy. These studies have indicated that the dodder plant itself acquires the virus in a manner suggesting that the virus moves from the host into the parasite with the food from the phloem. On the other hand, the entry of virus from the dodder into the still noninfected host appears to occur against the prevailing direction of food movement. Of course, one would not expect all viruses to be equally dependent on the phloem tissue for the movement between the dodder and the host. It is likely that the mosaic types of viruses would utilize their ability to move through parenchyma cells, whereas the yellows viruses would be restricted to the phloem in their passage between dodder and host.

The anatomic relation between the host plant and the dodder is certainly of interest in connection with virus transmission through the dodder plant. When the dodder stem comes in contact with a host plant it sends out an outgrowth, the so-called haustorium, that becomes firmly appressed to the surface of the host. The haustorium is really a modified adventitious root. Cells on the margin of the haustorium, which are in contact with the host surface, elongate and penetrate the tissue of the host and absorb some of the host cells along their way. These hypha-like cells are so numerous that soon they form a compact mass extending deep into the body of the host plant. Eventually the extending hypha-like cells reach the vascular tissues of the host.

From the standpoint of virus translocation we are particularly interested

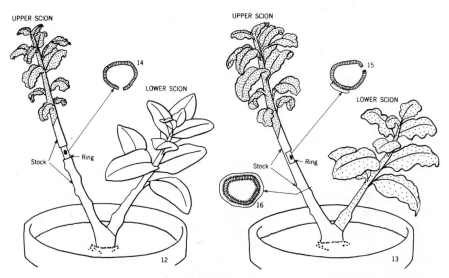

FIG. 12–16. Translocation of curly top virus in tobacco.—FIG. 12 and 13. Two tobacco plants, each produced by grafting two scions of *Nicotiana tabacum*, one above and one below, to a stock of *N. glauca*. The stem of the stock was "ringed"; that is, bark was removed in a ring-like area. The pith and the internal phloem also were removed through a small hole. In fig. 13 the ring was incomplete since some of the bark with external phloem remained attached to the xylem. In each plant the upper scion was inoculated with the virus. It developed symptoms. Since the ringed stem part in fig. 12 contained no phloem, the virus was unable to pass into the lower scion and the latter remained healthy. In fig. 13 the narrow phloem bridge in the ringed part allowed the virus to pass into the lower scion and the latter developed the symptoms.—FIG. 14 and 15 are cross sections of the ringed parts of stem from fig. 12 and 13, respectively. Only xylem appears in fig. 14. A small amount of bark with phloem (dotted) is attached to the xylem in fig. 15.—FIG. 16 shows a complete stem section with external and internal phloem (both indicated by dots) associated with the xylem (indicated by hatching). (*Fig. 12 and 13 from originals by Milton Shenkofsky.*)

in the phloem development in the haustorium, but the picture of xylem development, being better known, provides the necessary background. The parasite cells in contact with the water-conducting, or tracheary, cells of the host differentiate into equivalent kinds of elements, that is, tracheary elements. In the meantime the haustorium develops vascular tissue in its back part, in connection with the vascular tissue of the main body of the parasite. In this manner a continuous strand of water-conducting cells is established that unites the xylem tissues of the host and parasite and enables the parasite to take up water from the host. Haustorial cells also penetrate the phloem. Some of these cells apply themselves closely to the sieve elements of the host without destroying them. The contact between the parasite and host cells is very intimate. In fact, hypha-like processes encircle the sieve elements of the host like fingers of a hand. These hypha-like cells do not appear to develop the specialized characteristics of sieve elements, but they are in continuity with such elements in the older part of the haustorium. They appear to form a bridge between the sieve elements of the host and those of the parasite. An additional detail, that numerous plasmodesmata may be recognized in the walls of the parasite cells located within the host tissues, suggests a possible exchange of materials between parenchyma cells of host and parasite (provided, of course, that plasmodesmata are concerned with such an exchange). Thus it would seem that various kinds of viruses, those limited to the phloem or to the xylem or those occurring in various tissues at the same time, would find suitable pathways for moving from the host into the dodder plant and in the reverse direction.

Another problem in virus transmission that has been illuminated by anatomic research concerns the movement of viruses across a graft union. Bennett (1943) has found that when virus-diseased scions of tobacco were grafted to a healthy stock and left attached to the stock for periods of varying length, mosaic viruses were able to pass the graft union sooner than the curly top virus. This difference is readily explained by the evidence that phloem connection between the stock and the scion is established later than the junction of parenchyma (Crafts, 1934). The union of parenchyma tissues would suffice to transfer the mosaic viruses from scion to stock, whereas the curly top virus requires a bridge of phloem.

As with regard to mosaics, we assume that the curly top virus moves in the sieve elements in its long-distance travel. We have no direct proof for this assumption; only a circumstantial evidence. In young plant parts, recently invaded by the curly top virus, the first visible symptoms have been recognized at the level to which mature sieve elements were just reaching (they differentiate from the more mature regions of the plant toward the younger); and the degenerative changes were initiated in parenchyma cells located next to the sieve elements (fig. 18; Esau, 1935, 1941). It seemed as though an injurious substance issued from the mature sieve elements and affected the surrounding cells. Some of these cells became hypertrophied or degenerated completely; others formed a hyperplastic tissue by dividing repeatedly (compare fig. 18 with fig. 17). The injurious substance might have been the virus (or its precursor) that was transported in the sieve elements. A similar localization of the first symptoms in the vicinity of the youngest mature sieve elements was observed in the aster yellows disease (Girolami, 1955).

Thus we have an impressive collection of data that indicates a close rela-

tion between certain yellows viruses to the phloem tissue of the hosts. Moreover, we are also justified in pointing to the sieve elements as the possible
conduits for the movement of the viruses through this tissue. Can one go
equally far in depicting the relation of the Pierce's disease virus to the
xylem, the tissue which this virus affects primarily? In this disease, as in
curly top, the insect carrier—also a leafhopper—gives us a clue regarding the

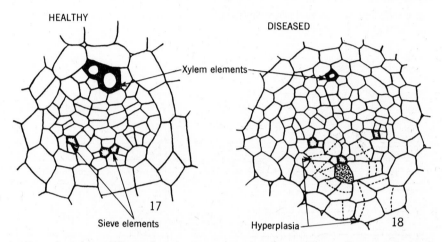

Fig. 17 and 18. Effect of curly top upon sugar-beet phloem. Cross sections of
vascular bundles from a healthy (fig. 17) and a diseased (fig. 18) leaf. Each bundle
has three mature sieve elements. Near the outermost sieve element in fig. 18 the
cells have increased in size (hypertrophy) and then divided so that an excessive
number of cells developed in this area (hyperplasia). The broken lines indicate recently formed walls, the dense stippling a cell with disorganized contents. (*Adapted
from Amer. Jour. Bot.: fig. 17 from Vol. 21, p. 641; fig. 18 from Vol. 22, p. 155.*)

place of entry of the virus into the plant. Whereas the sugar-beet leafhopper
seeks out the phloem in search of food (fig. 19), the grape leafhopper in at-
tacking the plant aims to reach the xylem (fig. 20). In a count of over one
hundred punctures that were made by carriers of the Pierce's disease virus in
grape canes and alfalfa stems, 88 per cent ended in the xylem (Houston and
coworkers, 1947). That these insects actually withdraw water from the plant
is graphically illustrated by the insect itself as it ejects large amounts of water
while working on the plant. This predilection for the xylem contents seems
puzzling. If it has to do with obtaining food, the sugar-beet leafhopper appears
to be a far more efficient insect since it utilizes the phloem sap, which is rich
in foodstuffs, for this purpose.

Experiments were designed to force the grape leafhopper to work on tissues
other than the xylem (Houston and coworkers, 1947). The bark on a grapevine cane was partially separated from the wood, and a metal shield inserted

between the phloem and the xylem. When an infective leafhopper was confined to the partially isolated bark the insect failed to transmit the virus.
When, on the other hand, it was given access to the xylem, indeed even when
it was restricted to the xylem, it introduced the virus into the plant. These
studies clearly show that the Pierce's disease virus must be placed into the
xylem for a successful inoculation of the plant with the disease. The previously
mentioned observation that the primary symptoms of Pierce's disease develop
in the xylem ties in well with the experience on transmission of the virus.

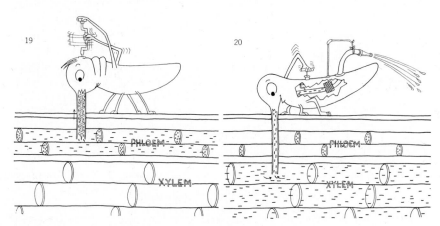

Fig. 19 and 20. Interpreting the feeding habits of the insect carriers of viruses.—
Fig. 19. The sugar-beet leafhopper obtains the food from the phloem tissue and
with it picks up the phloem-limited virus of the curly top disease and transmits it
to other plants again by puncturing the phloem.—Fig. 20. The grape leafhopper
punctures the xylem, pumps a large amount of water through its body, and with
it picks up the virus of the Pierce's disease. It transmits this virus to other plants
again by puncturing the xylem. (*From originals by Milton Shenkofsky.*)

With regard to the movement of the Pierce's disease virus within the plant,
some experiments have indicated a relatively rapid upward transport in alfalfa
stems, so that movement with the water may be assumed; but the evidence
is still too scanty to be conclusive. It could be that the virus is carried with
the water under certain conditions, but it probably also moves in the parenchymatous components of the xylem tissue which form an interconnected
system. In any event, it would be difficult to visualize the virus living and
multiplying in the water-conducting cells, for viruses are known to depend
on living cytoplasm for their multiplication; and mature conducting tracheary
elements of the wood are devoid of living contents. One may question also
the ability of a virus to leave a living parenchyma cell and enter a nonliving
cell or go in the opposite direction, from a nonliving into an unbroken living
cell. Some studies with mosaic viruses suggest that these viruses are unable to

pass in or out of the tracheary elements (see Bennett, 1940b, 1956; Esau, 1938). However, a xylem-limited virus may have some unique properties that bring about a specialized behavior in the tracheary elements.

CONCLUSION. The above discussion points out many of the areas in which anatomic studies have proved useful in research on plant viruses. The effects of viruses upon the cells and tissues of plants reveal—at least in part—the specific biologic relation of the virus to the tissues of the host and thus help to characterize and to classify the viruses. The anatomy of virus-diseased plants also has a broad, general significance in that a step-by-step recognition of viral effects increases our understanding of the reactions of plants to injuries. In this respect the anatomical investigations of plants infected with viruses are comparable with studies involving the use of growth-regulating substances and of surgical procedures designed to reveal the phenomena that are causally related to the development of the specific structures and forms in plants. In all these studies basic phenomena of development may come to light through responses of plants to effects that interfere with the normal development. The idea that studies of plant responses to diseases and other injuries enhances our general understanding of plant development—in fact, are indispensable for such an understanding—has been well expressed long ago by Goethe (see Esau, 1938) when he said: "Never can we obtain a complete comprehension [of a phenomenon] unless we consider the normal and abnormal both at the same time and contrasted with each other."

LITERATURE CITED

ARTSCHWAGER, E., AND RUTH C. STARRETT. 1936. Histological and cytological changes in sugar-beet seedlings affected with curly top. Jour. Agric. Res. 53:637–657.

BENNETT, C. W. 1934. Plant-tissue relations of the sugar-beet curly-top virus. Jour. Agric. Res. 48:665–701.

———. 1937. Correlation between the movement of the curly top virus and translocation of food in tobacco and sugar beet. Jour. Agric. Res. 54:479–502.

———. 1940a. Relation of food translocation to movement of virus of tobacco mosaic. Jour. Agric. Res. 60:361–390.

———. 1940b. The relation of viruses to plant tissues. Bot. Rev. 6:427–473.

———. 1943. Influence of contact period on the passage of viruses from cion to stock in Turkish tobacco. Phytopathology 33:818–822.

———. 1944. Studies of dodder transmission of plant viruses. Phytopathology 34:905–932.

———. 1956. Biological relations of plant viruses. Ann. Rev. Plant Physiol. 7:143–170.

——— AND KATHERINE ESAU. 1936. Further studies on the relation of the curly top virus to plant tissues. Jour. Agric. Res. 53:595–620.

BUTLER, E. G. 1930. Some aspects of morbid anatomy of plants. Ann. Appl. Biol. 17:429–443.

CRAFTS, A. S. 1934. Phloem anatomy in two species of *Nicotiana,* with notes on the interspecific graft union. Bot. Gaz. 95:592–608.

CURRIER, H. B., KATHERINE ESAU, AND V. I. CHEADLE. 1955. Plasmolytic studies of phloem. Amer. Jour. Bot. 42:68–81.

ESAU, KATHERINE. 1933. Pathologic changes in the anatomy of the sugar beet, *Beta vulgaris* L., affected by curly top. Phytopathology 23:679–712.

———. 1935. Ontogeny of the phloem in sugar beets affected by the curly-top disease. Amer. Jour. Bot. 22:149–163.

———. 1938. Some anatomical aspects of plant virus disease problems. Bot. Rev. 4:548–579.

———. 1941. Phloem anatomy of tobacco affected with curly top and mosaic. Hilgardia 13:437–490.

———. 1944. Anatomical and cytological studies on beet mosaic. Jour. Agric. Res. 69:95–117.

———. 1948a. Anatomic effects of the viruses of Pierce's disease and phony peach. Hilgardia 18:423–482.

———. 1948b. Some anatomical aspects of plant virus disease problems. II. Bot. Rev. 14:413–449.

FIFE, J. M., AND V. L. FRAMPTON. 1936. The pH gradient extending from the phloem into the parenchyma of the sugar beet and its relation to the feeding behavior of *Eutettix tenellus.* Jour. Agric. Res. 53:581–593.

GIROLAMI, G. 1955. Comparative anatomical effects of the curly-top and aster-yellows viruses on the flax plant. Bot. Gaz. 116:305–322.

HOUSTON, B. R., KATHERINE ESAU, AND W. B. HEWITT. 1947. The mode of vector feeding and the tissues involved in the transmission of Pierce's disease virus in grape and alfalfa. Phytopathology 37:247–253.

KÜSTER, E. 1925. Pathologische Pflanzenanatomie. 3d ed. Gustav Fischer. Jena.

LACKEY, C. F. 1953. Attraction of dodder and beet leafhopper to vascular bundles in the sugar beet as affected by curly top. Amer. Jour. Bot. 40:221–225.

LAMBERTZ, P. 1954. Untersuchungen über das Vorkommen von Plasmodesmen in den Epidermisaussenwänden. Planta 44:147–190.

SORAUER, P. 1909. Handbuch der Pflanzenkrankheiten. 3d ed. Paul Parey. Berlin.

ZECH, H. 1952. Untersuchungen über den Infektionsvorgang und die Wanderung des Tabakmosaikvirus im Pflanzenkörper. Planta 40:461–514.

7

RESEARCH ON XYLEM AND PHLOEM
Progress in Fifty Years

Vernon I. Cheadle

To many students in elementary botany classes who must learn something about structure of plants, even if only to practice use of the microscope, vascular tissues do not often excite much interest. And if one reads elementary textbooks, he recognizes that most of these do not serve very well in supporting the teaching efforts of instructors, who, unhappily, are seldom very confident of their own understanding of these tissues.

Yet a knowledge of vascular tissues is immensely important to an understanding not only of the activities of vascular plants in their present environment, but also of how they must have survived and prospered through the ages. Furthermore, these tissues or products derived from them have been important items in Man's economy since the time of his arrival as a thinking organism. This article is a review of progress in research during the last fifty years on some specific structural aspects of these important tissues.

INTRODUCTION. Vascular tissues are chiefly involved in rapid conduction in plants. They are composed of xylem—the chief water-conducting and supporting tissue—and of phloem—the chief food-conducting tissue. These seem to be prosaic definitions, but notice that though they mention nothing about structural details, they do provide the clues to the ability of plants to live on land. Is this economically or biologically important? Our economy is based first and foremost on plants—plants that grow on land—and they succeed in a land environment mainly (although of course not wholly) because they have xylem and phloem.

There are fascinating controversies among botanists concerning the origin of land plants. These controversies revolve around subject matter, most of which need not concern us here; but whatever stand one may take, he must agree that without xylem and phloem land plants could never have evolved to their present state of development. It seems generally agreed that land plants were derived from aquatic ancestors. If this is so, then we should recognize the essential differences between vascular plants and their aquatic ancestors and how these differences influence the ability of vascular plants to live on land. Aquatic plants are bathed in water, and thus water conduction throughout the plant is not of prime importance. And only when primitive aquatic plants developed vegetative bodies of great length (and consequent growth in deep water) was translocation of foods important. Thus we find food-conducting cells—perhaps they should be considered as phloem—in the stipes of such plants in the brown algae.

But how were plants able to migrate to the land and cover the face of the earth?

To grow on land and compete for available sunlight, it is evident that the structural plan of primitive aquatic plants will not do. The familiar roots and leaves of our present-day plants were apparently not present in the earliest vascular plants, but the available evidence indicates that they came, geologically speaking, soon after vascular plants arose. But even from the beginning, photosynthetic areas were carried into the air—as indeed they are during ontogeny (growth from germination to maturity) of present-day plants. Water had to be supplied to these food-synthesizing parts. It came from the only generally available source—the soil. Water and its dissolved salts moved into the underground stems of these primitive vascular plants and were undoubtedly transported rapidly upward through their xylem—just as they are today. The underground anchoring and absorbing stems would have starved had it not been for the translocation to them of food elaborated in the aerial parts of the stem. This translocation undoubtedly took place rapidly through their phloem—once again just as it does today. Our present-day plants, with leaves as special food-making parts and roots as special anchoring and absorbing organs, have the same basic vascular tissues, modified though the xylem and phloem may be.

The development of simple but typical xylem and phloem was a triumphant acquisition in the evolution of land plants. If we add to these tissues mechanisms for conservation of water and for gaseous interchange, we have assembled the means, as it were, for successful migration of plants from the sea to a secure footing on land.

It is undeniable, of course, that there are other factors contributing to the successful migration of plants to land. It is true, likewise, that still other factors are important in successful dissemination throughout the world's land areas, notably the innovation of seeds and of flowers and fruits. But there must be plants on land to disseminate, and it is my contention that without vascular tissues there would have been no typical land plants. The loss in varying degrees of vascular tissues by those derivatives of typical land plants that have migrated back into the water or have become saprophytes or parasites merely underlines the validity of this contention, for they lose (and in a manner apparently common to all) what no longer seems important in their survival.

The occurrence of xylem and phloem has been so evidently associated with the land habitat that when vascular plants are mentioned, it is understood that typical land plants are meant. The importance of vascular tissues has been emphasized in recent decades by use of a group name for all of them— the Tracheophyta (or Tracheata). This huge group of plants consists of a wide variety of forms, but all of them have vascular tissues—absence of them represents evolutionary loss. Among these plants are the present-day club mosses, horsetails, quillworts, ferns, gymnosperms, and angiosperms. Added to these groups, each of which has additional features that separate them one from the other, are those curious genera *Psilotum* and *Tmesipteris,* plants which give us some insight into what must have been the earliest land plants— though they themselves are considerably removed from these ancestors. Still more fascinating members of the Tracheophyta are the extinct groups: the Psilophytales and their primitive cohorts, giant horsetails and club mosses, primitive ferns, all seed ferns, many conifers, and the like, which at one time or another flourished and were lost, never to be known again except as fossils. And we have not yet more than a well-founded suspicion of what went on before these vascular plants, even the primitive Psilophytales with their lack of roots and leaves, arrived on their scenes. The antiquity of these forms can be partially recognized when one recalls one of Professor E. C. Jeffrey's apt expressions, "The pines are older than the birds that nest in their branches." And birds arose tens of millions of years before Man ever heard their songs.

Hundreds or thousands of fossil species, many hundreds of species in the lower vascular plants, thousands of ferns, hundreds of gymnosperms, scores of thousands of species of flowering plants—these are the materials that confront one who is interested in vascular tissues. These are the materials with endless variation in ontogeny and in construction of their mature vascular tissues—details that are often available for study only after painstaking preparation for observation.

In spite of the difficulties inherent in the study of vascular tissues, much is known of them; so much in fact that I hesitate in choosing those accomplishments that might exemplify the progress of research on vascular tissues, particularly in America, in the last fifty years. I have nevertheless arbitrarily chosen some lines of research I am most familiar with and another which recently has become lively.

Before proceeding to these, however, it may be useful to write briefly of the variation of patterns of conducting tissues that can be observed throughout the vascular plants. These patterns actually represent, of course, the occurrence of vascular tissues, the subject of this paper. Their interest here, however, lies more in the way they serve as a means of illustrating a phase in the development of knowledge about structure and the motivation which led to

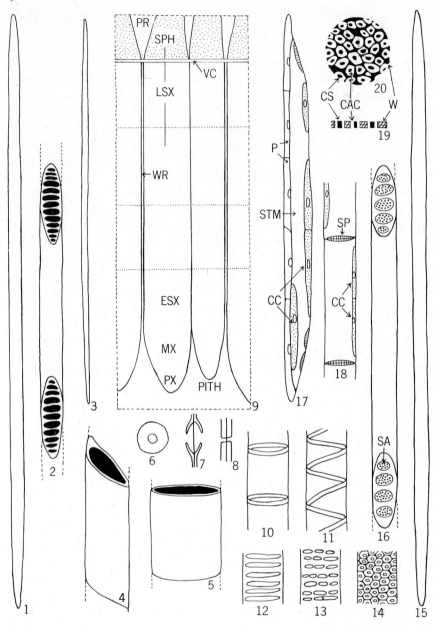

FIG. 1–20. All are figures of conventional structures drawn freehand; details of cell contents and side walls generally omitted.—FIG. 1. Outline of shortened tracheid, bordered pits as in fig. 6, 7, or 12–14.—FIG. 2. Vessel member, with scalariform perforation plates; perforations in black.—FIG. 3. Outline of wood fiber (with pits as in fig. 8).—FIG. 4, 5. Vessel members with single perforation (black) in

curiosity about this phase. If one merely uses a razor blade for sectioning and a 10× hand lens for observing, he can learn a great deal about the configuration of xylem and phloem in the plant. By using cross sections (taken at right angles to the long axis—they are thus similar to a normal slice of bread) and choosing young stems of many dicotyledons for research materials, it is apparent that the patterns of vascular tissues are remarkably constant throughout thousands of species, even though the details may differ. Many other dicotyledons could be chosen, on the other hand, in which the patterns are different; they may be, for example, more similar to those generally found in thousands of monocotyledons. If attention is turned to the ferns, even greater variation could be found. But if one similarly examined cross sections of vigorously growing young roots (a few inches or so back of the tip), he would find quite a different pattern, one which has some characteristic features that make it easy to distinguish roots from practically all stems just on the basis of the arrangement of xylem and phloem.

Late in the nineteenth century anatomists began pondering the evolutionary significance of these patterns, and from their efforts emerged the concept of the stele. The stele was considered as the central cylinder of the stem or root and was composed of the vascular tissues and others closely associated

---

slightly oblique end wall (fig. 4) or in transverse end wall (fig. 5).—Fig. 6. Bordered pit in surface view.—Fig. 7. Bordered pit pair sectioned through center. Borders of secondary wall of two cells concerned appear like opposed sets of two spread fingers; continuous pit membrane across the cavity actually separates the two cells—in a perforation the common pit membrane disappears.—Fig. 8. Section through a simple pit pair; no borders of secondary wall.—Fig. 9. Diagram of part of a cross section of stem four years old, showing pith, protoxylem (*PX*), and metaxylem (*MX*), which compose primary xylem, early secondary xylem (*ESX*), later secondary xylem (*LSX*), wood rays (*WR*), vascular cambium (*VC*), secondary phloem (*SPH*) with vertically oriented parts stippled, phloem ray (*PR*).—Fig. 10–11. Parts of two xylem conducting elements with annual thickenings (fig. 10) and spiral thickening (fig. 11).—Fig. 12–14. Parts of xylem conducting elements with scalariform (fig. 12), opposite (fig. 13) and alternate (fig. 14) pitting. Borders of pits not shown in fig. 12 and 13.—Fig. 15. Outline of shortened sieve cell; sieve areas not shown but would be of equal specialization and scattered along the entire wall.—Fig. 16. Sieve-tube member with oblique sieve plates [five oval sieve areas (*SA*) in upper and four in lower]. Dots merely represent sieve area in contrast to remaining part of end wall.—Fig. 17. Assemblage of cells derived from one phloem initial: sieve-tube members (*STM*) with sieve plates on end walls, strand of parenchyma cells (*P*) with nuclei, stippled companion cells (*CC*).—Fig. 18. Sieve-tube member in section, showing sieve plates (*SP*) on transverse end walls and two companion cells (*CC*).—Fig. 19. Diagram of part of sieve plate in section; connecting strands (*CS*) in black, wall (*W*) cross-hatched, callose cylinders (*CAC*) clear.—Fig. 20. Part of sieve plate in surface view; connecting strands (*CS*) in black, callose cylinders (*CAC*) clear, wall (*W*) in black.

with them, together with an outer boundary, the pericycle. The patterns of occurrence of vascular and associated tissues were to be reduced to a series of evolutionary modifications that would show the continuity of changes and something of how these changes were brought about. Some famous names in botany (Van Tieghem, Brebner, Jeffrey) were involved in these investigations. Confusing terminologies developed because of unawareness of the complexities of detailed differences in plant structure. Sometimes specious arguments arose over boundaries, origin of various kinds of steles and therefore their relative place in the evolutionary scheme devised for them, the influence of leaf traces, the interpretation of leaf bundles themselves, etc. It is no wonder that those whose chief interests lay outside these arguments have, in a word, cast a "plague on both your houses." They were unconsciously casting a plague as well, perhaps, on scientists who overzealously categorize information in the attempt to supply it to others in neat packages; organisms seem to resist, so to speak, such compartmentalization.

Those who were, or are, sympathetic to the evolutionary approach to anatomy are likely to recollect the historical scenes upon which development of the stelar concept proceeded. It should be recalled that the original notions concerning the stele appeared not long after Darwin's *Origin of Species* had motivated an immense surge of interest in evolutionary studies. Investigations of the patterns of vascular tissue seemed to be natural developments of this surge, and so these researches became quite fashionable for a time. If interpreted in this light, the stelar concept itself can be examined in its proper context and thereby properly evaluated. It cannot be denied that this concept has had an immense impact on anatomy and morphology. As Esau has emphasized in briefly reviewing the concept in her book *Plant Anatomy,* ". . . the stelar theory has been of unmistakable value in emphasizing the unity of structure of the vascular system and in stimulating extensive comparative research."

We know more about the details of conducting systems than we knew years ago, and we know there are aspects of vascular-tissue patterns that do not conform to the rigid terminologies employed in the stelar concept. We may look forward some day to a scholarly review of this concept with the hope that it may be used where instructive, and discarded where not, in our understanding of the vascular plant itself as a unit.

Having arbitrarily disposed of the stelar concept as it refers to vascular tissue, we may turn now to one aspect of xylem, the study of which was influenced by the same motivation that resulted in the stelar concept.

XYLEM. In an earlier paragraph, the patterns of vascular tissues within relatively young stems and roots were briefly discussed. If we turn our attention to the first xylem differentiated, in young stems particularly, we find that the earliest-formed cells are commonly featured by annular thickenings (fig. 10) of secondary walls. These together with the later-formed cells with spiral thickenings (fig. 11) constitute the xylem elements formed while the stem is still elongating as a whole—thus in accommodating over-all growth these cells themselves may be stretched as the stem elongates. Such cells comprise the *protoxylem* (fig. 9, *PX*). Those xylem cells subsequently formed as a result of cellular activity in the stem tip comprise the *metaxylem* (fig. 9, *MX*), whose mature cells are incapable of stretching because of the amount and interconnected nature of their secondary-wall thickenings (fig. 12–14). These two types of xylem together are called the *primary* xylem. In the stems of many plants, only primary xylem is formed, and any increase in the girth of such stems is due to increase in the size of the cells of other tissues. This is true, for example, of most monocotyledons, some herbaceous dicotyledons, and almost all ferns and club mosses.

In the stems of other plants, including many woody herbs as well as shrubs and trees, additional xylem is produced by the activities of a *vascular cambium,* a generating zone of cells (fig. 9, *VC*) that originates between the primary xylem and primary phloem. The girth of the stem in these plants thus increases by the formation and enlargement of cells produced by this cambium—*secondary phloem* (fig. 9, *SPH*) on the outer side and *secondary xylem* (fig. 9, *ESX* and *LSX*) on the inner side. Most of the cells in these secondary tissues are erect; that is, their long axes are parallel to the long axis of the stem. There are, however, sheets of cells—usually living—that are typically oriented at right angles to the elongate upright cells. These radially disposed, thin sheets of cells are the rays [wood rays (fig. 9, *WR*) or phloem rays (fig. 9, *PR*), depending on their location]. The vascular cambium which produces these two categories of cells—one perpendicular, the other horizontal—similarly has two types of cambial initials, one which is short and produces the rays, the other which is long (fusiform in shape) and produces all the vertical cells. A considerable body of data indicates that the actual make-up of the cambium in terms of the ray and fusiform initials is not static, but this information will not be considered further and neither will wood nor phloem rays.

We are now ready to consider the upright cells of the xylem, primarily in terms of their evolutionary development. The investigations which led to an understanding of the variations among these cells occurred within the last fifty years, and chiefly within the last thirty. Some of the Americans who were earlier involved in these studies are now gone, and some of them have been proved wrong in their conclusions. Jeffrey, for example, and the students who faithfully followed his pathways made mistakes, but E. C. Jeffrey will always be remembered for his stimulating and aggressive stands; he provoked the additional investigations that eventually were to correct his mistakes. A sounder, more meticulous, but no less imaginative American investigator took over from Jeffrey in developing the notions that now prevail about evolutionary changes in the wood. That man is I. W. Bailey.

To I. W. Bailey we owe, among other accomplishments, not only the most basic measuring device for evolutionary specialization of wood cells (cell length), but also an understanding of the use and limitations of wood specialization in determining the phylogenetic relationships among woody plants. His students and associates have developed, refined, and expanded his investigations to the point where the clarity of their conclusions stand unmatched in the study of evolution in plants. It is about this subject that the following paragraphs are written.

If one were to examine the separated, vertically oriented cells of woods of a great number of species of the angiosperms, he might readily be confused by the bewildering array of sizes, shapes, markings, and structure of the cells. Even in the nineteenth century, earlier anatomists had learned considerable about the cells and had accurately described many of their features, but it was not until the early years of the twentieth century that these cells were studied from an evolutionary viewpoint. And not until Bailey and Tupper published their notable study on length of elements in the secondary xylem in relation to certain other features—including the length of the fusiform initials from which they were derived—did we have a reliable device to use in any intelligent approach to the evolutionary problem represented by cellular variation in the xylem.

We must digress for a moment to review what variations there are in these vertically elongate cells of the xylem. To reduce details, let us omit reference to the typical living cells—wood parenchyma—important as they are, and concentrate only on conducting and supporting cells of the secondary xylem in the dicotyledons. These cells fall into three categories, one of which shows especially conspicuous variations. The first of these categories consists of tracheids (fig. 1 and others referred to in the legend for fig. 1). These are elongate cells, relatively narrow in diameter, squarish to rectangular in cross-sectional view, and with no openings from one cell to another. They are normally tapered gradually at either end and thus have no clearly defined end walls. Their secondary walls are interrupted by bordered pits (fig. 7) (thin places in the original primary wall overarched by the secondary wall). The bordered pits are often round (fig. 6) or transversely elongate (fig. 12). The transversely elongate pits (their occurrence in rows up the tracheid gives the appearance of a ladder; hence pitting of this nature is called scalariform) are primitive features, as indeed is the tracheid itself. Other types of pitting (fig. 13, 14) are considered more advanced.

In the second category of cells are those which are even more slender and thicker-walled than tracheids and which have no overarching borders on their pits (fig. 8). These cells are fibers (fig. 3), and there are all gradations between them and tracheids.

The third category of cells are those which differ from both tracheids and fibers in having actual openings (black in fig. 2, 4, 5) in their end walls; that is, if one were small enough he could crawl into and out of the cells through these openings—the original walls which were intact become clearly perforate. A series of these perforate cells arranged end to end forms a vessel, the most efficient conducting element in xylem. Such multicellular structures may extend, according to recent work, over the whole length of a tree trunk and even into smaller and smaller branches, and probably into the roots as well. This is an important factor in the possible spread of spores of some pathogens in the plant, for example, and hence the development and spread of a disease in an exceedingly short time. The number and shape of the openings in the cells vary considerably throughout the secondary xylem of dicotyledons. There may be a single large opening (fig. 5) in a transversely placed end wall (the remains of which in many species occurs in the form of a rim about the opening), or, at the other extreme, there may be a large number of transversely placed elongate openings (fig. 2) on steeply inclined end walls. Furthermore, the pitting on the side walls of these cells varies from scalariform to opposite to alternate. The cross-sectional aspect of vessels varies from rectangular to circular, their length from about as long as tracheids to extremely short, their diameters from about comparable to those of tracheids to large enough for the vessels to be seen with the unaided eye (contrast fig. 1, 2, 4, 5). Vessel members—the cells of a vessel—are extraordinarily variable.

For those interested in evolution, the fundamental question about these upright cells in wood is: are they related to one another, and if so, in what way? The two-pronged physiological definition of xylem as the principal water-conducting and supporting tissue in vascular plants immediately suggests that the earliest vascular plants had wood cells (tracheids) that served both in conduction and in support. From these must have developed cells (fibers) principally concerned with support and others (vessel members) especially effective in conduction. To those particularly inclined toward viewing the plant primarily as a functional mechanism, these "divisions of labor" seem perfectly reasonable as evolutionary events. To the morphologist, too, such ideas are eminently sound, but he is likely to ask: is there a way to clarify how and along what lines of an evolutionary nature such changes took place? If a concept explaining the grosser aspects of the changes could be developed, would its validity be supported by newly revealed information? Put in another way, could the concept, or some variation of it, be used in predictions?

Jeffrey in this country and Boodle in England were early investigators of the evolutionary development of vessels and other cells of the wood. Jeffrey correctly concluded that vessel members arose from tracheids and that those with scalariform perforation plates represent the beginning and that those with simple plates are the end points in the evolution of vessel members. But in supporting these ideas he used inconclusive evidence and, except for one unusual group of plants, even started with the wrong type of tracheid (in terms of pitting). Thus a somewhat tortuous explanation emerged for some of the variations we have cited. There was no real anchor, no conclusively proved starting point, upon which his conclusions could be based. Yet he and his students did provide a stimulus for the development of an evolutionary point of view in studying xylem, a stimulus that eventually resulted in one of the most completely documented illustrations of evolutionary changes in plants.

When Bailey and Tupper published their data in 1918 on the lengths of various types of tracheids, fibers, and vessel members in the secondary xylem of the stems of a wide variety of vascular plants and set these beside the length of the cambial fusiform cells from which these elements were derived, they provided a definite means for getting at the problem of evolution of xylem elements. Once again we are struck with the importance of discovery of a new approach to an old problem and how fruitful results of its use may become in the hands of those who recognize its potentialities. Bailey's work on the cambium itself showed that the fusiform initials are the origin of the vertical elements of the xylem. Furthermore, it was shown that there is a close relationship between the lengths of the initials and their derivatives. Thus as the fusiform initials become shorter and shorter, so do their derivatives in the xylem. In gymnosperms, the initials are extremely long; in the flowering plants they vary from rather long to extremely short. One other striking fact concerning the length relationships being discussed concerns the possible elongation of the derivatives of the fusiform initials. When the initials are extremely long, the derivatives increase in length very little. If the initials are short, those derivatives which become vessel members increase little or not at all and those destined to be tracheids increase somewhat, but those which become fibers increase considerably in length by growth at their tips (intrusive growth). This complication does not in any way seriously affect the use of length data, but merely makes it necessary to be wary in the over-all study of wood evolution.

With the recognition of a feature of wood that can be adequately measured, and therefore hallowed by statistical treatment, it was now possible to gather the data available—all from present-day plants—and from these provide a sound basis for theories on the evolution of vessels and other cells in the xylem. P. H. Frost, working in Bailey's laboratory, made the first definitive study about 1930 and then settled, for all unprejudiced anatomists, the controversies concerning the details of vessel evolution, especially in the secondary xylem of the dicotyledons.

We do not intend to discuss here all the details of Frost's studies or of those which preceded them and made them possible and worthwhile. A thorough presentation would emphasize how a conclusive statement in this field of research comes only from a tremendous backlog of information and how necessary it is in evolutionary studies to take broad samplings of the plants involved. It will be sufficient in our case to tell something of the approach to a study of this nature. This approach underlies much of the research in morphology as a whole, even though, as Sporne of England has recently emphasized, it is seldom acknowledged or described.

Using statistical methods, Frost's approach to the problem of the origin and evolutionary development of vessels emphasized two especially important concepts. They are both based on assumptions, the validity of which must be borne out by the harmony of the evidence when they are employed. One concept, as expressed in words pertinent to our purposes, states that if tracheids are more primitive than vessels of any type and are related to them in a direct line, then the most primitive vessels are those most similar to tracheids. The other concept, once again worded expressly for our purposes, is that rates of evolutionary development of various features (such as length and perforations) of vessels are correlated; that is, they occur at the same rate. If in certain restricted types of plants—generally unusual in other respects as well as in their secondary xylem—one or more features do not fit into the major, statistically determined trends, these become exceptions and illustrate minor tendencies, an example of which is the great length of vessels in the stems of vines. Frost dignified these aberrations by using them as the basis for a third concept called exceptions. It perhaps was necessary to so emphasize these aberrations, because some investigators chance upon exceptional forms and, on the basis of these relatively minor irregularities, love to dispute generalizations whose significance they never have really understood.

Frost found that tracheids are characterized by great length and that by association the longest vessel members are therefore most primitive. By use of the methods of association and of correlation, he statistically determined that among vessel members, the longest had narrow diameters, thin but evenly thickened walls, long end walls with numerous transversely elongate perforations, and scalariform pitting on the side walls. Hence all these features are primitive in vessels. Frost furthermore showed that there was a continuous gradation from these primitive, long vessel members to the shortest members, which are characterized by heavily—but unevenly—thickened walls, transversely placed end walls each with a single large circular perforation, and alternate pitting on the side walls. From these conclusions, as well as other information, Frost concluded that primitive vessel members with their long scalariform plates are derived from scalariformly pitted tracheids and that the really fundamental difference between the two kinds of elements was the loss of pit membranes in the end walls of primitive vessel members.

We have thus in secondary xylem a beautifully graded evolutionary sequence in the tracheid-vessel series which is correlated with a similar sequence in the shortening of fusiform initials in the cambium which gives rise to these cells.

Is there a comparable series in the primary xylem of the dicotyledons and of the monocotyledons? Later research by Bailey and Cheadle conclusively proved that the series is essentially the same in both these major groups of plants, the only real difference being that the cells themselves have greater average lengths and that there are greater technical difficulties involved in making accurate observations.

Let us see to what use some of the conclusions reached in the studies just described have been put. As an example, it has been possible to determine that vessels in the dicotyledons arose in woody plants (some present-day trees and shrubs lack them) in the secondary xylem and then in succession in the metaxylem (perhaps simultaneously in the last-formed metaxylem and secondary xylem) and protoxylem, that subsequent specialization of vessels took place in later-formed secondary xylem, early-formed secondary xylem, metaxylem, and protoxylem, successively. (See fig. 9, *LSX, ESX, MX, PX* for positional relationships.) So clearly established is this sequence that not a single exception is known; those occurring in the literature have been shown to be erroneous.

As a second example, in the monocotyledons, vessels arose first in the later-formed part of the metaxylem of roots and then appeared successively upward in the plant. The same sequence is true of the specialization of vessels. Furthermore, vessels arose and specialized in succession in the later-formed metaxylem, early-formed metaxylem, and protoxylem of any particular organ of the plant in the monocotyledons. There are no reliably reported exceptions to these statements. So clear is the situation in the monocotyledons that given the information on vessels in the stem of a plant, one can predict without exception the limitations of specialization within which vessel variation may be present in the remainder of the plant. In terms of evolutionary studies, these sequences are fabulous illustrations of evolutionary change. Furthermore, there are no identifiable evidences of retrogression; the sequences are unidirectional.

As a third example, using the specialization of vessels as a base, it has been possible to determine the evolutionary specialization of the arrangement of vessels in the wood. For illustration, those woods in which the vessels are distributed singly throughout mostly have primitive vessels. Conversely, when the vessels are arranged in aggregations, the vessels are likely to be specialized. In those woods having large vessels in the first wood laid down after a resting period (such as winter) and small vessels in later wood, the vessels are chiefly specialized.

Two other examples can be cited. The proper reading of the tracheid, fiber-tracheid, fiber series can also be made by using correlation with specialization of vessels in the same woods. The evolutionary specialization in patterns of wood parenchyma have also been more or less clearly established by utilizing variations among the accompanying vessels as a measuring device.

While the major evolutionary tendencies within secondary xylem, of which the above are examples, can thus be established, it should be carefully noted that it is principally the different rates of specialization of these features in any given wood that provide the important methods of microscopically distinguishing one wood from another. Much of this type of work, incidentally, has been done by researchers in other countries.

There is another aspect of the use of specialization of vessels, and of xylem generally, that should be mentioned. If it is accepted that specialization in vessels is a unidirectional evolutionary sequence, then this sequence is of immense value as a means of determining the phylogenetic placement of plants in the schemes of natural classification. For example, it is clear that typical herbs in the dicotyledons must have arisen from woody ancestors, for, on the one hand, herbs generally have extremely specialized vessels and, on the other, there are some woody species in the dicotyledons that lack vessels of any kind. As another example, the vessel situation in herbaceous monocotyledons is such that they could not have originated from the dicotyledonous herbs suggested as their forebears by some writers. Like any other feature concerning plants, the tracheid-vessel series must be intelligently employed. But this series has the obvious advantage of being the most clearly documented of any that might be used. Because of its unidirectional development, it can always be employed as a negating factor; for example, a plant with highly specialized vessels in the secondary xylem could not have given rise to one with only normal tracheids in secondary xylem. The application of the tracheid-vessel series in this sense is its most compelling attraction as a tool for use in developing a natural classification.

If there are those who believe that xylem has been pretty well worked over, even from an evolutionary standpoint, let it be said at once that there are problems both large and small still to be solved. If we are to make the best use of vessels in classification, there are enormous numbers of plants still to be examined. It is especially necessary further to investigate herbaceous, aquatic, and parasitic or saprophytic dicotyledons. The same is true of a wide variety of monocotyledons, not so much to test further the generalities that have been made in the last few years as to establish a more complete inventory for use in phylogenetic classifications or in interpretation of the loss of xylem in certain aquatics and other plants in which typical xylem is lacking. Without such investigations, we lose full use of an effective tool in evolutionary studies.

Before closing this brief account of some aspects of progress in research on xylem, I should make clear that there have been many other extensive investigations on this conducting and supporting tissue. In particular, we should acknowledge the beautiful work on cell walls by Bailey and Kerr and others and the huge literature on wood identification and wood technology by numerous workers in this country, to say nothing of those abroad. But the progress in these and other important fields in the last fifty years must be told by others.

PHLOEM. The second general area of research I should like to review concerns phloem. In spite of the fact that xylem and phloem are intimately related in vascular plants, progress on investigations of the structure of phloem has been slow. There are several reasons for this. In contrast to the xylem, the phloem has soft conducting cells which are commonly crushed as new secondary tissues are produced by the vascular cambium. As a matter of fact, the outer (older) phloem in most older stems is successively sloughed off by the formation of cork by cork cambia. Again in contrast to the conducting cells in xylem, the actively conducting cells of phloem are living, or are at least in a labile form generally associated with the living state, and thus many aspects of phloem cannot be studied in dried material —the extensive usable wood collections over the world are not matched by comparably useful bark collections. Likewise, herbarium materials cannot often be effectively used in phloem studies, although they frequently can in researches in xylem. These same contrasting features of phloem and xylem are related to the paucity of good fossil material of phloem and the relatively frequent appearance of fossil remains of beautifully preserved xylem. To compound the difficulties, the ontogenetic changes that occur both with regard to cell divisions and to cellular content are much more complicated in phloem. The foregoing peculiarities of phloem, when added to the heterogeneity of the tissues as often represented by mixtures of hard- and soft-celled constituents, make technical preparation itself a formidable obstacle to progress.

It is paradoxical, in one sense, that although our understanding of phloem is not equal to that of xylem, there have been more recent and more widely disseminated reviews of both structure and function of phloem than there have been of xylem. The recent accounts by K. Esau and by A. S. Crafts in the *Botanical Review* and by Esau and others in the *American Journal of Botany* are especially worth reading. Another aspect of the literature on phloem should be stressed at this point. Although the best-informed investigator of phloem is undoubtedly an American scholar, there have been more publications abroad on this tissue—and this is true recently as well as in the past—than in the United States. The summary of important research accomplishments in the last fifty years in this country will consequently not be as representative of the total new knowledge of phloem as was that for the xylem. After a rather lengthy orientation, accordingly, a condensed review will be given of certain aspects of phloem research.

In relation to the subject matter arbitrarily chosen for discussion of xylem, it was shown that the intellectual drive involved in the reviewed research on wood lay in curiosity about the evolutionary development of various kinds of cells and assemblages of them. This has not been the chief motivation in the study of phloem in this country. The principal objective in published research on phloem has been a more complete understanding of its functioning as the chief food-conducting tissue. As a matter of fact, many of the detailed papers on phloem anatomy have appeared as side issues, more or less, to the main objective of understanding phloem physiology. It is worth stressing that recognition of the relationship between structure and function has had a sobering effect on physiological speculation.

As pointed out earlier, we do not have a large fund of information on some aspects of phloem, and this is especially true in terms of comparative studies. And in spite of a considerable body of data on the physiology of conduction of food in the phloem, there is still controversy over the mechanism of translocation of these materials. Perhaps because of this, interest has centered on the cytophysiology and structure of the principal conducting elements themselves. As we make our short inventory of the cellular components of the phloem, let us keep in mind the importance of these elements, so unusual that Katherine Esau has referred to them singly as "the nonconformist plant cell."

Disregarding for the moment the unusual food-conducting cells in certain primitive (nonvascular) plants, the vertically conducting elements in the phloem consist of sieve cells and sieve tubes. Sieve cells (fig. 15) occur in most of the vascular plants below the angiosperms, whereas sieve tubes, composed of longitudinally oriented series of cells known as sieve-tube members (fig. 16, 18), occur in the angiosperms. Parenchyma cells are also important constituents of the phloem, and they occur in varying degrees of relationship to the sieve cells or sieve tubes. Certain parenchyma cells, for example, arise from a phloem initial that immediately thereafter becomes a young sieve-tube member and are known as companion cells (fig. 17, 18) because of their close relation to these conducting cells. In addition to parenchyma, there are often fibers, or sclereids, thick-walled cells that tend to make the phloem in some species exceedingly hard or tough. Disregarding some unusual cells or cell complexes, the final constituent to note is the phloem ray, previously mentioned when the radially disposed sheets of cells in secondary vascular tissues were casually described.

The sieve elements (this term is used when sieve cells, or sieve tubes, or sieve-tube members are meant) have a combination of features that, taken as a whole, make them unique among plant cells. The most common features may be given in a brief description of the ontogeny of sieve elements. Whether such elements arise in the primary body of the plant or in the secondary, they of course at first have a nucleus. In most plants, this nucleus normally disintegrates during maturation of the sieve elements, although the nucleoli may escape and retain their identity within the cell. The cytoplasm becomes so thin and unstainable (with ordinary histological stains) that the cells in a sense appear to be clear and often can be tentatively identified on this basis. Plastids, or structures comparable to them, generally appear in the sieve elements, but grains of typical starch do not form in these plastids.

A fourth feature of sieve elements—the sieve areas—is associated chiefly with the wall. Young sieve elements, and young parenchyma cells generally, characteristically have thin areas in their walls through which narrow cytoplasmic strands (plasmodesmata) presumably interconnect with those of similar neighboring cells. In sieve elements, the thin areas (primary pit fields) become more clearly differentiated by an increase in the size of the plasmodesmata and by the deposition around each of an elongate collar of callose—the callose cylinder (fig. 19, 20, CAC). At this stage the plasmodesmata are best called connecting strands (fig. 19, 20, CS), according to Esau, because they may consist of something more than typical cytoplasm (e.g., slime).

Sieve areas are presumably of great importance in vertical conduction. One indication of this is that the sieve areas on the end walls of sieve elements in the angiosperms, particularly, are more highly differentiated (larger connecting strands and callose cylinders) than they are elsewhere. So obvious is this in most observed angiosperms that the sieve elements can be said to be arranged in longitudinal series known as sieve tubes, each cell of which is called a sieve-tube member (fig. 16, 18). (The length of sieve tubes is unknown.) Sieve tubes are thus to the phloem what vessels are to the xylem. Another indication of the importance of sieve areas in translocation is that during dormancy of sieve elements, or during senescence, excessive amounts of callose occur around the connecting strands and over the entire sieve area, thus effectively reducing the size of, or even breaking, the interconnection of the strands between two cells. In those plants in which sieve elements become reactivated following dormancy, the callose is reduced in amount and the connecting strands enlarge and apparently re-establish continuity between adjacent sieve elements. On the other hand, at the cessation of conducting activity of sieve elements, both the connecting strands and the callose disappear, leaving empty pores in the sieve areas—at this stage they really appear as sieves. The sieve elements at this time also become devoid of cellular contents and may even be obviously filled with air; they may or may not become crushed at this nonconducting stage, depending upon the species and cellular make-up of the phloem. It is hardly conceivable, in view of the changes just reviewed, that sieve areas are not intimately associated with translocation.

The four features (absence of nuclei, relatively thin, poorly staining cytoplasm, absence of typical starch, sieve areas) seem generally common to all sieve elements, except for the inevitable minor exceptions (e.g., somewhat degenerate nuclei in *Isoetes*); and it is at the stage when these typical features are evident that the elements presumably become functional in rapid conduction of food materials. It appears, then, that the functioning of these elements is associated with their cytological condition. If true, it is obvious why the cytology of sieve elements should be of interest to physiologists and why cytological details should be accurately reported.

There are still other details of sieve elements that merit brief mention. Slime and additional details of the wall structure are examples. Slime is noted here chiefly because it often occurs abundantly in the sieve elements of those plants used for class study (e.g., cucurbits). It appears in various forms, and these may represent seasonal changes or stages of development of the sieve elements. The additional feature of the wall in the sieve elements of many species of plants concerns variability in thickness. In fresh sections, the thicker walls, especially, often have a pearly luster, hence the name nacré applied to such walls. There is little specifically known of this feature of sieve elements, and hence nothing more will be said of it at this juncture; it will be referred to briefly again later.

The early important information on phloem from American laboratories came from MacDaniels, whose paper in 1918 on phloem of woody plants corrected Hemenway's observations and unsubstantiated notions on the evolution of sieve tubes in relation to the phylogeny of the dicotyledons. It should be remembered that in 1918 the important work on the vascular cambium and the length of its xylem derivatives had not yet been published. Hence MacDaniels' accurate observations could not be adequately interpreted against a background of reasonable generalizations about the cambial derivatives. Nevertheless, it is evident from the early work that in the evolution of sieve-tube members they not only became shorter, but also their end walls became more nearly transversely placed (fig. 16, 18).

As was mentioned previously, an American—Katherine Esau—is the best-informed investigator of phloem structure. Her entrance into this field was primarily motivated by an interest in the translocation and effect of virus particles. And Alden S. Crafts, the leading physiologist in the field of translocation in this country, pursued research in phloem anatomy in the effort to learn more about the mechanism of translocation. In fact, aside from a very few papers, the important American literature on phloem is primarily a reflection of curiosity about vertical conduction in the phloem. This is understandable because of the importance of translocation in terms of nutritional relationships in the plant as a whole and of the movement of other substances, such as herbicides and viruses, with the translocation stream. The latter two materials are dealt with by other authors of these Jubilee papers.

Crafts' major contributions to phloem anatomy, introduced at about the time that K. Esau commenced her studies, were twofold. In the first place, he brought into modern focus a good deal of European data on phloem structure. Secondly, he clearly demonstrated, and has continuously emphasized, the interrelationship of structure and physiology of the sieve elements. With this background of phloem study, his eloquent, imaginative, consistent defense of the mass-flow hypothesis as an explanation of translocation in the phloem has forced those who oppose it to broaden their own horizons in coping with his arguments. Crafts' curiosity about the essential nature of food-conducting elements led him to a relatively broad survey of brown algae, bryophytes, gymnosperms, and angiosperms. From this survey came some of the generalities about sieve elements that were given above in the description of phloem. He particularly stressed the notion that the protoplasmic peculiarities of sieve elements make them unique among living cells. From this conclusion came, almost inevitably, the concept that cells with all or most of these characteristics in the bryophytes and the brown algae must be sieve elements, even though xylem is absent. This occurrence of at least sieve-element-like structures has important implications with regard to the universal occurrence of some common structural peculiarities in food-conducting elements and hence the relation of such structures to function; the problem of relationship of vascular plants to brown algae and to the bryophytes; and the presumed antiquity of phloem in contrast to xylem. All these implications are of deep interest to those concerned with the biology of phloem or with plant phylogeny.

The greatest impetus to phloem study in America, however, has come from Katherine Esau's research papers and reviews. Keen observer, meticulous writer, excellent illustrator, linguist, her accomplishments in phloem research and related studies have set the highest standards. An interest in studies of the anatomic effects of sugar-beet virus and its movement in the plant led naturally to broader and broader investigations of phloem. Once again, studies intended originally to be chiefly practical in outlook turned almost immediately into fundamental investigations upon which all practical applications appear to depend. It is almost axiomatic that we quickly exhaust our basic information when it is needed in the detailed solution of more obviously practical problems.

Esau's knowledge of the literature has led to clarification of terminology as well as a sound basis for various approaches to study of the phloem. The terminology in Cheadle and Whitford's papers on the evolution of sieve tubes in the monocotyledons in 1941 and subsequent years, for example, is primarily an outcome of conversations with her. Utilizing her understanding of developmental anatomy, she made detailed investigations of the phloem of tobacco, grape (including seasonal changes), and other plants. She described the unique release of nucleoli from nuclei during developmental stages of sieve elements in a number of plants. Esau took a major part in a study on plasmolyzability of sieve elements that settled a controversy of long standing over this aspect of sieve elements. In later years, with her colleagues, she has broadened further her studies of phloem structure over a wide range of plants. These studies have chiefly made clear how vague and unsatisfactory is our total understanding of variation in the phloem.

One of the latest papers has shown, for example, the differences in some of the divisions within the phloem derivatives of the vascular cambium. The divisions [in planes more or less at right angles (anticlinal) to that of the cambium] may be vertical to almost transverse. The derivatives of the divisions that are nearly transverse obviously are shorter than the fusiform cambial initial from which they were indirectly derived. Some of these derivatives become sieve elements. Since they do not elongate before maturation, it is clear, accordingly, that length of sieve elements may have no obvious relation to the length of fusiform cambial initials. Length—the cornerstone of evolutionary studies of xylem elements—thus can be used only when one knows the developmental history of the sieve elements; this is a crucial obstacle to overcome in similar studies of phloem elements.

Another interesting aspect of divisions within the cambial derivatives (phloem initials) is related to the number of divisions that may occur. For example, it has often been considered that a given phloem initial in the dicotyledons acts as a sieve-tube mother cell, and by one or more divisions produces one or more small companion cells [which may undergo transverse divisions themselves (fig. 18)]. It is now clear that the phloem initials may undergo several longitudinal (anticlinal) divisions prior to those which produce companion cells. The products of these divisions may be sieve elements or parenchyma cells (fig. 17, *P*) or both. If they are to be sieve-tube members (fig. 17, *STM*), they in turn undergo divisions resulting in the formation of companion cells (fig. 17, *CC*). A widely varying assemblage of cells may thus arise from what has heretofore been considered as a sieve-tube-member mother cell. In addition to companion cells, accordingly, there are at least two kinds of parenchyma cells in many species of the dicotyledons, those which are derived as noted above and those which arise directly (usually after one or more transverse divisions) from a phloem initial. Those arising in the latter manner are almost invariably larger than those indirectly derived in the same species.

The significance of these divisions in relation to food conduction in sieve elements is yet unknown, but they must be considered in any theories concerning the mechanism of conduction. Reduction in size of the potential conduits, together with the insertion of additional end walls, must make some impact on the efficiency of translocation.

The problems for study in phloem anatomy are numerous and varied. They concern, for example, structure not only as related primarily to conduction but also as related to toughness of the bark. Some problems of special importance to physiology concern the sieve areas, and particularly the minute composition of connecting strands; the functional duration of sieve elements—our general ideas will almost certainly be changed by study of tropical and semitropical dicotyledons and of perennial monocotyledons in all climates; the occurrence and number of companion cells and whether they are lacking in any significant number of species—time-consuming and difficult research; the frequency and precise positional relationships of various other parenchyma cells; and the influence of fiber distribution on longevity of sieve elements. It may be, too, that the evolutionary development of the various types of sieve elements may supply critical information on the physiology of food-conducting cells.

In connection with the size of the lumen of the sieve element, through which food substances presumably pass, it would be wise for students of translocation to consider the extraordinary thickness of walls of sieve elements in many species. Even after complete dehydration, many of these walls are so thick that the lumen is almost completely obstructed. This aspect of structure in relation to translocation is almost universally ignored, chiefly because such thick walls are not commonly present in the usual experimental plants. Here is a problem that needs critical attention.

Fibers and sclereids need further study, particularly of their ontogenetic variations and of their special relation to other elements in the phloem. The ontogeny of fibers that occur in what has ordinarily been assumed to be the pericycle needs to be studied in a wide variety of angiosperms, particularly, for these fibers actually originate in primary phloem in many species and perhaps in most.

Truly the field of phloem anatomy is a wide-open one. We need more investigators; only a few botanists, including Artschwager and, more recently, Schneider, seem interested in solving the problems presented by this extraordinary assemblage of cells. Those of us in this field invite our colleagues to join in the quest for knowledge—there are problems enough for scores of researchers in this country in addition to those active in other parts of the world.

INITIAL VASCULARIZATION. I should not close this article on vascular tissues without some comment on concepts of the initial vascularization of the shoot—an important aspect of development of primary tissues in general. A critical evaluation of the research on this subject in the decade preceding 1954 has been given by Esau, and earlier work has been reviewed by Wetmore and others. The following, accordingly, is a brief summary made from a different point of view and is not meant in any sense to be critical. The comments will lay stress on the individuals involved and the importance of our fund of basic morphological information to those who must use it in interpreting experiments designed to extend our understanding of causal relationships in morphology.

It is not surprising that the more or less indefinite apical growth of the vegetative shoots (and roots, for that matter) in vascular plants should

attract the attention of morphologists, for in this type of growth we have
one of the most essential differences between typical animals and plants. If
we think about this growth for a moment, one of the striking facts that
should occur to us is that in moving downward, so to speak, from the apex of
an actively growing shoot of a tree, for example, we soon pass through all
the stages that represent longitudinal growth of the stem; thereafter what
we observe is chiefly related to increase in girth. What may not often occur
to us in such observations, perhaps, is that we have the possibility of studying the interplay between whatever influences may reside in young undifferentiated cells on the one hand and more mature assemblages of cells on
the other. There is, in addition, the effect of cells in various stages of differentiation to be considered. It should be obvious, accordingly, that a clear
understanding of the changes in the various regions of a young tip in a normal
plant must precede any understanding of what may occur when normal
growth of the tip is disturbed. Most of the research up to recent times has
been devoted to the development of an understanding of the normal sequence
of events in primary growth of shoots.

Through the efforts especially of A. S. Foster and some of his students and
colleagues, we have learned from research in this country much about the
make-up of the shoot apex. We know from this work, for example, that the
meristematic cellular constituents of the shoot apex are not haphazardly arranged, but that they have, within certain limits, a recognizable organization.
Furthermore, the patterns of organization are even arranged by some writers
in several loosely defined categories, although these are not mutually exclusive. It is helpful to be aware of the cellular organization in the shoot apex,
because descendants from cells in these apices indirectly produce the leaves
and eventually become differentiated as the primary body of the stem. In
this connection, the precise relationship between the initial vascularization—
formation of procambium and later differentiation of the xylem and phloem
—of the stem and that of the leaves developing from it may be of the greatest
value to experimental morphologists. Important as information concerning
the shoot apex proper is, however, the descriptive research concerning it ordinarily has not considered derivative groups of cells far enough down the stem
to provide adequate information on the ontogeny of primary vascular tissues.

In this country, the earliest important emphasis on primary vascularization—development of the primary vascular tissues—again appeared in Esau's
papers. In attempting to clarify the "host-virus relations in the curly top disease" in tobacco, she found it necessary to undertake a critical analysis of the
ontogenetic history of primary vascular elements. It became essential, too,
for her to distinguish between primary and secondary elements, as well as
between procambial cells (direct precursors of primary vascular elements)
and other meristematic cells. Esau later answered her own plea for further
critical research of this type by detailed studies of a number of species. From

these studies came an understanding of the relation of appearance and size of vascular tracts in the stem to phyllotaxy (arrangement of leaves). They demonstrated, also, the difficult and painstaking nature of this type of research. Her students and many of Foster's have since completed other investigations of this type. Wetmore and his students also early followed a comparable type of research in a greater variety of vascular plants before turning chiefly to the extremely valuable experimental work that has characterized publications from his laboratory in recent years.

It seems abundantly clear from the comments just made that a thoroughgoing knowledge of origin of procambium in stems and leaves, both in relation to time and position, together with a comparable understanding of the differentiation of primary xylem and phloem, is difficult to achieve. It is just as clear, moreover, that any departure from a normal sequence of events cannot even be recognized as such without this knowledge and understanding.

It is a tribute to the professional courage of experimental morphologists that in spite of these obstacles, they have launched into programs of exciting research on shoot tips (see other contributions in this Jubilee series). By the use, where appropriate, of tissue-culture techniques developed in the latter decades of this half century—these in turn were based upon nutrient culture techniques involving whole plants—and of surgical procedures, the way has been opened not only for studies of structure in relation to growth, but also for a thoroughgoing program of biochemical research in connection with them.

We are thus on the threshold of an era in which much can be learned about the causal relationships of form in plants, about various mutual influences of differentiated and undifferentiated groups of cells. The literature to date has shown that some of the details of vascularization of the shoot, especially in relation to the leaves, can be used as important testing devices for determining the causal influences we have briefly mentioned. Those of us who by inclination or opportunity find our own research interests in other aspects of morphology hope to gain much by rapid progress in these experimental aspects of structure and form in plants. My plea is that we do not slow down essential progress by excessive speculation based upon incomplete knowledge of initial vascularization in normal plants and by crowding the literature with unsatisfactory, if not actually misleading, casually descriptive papers purporting to serve as the bases for such speculations. It seems obvious that carefully prepared descriptions of adequately investigated typical plants will provide the only sound basis upon which to interpret experimentally induced variations. At the same time, such descriptions will add to our inadequate knowledge of structure in normal plants.

CONCLUSION. The remarks just concluded on certain arbitrarily chosen studies of vascular tissue chiefly referred to the individuals and the intellectual motivations concerned with these studies during the past fifty years.

One feature of all the investigations of plant structure mentioned might be stressed again: the large amount of research in this field necessary to make a noteworthy addition to our knowledge. To many of us, nevertheless, a study of anatomy or of some other phase of morphology is a satisfaction in itself if it provides even a small, but well-substantiated, addition to the literature.

Viewed as a whole, highly satisfactory progress has been made during the last fifty years in anatomical research. And just as cytology was so obviously invigorated by the demands made on it by genetics, so we may expect anatomy to be further invigorated in the next fifty years by demands from a wide variety of other disciplines in plant science. There is no attainable limit to what may be learned or to how it may be put to use.

8

BOTANY AND MORPHOGENESIS

Edmund W. Sinnott

No botanist needs to be persuaded that his science is of fundamental importance. In some respects it stands above all others, for it deals with the processes that make life possible—photosynthesis and many other basic syntheses. Studies concerned with metabolism, cytology, genetics, ecology, and evolution draw heavily on plant material for their progress. Botany contributes to almost every aspect of the life sciences and will continue to do so actively in the future.

There is one biological discipline, however, in which all others seem in a sense to converge—the problem of how growth and development are controlled and an *organism* is produced. This in its simplest statement is the problem of *form* in living things, one to which thinkers from Aristotle and Goethe to Joseph Needham and Agnes Arber have pointed as the central one. It is the basis of morphology, a science which Darwin declared to be the very soul of natural history.

The *dynamic* aspects of the form problem come to focus in that field of biology that is variously called experimental embryology, causal morphology, *Entwicklungsmechanik,* or, perhaps most appropriately, morphogenesis. It deals with the organizing capacity of protoplasm by which random material, when drawn into the body of a plant or animal, becomes organized into a living system with a precise form and structure. The embryo or embryonic center marches on in its development through a regular series of stages to the production of a mature organism and tends to do this even if its normal course is experimentally disturbed. This fact of *organization,* whatever the explanation of it may turn out to be, still remains the great biological enigma and confers on the sciences of life that autonomy that distinguishes them from the physical sciences. The latter, as Whitehead suggested, may be concerned with "organisms" of a very simple sort, like the atom, but these are far from the elaboration and significance of living ones.

Plants provide particularly favorable material for morphogenetic investigation. They are less tightly organized than animals and therefore pose most problems of morphogenesis in relatively simple terms. The complexity that the presence of a nervous system introduces into animal development is missing in plants, and the basic activities and possibilities of relatively undifferentiated living stuff can here be studied most directly. Plants also are usually more tractable than animals and easier to deal with experimentally. It is therefore evident why a study of plant development has made so many notable contributions to this field in the past and is so promising for a further understanding of morphogenetic problems. It will be profitable in this anniversary year to examine, even very briefly, what has already been accomplished and what the possibilities are for further progress here.

In the history of morphogenesis one often thinks first of the great names in zoology—Roux, Driesch, Wilson, Morgan, and many more—who studied the problems of experimental embryology so fruitfully, among amphibia and various invertebrates, more than half a century ago. Let us not forget, however, that Vöchting, Goebel, and their colleagues at this time were laying a firm foundation for morphogenesis in plants as well. Driesch's famous aphorism, "The fate of a cell is a function of its position," which states so compactly the essence of the phenomenon of organization, was uttered about the turn of the century, but one can find almost these same words in Vöchting's little known *Organbildung im Pflanzenreich,* published in 1878.

One reason for the more rapid morphogenetic progress among zoologists at first was the fact that they had easy access to the early embryonic stages of their organisms whereas in seed plants the young embryo, buried inside integuments and ovary wall, is difficult to study experimentally. In one respect, however, the structure of these higher forms gives the investigator a great advantage in developmental studies, for in their meristems they possess permanently embryonic regions. A single plant thus provides readily accessible and genetically uniform material in abundance where many stages in the developmental process can be studied in one individual. This advantage is now being actively exploited, especially by those who work with apical meristematic regions. Here the steps in the development of lateral organs can readily be traced. The occurrence of cell layering in these meristems has been studied, and in some cases, particularly in periclinal chimeras, it is possible to trace particular organs or tissues to specific layers. The subepidermal layer in the shoot has been found to be the one from which sporogeneous tissue is derived and may thus be thought of as the germinal layer, a sort of germ plasm.

That layering in itself has little significance, however, is shown by the fact that plants where the meristematic apex is irregularly cut up into cells, as in many gymnosperms, develop in as regular a pattern as do layered ones. Evidently the particular cellular configuration of an embryonic region—and this is still clearer in determinate meristems—has little direct effect on the character of the structure which develops from it. It is the whole meristematic mass that behaves as an orderly developmental unit.

Studies of determinate meristems, as in the growth of leaf and fruit, and of lateral ones, especially the vascular cambium, offer a wide and little-exploited field for research. Intensive experimental work on meristems of all kinds is producing a new sort of experimental embryology, quite different from that in zoology but destined to be very fruitful.

The relation of the character of individual cells to morphogenetic proc-esses is a problem almost as old as the cell theory itself. It can readily be examined in plant material since the cell here has a firm wall, usually is closely attached to its neighbors, and maintains a relatively constant size and shape. The fact that in most cases the size of a plant organ is related to the number rather than to the size of its constituent cells may be taken as evi-dence that the cell is not the basic morphogenetic unit. This conclusion, for which there is much other evidence, is of great theoretical importance if true. In some cases, of course, notably in polyploid forms, organ size *is* re-lated to cell size. Cell-size differences often reflect environmental influences, also, as in etiolation and physiological dwarfing.

The shape of cell varies greatly and is a major aspect of differentiation. The origin of these different shapes is a morphogenetic problem in itself, in-volving polarity, geometry, and the fine structure of the cell wall. In most cases, however, cell shape has little influence on organ shape and is relatively unimportant at higher levels of development.

In some cases the plane of cell division has a definite relation to the direc-tion of growth and it is often closely concerned with differentiation. The in-fluence of external factors such as light, pressure, chemical gradients, and electricity on plant form can often be studied most directly through their effect on the plane of cell division. These facts make it clear that a study of cellular characters is by no means unimportant in developmental problems. The simplest types of plants, notably some of the algae, offer a particularly attractive field for work of this sort.

In discussing problems in plant morphogenesis above the cellular level one can do little more in brief space than point to some of the promising areas for research.

One of these is correlation, which in a sense is the problem of organization itself. Much work has been done on the relation of one structure to another, as of the terminal bud to buds below it; on the relative sizes of plant organs, such as root to shoot and cell to organ; and on the relative dimensions of growing plant parts—all these both in normal development and under various experimental conditions. Some of these correlations may be called nutritive, as where root growth depends on food production in the shoot; stimulatory, as where root growth is initiated by auxin, produced in a bud or otherwise; inhibitory, as where one structure inhibits the growth of another, as a terminal bud sometimes inhibits a lateral one; or compensatory, as where removal of one part results in abnormally large growth of another. The correlations evident in the development of specific forms, where physiological factors are not directly involved, are obviously under genetic control. Allometric analyses of the development of such forms have been fruitful although as yet little more than descriptive. The term "growth correlation" used to be thought of as a convenient catchall for unsolved problems in development, but the discovery of various mechanisms involved in it, especially among plants, has begun to bring order out of its confusion.

Polarity is also a conspicuous feature in development. Most organisms are built around a polar axis, the two ends of which are unlike. This is especially conspicuous in plants. Polarity here is manifest in various ways. One of these is in the basic difference between the root pole and the shoot pole and the structures each produces. Polarity is evident even in isolated pieces of a plant axis, as shown by the polar regeneration of roots and shoots in pieces of young stems and of fleshy roots. In some of the simple plants this polar character has been shown to be present even in individual cells as they regenerate, a fact which the firmness of plant tissues and the fixed position of their cells make it possible to prove more easily than in animals.

There must be a physiological polarity underneath that which is visible in structure. The simplest and best-known example of this is the polar flow of auxin, which is almost always from the apical end of the axis basipetally and is usually difficult to reverse. The actual mechanics of this one-way flow is unknown, but it seems not to be electrical in character. Bioelectric factors are evidently involved in some cases of physiological polarity, however. Since auxin tends to accumulate in the lower portions of the axis and since a relatively high concentration favors root development and a lower one shoot development, this fact may account for the polar nature of regeneration in these structures. Transverse as well as longitudinal polarities have been demonstrated. All this emphasizes the morphogenetic importance of the factors which determine the direction of movement of growth substances and nutrient materials in the plant. Perhaps a complex pattern of specific polarities is the basis for the patterns of tissues and organs. However this may be, the actual nature of polarity itself is obviously a major problem. A study of it in its relatively simple manifestation in plant axes has been very fruitful and seems to be the place where this basic problem may be attacked most hopefully.

Symmetry is another morphogenetic phenomenon of the first importance. Here, again, plant material makes a unique contribution, since plant axes are prevailingly vertical instead of horizontal, as in animals. The radial symmetry of leaves spirally arranged around this axis, and of flowers and floral parts, shows simple mathematical relationships. There is some difference of opinion as to how these phyllotactic patterns originate, but they are probably due to geometrical relationships between the primordia of lateral structures in meristems of different sizes and different degrees of crowding. Phyllotaxy has always intrigued morphologists since it is a place where organic form can be interpreted in mathematical terms. At least it is clear that symmetry of this sort, simple though it be, is quite different from the rigid symmetry of crystals, to which it has often been compared. It may perhaps be based on a fundamental spiral tendency in living stuff itself which is evidenced in traits as different as the spiral pattern of cellulose micelles in the cell wall and spiral growth movements and nutation.

The distortion of radial symmetry to dorsiventral or other types has often been studied. In some cases this is due to the direct effect of an external factor like light or gravity; in others it has become fixed through evolutionary changes. Nowhere can the relation between environmental and genetic control of organic form be studied in simpler manifestations than in these two types of dorsiventrality in plants. The polarity and symmetry that are inherent in the structures protoplasm builds and that are so vividly expressed in plants seem to be the basis of most organic patterns.

But a plant is more than a polar axis with symmetrical structure. Its parts are different from one another. The first difference is between the two ends of the polar axis. In the course of development from spore or seed various lateral organs appear along this axis, such as leaves in higher plants. In most cases these are produced in a series of successive members, from juvenile stages through various levels in the adult and culminating in the formation of reproductive structures. The plant thus has a definite life cycle. The successive multiple parts of which the body is composed often show progressive differences in structure, and evidence is accumulating that there are also physiological differences among them. In animals these various steps in the life cycle are manifest in changes within a single individual, but in plants the steps are spread out among the successively differentiating parts. Plants offer the student of development an advantage in this regard since he can separate the various stages in the process instead of having to follow them in a single unfolding system.

This system is not an unchanging one in differentiation. The potency of a cell or group of cells is altered as the organism develops. Originally it may be able to produce, by regeneration, an entire individual and is thus totipotent. This ability is reduced little by little until only one fate is left for a cell unless it becomes embryonic again. The reactivity of a cell also changes. The response it will make to a given factor in the environment may be very different at successive stages of development. This is related to the 'rhythmic physiological alterations which the whole plant undergoes. Furthermore, both the potency and the reactivity of a cell may become very different in various parts of the plant as differentiation progresses.

The ease of regeneration in plants can often be used to test the degrees of differentiation that occur during the life cycle. In many cases it has been found that cuttings from different parts of the plant, and thus from different developmental levels, produce plants with persistent differences. Cuttings from the flowering branches of English ivy, for example, produce plants very different from ones made from the earlier vine-like portions. Cuttings from seedlings will often produce plants unlike those taken from adult parts.

The paradox of differentiation is that it occurs in living stuff that is genetically uniform. One great contribution that plant science has made to morphogenetic problems is the proof that this is so. Cuttings can be produced not only from stems but from roots, leaves, hypocotyls, inflorescences, and even floral parts. In many cases, individual cells or groups of cells from parts of the plant body can be induced to divide, become meristematic, and ultimately regenerate new plants. This can be done by applying growth substances, isolating pieces of plant tissue, or in other ways. The plants produced from these various regions are all like the parent plants (save that the cells are sometimes polyploid), thus indicating that all parts of the plant are genetically alike. How the differences arise from these identical cells is obviously a major problem.

The very beginning of differentiation can often be traced, in plants, to a particular cell division where the two daughter cells are dissimilar, as in the origin of root-hairs, stomata, glandular cells, and other structures. Here the process of differentiation is pin-pointed, so to speak, and offers an excellent opportunity to find just how it begins and what causes it. The relative rigidity and stable position of plant cells make them particularly favorable for such studies.

In more complex cases the origin of a new tissue within a relatively undifferentiated cell mass may be observed, as in the development of the endodermis, the veins within the leaf mesophyll, or the fibrous net in a cucurbit fruit. All such examples offer opportunity to study differentiation more directly and easily both visually and by microchemical methods than can usually be done in animal tissues.

Plants have notable powers of regeneration, and the student of morphogenesis has long used this ability in his investigation. Several examples of this have already been cited, notably the ability to grow whole plants from single cells or small groups of cells.

The regenerative process in animals usually consists in remolding an organ, experimentally deprived of some of its normal structures, into a complete whole. In plants this process is more various. Sometimes it resembles that in animals, as when the tip of a root restores itself when only a small piece is cut off. Sometimes a larger portion of an organ may be restored, as when a leaflet is replaced after its removal. Far more commonly, however, there is no true repair of a structure but instead a restitution of it by the development of new young parts, often from a callus layer. This is what normally happens, for example, in the formation of roots on decapitated roots, or adventitious buds on decapitated shoots, or roots on stem cultures, and in similar cases. In such instances important information can be gained as to the physiological basis of regeneration, such as its relation to polarity, gravity, and growth substances.

Tissue regeneration in plants often provides clues impossible to find in normal development. In the regeneration of a vascular strand after it has been cut, for example, a new bundle is often formed by the transformation of large cells that would normally be parenchymatous. In such a cell cytoplasmic granules can be seen to aggregate into a pattern which marks the future reticulate lignified wall. Since the problem of differentiation, as is often remarked, must be studied in the cytoplasm because the nucleus is the same in every cell, these examples of tissue regeneration provide good material in which to investigate the behavior of the cytoplasm on a much larger scale, so to speak, than in normal tissue.

Orderly development sometimes breaks down, in plants as in animals, because of various internal or external factors. These cases of atypical growth are useful for a study of the developmental process itself. Most plant galls are self-limiting and rarely, if ever, assume a type of growth that can be called malignant. The intensive work on crown gall, however, has provided some important clues for a comparison between galls and true cancers.

The great variety of abnormalities that are to be found show the remarkable possibilities that plants possess. Galls produced on a wide range of plants by the deposition in them of the eggs of certain insects, notably the cynipid wasps, are highly specific in form and often complex in structure. Tumors and fasciations of various kinds are not infrequent. All these provide opportunity for a wide field of research on form-determining factors, a whole science in itself and destined to be of great importance in morphogenesis. Nothing quite like them is known in the animal kingdom.

Tissue culture, of course, is the almost complete collapse of organization. In plants, however, it is rarely possible to produce the real tissue culture that has been developed with animal material, where a particular type of cell multiplies indefinitely. A certain amount of differentiation is present in most plant cultures, and such cultures have a strong tendency to form growing points and produce organized bodies again. The degree of this tendency is affected by various external factors, notably some of the growth substances, a fact that provides a direct means of studying the phenomenon of organization itself.

Roots, leaves, fruits, and even whole plants may now be cultured in sterile media, and this makes possible a study of development under a completely controlled environment. This has already been of much value for the solution of physiological problems, but its great promise for studies in morphogenesis has yet hardly begun to be utilized.

A wide field for morphogenetic research is open through experimental manipulation of the environment. Plants provide particularly favorable material for studies of this sort, for a plant, as a result of its fixed habit, is much more sensitive to environmental factors than are most animals, since the latter can in some degree choose or modify their surroundings. We must recognize that there is not only an external environment but an internal one, and that changes in the latter, as in water content, acidity, electrical potential, and chemical substances, may have important effects on development. These inner factors are part of a highly organized system that exists in the midst of a much less organized environment.

The effect of a given factor on an organism is a much more complex process than it is on a lifeless object. In the latter the factor produces a direct and predictable result, as when water moves a wheel or light modifies a photographic plate. In a plant or animal, however, the factor acts as a trigger, or stimulus, which sets off a response. This response is the result of regulatory reaction by an organized living system, and since the nature of this system is not fully understood, the response is sometimes difficult to forecast. It is the presence of this organized, self-regulating system that makes experiments with living things so much more complex than with lifeless material.

The morphogenetic effects of various internal and external factors are often hardly to be distinguished from their physiological ones, and much of the knowledge that physiology obtains about biochemical and biophysical processes and protoplasmic activity has made important contributions to our knowledge of developmental processes. This has been particularly evident in the physiology of light effects, water relations, and growth substances.

For convenience one may classify environmental factors into physical ones, chemical ones, and a third group—genetic or biological—which have not been analyzed into simpler terms.

Among the first factors to be examined was water. The effects of a shortage of this essential substance in the production of xeromorphic structures was early recognized. These were at first thought to be adaptive in character. This is doubtless true for such as are inherited and have proved their value in selection. There is evidence, however, that the xeromorphy which results from shortage of water during development, either because of its lack in the environment or the inability of a given plant to obtain it, is due to a direct effect on plant structure and is without much adaptive significance. This effect is shown chiefly in reduced cell size and increased deposition of cellulose. Studies in water relations are not as common as they used to be in plant physiology, but their contribution to developmental problems is far from exhausted.

Light, a factor of peculiar importance in plants because of its role in photosynthesis, has implications for development that were unexpected in earlier years. The influence of the photoperiod on flowering has made possible one of the most direct means of attack on the problem of differentiation. These studies have told us much not only about the relative development of reproductive as opposed to vegetative structures, but about the differentiation of other characters, as well. The direct effect of differences in the intensity and the quality of light on plant structure has also provided important morphogenetic information.

Temperature has been found to be of importance in speeding up or slowing down early stages in growth and thus affecting the character of the developmental cycle. The concept of phasic development, of changing physiological states during growth, has largely grown from studies of temperature effects. These are closely concerned with the effects of light and of growth substances.

Mechanical factors, such as tension, compression, and swaying during growth, have been found to affect plant structure in various ways. They seem to be particularly effective on cambial growth. A tree that is freely swayed by the wind, for example, will grow considerably thicker than one which is prevented from swaying. Sometimes the influence of mechanical factors is direct, as in the determination of the plane of cell division, but oftener it is apparently indirect and simply influences the distribution or operation of other factors.

The field of bioelectricity is an extraordinarily difficult one, but enough substantial results have been obtained to make sure that it is importantly concerned in many developmental processes. This is what we should expect from our knowledge of animal physiology, but the advantage of similar work with plants is that their effects are simpler and not complicated by the presence of a nervous system.

One of the active and fruitful fields of research in plant morphogenesis is a study of the effects of chemical substances. The role of various individual elements in plant development has long been examined, especially in connection with agricultural practices. More important is the ratio between some of them, notably between carbohydrate, on the one hand, and water and available nitrogen, on the other. This ratio affects the relative development both of vegetative to reproductive structures and of root to shoot.

Still more significant are the various growth substances. Auxin is known to be involved in almost all the developmental processes of plants—cell division, cell enlargement, cambial activity, polarity, differentiation, and dominance. Other normally occurring hormone-like substances are concerned with wound healing, the induction of flowering, reproductive processes in algae and fungi, and other activities which have important implications for morphogenesis. Of only a few are their precise chemical nature and action known. A wide variety of synthetic substances provide valuable means for experimental work. A study of the role of growth substances is now the most active one in morphogenetic research.

To the environmental factors which have been mentioned the plant reacts in various ways. What this reaction will be is determined by the genetic constitution of the plant itself. A gene does not control a specific trait but a specific reaction to a specific environment. We thus must approach the problems of morphogenesis from a study of the inner genetic mechanisms as well as the outer factors to which it reacts.

The role of genes in the control of various metabolic processes is beginning to be understood. Each seems to mediate a particular process—perhaps by the production of a particular enzyme—in a successive series of processes. How genes control development, however, is far more difficult to understand and is the least explored field of morphogenesis. Gene action must evidently control *relationships* between parts or processes. There is good evidence that the inheritance of form is independent of that of size and that what is inherited is not particular dimensions but particular growth ratios or patterns. For studies of form inheritance the rather rigid structures of plants, notably leaf, flower, and fruit, provide particularly favorable material.

There are other points of contact between genetics and morphogenesis. Multiplying the chromosome complement through ploidy has various effects on development. It tends not only to increase cell size but often organ and body size. It also characteristically increases transverse dimensions more than axial (polar) ones and thus affects the shape of leaves and fruits. Heterosis, though its genetic basis is still not fully understood, also affects development profoundly. Both polyploidy and heterosis are commoner and easier to study in plants than in animals.

Plants have the further advantage that tissue mixtures of various sorts can be made easily between diverse forms which are sometimes rather widely separated taxonomically. The mutual effects of stock and scion have long been studied. It is chimeras, however, and especially periclinal ones, that are of the most importance here. In the latter, tissues from plant types differing in the size and form of their organs may be brought together in a most intimate fashion, and in varying proportions, to form essentially normal plants. The morphogenetic effect of each component can here be readily observed.

Such are some of the more important of the problems of morphogenesis as these are approached through studies with plants. It is clear that many of them are simpler and more readily open to investigation with botanical materials than by other means. We can be proud of the accomplishments of botanists in this field in the past, and there are prospects of much fruitful research in the years to come.

With whatever material one works, the problems of morphogenesis present extraordinary difficulties. One deals here with the central and most distinctive feature of living things—organization and self-regulation. He must never underestimate the magnitude of the task that confronts all explorers in this difficult realm. The great advances that have been made in many aspects of biology in recent years, particularly in metabolism, should not blind us to the fact that at this point on the frontier progress has long been interrupted. Save for being able to pose the problem of organic self-regulation in clearer terms we are not much farther along than were Vöchting and Driesch at the end of the nineteenth century.

This is not surprising, for one is here at grips with the very nature of life itself—not life simply as a series of chemical changes but as an integrative process. Because of this the student of morphogenesis lacks in many cases the advantage of employing the basic scientific technique of analysis, which has proven so successful in the physical sciences. No internal activity, or environmental factor, can be isolated in its effect or studied as a single variable, for each is concerned, to a greater or less extent, with the *entire living system*. Though the plant may seem to be made up of independent units in inheritance, it is not so in development. The influence of a given genetic factor is usually more conspicuous on one trait or group of traits than on the others, but modifying the organized framework in one respect affects the entire system to some degree, as the widespread occurrence of the multiple effects of genes makes clear. Similarly, the reaction of a plant to a particular external factor depends on what the other factors are. The effect of light is modified by temperature and inner rhythms. What auxin will do depends on the place and the process on which it operates. In metabolism, one can often break down the complex series of chemical changes and study the particular steps in each, but in the processes of regulation the changes have complex interrelationships and homeostatic activity which we do not yet understand. Of such a process, L. J. Henderson once said, "Sooner or later, when the problem is studied, we come upon the fact that a certain organ or group of cells accomplishes that which is requisite to the preservation of the equilibrium, varying the internal condition according to the variation of the external conditions, in a manner which we can on no account at present explain."

The process of organization and regulation is of significance beyond the boundaries of biology itself. Being concerned with the essential quality of life, it is important in the fundamental problems of all living things, including man himself. Biological organization must even be taken into account in certain philosophical questions, and it is here that the life sciences may have an important contribution to make to man's understanding of his own nature. It has been suggested by several biologists, for example, that there is a basic identity between the self-regulation shown in development and that shown in behavior, and that the origin of psychical traits, and thus perhaps of mind itself, may be found in the same protoplasmic activities that are concerned in morphogenesis. The march from fertilized egg to the formation of a mature individual, a march in which the organism tends so stubbornly to persist even when it is blocked experimentally, suggests that in the organism there is a protoplasmic norm or series of norms *to* which it regulates its activities. This may be thought of as a primitive purposiveness. Such is not the sort of purposiveness, often wrongly invoked by the teacher of elementary biology, which assumes that the organism naturally tries to do what is best for itself, as a person would; it is rather the purposiveness implicit in the very fact of the organism as a self-regulating system. In our fear of being teleological we sometimes forget that the organism itself is in a real sense teleological.

These problems are far from those with which we are dealing in the laboratory, and some biologists pride themselves on being entirely unconcerned with such matters. Biology is everywhere now pressing so closely on philosophical questions, however, that the student of life at its lowest levels should take an intelligent interest in problems presented at its most complex ones. The botanist is dealing with the very simplest manifestations of life, uncomplicated by the intricacies of structure and function necessarily present in animals. It may be that in the end what he discovers in plants about the nature of life will prove to be important for an understanding of man himself.

9

CYTOLOGY: THE STUDY OF THE CELL

Ralph E. Cleland

In their efforts to learn about life and living beings, biologists have developed many specialties, for although they know but a tiny fraction of what they need to know in order to understand fully what life is and how it functions, the sum total of biological knowledge is already far too extensive and complex for any one man to grasp it all. And so, some biologists have concerned themselves primarily with the identification and recognition of the different kinds of organisms, others with the manifold structures which these organisms have developed; still others have sought to analyze their activities, how they nourish themselves, grow, and reproduce, how they behave in their native surroundings and under controlled conditions.

Most of these and other specialties, however, attack the problem of the nature of life only indirectly, by studying the varied manifestations of life, the results of life activity. It is only by a study of that part of a living organism which is itself alive (the so-called protoplasm) that one can hope to gain an understanding of what life is in essence, what lies at the bottom of and is responsible for the phenomena which together make up what we call life. To achieve this goal, one must turn to the cell, for protoplasm exists, with very few exceptions, not in large masses, but in minute units which are called cells. Cytology is the study of the cell, and it is, therefore, of all fields the one which comes closest to the heart of the major quest of biology—the understanding of life in its essence.

The cell is a marvelous microcosm, extremely small, yet unbelievably complex. Although protoplasm is incomparably the most complex system known, it is organized into units whose size, or lack of size, is difficult for the average man to grasp. As the late Professor Sponsler (1940) has pointed out, the average-sized cell has a volume about one-millionth that of the average raindrop. It might seem that a unit of matter so small would be incapable of containing a substance as complicated as protoplasm. The complexities of protoplasm, however, are at the molecular level. It is an organized system of molecules of myriad kinds, some simple, some ranging up to the most complex molecules known, each kind of molecule having its own chemical properties, the sum total of all these properties adding up, when the molecules are organized in just the right way, to what we call life. The huge complexity of protoplasm does not require great mass or bulk, for even the largest molecules are minute in comparison with the size of the cell, and the space necessary to accommodate the total organization of these molecules is easily provided by the average-sized cell.

That there is plenty of space for a system as complicated as protoplasm in the cell is shown by a comparison of the size of an average cell with that of the various molecules which make up protoplasm. Protoplasm is composed of a skeletal framework made up of protein molecules, to which molecules of other kinds are attached, the whole suspended or dissolved in water. One of the substances found in some abundance in the cell is sugar. As Sponsler has pointed out, there is room in an average-sized cell for 64 trillion molecules of glucose (grape sugar), each with a molecular weight of 180 (i.e., it is 180 times as heavy as a hydrogen atom). It would take a person, counting at the rate of one a second, over 2 million years to count 64 trillion. The protein molecules which form the structural framework of the protoplasm are much larger than glucose molecules, averaging about 36,000 molecular weight. A cell with a volume a millionth that of the average raindrop is large enough to accommodate over 60 billion such protein molecules of average size (about 25 times as many as there are people on the face of the earth). Some of the protein molecules in the cell, however, may have molecular weights as high as 6 million. There would be room for as many as 500 million molecules of this size in such a cell. It is evident, therefore, that a cell could even be much smaller than a millionth the size of an average raindrop and still be abundantly able to enclose an enormous number of molecules of all sizes and sorts and to permit a molecular organization so complex that its properties would total that of life itself.

The cell has been known for a long time, but its nature, its organization, and the ways in which it functions have only recently begun to be elucidated. Back in 1665, Robert Hooke, an Englishman, constructed one of the first "microscopes" and with it saw many things never before seen by the eyes of man—among them, the box-like structure of cork. The compartments which he found to compose the structure of cork he called "cells"—he thought that they were empty compartments, as indeed in cork they were, since cork cells die soon after they have been formed and hence lose their contents. It was not until nearly 200 years after Hooke that it became evident that living cells are not walls surrounding empty spaces, but are masses of material surrounded by walls or membranes. The gradual revelation of the structural characteristics of this material, the discovery that it is endowed with the power of movement and able to react and respond in various ways to various stimuli, was the work of 19th-century investigators. The 1870's and 1880's were especially significant in the history of cytology. It was during this period that chromosomes were discovered, that the details of cell division were worked out, that the foundations for the study of the structure, chemical composition, and behavior of protoplasm were laid.

If one were to ask why it took so long after the cell was first seen for the science of cytology to be born, the answer is easy. Cytology, dealing as it does with units of microscopic size, had to await the development of magnifying apparatus of sufficient strength and resolving power to enable objects as small as a cell to be studied in detail. Such instruments were not developed until the latter third of the 19th century. As soon as they became available, an entirely new field of study was opened up.

Ever since its birth, cytology has been limited in its achievements by the instruments and methods at its disposal. On the observational side, it has been limited by the ability of available equipment to magnify and resolve. The microscope which uses ordinary light can only magnify in a really satisfactory manner up to about 1500 diameters, and this result has only been achieved by the use of special types of optical materials, such as fluorite. At higher magnifications, the image begins to lose definition, to become more and more fuzzy. Many of the secrets of structure and behavior which cytologists are seeking to uncover depend upon the analysis of structures which lie beyond the resolving power of the ordinary microscope.

Various improvements have been made from time to time on the light microscope. Quartz lenses have permitted the use of ultraviolet light which, because of its shorter wave lengths, permits a higher resolving power than does visible light. An ultraviolet microscope, however, can be used only photographically, since ultraviolet light is invisible to the human eye. One must take photographs and study these, rather than look at the material directly, and this creates a barrier to rapid and convenient study which, together with the excessive cost of a quartz optical system, has greatly limited the use of the ultraviolet microscope.

Dark-field microscopy has provided another useful supplement to the light microscope. It depends upon visible light which is introduced obliquely into the material being studied and is reflected off the surface of particles to the eye of the observer. When light from below is cut off and only the light reflected from the surfaces of particles is seen, the presence of particles too small to be resolved by the ordinary microscope is revealed.

In recent years, other mechanical developments have been added to the cytologist's arsenal of weapons. One of the most serious sources of error in cytological study stems from the fact that protoplasm in its living state is so transparent that one can look right through it with the ordinary microscope and fail to see most of the structures which it contains. This has made it necessary to use dyes which will stain different structures differently or stain particular structures and leave others unstained. Such dyes, however, will function as a rule only after the cell has been killed. The cytologist is compelled, therefore, to kill the cell first, then stain it. This necessity introduces into the work an element of uncertainty, for one is confronted with the possibility that the killing process has altered the fine structure of the cell or has rendered parts of the cell soluble in the reagents that must be used in the staining and mounting process. To be able to get away from the necessity of killing the cell, to find a way of seeing the structures in living protoplasm, has been the dream of the cytologist from the beginning. He now has two new kinds of microscopes, the phase-contrast microscope and the interference microscope, which utilize certain optical principles hitherto unused in microscopy to make many of the constituent parts of the cell stand out from their surroundings when the protoplasm is still living, so that they can be studied in respect to both their structure and behavior.

Perhaps the most spectacular mechanical development which in recent years has become available to the cytologist is the electron microscope. This instrument is capable of providing sharply resolved images at magnifications 10 times that of the light microscope. Although there are certain drawbacks to its use, the greatly increased magnification which it affords has brought it into great prominence as a cytological tool. The drawbacks to its use, beside the great cost of the instrument, are the fact that it must be used primarily as a photographic instrument; the fact that the material studied must be very thin, since electrons will not pass through thick layers of matter; and the requirement that material must be studied in a vacuum, since electrons will not penetrate air. These difficulties are gradually being overcome to a considerable degree. Microtomes have been invented which will cut amazingly thin sections, and good methods are being developed whereby the object of study can be evacuated and consequently desiccated, with much less distortion of the fine structure than was the case at first. The use of the electron microscope as a photographic instrument is in one respect an asset; for it is possible to take pictures at magnifications of 15,000 diameters or more on fine-grained film, from which enlargements can be made which retain sharp definition up to magnifications of 50,000 or more.

The electron microscope is making as drastic a revolution in cytological knowledge as did the light microscope in the 1870's and 1880's. It is revealing an amazing intricacy of structure in the cell beyond anything dreamed of a few years ago. Resolving powers as low as 8 Ångstroms are being achieved; i.e., it is possible to reveal particles as small as one thirty-millionth of an inch in diameter. The discovery of structures and types of organization within the cell hitherto unsuspected is a long step in the direction of understanding the nature of the living machine and how it functions.

At its inception, cytology was a distinct science which showed relatively little relationship to other sciences. Its objective was to know the cell, its structure and behavior, and this did not seem to have much bearing upon the other branches of biology then in vogue. The identification and classification of plants and animals did not seem to depend upon cellular phenomena. Physiology was still concerned with the functions of organs and tissues and had not reached down to the cellular level. Genetics was a science yet unborn, and biochemistry was in its infancy. Cytologists did not need to master the techniques of other sciences, nor were these sciences in turn concerned with the findings of cytology. In only one direction was cytology a science which involved more than one discipline. It was equally a botanical and a zoological field. Plant and animal cytologists had much more in common than either of them had with other branches of botany or zoology. And the fundamental discoveries were equally shared by those working on plants and on animals. Except for this one relationship, however, cytology remained a science apart for some decades.

The position of cytology changed, however, as it began to feel the need for techniques from the other sciences to supplement its own and as other sciences began to discover that the solution of their own problems required going back to protoplasm itself, where alone the answers to the really fundamental questions are to be found. On the one hand, cytologists began to utilize for their own purposes the techniques of genetics, biochemistry, and histochemistry. On the other hand, they found themselves helping to furnish the answers to the questions which the geneticists, the biochemists, the taxonomists, and the evolutionists were raising. Cytology rather suddenly became, therefore, an experimental, as well as an observational, science, and it became a fundamental contributor to, if not an integral part of, other important branches of biology.

This transformation of the science of cytology began at the turn of the century with the rediscovery of Mendel's work. This discovery marked the birth of the science of genetics, and immediately this new science found a use for cytology. Cytologists had been studying for some time the way in which the cell and the nucleus within the cell divide and the behavior of the chromosomes, the sausage-shaped structures within the nucleus. They had been speculating about the possible hereditary significance of the phenomena of nuclear and cell division, of the peculiar cell divisions which occur at the formation of reproductive cells, and of fertilization. When Mendel's work was finally brought to light in 1900, cytological analyses had reached a point where the parallelism between chromosome behavior and gene behavior could be appreciated. It was Sutton (1903a, b) who was the first to make this parallelism clear and to show convincingly that hereditary determiners are distributed among the chromosomes and carried by them. From this time on, cytology became a handmaiden of genetics, and its importance to genetics soon became so apparent that the two sciences became to a considerable extent fused into the new synthetic science of cytogenetics.

As a result of these developments, cytologists can no longer confine their interests and competencies to the killing, sectioning, staining, and observing of cell structures. A cytologist needs to be a geneticist as well. Whether he is primarily interested in the nucleus and its chromosomes, or in the region which surrounds the nucleus, the so-called cytoplasm with its inclusions, he must still be something of a geneticist, for it is now known that the cytoplasm—that part of the cell which surrounds and nourishes the nucleus—has also an important role to play in heredity. And he must in addition become almost inevitably a biochemist, and preferably a biophysicist as well, for many of the most intriguing problems of cytology now have to do with the identification and analysis of key chemical compounds in the cell and the roles which these specific compounds or classes of compounds play in heredity and other cellular activities.

Again, cytology has proved in recent years to be of marked use in the solution of the problems of taxonomy and evolution. Much can be learned regarding the relations between species or races by a comparative study of chromosomes, with respect either to their numbers or their structures. It has been discovered that evolutionary development often involves alterations in chromosome number or structure, so that analysis of these cytological characteristics may shed important light on evolutionary history and on species relationships.

In still another direction, cytology has proved to be of fundamental importance, namely, in the solution of physiological problems. Physiology has become increasingly concerned with something more than the functions of tissues and organs, the behavior of organisms and their reactions to environment. When one has analyzed these activities he is still confronted with the question as to the basic causes of these phenomena and is inevitably forced back to the protoplasm itself—to its chemical and physical properties, to the way in which the cell and its constituent parts behave, to the question as to what parts of the cell initiate the processes which eventuate in physiological activity, how these essential ingredients in the cell maintain and reproduce themselves and become distributed to the daughter cells when a parent cell divides. Cytology has thus found itself concerned with the most fundamental questions which a biologist can ask.

A modern cytologist, therefore, must be a man of parts—a broadly trained person—ideally a biologist with chemical, physical, mathematical, and statistical competence. Furthermore, the type of material upon which he works is likely to vary according to the problem with which he is concerned. He may at one time work with bacteria, at other times with fungi, or viruses, or flowering plants, or animals. Many eminent cytologists have utilized a wide variety of materials, plant and animal, in the course of their experiments. Since cytology involves all organisms equally, a cytologist should be a biologist in the broadest sense if he is to be truly competent.

At the present time, cytologists are concerned with a great variety of problems, so many that it will be possible to do no more than refer briefly to two or three of the more important, upon which the limelight is focused at the moment.

One of the fundamental problems upon which marked emphasis is now being placed relates to the nature of the gene. Mendel long ago showed that heredity is based upon the existence of separate and distinct determiners which are transmitted from parents to offspring through sperm and egg. The characteristics of an individual depend upon what determiners of heredity it receives from its parents. These determiners have become known as genes. What, then, is a gene? What is it composed of? Where is it situated in the cell? How does it produce its effects? How is it distributed from one generation to another? Do all cells in a body contain full sets of genes? If so, how do genes multiply, so that the two daughter cells derived from a single cell will each have all the genes which the parent cell had? Can genes change? If so, what is the nature of these changes, and how are they accomplished? Are genes discrete chemical entities? There are some biologists who claim that they are not.

It is obvious that the answers to these questions lie at least in part in the area of cytology. Whatever their nature, genes are cellular entities. By a combination of techniques from a number of relevant disciplines, much has been learned about the gene already, and the major emphasis now being placed upon this problem ensures that much more will be learned in the near future.

The first problem relating to the gene is its location in the cell and its cytological identification. Much progress has been made along this line in recent years. Genetical methods have demonstrated the fact that, as a rule, genes are duplicated every time a cell divides so that each daughter cell receives a full set of the genes which the parent cell had. The geneticist has shown that genes are associated in blocks, which tend to be inherited together, and they have found that the genes are associated within each block in linear order, like beads on a strings, each gene having its particular position in the string between specific neighbor genes. They have also found that genes may occasionally change their position, and a variety of ways have been discovered by which this can be accomplished. A section of the gene string in a given block of genes can become inverted in position, the genes in this section coming to lie in reverse order; or a group of genes may be moved to a different position in the block; or different blocks may exchange sections of their gene strings. Sometimes genes seem to vanish completely, or they may be duplicated so that a gene is represented more than once in a set of genes. All these facts regarding the arrangement and order of the genes and possible rearrangements of this order have been detected by genetic means, but such findings have not in themselves related the genes to any particular structure or region in the cell as observed microscopically. This has been accomplished by cytological investigation. When Mendel's paper was discovered in 1900 and the laws of the distribution of hereditary determiners were thus brought to light, the cytologists found that they had already seen with the micro-

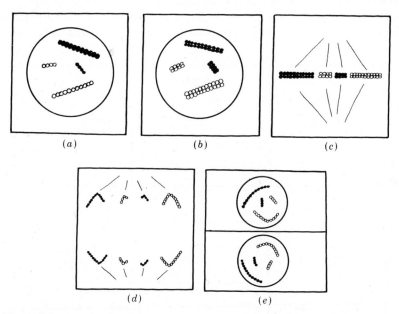

Fig. 1. Diagrams to show the ordinary process of cell division (mitosis).—*a*. Four chromosomes are shown in the spherical nucleus, each chromosome containing a series of genes. Chromosomes drawn in black are descended from one parent, white chromosomes are descended from the other parent.—*b*. Each chromosome splits and becomes double.—*c*. The nuclear wall vanishes, a spindle-shaped area develops, the split chromosomes become aligned across the middle of the spindle.—*d*. Forces, the nature of which are not understood, pull the halves of split chromosomes apart.— *e*. The daughter chromosomes are gathered into new nuclei and the cell is cut in two. Each daughter cell is exactly like the parent cell in its chromosome make-up. Each nucleus has two complete sets of chromosomes and genes, one descended from one parent, the other from the other parent.

scope structures in the cell whose behavior exactly corresponded to the behavior of the genes (fig. 1). It had been found that certain bodies which had been termed chromosomes were indeed divided equally whenever a cell divided, each chromosome becoming split longitudinally, one-half going to each daughter cell. These and no other bodies in the cell were distributed with exactitude to the daughter cells. It was found that the number of chromosomes in a cell corresponded exactly to the number of blocks of genes existent in that cell, that larger blocks of genes corresponded to larger chromosomes, and

vice versa. The behavior of the chromosomes at the time of reproductive
cell formation also fitted exactly that of the genes, so that the chromosomes
were distributed to the germ cells according to the same rules which governed the distribution of the genes (fig. 2). Furthermore, whenever a case
was found where the chromosomes behaved in an unorthodox manner in this
regard, it was found that the genes behaved in corresponding fashion, and
whenever genes were found to have changed places, via inversion or transfer

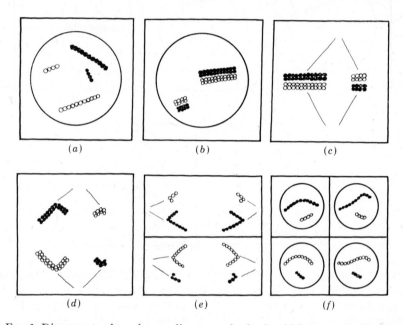

Fig. 2. Diagrams to show the peculiar type of mitosis which occurs at the formation of reproductive cells.—*a*. A nucleus with four chromosomes.—*b*. Chromosomes
descended from different parents and carrying corresponding genes form pairs with
each other. Each chromosome also becomes split.—*c*. The spindle is formed and
paired chromosomes become aligned across its center. Note that the same chromosomes are present as in fig. 1*c*, but their arrangement is different.—*d*. Corresponding chromosomes are separated. In this case, the separation is not between half
chromosomes but between whole chromosomes.—*e*. A second division separates the
half chromosomes from each other.—*f*. As a result, from each cell which has undergone this process of "reduction," four cells result, each with only a single set of
chromosomes, instead of the two complete sets found in the parent cell. These cells
become or give rise to sperm or egg cells. When sperm and egg unite, each carrying
a single set of chromosomes, a fertilized egg with two sets will be formed. From
this, by ordinary mitosis, multitudes of cells will be produced, each with two sets,
and the body will thus consist of cells with two full sets. *Note:* The diagrams in
fig. 1 and 2 are oversimplified with respect to certain details, but the essential features and the end result are correctly pictured.

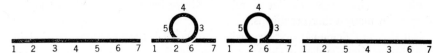

FIG. 3. Diagrams to illustrate one way in which chromosome structure can be altered. Some of the genes of the chromosome diagramed are designated 1 to 7. At the left, an unaltered chromosome. In the next diagram, the chromosome has formed a loop. In the diagram at the right the chromosome has straightened out, but some of its genes now lie in reverse order (an "inversion" has occurred).

of segments, cytologists were able to demonstrate that corresponding segments of certain chromosomes had suffered the same alteration (fig. 3, 4).

In recent years, the cytologist has been greatly helped in this work by the discovery in certain organisms of giant chromosomes, whose structure can be relatively easily analyzed. Thus, in the fruit fly, one of the most completely analyzed organisms from the standpoint of genetics, the chromosomes in the salivary glands and other organs of the larva become enormously swollen. They show under the microscope a banded structure, with thinner or thicker bands arranged in a constant pattern so that the cytologist can analyze this pattern and learn to recognize each chromosome and chromosome part (fig. 5). When a portion of a chromosome becomes inverted, or is exchanged for a part of some other chromosome, the geneticist is able to show by his analyses exactly what alteration has occurred, and the cytologist is able to demonstrate exactly what parts of what chromosomes have been affected. Thus it has been possible to relate each block of genes to a given chromosome, and even to place individual genes in the cytological chromosome. There is a possibility that each band in the salivary-gland chromosome corresponds to a gene or a group of closely associated genes. Numerous genes have actually been equated with specific bands in the chromosome. In plants, no such giant chromosomes have been found, but there are cases where a fair amount of correlation can be demonstrated. In maize, McClintock and others have been able to relate many areas in the gene map, as determined genetically, with corresponding areas in the chromosomes, as seen

FIG. 4. Another type of alteration in chromosome structure ("translocation"). A chromosome whose ends are designated 1 and 2 exchanges segments with a non-corresponding chromosome with ends 3 and 4. As a result new chromosomes are formed, with ends 1 and 3, and 2 and 4.

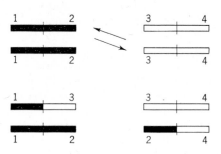

under the microscope. Similar correlations have been established in varying degrees in many other organisms.

All this has demonstrated beyond question that the genes are carried in the chromosomes and that the laws of the distribution of genes from parent to offspring are in reality the laws governing the distribution of the chromosomes from one generation to the next. This localization of the genes within the cell is the first important step toward an analysis of the structure and chemical composition of the gene. It enables us in our further studies to concentrate on the chromosomes. By studying their structure in detail and analyzing them chemically, it may be possible ultimately to understand the true nature of the genes contained in the chromosomes.

In undertaking this further exploration, additional techniques are required, particularly the techniques of biochemistry and histochemistry, supplemented by the findings of electron microscopy and X-ray diffraction studies. Already much has been learned by these methods, but this constitutes only a bare beginning of what must be learned before we can have an adequate understanding of the gene and its nature. As a result of biochemical analyses, something is now known of the chemical composition of the chromosomes, and convenient histochemical techniques have been developed to test for the presence or absence of certain of these compounds. These methods make it possible to treat the chromosomes with various reagents or with enzymes and determine by microscopic observation the effect of such treatments on the structure of the chromosomes.

FIG. 5. Photograph of salivary chromosome from *Sciara*, the mushroom fly. Note that the bands vary in thickness and structure. They can be recognized and identified, and the whole sequence mapped, so that, if a structural alteration occurs, its presence can be detected and its nature determined by microscopic examination. (*Courtesy of Dr. Charles W. Metz.*)

The biochemical approach has shown that the chromosome is composed of two principal classes of substance, nucleoproteins and a globular type of protein. Nucleoproteins are compounds composed of nucleic acids, associated with protein. The protein associated with nucleic acid seems to be of a relatively simple type—mostly histone. Nucleic acids exist in the form of complicated molecules, each composed of units known as nucleotides: each nucleotide consists of a purine or pyrimidine base attached to a sugar, which is in turn attached to a molecule of phosphoric acid. The nucleotides are arranged in parallel, somewhat like the rungs of a ladder, which are attached to each other, but only at one end. The rung consists of the base and sugar; the part which attaches the rungs together at one end is the phosphoric acid. The latter also attaches the nucleic acid to the associated protein (fig. 6).

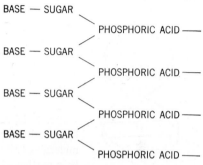

FIG. 6. Diagram to show relation of various chemical entities making up nucleic acid. The bonds to the right attach the phosphoric acid to protein, usually histone. Each horizontal chain of base-sugar-acid constitutes a nucleotide. A nucleic acid molecule consists of a long chain of nucleotides, of which there are several kinds. The order in which the different kinds of nucleotides are arranged and their relative frequency determine the specific chemical characteristics of the nucleic acid molecule. Nucleic acid can exist in myriad forms.

Considerable progress has been made in recent years in the field of nucleic acid chemistry. With the help of X-ray diffraction the three-dimensional structure is being elucidated. The work of Watson and Crick (1953a, b), for instance, suggests that nucleic acid molecules exist in pairs, the two molecules wound around one another, with the nucleotides extending horizontally inward (fig. 7). Each nucleotide is attached to a nucleotide of the other nucleic acid molecule by its base, in a very precise manner, the two nucleic acid molecules together thus resembling a twisted ladder. It used to be thought that the nucleotides containing the two purine bases adenine and guanine and the two pyrimidine bases thymine (or uracil) and cytosine were present in a nucleic acid molecule in equal numbers and arranged in a regular sequence. This is no longer found to be true. Not only are the various nucleotides present in varying proportions, but there are also more than four kinds of nucleotides now recognized. Far from there being but a single pattern of arrangement of four nucleotides, a very great variety of arrangements of an unknown number of different nucleotides is indicated.

In addition to the nucleoproteins, certain more complicated proteins are present also in the chromosomes, proteins of a globulin type. They consti-

tute, however, a relatively small proportion of the chromosome, the nucleoproteins accounting for the bulk of its material.

The question of first importance in this study of chromosome chemistry
is what part of the chromosomal structure constitutes the gene? Genes show
great diversity in their functional activities. Not only are there thousands
of different kinds of genes in a single organism, doing thousands of different
things, but the genes in different organisms differ, at least in part, from each

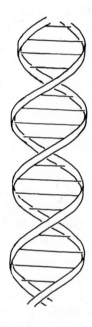

FIG. 7. Diagram to illustrate the Watson and Crick
hypothesis of nucleic acid structure. Two nucleic acid
molecules twist around each other with the sugar and
base portion of their nucleotides extending horizontally
inward. The nucleotides of opposite nucleic acid molecules are attached to each other at their inner ends in
a very precise manner, thus constituting the "rungs" of
the twisted ladder.

other. The total number of different genes in all the species of plants, animals, and microorganisms is undoubtedly very great. What part of the chromosome is capable of existing in such myriad forms? Apparently not the
histones, for they are relatively simple structures; probably not the globular
proteins, which constitute such a small proportion of the chromosome. The
suspicion falls on the nucleic acids which recent students have shown are
capable of an enormous variety in their structure. This surmise is strengthened by the finding that self-duplicating bodies in the cell seem all to contain
nucleic acid: since one of the chief characteristics of the gene is its ability to
reproduce itself, this suggests that nucleic acid is tied in with its structure
in some way. It is probable, however, that not all nucleic acid is genic in
character. Some organisms, such as members of the lily family, for instance,
have relatively enormous chromosomes, and the chromosome set has a relatively huge amount of nucleic acid compared with such organisms as the fruit
fly or man. It is not likely, however, that the lily has more genic material

than the latter organisms. The quantity of nucleic acid present in a set of chromosomes, therefore, is probably not a measure of the number of genes present. We are not justified in exactly equating genes with nucleic acid. It is likely that genes are not pure nucleic acid but a combination of nucleic acid and protein, the nucleic acid imparting to the gene its specificity. The chromosomes may also contain nucleic acid which is unbound to protein. Only when properly combined can nucleic acid and protein take on genic properties.

Recent work by McClintock (1951), Lewis (1951), and others suggests that the gene may be in reality a compound structure, its parts separable under certain conditions. It has also been found that the action of a gene may depend to some extent on its position in the chromosome. There are in most organisms so far studied certain regions of the chromosomes which seem wholly or almost devoid of definitive genes. These areas, known as heterochromatic regions, are imperfectly understood as to their structure and function. It has been found, however, that when a gene whose normal position is distant from heterochromatin is transferred to a heterochromatic region, its behavior may become fluctuating—it may function in some cells and not in others, and a mottled or mosaic effect may be produced. This kind of "position effect" is especially well known in the fruit fly, but Catcheside (1947) has found a very striking case in *Oenothera,* the evening primrose, and a few other cases are known. The chemical basis for this behavior is not understood.

From this brief account it is clear that much progress has been made in the attempt to understand the nature of the gene and how it functions. We know where genes are in the cell, and we can follow many of them when they become transferred from one place to another, or when they change their function. We have learned some facts regarding the chemical structure of the chromosomes of which they are a part. We have a long way to go, however, before our knowledge of genes becomes in any way complete or adequate. This is one of the main emphases of the cytologist at the present time, and in this quest he must use a great variety of technical approaches in addition to those of microscopy, or else collaborate with those who are capable of using these techniques.

Another focus of interest which is occupying the attention of many cytologists at the present time is the cytoplasm—that portion of the cell which lies outside of, and surrounds, the nucleus with its chromosomes and genes. For a long time cytologists tended to place relatively little emphasis on the cytoplasm, largely because there seemed to be so little that could be observed microscopically in this portion of the cell. Bodies as striking as chromosomes were seldom present; very few definitive activities seemed to accompany cell division, in contrast with nuclear division. Some bodies, to be sure, were to be seen, but except for plastids (chloroplasts, etc.) none of

these were large enough to show much structure under the ordinary microscope and none seemed to undergo any sort of marked change or cyclical
modification. There seemed little, therefore, that the cytologist could learn
about this portion of the cell (fig. 8).

This situation is rapidly changing, however, in view of the discoveries by
both the geneticists and the biochemists. The geneticists have discovered that
the cytoplasm has a role in heredity which is far larger than had originally
been suspected. The plastids, for instance, have been shown to have hereditary

Fig. 8. A diagram of a cell. The central sphere is the nucleus, the rod-
shaped bodies the chromosomes. The
region outside the nucleus is the cytoplasm, and in it are shown the more or
less spherical plastids and the much
smaller spherical or rod-shaped chondriosomes.

characteristics of their own which to a degree are independent of those of the
genes. To be sure, the genes set up the conditions under which the plastids
operate, and if the wrong genes are present, a given kind of plastid may not
be able to function successfully. There are also cases where a gene may
succeed in bringing about a more or less permanent change in the structure
or function of a plastid. On the other hand, cases are known where plastids
remain uninfluenced by foreign genes, in whose presence they are unable to
function, but to whose influence they fail to yield—so that if they are removed from the presence of the uncooperative gene and find themselves
again in a congenial genic environment, they can again function normally,
unchanged in their fundamental characteristics by having been associated
with the wrong kind of gene. Hence, plastids seem to have a degree of independence of the gene. In the evening primroses, for instance, several genetically distinct classes of chloroplasts are known (Schötz, 1954). They retain
their own specific characteristics indefinitely, no matter what kinds of genes
they are exposed to. If they are subjected to the wrong kinds of genes, they
will be unable to function, but relieved of these genes, they will continue to
function as before. Each class of plastid reacts differently to the various types
of genes which exist in the population, and each retains its own characteristics
no matter what the vicissitudes to which it is subjected. On the other hand,

plastids in the evening primrose are known to have mutated on rare occasions, as a result of which they have taken on new characteristics (Schötz, 1954).

Plastid inheritance is therefore a well-known phenomenon and has been studied intensively in a number of organisms. Since plastids or their precursors are usually transmitted through the egg but not the sperm, their inheritance is usually maternal in character; i.e., the offspring receives its plastids only from the mother. There are exceptions, however, where plastids may also be introduced into the offspring along with the sperm.

But it is not only the plastids which are of interest from the standpoint of cytoplasmic inheritance. The work of Sonneborn and others has drawn attention to the fact that certain hereditary characteristics require the interaction of both the genes and certain elements in the cytoplasm. The "killer" characteristic in *Paramecium,* a one-celled animal, is a case in point (Sonneborn, 1946). Some individuals in *Paramecium aurelia* are capable of excreting a substance into the surrounding water which will kill other "sensitive" animals. To be a killer a cell must have a certain gene (K) and in the cytoplasm it must have minute particles which are known as kappa particles. If both are present, the animal is a killer. If, however, the K gene is present and the kappa particles absent, the cell cannot produce the killer substance. Kappa particles are self-reproducing bodies, but they can live and reproduce only in the presence of the K gene. In the absence of this gene they soon vanish. The K gene, on the other hand, cannot synthesize new kappa particles. If none of the particles are present in a cell possessing K, none can be formed. In other words, kappa particles must come from preexisting kappa particles. The conditions under which these particles can divide and function are set up by the K gene, but the K gene cannot create new particles. The particles are therefore dependent upon the gene for the proper environment in which to continue existence, but not for their origin; the gene is dependent on the particles to carry out the process of killer-substance formation. Thus a Mendelian or hereditary character is dependent for its expression on both a gene and a type of cytoplasmic particle. A number of other cases of this type of inheritance are known.

Another type of particle in the cytoplasm is the chondriosome, or mitochondrion. Chondriosomes have been known for 50 years or more, but they have not received much attention until recently. They are ordinarily minute spherical or rod-shaped bodies, about the size of bacteria, with which they have been confused by some investigators. For a long time their function remained obscure, although their universal presence in all plant and animal cells indicated that they had a vital role to play. In recent years, however, a combined biochemical and cytological approach has shown that they are the chief centers of respiration, the regions where most of the enzymes are situated which together bring about the liberation of the energy needed by the protoplasm. This discovery has added a new importance to the chondriosomes and has focused renewed attention upon them. Cases are now known where chondriosomes appear to have mutated—to have changed their fundamental character by the loss of certain enzymes which they normally possess. For instance, Ephrussi (1951) found in yeast a case of mutation as a result of which cells previously capable of complete aerobic respiration were now capable only of the less complete anaerobic type of energy release because of the loss of the enzyme cytochrome oxidase. He found by the use of Nadi reagent (a test for the presence of cytochrome oxidase, which helps to make possible the use of oxygen in energy release) that, whereas unmutated cells had particles in the cytoplasm which would stain blue with this reagent, thus showing the presence of cytochrome oxidase, the cells no longer capable of aerobic respiration no longer showed stainable bodies. Thus, aerobic respiration was related to stainable bodies or chondriosomes, and the loss of an enzyme essential to the carrying on of aerobic respiration was shown to have occurred in these bodies, confirming the conclusion that they are centers of respiratory activity.

The renewed interest in the cytoplasm has resulted in an increased use of the electron microscope in order to learn more about the structure of the bodies found in this region. Since these bodies are so small, their structure is beyond the capabilities of the ordinary microscope to elucidate, and electron microscopy seems the only feasible way now available to get at the details of their architecture. The results of recent studies by such workers as Frey-Wyssling (1953), Steinmann (1952), and Sjöstrand (1956) have revealed an amazing complexity of organization in bodies which had previously been considered to be essentially structureless. Chloroplasts, which can often be seen under the ordinary microscope to be filled with granules, or "grana," are now found to present a finely layered appearance, the grana as well as the surrounding material having such a structure. The grana, which contain the chlorophyll, seem to be composed of alternate layers of protein and fatty material, and since the tadpole-shaped chlorophyll molecule is attracted at its head end by water and at the tail end by oil, it takes up a position with its head in the protein layer and its tail in the lipid layer. Thus the chlorophyll becomes oriented in a very orderly and precise manner.

Chondriosomes also appear to have a very intricate and precise structure. The work of Sjöstrand and others shows that they have a double membrane with cross membranes extending part or all the way across the body. Like the chloroplasts, therefore, they also have a form of lamellate structure. Sjöstrand has also shown that, in some kinds of cells at least, the cytoplasm itself has a very elaborate structure, composed of closely folded, parallel membranes which separate the protoplasm proper from a watery material which fills part of the cell.

Thus, the electron microscope is making possible an increasingly detailed analysis of the finer structures of the protoplasm, the general ground substance, as well as the definitive bodies which exist in the cell. Interestingly enough, more success has attended the study of cytoplasm by these means than of the nucleus. Thus far, it has not been possible to prepare nuclear material for electron microscopy without a considerable amount of distortion which tends to obscure the results obtained.

A third center of interest among cytologists arises from the fact that cytological studies can throw considerable light on the relationships of species and races and can furnish clues as to the paths along which evolutionary progress has been made. The nature of the evidence which cytology is able to present varies with the material. In some cases, a comparative study of chromosome structure will indicate relationship. Chromosomes have definitive shapes and sizes, and it is often possible to recognize particular chromosomes under the microscope. In many genera, it is possible to compare the various species or subspecies from the standpoint of chromosome structure. Species which have similar or identical chromosomes so far as morphology is concerned are considered to be more closely related than species whose chromosomes differ in these regards. Other lines of evidence must of course be brought to bear on the problem, but chromosome structure has often proved to be a characteristic of great value in determining relationships.

In other cases, relationships can be determined or confirmed by analyzing the structural alterations which have occurred in the evolution of the group. Thus, in certain species of *Drosophila,* the fruit fly, inversions of chromosome segments have occurred with relative frequency. In some cases, sequences of inversion can be followed, especially where a portion of a previously inverted segment becomes involved in a second inversion. Dobzhansky and his students (da Cunha, 1955; Dobzhansky, 1944) have been able to learn much regarding the evolutionary history of certain species by analyzing the inversions which have occurred and determining the sequences of their occurrence. In other organisms, other types of structural alteration have proved of value. For instance, in the evening primrose (*Oenothera*), the author and his students (Cleland et al., 1950) have found that exchanges of segments between non-corresponding chromosomes have occurred with unusual frequency and it has been found possible to analyze many races from the standpoint of the interchanges which have occurred. Races which show evidence, at least in part, of the same interchanges are considered, other things being equal, to have been derived from common ancestors in which these interchanges occurred. The more closely races resemble one another in respect to the interchanges which have occurred in the course of their evolution, the more closely related they are considered to be, and vice versa. As a result of cytological and genetical techniques, the evolutionary story of the evening primrose is being revealed, and this in a genus which has for many years been the despair of taxonomists who have tried to ferret out the relationships by strictly taxonomic methods.

In plants another cytological phenomenon has proved to be of great importance in determining relationships. It not infrequently occurs in plants that the chromosome number becomes altered. Chromosomes may occasionally be lost, or additional chromosomes may be added. Of greatest significance are the cases where the ordinary or diploid chromosome number becomes doubled, producing what is known as a polyploid. It has been found that polyploidy has been a major factor in plant evolution. A polyploid does not produce fertile progeny easily when crossed with its parental diploid, because the progeny will have an odd number of chromosome sets and will fail to a large extent to produce sperms or eggs with complete sets of chromosomes. A polyploid, therefore, has a degree of reproductive isolation which enables it to carry on an independent existence and to evolve along its own line. A very large number of species of plants show evidence of chromosome doubling in their evolution—in fact, doubling has occurred more than once in the ancestry of many plants. A curious fact has been discovered in the course of studies of polyploidy: if doubling occurs in a plant whose parents were very closely related, the resultant polyploid is likely to be more sterile and less able to maintain itself than if its parents had been very unrelated. This fact, the reason for which we cannot go into here, is of great practical value. It is often advantageous to combine the desirable traits of different varieties or species, but when one crosses these, the resultant hybrid proves to be sterile— the chromosomes of the two species are too unlike to pair and separate properly during the process of germ-cell formation. Such a cross would not be able to propagate itself, therefore, were it not for the possibility of polyploidy. If one induces the chromosomes to double in such a hybrid (and this can be done easily with the use of colchicine or other chemical), the resultant polyploid, which will still possess the desired combination of characters, will be found to be perfectly fertile and capable of passing its desirable combination of genes to succeeding generations. The wider the cross and the more sterile the hybrid, the more likelihood that a polyploid derived from it by chromosome doubling will be perfectly fertile, and vice versa.

In the course of evolution, chromosomes are apt to suffer various major or minor alterations in structure. They may lose small segments, or certain segments may become duplicated. They may experience inversions, or they may exchange segments with other chromosomes. As a result, chromosomes in races which were originally derived from a common ancestor may become very different in structure, so different that if they are brought into the same plant by appropriate crossing they can no longer associate in pairs as corresponding chromosomes are supposed to do at the time when germ cells are produced. Cytologists can study the behavior of chromosomes in hybrids and from their behavior at this stage judge as to their similarity of structure and hence their evolutionary relationship. By techniques of this sort, much has been learned about the ancestry of plants important to our economy, such as wheat and oats.

From this very cursory and superficial account, it can be seen that cytology is capable of throwing light upon many fundamental problems of biology. It is especially concerned with the basic problems of protoplasm—its structure, chemical composition, and behavior. It is also of importance in the solution of problems in other areas of biology, such as taxonomy and evolution, plant and animal breeding. It is not an exaggeration to say that there is no branch of biology to which cytology does not contribute. It is even being used at present to predict the sex of a human child before birth (Anon., 1956).

Cytology demonstrates in unusual degree the essential oneness of living nature. The average person is apt to be impressed more with the diversity than with the unity of life. Plants seem so different from animals. Bacteria seem so different from either plants or animals. The millions of different species of animals and plants, the range from amoeba to man, from the microscopic alga to the sequoia tree, are evidence of the ability of protoplasm to take on myriad forms, to adopt multitudinous variations of structure without losing that structural key which makes it alive. Truly the diversity of living material is a profoundly impressive fact. And yet, it is also an amazing fact that through all this diversity there runs a unity of structure and function which is equally impressive, and most of this unity reveals itself at the cellular level. It is a striking fact that practically all organisms, plant or animal, follow the same laws of heredity, based upon the presence of genes carried in chromosomes. These chromosomes divide and are transmitted, when cells divide, to the daughter cells by the same process of mitosis and are parceled out to the individual reproductive cells by the same mechanism of meiosis. Practically all cells in all organisms have mitochondria, and associated with these are to be found the same respiratory enzymes and the same complicated chemical cycles by which energy is liberated. Even the green chlorophyll which seems to be such a distinctive and unique feature of green plants is structurally very closely related to the heme molecule which forms the colored part of the hemoglobin of the animal blood system. When one descends to the cellular level, most of the differences which distinguish one class of organism from another seem to disappear, and there remains a common core of essential structure and function which appears to have been developed very early in the evolution of life and to have been retained by all forms of life as they have deviated from one another. The deviations have involved relatively unessential aspects; the essential features of living protoplasm have been retained by all organisms—otherwise they would not have been able to survive.

This fact has very important practical applications. Cells have the same fundamental attributes, whether they belong to bacteria, the higher plants, or animals. An agent or condition which effects the functioning of one kind of cell is likely to have similar effects on other cells. Many of our most pressing biological problems involve the cell and the behavior of protoplasm. Cancer, for instance, is a condition in which cells have lost the inhibitors which retard and control growth and cell division. The brakes have been released, and the processes of growth and multiplication are unrestrained. The solution of the cancer problem will not be achieved by attempts to cure cancer, nor will it necessarily come by the study of human tissues, since cancers are found in many other organisms, even in plants. It will not be found until we know what makes cells grow and multiply, what controls and regulates these processes, what substances are capable of throwing a monkey wrench into the regulatory machinery, and what part of the machinery they affect. Then, and only then, will we be in a position to take the necessary measures to prevent the uninhibited growth of cells or to arrest such growth once it has started. Since the essential machinery is the same in all kinds of cells, this problem can be attacked by the study of any kind of cell. It will not be surprising if some of the keys to the solution of the human cancer problem (there probably is no one key) will be discovered by studies of plant cells. The more widespread the study of the mechanism of cell growth and division, the sooner the essential clues will be discovered.

This is but one illustration of the fact that, at the cellular level, all life displays a unity which superficial observation of plants and animals fails to reveal. Protoplasm in all organisms is organized in essentially the same way. In basic behavior and characteristics, protoplasm is essentially the same in all organisms, though it is obvious that in the finer details of chemical composition and organization, the protoplasms of different organisms differ. It is the presence of protoplasm which distinguishes the living from the lifeless.

This unity is something which involves not only plants and animals. It includes man as well. Detailed study of cellular structure and protoplasmic behavior in man shows that these are essentially the same as in other organisms. The chromosomes in man are typical in structure and behavior; they divide in normal fashion and are distributed to sperm and egg in the usual manner. Thus the physical basis of heredity is the same in man as it is in animals and plants. There is no reason to suppose, therefore, that man is any different from the plants and animals from the standpoint of heredity, or of the mechanism by which his characteristics are determined and transmitted from parent to offspring. His characteristics are as fully gene-controlled and as fully dependent on chromosome behavior as are the characteristics of fruit flies and lilies. Since intensive studies of many organisms have shown that gene control extends not only to external or structural features, but also to the physiological processes, even to the behavior of the chromosomes themselves, there is no reason to consider that all characteristics in man—physical, physiological, and psychological—are not also controlled by genes lying in the chromosomes. This does not in any way imply that environment does not have an effect in modifying or even suppressing the action of the genes. Environment will not, however, create characteristics for which no genic basis exists. It can merely act upon the gene-induced traits and modify them if it can. All the evidence supports the conclusion that man's traits are induced in the same way and subject to the same external influences as in other forms of life.

From this brief discussion it is evident that cytology deals with the most fundamental properties of living beings—how the living material is organized and constructed, how it carries on its multitudinous processes, how it is governed, how it reproduces and transmits to successive generations the powers which it possesses. The answer to all the basic riddles of living nature, so far as they are capable of solution, are to be found in the cell, the happy hunting ground of the cytologist.

LITERATURE CITED

ANON. 1956. Tell child's sex before baby born. Sci. News-Letter 69:85.

CATCHESIDE, D. G. 1947. The P-locus position effect in *Oenothera*. Jour. Genet. 48: 31–42.

CLELAND, RALPH E. (Ed.). 1950. Studies in *Oenothera* cytogenetics and phylogeny. Indiana Univ. Publ. Sci. Ser. 16.

DA CUNHA, A. B. 1955. Chromosomal polymorphism in the Diptera. Advances in Genet. 7:93–138.

DOBZHANSKY, T. 1944. Chromosomal races in *Drosophila pseudoobscura* and *Drosophila persimilis*. Carnegie Inst. Washington Publ. 554:47–144.

EPHRUSSI, BORIS. 1951. Remarks on cell heredity. *In* Genetics in the 20th century, pp. 241–262. Macmillan.

FREY-WYSSLING, A. 1953. Submicroscopic morphology of protoplasm. Elsevier. Houston, Tex.

LEWIS, E. B. 1951. Pseudoallelism and gene evolution. Cold Spr. Harbor Symp. on Quant. Biol. 16:159–174.

MCCLINTOCK, B. 1951. Chromosome organization and genic expression. Cold Spr. Harbor Symp. on Quant. Biol. 16:13–47.

RENNER, O. 1924. Die Scheckung der Oenotherenbastarde. Biol. Zentralbl. 44:309–336.

SCHÖTZ, F. 1954. Über Plastidenkonkurrenz bei *Oenothera*. Planta 43:182–240.

SJÖSTRAND, F. S. 1956. The ultrastructure of mitochondria. *In* Fine structure of cells, pp. 16–30. Int. Union Biol. Sci. Publ. Ser. B., No. 21. Paris.

SONNEBORN, T. M. 1946. Experimental control of the concentration of cytoplasmic genetic factors in *Paramecium*. Cold Spr. Harbor Symp. on Quant. Biol. 11: 236–248.

STEINMANN, E. 1952. An electron microscope study of the lamellar structure of chloroplasts. Exptl. Cell Res. 3:367–372.

SPONSLER, O. L. 1940. Molecular structure in protoplasm. *In* The cell and protoplasm, pp. 166–187. Publ. 14, Amer. Assn. Adv. Sci. Washington, D.C.

SUTTON, W. S. 1903a. On the morphology of the chromosome group in *Brachystola magna*. Biol. Bull. 4:24–39.

——. 1903b. The chromosomes in heredity. Biol. Bull. 4:231–251.

WATSON, J. D., AND F. H. C. CRICK. 1953a. A structure for desoxyribose nucleic acids. Nature 171:737–738.

—— AND ——. 1953b. The structure of DNA. Cold Spr. Harbor Symp. on Quant. Biol. 18:123–131.

10

INDUCED POLYPLOIDY

O. J. Eigsti

More food and fiber are produced from polyploids than from the related species that are diploid. This fact is well known to agriculturalists. Species of the rank of polyploid are also distinguished by their mode of origin; that is, polyploids may arise suddenly from parental diploids. Thus, in two botanical fields, polyploidy attracts considerable attention: (1) in the area of crop improvement (Levan, 1945), and (2) in the mechanisms of evolution (Stebbins, 1950).

The present human population depends upon the greater increases in annual production that come from the polyploids against the lesser quantity that would be available if only diploids were under cultivation. Our daily bread is made almost entirely from the flour obtained from hexaploid and tetraploid species of *Triticum* (Sears, 1948). Cotton in largest supply is produced by the tetraploid rather than the diploid species. A long list of economically important plants that are also polyploid could be prepared from the many cases reported in the literature by Eigsti and Dustin (1955) and Krythe and Wellensiek (1942).

About one-half the species of flowering plants are polyploid (Stebbins, 1950). Among certain families, the proportion of polyploids to diploids is higher than 50 per cent. Undoubtedly Darwin would have devoted an important chapter to the subject of polyploidy and origin of species had the present information been available such as the investigations by Clausen, Keck, and Hiesey (1945). During the last half century many excellent experiments have confirmed the origin of polyploids from their parental diploids, notably papers and books by Stebbins (1950), Beasley (1940), McFadden and Sears (1945), Kihara and Lilienfeld (1948), and others. Usually the diploids were suspected as parents for one or more reasons, and from these cases interspecific sterile hybrids were made. Subsequently a doubling of the chromosomes yielded the fertile polyploids, or equivalent species. Such synthetic types as Frandsen (1947) made with *Brassica* resemble the natural species very closely and are not easily separated into the respective populations.

As we learn more about the role of polyploidy in origin of species we can expect to see an improvement in our approach to the improvement of crops that are in part or exclusively from species that are polyploid (Levan, 1945).

Agriculture in its historical perspective shows a parallelism between the introduction of new crops and the greater prevalence of species with higher and higher numbers of chromosomes. Thus, within a given group, the newest species introduced to agriculture are usually those with the highest number of chromosomes; or those species with a long record in domestic use generally are diploid. Good cases are found among the species of *Triticum,* where it is well known that hexaploid wheat, *T. aestivum,* is the newcomer to agriculture (Sears, 1948). In fact, there are no species of hexaploids outside cultivation. At least, up to now there are no wild 42-chromosome types of *Triticum* on record. The tetraploid, or 28-chromosome *Triticum,* preceded the hexaploid and may have played an important role in the origin of the hexaploid 42-chromosomal cultivated forms (Thompson et al., 1943). Finally, the diploids, of which *T. monococcum* is an example, have been associated with agriculture from its dawning period, in certain centers of civilization. *Triticum monococcum* is cultivated today in central Europe, but the production is extremely limited in comparison with the acreage now planted with polyploids of *Triticum* (Sears, 1948). The introduction of more productive varieties often meant the introduction of species that were polyploid. In the future we can look for this trend to continue, and with newer techniques, reviewed by Eigsti and Dustin (1955), for making polyploids, there is great hope for the development of new and more productive crops.

The tetraploid cotton, *Gossypium hirsutum,* is another interesting introduction wherein the practice of agriculture played its role in making possible the close contact between the diploid species, one of Asiatic origin and the other American. Both are involved in the present-day tetraploid American Upland Cotton (Beasley, 1940; Stephens, 1950). The diploids had to make contact at some point where the hybridization could take place. Then doubling of the chromosomes within the sterile diploid hybrid resulted in the origin of fertile tetraploids. Man was able to recognize in the tetraploid the increased productivity. When and exactly where the hybridization took place is unknown. If more facts are established, one can predict that botanists will furnish some of the data to show how the diploids of two continents came together prior to the origin of the American Upland Cotton (Stephens, 1950).

The superiority of ornamentals and horticulturals (Emsweller, 1949; Dermen, 1952; Mehlquist, 1949; Darrow, 1950) that are known as natural polyploids keeps alive keen interest in polyploidy as a practical means for producing new and better flowers and fruits. Kamemoto (1952) reports exceptionally valuable orchids that are triploid. The outstanding irises judged best by experts are in many cases tetraploids. If we limited competition among *Iris* to diploids, we would at once eliminate many of the most prized varieties. Among many horticultural varieties, the triploids and tetraploids are well known for their valuable contributions in one or several ways.

A NEW ERA. *The rediscovery of colchicine*. Realizing, then, both theoretical and practical implications of mitotic arrest and polyploidy, it is not surprising to learn that the development of good methods for inducing polyploids conveniently and efficiently should attract so much attention (Dustin, 1934; Ludford, 1936; Gavaudan et al., 1937; Blakeslee and Avery, 1937; Nebel and Ruttle, 1938; Eigsti, 1938; Levan, 1938; Havas, 1940; Eigsti and Dustin, 1955). Some speculations were made beyond the factual limitations. Such was the unusual interest created when colchicine became known as an agent for doubling the number of chromosomes.

This chemical, colchicine, was demonstrated by Levan (1938) to be specific and efficient in creating polyploid restitution nuclei, opening a new era for induction of polyploidy (Eigsti and Dustin, 1955). The action on dividing cells of roots, stems, pollen, and other embryonic tissues led to a new and important tool for plant scientists.

Colchicine was not a new idea for arresting mitosis. A heat treatment was suggested by Belling in 1925 and was successfully applied with maize (Randolph, 1941). Also, cold-heat shock methods were useful in studying polyploidy at the chromosome laboratory at Svalof, Sweden. Levan reported that this elaborate machinery for producing polyploidy by heat and refrigeration became museum pieces overnight after colchicine methods had been developed. This rediscovered chemical, first observed by Pernice in 1889, was so superior, so effective, and so readily applied that its use with many kinds of plants was assured. Laboratories already investigating polyploidy switched to the new procedure, while in other places new programs were started that had not been previously conceived along the lines of polyploidy breeding. It was hoped that new varieties would be developed quickly. The acceptance of this method of plant improvement was widespread, and numerous papers were published beginning in 1938. Something new in research had arrived according to Wellensiek (1938), who reported a "colchicine fad."

Colchicine freed of its impurities is a white powder obtained from any one of a number of species of plants, but notably from the genus *Colchicum* (Cook and Loudon, 1951). Pharmacists recognize only *C. autumnale* L. as the official drug plant, although *C. luteum* Baker is admitted in India, where this spring-flowering species is abundant and is also an excellent source for the drug (Eigsti and Dustin, 1955).

The pure substance is in the form of needles and has a melting point of 155°C. It is colorless, readily soluble in water, chloroform, or alcohol. While colchicine is often classified as an alkaloid, such classification is open to question on the basis of additional chemical study of the past two decades as reviewed by Loudon (chapter 6, Colchicine) and by Eigsti and Dustin (1955). The compound is described as methyl ether of an enolone containing three additional methoxyl groups, an acetylated primary amino group, and three nonbenzenoid double bonds. The structure is novel chiefly in respect to the two fused 7-membered ring of its tricyclic system (Loudon, 1955). Complete synthesis offers no needed economic replacement since the natural product is abundant and completely effective. However, more complete estimate of the pattern of atoms and specific action upon mitotic processes offers promise of discovering new ways to control cellular activities. For improved chemotherapy more knowledge of atomic specificity in relation to biological processes would be valuable. Here is an excellent field for future research.

When colchicine comes in contact with dividing cells the spindle fibers are at once reduced, as well as structurally changed. Other cells are uniformly arrested at the metaphasic stage. Such action leads to a restitution nucleus with double the number of chromosomes. Metaphasic arrest by spindle inhibition is the central feature of the "C-mitosis" as described by Levan (1938), a process familiar to many biologists (Eigsti and Dustin, 1955).

The chemical acts specifically upon the spindle and has not been demonstrated conclusively to alter chromosomal structure. Its selective reaction is total for all cells in mitosis. No serious consequences occur in cells after the drug has been dissipated from the cell, except that more chromosomes are present than before contact with the substance.

As the cell recovers from a treatment, a new spindle is formed and the restitutional nucleus undergoes a regular mitosis, now as a polyploid cell. If sufficient numbers of cells in a given area are simultaneously changed from diploid to tetraploid, the new tissue will be tetraploid. However, experimental conditions may allow only a few tetraploid cells, the majority remaining diploid. A more rapid growth by diploid cells causes presumable tetraploids to revert back to diploids. Success can be obtained only when specific conditions are well understood and entirely accounted for in the procedures designed to create tetraploids.

Five interacting factors must be considered for successful experiments designed to induce polyploids (Eigsti and Dustin, 1955). These are (1) concentration of the solution, (2) exposure schedule, (3) number of chromosomes of species treated, (4) specific stages of mitosis, and (5) general conditions for growth. More experimenters use the 0.2 per cent aqueous solution than any other concentration. This strength can be recommended generally for inducing polyploidy. A direct contact between the chemical and nucleus must be maintained for not less than 48 hours. Even longer exposures are used. Schedules providing an intermittency for the treatment are applicable where roots may be treated by alternate immersion in colchicine 12 hours and water 12 hours, extending the total treatment to 3, 4, 5, or 6 days. A drop of the 0.2 per cent solution may be applied to very young seedlings each morning and evening for a period of 4 or 5 days. Care should be taken to reduce evaporation from the treated area.

SOME NOTABLE ADVANCES WITH POLYPLOIDS. A revolutionary practical application has been made to watermelons by Kihara (1952) and his associates (Yamashita, Kondo, Matsumoto, Nishida, and Nishiyama; see also Kihara and Nishiyama, 1947; Kihara and Yamashita, 1947). Triploid seedless watermelons, as true sterile hybrids, are a significant achievement. This new crop with its novel features has been adapted successfully on a large scale. A basic requirement for the seedless watermelon is an induced tetraploid parent that provides "triploid seed" from which triploid plants are derived.

Seedless fruits have special value in commerce, with premiums given to such products. This is true for seedless watermelon, as well as bananas, grapefruit, grapes, pineapple, and oranges. Scientists have added the seedless watermelon only recently.

The general scheme for making triploids follows several necessary steps. First, the tetraploid $4\times$ seed parents are developed by treating diploids with colchicine. Next, hybridizing the correct tetraploid with the best diploid yields seed for seedless watermelon plants. Triploids are sterile because the unbalanced number of chromosomes creates a meiosis, with three sets of homologous chromosomes coming together in the pairing process. The unequal chromosomal distribution causes ovular and pollen abortion; hence a seedless fruit develops from the triploid when pollinated with viable pollen. Diploid pollinators are planted with a 1 to 4 ratio, that is, one diploid to four triploids. Fruit yield is directly related to pollination. Tetraploid plants may provide the fruiting stimulus; however, these strains have fewer viable pollen because tetraploids have reduced fertility. If neither the tetraploid nor the diploid is flowering when triploids blossom, no seedless fruit will be formed.

Under certain conditions and among specific triploid hybrids, the ovules may develop into a hardened seed coat, of course, without embryo. Botanically then such fruits are seedless, but horticulturally they cannot be classed as seedless, since these hardened "seeds" are quite as objectionable as true seeds. There is some tendency for "false-seed" formation among the first set of fruit and perhaps again greater tendencies toward the end of the season. In other cases, a particular combination of tetraploid and diploid parents will always produce these false seeds at any part of the season. The prominence of false seed has created unfavorable impressions among growers and caused some disappointment when triploids were first marketed. As better cultivation practices were developed and the selected specific hybrids were used that eliminated this feature, better seedless watermelons have rapidly gained acceptance at the consumer level.

The finer texture of flesh, probably a feature of the triploid cell, more uniform distribution of sugar from center to rind, an increase in sugar content, the better keeping quality, all are results of seedlessness and triploidy, adding special value to this new hybrid. Also, certain superior specific combinations have shown excellent hybrid vigor, thereby increasing the total fruit production over a longer period of the season than the diploid (fig. 1).

FIG. 1. Excellent fruit of seedless watermelon. (*Photo by H. R. Knaus.*)

The seed for the triploid plant does not germinate as readily as diploid, particularly when the soil temperatures are below 85°F. This difficulty has been overcome by seedling culture in greenhouses or in covered and heated beds. After 20–30 days, seedlings thus cultured may be transplanted to the fields. Direct seeding into the field is not as successful, unless the daily soil temperatures are above 85°F. Usually, in early summer and late spring unfavorable cold soil conditions occur. However, once the triploid seedlings are past the second or third leaf stage, a hardiness to cold counteracts unfavorable soil conditions (Eigsti and Dustin, 1955).

Reduced fertility of the tetraploid seed parent reduces the seed production. Since the tetraploid must be used as the seed parent there is no prospect for increasing seed production by reciprocal crosses. The fertility shown by the

FIG. 2. Triploid fruit in cross section showing ovules.

tetraploid parent is directly related to "seedlessness" in the subsequent triploid hybrid.

Consumer acceptance rises when good-quality seedless fruit can be brought to the market. Where seedless fruit is produced in volume, the wholesale market awards premium prices over the price of regular fruit. Plant breeders have new approaches with polyploidy and watermelon improvements (fig. 2).

Induced polyploidy has contributed another significant achievement in tobacco improvement. Cultivated tobacco is attacked by a serious mosaic, a disease to which many varieties of *Nicotiana tabacum* are susceptible. Another species, *N. glutinosa*, carries disease resistance, but it is otherwise unfit for cultivation. If the resistance factor could be transferred to the commercial varieties, a long step in tobacco improvement could be taken. A review by

Valleau (1952) gives numerous important details about this achievement. Mosaic resistance was obtained when chromosomes were substituted, viz., *glutinosa* chromosomes exchanged for *tabacum* chromosomes that led to mosaic resistance (Clausen, 1945). Tobacco breeders have access to mosaic-resistant strains for the future development of new and better varieties. Such genic transfer from one species to another is a considerable accomplishment. Not only has its practical contribution meant much, but excellent theoretical work has been done with *Nicotiana* (Smith, 1939).

Three root crops may be improved by induced polyploidy: sugar beets (Matsumura, 1953), radish (Nishiyama, 1952), and turnips (Josefsson, 1953). The triploid sugar beet has the capacity to produce more raw sugar per acre, because the percentage of sugar per unit of beet remains proportional to size of the root as it increases (Peto and Boyes, 1940), whereas the diploid beet reduces yield of sugar per unit when the root approaches the largest size possible. This basic difference between diploids and triploids means that greater efficiency is in favor of triploids over diploids (Matsumura, 1953). After many selections and careful plant breeding, better and new strains of tetraploid sugar beets are now reported in Sweden. At first, the tetraploids proved inferior, on an over-all basis, to the best diploids, but applied work on improvement has brought new tetraploids with promise of superiority in production of sugar. The tetraploid radish carries favorable disease resistance, overcomes pithiness, and grows better under specific cold conditions than the diploid. In Sweden a third root crop, the turnip, has been improved with the use of tetraploid strains. Increases in the acreage of tetraploids have followed the introduction of new and useful varieties of induced polyploids.

Some new varieties of tetraploid rye have been introduced to agriculture by Muntzing (1951) and others. Again, the first expectations for the "raw" tetraploids were too high. Since then, selections have advanced new superior polyploid strains. One tetraploid with wide adaptation for Europe and parts of the U.S.A. is called Petkus tetraploid rye, first developed in Europe. The advantages shown by the tetraploid rye must be balanced against certain disadvantages before a superiority for tetraploids or diploids can be decided.

Rye wheat hybrids made fertile by inducing polyploidy have been known for many years. Certain advantages along with disadvantages attend these polyploids, technically called the *Triticales*. The protein quality of the flour shows superiority to rye flour. These hybrids develop on soil not suitable for bread wheat. Inherent to new *Triticales* are the usual problems of low fertility, lack of genotypical balance, and the need for suitable agronomic types attractive to farmers as well as millers of flour.

Among the genus *Triticum* and related genera many induced polyploids have been made (Sears, 1948). Much of this work contributes primarily to an understanding of the origin of species and the mechanisms of evolution, although practical breeding plans are greatly enlarged with induced amphiploids that now carry certain desirable traits transferable to hexaploid wheat from other genera. Induced polyploidy provides a key to wheat improvement.

As soon as colchicine methods became known, certain interspecific hybrids of cotton were treated by Beasley (1940) and other cotton geneticists with this drug. It was proved conclusively that our present Upland tetraploid cotton *Gossypium hirsutum* was indeed the composite of an Asiatic diploid and an American diploid. Cytological and genetical investigations within the genus *Gossypium* expanded at a fast pace with the rapidly introduced methods for making polyploids. No group of economic plants offered greater promise as a subject for polyploidy breeding. At the same time the problems confronting these programs have been as complex as any group (Stephens, 1950). Theoretical and practical work should be integrated as progress is made with induced polyploidy and cotton.

Larger and larger flowers are frequently desirable. When colchicine methods were perfected to make new polyploids, many projects were launched to create large-flowered tetraploids. Success was not as outstanding as desired, because features such as reduced seed germination, longer growing periods, lack of uniformity, along with other disadvantages, tended to reduce the advantages gained with polyploidy.

Among ornamentals certain triploids are outstanding in comparison with diploids. Triploid orchids have brought higher prices than diploids (Kamemoto, 1952). Mehlquist (1949) showed that polyploidy is a good procedure applied properly to specific flowers. The longer flowering period, greater uniformity, increased vigor, and additional size are noteworthy. The propagation becomes a problem since triploids are sterile. Tetraploid lilies induced from diploid by Emsweller (1949) have been developed, with the polyploids giving greater elegance, size, and beauty. Fruits of many kinds come from polyploids (Darrow, 1950). Some of the best varieties of apples are triploids, while others are special chimeral types (Dermen, 1952). These problems represent the specific challenge to specialists.

Other projects that consider forage crops (Levan, 1945), *Brassica* (Frandsen, 1947), *Solanum, Mentha,* the Gramineae, cucurbits, and numerous economic types might have been more extensively reviewed. The bibliographies by Eigsti and Dustin (1947, 1949) and their review (1955) should be consulted.

There is a rapid method for creating pure-breeding inbred lines by doubling the chromosomal numbers of monoploids to give the plant breeder a wealth of useful germ plasm. Specific maize-breeding projects include monoploid techniques executed by qualified scientists, yielding valuable materials for practical and theoretical consideration.

PRINCIPLES. *Polyploidy as a breeding procedure.* When many polyploids became available among the numerous crops tested, probably our greatest contribution came from the insight gained to general principles governing polyploidy as a breeding method, rather than the actually improved varieties added to agriculture (Levan, 1945). These concepts appear to be more valuable than the actual tetraploids developed from diploids. Practical men became alarmed and disappointed because so many polyploids proved wholly useless. In many cases, the results consisted in new and better knowledge about polyploidy. Information can be more valuable than a direct benefit from specific plants.

Some of the principles now recognized in the breeding of polyploid crops are (1) first-generation polyploids as "raw" polyploids and as such unselected genotypes; (2) large populations necessary; (3) selection all important; (4) choice of diploid and the need for diploids instead of tetraploids for starting material; (5) optimal numbers of chromosomes for a maximum efficiency; (6) use of cross-fertilizing species; (7) transfer of genes from one species to another; (8) fertility and sterility barriers; (9) advantages compared with the attending disadvantages; (10) procedures for testing the polyploids against the diploids.

Many plant breeders often expected the first-generation tetraploids to provide the superior strains in contrast to the diploid. Such improvements were anticipated with the development of the polyploid. As a matter of fact, the task of plant breeding only begins once the tetraploids have been created. These "raw" polyploids are unselected and unbalanced genotypes even though the starting diploids may have been carefully selected varieties.

With the efficiency of colchicine in contrast to other methods, large populations could be handled. Instead of developing a few tetraploids from a few diploids, hundreds of tetraploid individuals should be included. The largest possible combinations of genotypes must be transformed from the diploid to the tetraploid level. Effective selection can be done only with large populations. Such selection is now regarded as essential if success is expected with polyploids induced from diploids.

It should hardly be necessary to state that diploids rather than the already polyploid species are prerequisites for a good polyploidy-breeding program. Since there are many natural tetraploids available, numerous breeding projects failed because their starting material was unsatisfactory in this respect. There seems to be an optimal number of chromosomes that is tolerated for each species. Numbers above or below that optimum usually lead to inferior performance. Sometimes triploidy is optimal, rather than tetraploidy or diploidy.

Cross-fertilizing species as a group tend to be more useful in creating favorable tetraploids than self-fertilizing species. Also, the transfer of genes from one species to another can be done at the polyploid level and not at diploid levels. Higher chromosomal types act as a bridge across the species barrier. Within certain groups this potential for crop improvement is exceedingly great.

Everyone should be aware of the universally attendant characteristic of reduced fertility among tetraploids. If the crop depends on seed production, then fertility levels are directly related to yield factors. A low-fertility tetraploid cannot be expected to yield as well as the high-fertility diploid unless the greater-sized seed from the tetraploid offsets the reduced numbers of seeds. Along with reduced fertility, longer growth period, vigor, and physiological factors go with tetraploids. Sometimes the new feature is an advantage, and sometimes a disadvantage. The ultimate success of any tetraploid depends upon balance in favor of tetraploids as offset by the disadvantages included therewith. Sometimes the advantages and disadvantages can be correctly assessed before the experiment is begun (Eigsti and Tenney, 1942). When the disadvantages outweigh the advantages there can be little hope for practical success. Amphidiploidy offers a way to overcome the disadvantageous sterility barrier. Whenever possible such hybrids need to be used.

The testing procedures need consideration. For example, tetraploid rye cannot be grown beside diploid rye in order to measure relative performances because the diploid pollinates the tetraploid, and the subsequent triploid grains being sterile, the yield of the tetraploid is greatly reduced (Muntzing, 1951). In these cases, special designs for test are necessary. Also, it is necessary that triploid watermelons be cultivated with some degree of care in the early growth period, otherwise the performance of triploids will fall below the parental types (Kihara, 1952). These and many other signs of caution need to be heeded.

SUMMARY

Since polyploids are so important in practical agriculture and since polyploidy is one of the methods of species formation, the future study with induced polyploidy holds many good opportunities for crop improvement as well as more information as to ways that new populations originate in nature. The tool for making polyploids has been found; the end of its usefulness is by no means totally in sight.

LITERATURE CITED

BEASLEY, J. 1940. The production of polyploids in *Gossypium*. Jour. Hered. 31:39–48.

BELLING, J. 1925. Production of triploid and tetraploid plants. Jour. Hered. 16:463–466.

BLAKESLEE, A. 1937. Dédoublement du nombre de chromosomes chez les plantes par traitement chimique. C. R. Acad. Sci. Paris 205:476–479.

———— AND A. AVERY. 1937. Methods of inducing doubling of chromosomes in plants. Jour. Hered. 28:393–411.

CLAUSEN, J., ET AL. 1945. Experimental studies on the nature of species. Carnegie Inst. Wash., D.C., Publ. 564:1–174.

CLAUSEN, R. 1945. Mosaic resistance transferred from wild tobacco to cultivated varieties through the science of genetics. California Agric. 3(7):7, 16.

COOK, J., AND J. LOUDON. 1951. Alkaloids: Colchicine. Ed. by Holmes and Manske. Vol. 2, pp. 261–325. Academic Press. New York.

DARROW, G. 1950. Polyploidy in fruit improvement. Sci. Monthly 70:211–219.

DERMEN, H. 1940. Colchicine, polyploidy and technique. Bot. Rev. 6:599–635.

———. 1952. Polyploidy in the apple. Jour. Hered. 43:7–8.

DUSTIN, A. 1934. Contribution a l'étude des poisons caryoclasiques sur les tumeurs animales. Bull. Acad. Roy. Méd. Belg. 14:487–502.

———, L. HAVAS, AND F. LITS. 1937. Action de la colchicine sur les divisions cellulaires chez les végétaux. C. R. Assoc. des Anat. 32:170–176.

EIGSTI, O. 1938. A cytological study of colchicine effects in the induction of polyploidy in plants. Proc. Nat. Acad. Sci. (U.S.) 24:56–63.

——— AND P. DUSTIN. 1947. Colchicine bibliography. Lloydia 10:65–114.

——— AND ———. 1949. Colchicine bibliography. Lloydia 12:185–207.

——— AND ———. 1955. Colchicine in agriculture, medicine, biology and chemistry. 470 pp. Iowa State College Press. Ames, Iowa.

——— AND B. TENNEY. 1942. Colchicine—a report on experiments. 40 pp. Univ. Okla. Press. Norman, Okla.

EMSWELLER, S. 1949. Polyploidy in Lilium longiflorum. Amer. Jour. Bot. 36:135–144.

FRANDSEN, K. 1947. The experimental formation of Brassica napus L. var. oleifera DC. and Brassica carinata Braun. Dansk. Bot. Ark. 12:1–16.

GAVAUDAN, P., AND N. POMRIASKINSKY-KOBOZIEFF. 1937. Sur l'influence de la colchicine sur la caryocinèse dans les meristèmes radiculares de l'Allium cepa. C. R. Soc. Biol. Paris 125:705–707.

HAVAS, L. 1940. Colchicine chronology. Jour. Hered. 31:115–117.

JOSEFSSON, A. 1953. Tetraploida rovor, förädling och Forsök vid Sveriges Utsädesförening. Sveriges Utsädesf. Tidskr. 3:165–180.

KAMENOTO, K. 1952. Further studies on polyploid Cattleyas. Bull. Pac. Orchid Soc. Hawaii 10:141–148.

KIHARA, H. 1952. Triploid watermelons. Proc. Amer. Soc. Hort. Sci. 58:217–230.

——— AND F. LILIENFELD. 1949. A new synthesized 6× wheat. Hereditas Suppl. Vol.: 307–319.

——— AND I. NISHIYAMA. 1947. An application of sterility of autoploids to the breeding of seedless watermelons. Kihara Inst. Biol. Res. Seiken Ziho 3:92–103.

——— AND K. YAMASHITA. 1947. A preliminary investigation for the formation of tetraploid watermelons. Kihara Inst. Biol. Res. Seiken Ziho 3:89–92.

KRYTHE, J., AND S. WELLENSIEK. 1942. Five years of colchicine research. Bibliog. Genetica 14:1–132.

LEVAN, A. 1938. Effect of colchicine on root mitosis in Allium. Hereditas 24:471–486.

———. 1945. Polyploidiforädlingens Nurvarande Lage. Sveriges Utsädesf. Tidskr. 1945:109–143.

LOUDON, J. 1955. Chapter 6 in Colchicine, ed. by Eigsti and Dustin (1955). Iowa State College Press. Ames, Iowa.

LUDFORD, R. 1936. The action of toxic substances upon the division of normal and malignant cells *in vitro* and *in vivo*. Arch. Exp. Zellforsch. und Mikr. Anat. 18:411–441.

MATSUMURA, S. 1953. Improvement of sugar beets by means of triploidy. 134 pp. Sciencesha 5 Higashikatamachi, Bunkyo-ku, Tokyo, Japan.

McFADDEN, E., AND E. SEARS. 1945. The artificial synthesis of *Triticum spelta*. Genetics 30:14.

MEHLQUIST, G. 1949. Role of genetics in floriculture. Genetics 24:75.

MUNTZING, A. 1951. Cyto-genetic properties and practical value of tetraploid rye. Hereditas 37:1–84.

NEBEL, B., AND M. RUTTLE. 1938. The cytological and genetical significance of colchicine. Jour. Hered. 29:3–9.

NISHIYAMA, L. 1952. Polyploid studies in Brassiceae. III. Mem. Research Inst. Food Sci. Kyoto Univ. 3:1–14.

PERNICE, B. 1889. Sulla cariocinesi delle cellule epiteliali e dell' endotelio dei vasi della mucosa dello stomaco e dell' intestino, nello studio della gastroenterite sperimentale (nell' avvelenamento per colchico). Sicilia Med. 1:265–79.

PETO, F., AND J. BOYES. 1940. Comparison of diploid and triploid sugar beets. Canadian Jour. Res. Sec. C. Bot. Sci. 18:273–282.

RANDOLPH, L. 1941. An evaluation of induced polyploidy as a method of breeding crop plants. Amer. Nat. 75:347–65.

SEARS, E. 1948. The cytology and genetics of the wheats and their relatives. Advances in Genet. 2:239–270. Academic Press. New York.

SMITH, H. 1939. Induction of polyploidy in *Nicotiana* species and species hybrids by the treatment with colchicine. Jour. Hered. 30:290–306.

STEBBINS, G. 1950. Variation and evolution in plants. 643 pp. Columbia Univ. Press. New York.

STEPHENS, S. 1950. The internal mechanism of speciation in *Gossypium*. Bot. Rev. 16:115–149.

THOMPSON, W., ET AL. 1943. The artificial synthesis of a 42-chromosome species resembling common wheat. Canadian Jour. Res. Sec. C. Bot. Sci. 21:134–143.

VALLEAU, W. 1952. Breeding tobacco for disease resistance. Econ. Bot. 6:69–102.

WELLENSIEK, S. 1939. The newest fad, colchicine and its origin. Chron. Bot. 5:15–17.

11

CYTOGENETICS AND EVOLUTION
OF THE GRASS FAMILY

G. Ledyard Stebbins

During the past half century that part of botany, and in fact all biological science, which deals with evolution and classification has entered a new era, dominated by the rise of cytology and genetics and their use as new tools for solving evolutionary and taxonomic problems. This union of disciplines has yielded striking results, and the new relationships uncovered by it have often been supported by data from still other fields, such as anatomy, embryology, and physiology. Thus plant evolutionists are gradually progressing toward their avowed goal: the understanding of the complex interrelationships between and the evolutionary origin of the myriad diverse types of plants existing on the earth and the establishment of general principles which have governed this evolution.

No group of plants has been more radically affected by this new approach than the grass family. There are several reasons for this. In the first place, grasses are very important to us. They feed our cattle, sheep, and other livestock. A few species of the family, the cereal grains, have become our staple foods, while another, sugar cane, sweetens our lives. If we are home owners, we cut the grass every week so that we can enjoy the soft turf and cool green expanse of our lawns; and while resting we often pluck its leaves or stems, admire their structure, or teach our youngsters how to turn a grass leaf into a shrill whistle by placing it between our thumbs. If we live in a dry climate and hike over the hills in summer, we come home to spend hours plucking the seeds of the weedy or "stickery" grasses out of our clothing or our dog's hair. In many parts of the world one group of grasses, the bamboos, are the staple building material for houses and bridges.

Because of these many uses, the study of grass classification, or taxonomy, does more than satisfy our curiosity about the diversity of living things and the way in which they have evolved. Cereal and sugar-cane breeders have learned that many species of wild grasses are closely enough related to the cultivated crop species so that hybrids between them can be obtained. By back crosses or introgression from such hybrids, the gene pool available to the cereal or cane breeder can be enlarged to include extra genes for vigor, disease resistance, and such valuable qualities as high protein content of the grain. Breeders of forage grasses are trying out interspecific hybrids as a means of obtaining greater vigor, as well as resistance to drought, cold, or unfavorable soil conditions. Specialists in lawn and turf management find that an understanding of grass taxonomy is most helpful to their work. For all these purposes, the most useful system of classification is one which reflects as nearly as possible the true genetic and evolutionary relationships of the species concerned.

A second reason for the changing grass taxonomy is that grasses are difficult for the taxonomist. In the words of Edgar Anderson, they are "streamlined." Their leaves are all alike in shape, and their stems vary relatively little in branching pattern. Their flowers are so reduced that the calyx and corolla, though probably present in the form of small scales (palea and lodicules), are very hard to study, and their ovary is reduced to a simple, 1-seeded caryopsis. An amateur in systematic botany who has not tried to recognize the genera and species of grasses could visualize the plight of the grass taxonomist if he should try to place into genera and species a large number of specimens of, say, the rose family which he had mutilated by cutting off all the flowers at the summit of their pedicels and trimming the leaves down to a narrow ribbon. If he did this, he would find his attention becoming focused on the inflorescence, particularly the pattern of its branching and the shape of the reduced leaves or bracts which subtend the branches. These are exactly the characters which grass taxonomists have traditionally emphasized.

The near revolution which is now taking place in grass taxonomy began when a few anatomists like Grob, Duval-Jouve, and Pée-Laby began to examine and compare the leaves of grasses under the microscope. They found that the smooth surface of the grass epidermis, so plain to the naked eye, appears under the microscope as a mosaic of highly distinctive cells: siliceous cells, parenchyma cells, hairs of various types, and specialized cells surrounding the stomata. An equal diversity of cells and tissues can be seen on examining a grass leaf in cross section. Furthermore, these cell patterns are characteristic of a species, and often diagnostic also of genera and tribes. But when grasses are classified on the basis of these anatomical characteristics, the arrangement of genera which emerges differs strongly from the classical system based upon characteristics of the inflorescence. It is perhaps for this reason that grass taxonomists paid little attention to these anatomical studies. But in 1931 there appeared the first important work on the cytology of grasses, the monumental treatise of the Russian cytologist Avdulov. He found that if one classifies grasses on the basis of the number and size of their chromosomes, one forms a system strikingly similar to that based on anatomy and histology, and equally different from that founded on the traditional characteristics of the inflorescence. He therefore studied additional characters: the shape of the first seedling leaf, the organization of the starch grains in the leaf and caryopsis, the organization of the resting nucleus, and the geographic distribution of the genera. All these bore out the system based upon anatomy and chromosomes. More recently, confirming evidence has been obtained from studies of lodicules, caryopses, embryos, root-hair development, and the reaction of germinating seeds to a weed-killing organic chemical compound, IPC. We thus find that the realignment of genera and tribes proposed by Avdulov is supported by nearly all the characteristics which we can study, and so appears to reflect genetic and evolutionary relationships better than the traditional system. This situation has been recognized by an increasing number of taxonomists, particularly Dr. C. E. Hubbard of Kew, England. He has pointed out the unnaturalness of some traditional genera, such as *Lepturus,* which he has severed into four genera belonging in different tribes. A radical rearrangement of genera and tribes of grasses is in the making, some features of which will be presented below. His system has been adopted by the authors of a recent *Flora of the British Isles* (Clapham, Tutin, and Warburg, 1952). Pilger (1954) proposed a system of classification which incorporated some of the newer characteristics, but it remains unnatural in a great many respects. The changes mentioned above have affected chiefly the broader classification of higher categories of grasses. But the problems of grass taxonomy do not end with the tribes and genera. Specialists who can recognize most genera of grasses at first sight still have great difficulty in delimiting their species. When one compares the diverse treatments which various monographs and floras present for such genera as *Festuca, Poa, Agropyron, Andropogon,* and *Panicum,* one realizes that even the experts have difficulty recognizing the species of grasses.

Cytogenetics has clarified the most important reason for this difficulty, although this new approach has not simplified the problem of delimiting species. Species delimitation of grasses is intrinsically difficult because interspecific boundaries have been blurred by hybridization and chromosome doubling, or polyploidy. Because of the widespread action of these two processes, the evolutionary "tree" of most grass genera is not a simple branching affair, but a highly complex network. Most of the common species of grasses are not descended from a single ancestral type, but contain in varying proportions gene combinations derived from two, three, four, or more separate and sometimes widely divergent ancestors.

This situation, however embarrassing it may be to the taxonomist, provides a gold mine for the evolutionist who has enough patience, persistence, and insight to analyze its problems. Evolution by polyploidy is essentially unidirectional; the polyploids are, as a rule, derived from relatives with lower chromosome numbers. Furthermore, although hybrid polyploid or amphiploid species are constant and may even be ancient in the geological sense, the diploid ancestors of many such species still exist and can be recognized by their external morphology. Once the suspected ancestral species have been identified, the supposed evolutionary course of hybridization and chromosome doubling can be repeated in the garden or greenhouse, and the hypothesis about phylogeny can be subjected to the acid test of prediction and verification by experiment. No other type of evolutionary phylogeny on the level of species or genera can as yet be subjected to this rigorous test. Although experiments of this type have been performed in many different plant families, the grasses provide particularly favorable material for them, not only because of their high percentage of polyploidy, but also because their species are widespread and common, and most of them can be raised and hybridized under controlled conditions with relative ease.

The few phylogenetic patterns of polyploidy in grasses which have been analyzed by this method have had an important bearing on problems of plant geography, particularly the interpretation of past migration and dispersal on the basis of the distribution of modern species. In some instances the ancestry of amphiploid or hybrid polyploid species has been diagnosed, and one or both of the immediate parents of the amphiploid have been found to occur in areas widely separated from its own area of distribution. Such discrepancies call for an explanation in terms of altered geographic distributions in past geological epochs, since we must assume that at the time of its origin, the amphiploid occurred together with both of its parental species. If, in attempting to explain these alterations in distribution, we become thoroughly familiar with the fossil evidence and with geological evidence about past climates and the distribution of land and water, we can often use polyploids to provide valuable evidence about this phase of historical plant geography.

In the preceding section, the broad outlines of the new orientation in grass taxonomy and evolution have been sketched. The subsequent sections will be devoted to amplifying this sketch with specific examples and will pose some problems for future investigators.

GENERAL TRENDS OF EVOLUTION IN THE GRASS FAMILY

The nearest approach to a complete system of classification based upon these newer characters was made by Prat (1936), who illustrated most of the characters mentioned above and constructed a phylogenetic tree on the basis of them. The difficulty with this "tree," as with nearly all such efforts, is the assumption that the ancestral type of a given group has been preserved to the present day and can be identified among living forms. The very age of the grass family, which already existed in the Cretaceous period, speaks against such an assumption. In other plant groups, such as the conifers, as well as in numerous orders of animals well represented in the fossil record, the fossil evidence shows clearly that the primitive members of the group concerned died out relatively early in its evolutionary history, and the modern genera are all specialized in one way or another.

In the grasses, both Prat and Bews (1929) have considered the bamboos to be ancestral to the other tribes. This viewpoint is reached because bamboos undoubtedly have more primitive flowers; i.e., their floral structure approaches the generalized monocotyledonous, or lily-like, type more than does that of any other members of this highly specialized family. But although the bamboos are undoubtedly primitive in floral characters, they are nevertheless highly specialized in many other ways. They have a complex pattern of branching, highly specialized leaves, often on distinct petioles (which are, however, absent from the young shoots), and an elaborate system of rhizomes. Their tree-like habit of growth is itself probably a secondary specialization, as suggested by Agnes Arber (1934), since it is entirely different from the growth habit of any other trees, either mono- or dicotyledonous, and the groups of monocotyledons which on various grounds are believed to be most closely related to the Gramineae (Flagellariaceae, Restionaceae, primitive Liliaceae) are all herbaceous. The earliest members of the grass family, therefore, probably had flowers somewhat like those of some modern bamboos, but their growth habit and general appearance were in all likelihood more like that of the more familiar herbaceous grasses.

Hence, the following picture emerges of the broad outlines of the course of evolution in the grass family. The earliest grasses were herbs with stems having few to many nodes, relatively simple racemose or paniculate inflorescences, and spikelets with numerous florets, the bracts or glumes being undifferentiated like those of primitive bamboos. The flowers themselves were trimerous, with a perianth of three and perhaps six members, six stamens in two series, and an ovary with a single ovule and three styles and stigmas. They were probably already wind-pollinated, but descended from ancestors with a well-developed perianth and insect pollination. They probably existed in the middle of the Cretaceous period, judging from the scanty fossil evidence that is available, and inhabited regions with a tropical or subtropical climate. From this primitive, now extinct group evolved a series of lines adapted in different ways to various habitats, as typical of adaptive radiation in all groups with a known fossil record. Three of these lines had unusual success. The first two developed primarily in the tropics. These were Panicoideae and the Chloridoid-Eragrostoid line. They probably came from closely related ancestors and evolved in similar directions. Their evolution was characterized by the retention of primitive features in the leaf epidermis, caryopsis, embryo, and seedling, but by specializations in the leaf anatomy (distribution of chlorophyll-bearing tissue) and particularly the inflorescence and spikelets. The predominant trend, expressed in every genus of the Panicoideae, is reduction of the fertile florets to one per spikelet. In the Panicoideae this affected chiefly the lower florets of the spikelet, while in the Chloridoid-Eragrostoid line the upper florets were more strongly affected. In addition, various branches of both lines, but particularly the Panicoideae, have developed a tremendous diversity of specialized adaptations for seed dispersal (fig. 1). Among the most striking examples are the bristly involucres of the elephant grasses (*Pennisetum*), which evolved further through fusion of bristles to form the involucre of the sand burs (*Cenchrus*); the long-awned, pointed callused fruits of tanglehead, or Pili grass (*Heteropogon*), which simulate those of *Stipa*, discussed below; the upper leaf sheaths of Job's tears (*Coix*), which have become inflated, hardened, and polished so that they resemble beads; and the enlarged, indurated rachises, or cobs, of the maize tribe (*Maydeae*).

The third dominant line, that of the Festucoideae, are the principal grasses of temperate climates. They became specialized largely by reduction in the leaf epidermis, caryopsis, embryo, and seedling. The specialization of the inflorescence and spikelets lagged behind that of the Panicoideae, although it reached a high level in several genera of the Agrostideae and Phalarideae. The large chromosomes of the Festucoideae are probably a later specialization, as suggested by Avdulov, since they do not occur in any grasses which are primitive in morphological characteristics. Avdulov's suggestion that large chromosome size evolved as an adaptation to winter cold is, however, hard to justify on the basis of any known facts of chromosome chemistry or cellular physiology. It is, however, an intriguing speculation, particularly since it is paralleled to some extent in other families. In the Commelinaceae, Liliales, Leguminosae, and Polemoniales the largest chromosomes are found in species inhabiting temperate climates; although, of course, many families with consistently small chromosomes (Cyperaceae, Juncaceae, Rosaceae) are dominant in these same temperate regions. The relationship between chromosome size, cellular metabolism, and growth is a subject which certainly deserves attention and about which new discoveries of considerable evolutionary significance might be made.

A less successful line of radiation, the bamboos, became dominant only in the moist forests of the tropics. Some of its members have developed extreme vegetative specializations, such as the habit of climbing over other vegetation by means of elaborate systems of spines or thorns developed on the stems. As mentioned above, many species of bamboos have very primitive reproductive structures, but others are highly specialized in this respect.

Three additional lines of grass evolution were highly successful in even more limited ways. The Arundineae, or reed grasses, which retained the apparently primitive chromosomal condition of a basic number of $x = 6$ or 12,

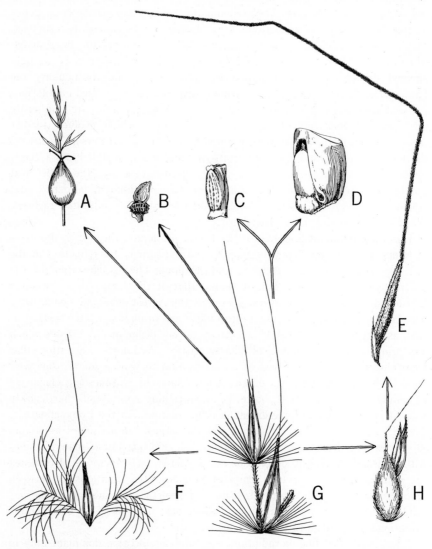

Fig. 1. Fruits of various species of the tribe Andropogoneae, showing adaptive radiation in respect to specialization for seed dispersal. All drawings from Hitchcock and Chase (1950) reproduced at a magnification of ×3, except for *A*, which has a magnification of ×1⅔. *A, Coix lacryma-jobi; B, Hackelochloa granularis; C, Manisuris cylindrica; D, Tripsacum dactyloides; E, Heteropogon contortus; F, Andropogon virginicus; G, Erianthus coarctatus; H, Sorghum halepense.*

remained primitive in some other respects, such as the lack of reduction in the spikelets, and preserve a considerable diversity in epidermal and anatomical structures. Isolated genera of this group, such as the common reed (*Phragmites*), though probably very old, are still successful throughout the world, while others such as pampas grass (*Cortaderia*) have developed chiefly in the Southern Hemisphere. Still other genera of Arundineae (*Ampelodesmos, Lamprothyrsus*) are relics, surviving in only a restricted part of the world, although they are successful and common in their areas of distribution.

The Oryzoid line, of which the best-known member is cultivated rice, has developed some of the most successful grasses of wet places. One peculiarity of this line is that many of its species have preserved the primitive condition of six stamens per floret, a condition existing elsewhere in the family only in the bamboos and a few other isolated genera. The most characteristic morphological feature developed in this line is the strong flattening of the spikelets and pronounced reduction in both glumes.

The Stipoid line is probably an offshoot of the danthonoid-arundinoid complex which became highly specialized in fruit structure. The development of a thick, tough fertile scale, or lemma, with overlapping margins was followed by further specialization in two directions. In the genus *Stipa*, or needle grasses, the fruit became much elongated, and the rachilla, or spikelet axis, immediately below it became modified into a sharp-pointed callus. At the same time, the awn at the fruit apex became much elongated and twisted in such a way that it winds and unwinds with changes in moisture. In this way the fruit has been converted into a drill, which effectively buries the seeds in the ground and increases their chances of successful germination under low moisture conditions. A further specialization, the development of hairs or plumes on the awn, is an aid to seed dispersal by wind, and particularly by animals, through clinging to their hair. In the other genera of this line, such as the rice grasses (*Oryzopsis*) and two principally South American genera (*Nassella, Piptochaetium*), the fruit has become rounded in shape, the lemma possesses a hard, shining surface, and the awn is relatively weak. At first sight, these fruits would appear to be very poorly equipped for wide dispersal, an appearance which is not borne out by the extensive distribution of many species of *Oryzopsis*. A suggested explanation for their dispersal is that these hard, shining fruits are particularly resistant to the digestive juices of animals, and so are carried long distances in the intestines of mammals and the crops of birds. At any rate, both *Stipa* and *Oryzopsis* have become among the most successful grasses of cold steppe regions.

In addition to these seven successful lines, the grasses contain many peculiar monotypic, ditypic, or small genera with very uncertain affinities. Among the most striking examples are *Nardus* and *Lygaeum* in Europe,

Anomochloa, Streptochaeta, and *Pariana* in the American tropics, and several strange endemics in Madagascar, described by A. Camus. These oddities are a continual source of worry to taxonomists who wish to construct a neat, well-ordered system. To the evolutionist familiar with several different families, they are recognized as being a common phenomenon. They apparently represent either the last vestiges of evolutionary lines which were successful in the past and are now nearly extinct, or the culmination of evolutionary trends which have been successful in only one specialized ecological niche.

SYNOPSIS OF THE PRINCIPAL CHARACTERISTICS ON WHICH THE NEW SYSTEM IS BASED

Figure 2 shows the evolutionary interrelationships of the principal tribes and genera of grasses. This diagram has not been made in the form of the customary evolutionary tree, with connections between the groups which are supposed to represent extinct common ancestors. In a family like the grasses, of which the fossil record is negligible, the actual connections between the modern groups can never be known and speculations about them may be more misleading than enlightening. I have adopted, therefore, a scheme which has been proposed by several authors and elaborated in particular by Sporne (1956). The modern groups are represented as cross sections of the branches of the evolutionary tree, with the distance between branches representing as nearly as possible my conception of the degree of resemblance or difference between the groups. Since this conception is based on many characters, it should be in some sort of multidimensional form, and any attempt to reduce it to the two-dimensional shape of a single surface naturally produces distortion. Broken lines on the diagram indicate, therefore, that the groups on either side of them are farther apart from each other than their position on the diagram would indicate. An attempt to express different degrees of evolutionary specialization has been made by placing a star in the position of the hypothetical primitive, generalized extinct type which formed the beginning of the family and by arranging the groups at distances from this star which correspond roughly to their degree of evolutionary specialization.

In fig. 3 and 4, the condition with respect to eight of the most significant diagnostic characters is illustrated for the three major subdivisions of the family, as well as for the relatively primitive group Bambuseae. Table 1 lists the condition with respect to these characters of four of the smaller groups and of four well-known genera which do not fit well into any of the eight groups listed in the diagram and table. The assignment of these genera, as well as of about 20 others, to tribal or subfamily groupings must await further study and may always be largely a matter of subjective judgment.

In addition to the eight characteristics illustrated, four others are worthy of mention, since they show a connection between evolutionary divergence in morphology and in physiology. The first is the way in which root-hairs de-

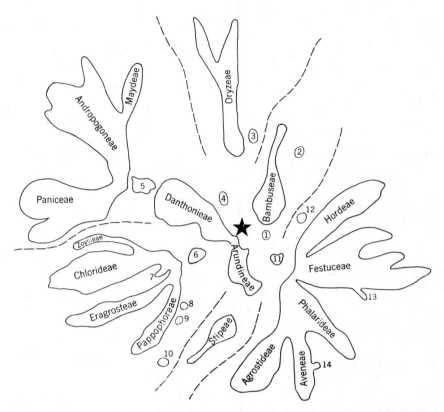

FIG. 2. Diagram showing the evolutionary interrelationships of the principal sub-families and tribes of the Gramineae. The irregular outlines represent approximately the relative size and diversity of the groups named in them, and the distance of a group from the star in the center is a rough indication of its degree of evolutionary specialization. The numbers represent single genera or small clusters of genera which are not easily placed in any of the major groupings, as follows: 1, *Streptochaeta;* 2, *Pariana;* 3, *Pharus;* 4, *Centotheceae;* 5, *Arundinelleae;* 6, *Uniola, Brylkinia;* 7, *Distichlis, Aeluropus, Vaseyochloa, Ectosperma;* 8, *Orcuttia;* 9, *Neostapfia;* 10, *Aristida;* 11, *Melica, Glyceria, Schizachne;* 12, *Nardus;* 13, *Monerma;* 14, *Scribneria.*

velop from epidermal cells (Reeder and Von Maltzahn, 1953; Row and Reeder, 1957). In the Panicoideae as well as in the Chloridoid-Eragrostoid group, the epidermal cells in the region of root-hair development are all alike in size, and any one of them can give rise to a root-hair. Furthermore, the root-hair emerges from the middle of the cell and at a right angle to the axis of the root. In the Festucoideae, on the other hand, the mature epidermal cells in the root-hair zone are of two types, long and short. Only the

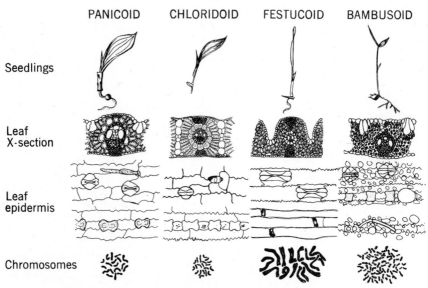

FIG. 3. Chart showing the differences between the four largest subdivisions of the grass family (Panicoideae, Chloridoid-Eragrostoid group, Festucoideae, Bambuseae) in respect to four diagnostic characteristics of the vegetative parts. Individual drawings as follows: Seedlings: *Panicum* sp., *Chloris cucullata, Festuca elatior* (*all from Prat*, 1936); *Pleioblastus Simoni* (*from Makino, Flora of Japan*). Cross sections of leaves: *Panicum dichotomiflorum* (*original, from preparation by V. I. Cheadle*); *Eleusine tristachya* (*from Hubbard*, 1948); *Lolium perenne* (*from Hubbard*, 1948); *Arundinaria argentea striata* (*original, from preparation by V. I. Cheadle*). Epidermis of leaves: *Digitaria sanguinalis* (*original, specimen from campus, University of California, Berkeley*); *Cynodon dactylon* (*from campus, University of California, Berkeley*); *Festuca arundinacea* (*from campus, University of California, Davis*); *Chimonobambusa marmorea* (*campus, University of California, Berkeley*). Chromosomes: *Panicum eruciforme, Chloris barbata, Lolium multiflorum, Bambusa* sp. (*all from Avdulov*, 1931). Chromosome drawings all reproduced at a magnification of ×980; other drawings at various magnifications.

shorter cells can give rise to root-hairs. The hairs, furthermore, emerge from the apical end of these cells and project forward at an angle of about 45 degrees with the axis of the root. A speculation worthy of mention, since it could be tested experimentally, is that the method of root-hair development found in the Festucoideae is a specialization adapting these grasses to relatively rapid elongation of the roots and assimilation of water and minerals.

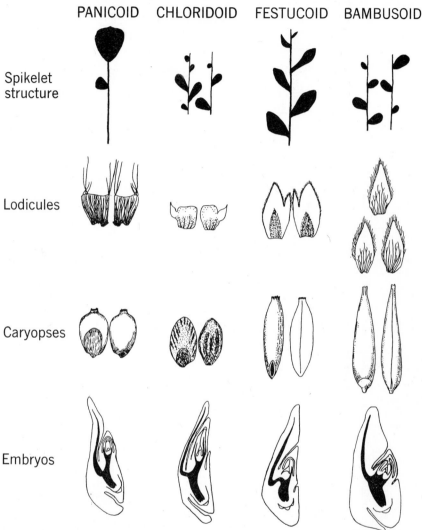

PANICOID   CHLORIDOID   FESTUCOID   BAMBUSOID

Spikelet structure

Lodicules

Caryopses

Embryos

FIG. 4. Chart showing the differences between the four largest subdivisions of the grass family with respect to four reproductive characteristics. Diagrams showing mode of reduction and abortion of florets of the spikelets (*all from Prat, 1936*). Lodicules and caryopses: *Sorghum halepense* (*original, from University of California campus, Davis*); *Eleusine indica* (*original, from Story County, Iowa, Caldwell no. 60, University of California Agronomy Herb.*); *Agropyron junceum* (*from Hubbard, 1948*); *Arundinaria japonica* (*from Hubbard, 1948*). Embryos: *Sorghum vulgare, Chloris verticillata, Festuca elatior* (*all from Reeder, 1953*); *Arundinaria tecta* (*original drawing of J. R. Reeder*). Magnifications various.

Table 1. Condition of various smaller groups of grasses with respect to the characters illustrated in fig. 3 and 4

Group	Seedlings	Leaf anatomy	Leaf epidermis	Chromosomes	Spikelets	Lodicules	Caryopses	Embryos
Danthonieae	Festucoid	Festucoid and Panicoid	Festucoid and Panicoid	Medium-small $x = 6, 7$	Festucoid	2, Various	Modified Panicoid	Panicoid
Arundineae	Panicoid	Modified Festucoid	Panicoid	Small $x = 12$	Festucoid	2, Modified Bambusoid	Panicoid	Panicoid
Stipeae	Festucoid	Festucoid	Festucoid	Small $x = 11, 12$	Modified Panicoid	3, Bambusoid-Festucoid	Festucoid	Modified Festucoid
Oryzeae (incl. Ehrharta, Zizanieae)	Festucoid-Panicoid	Festucoid	Modified Bambusoid	Small $x = 12$	Modified Panicoid	2, Bambusoid-Panicoid	Modified Festucoid	Festucoid
Uniola	Panicoid	Panicoid	Festucoid	Small $x = 12$	Festucoid	2, Modified Bambusoid	Panicoid	Chloridoid
Aristida	Festucoid	Modified Chloridoid	Panicoid	Small $x = 11$	Modified Panicoid	Modified Bambusoid	Festucoid	?
Glyceria	Festucoid	Festucoid	Festucoid	Small $x = 10$	Festucoid	Modified Chloridoid	Festucoid	Festucoid

Second, there are two types of starch grains in the grasses, compound and simple. Although there are some exceptions, the tribes and subfamilies are generally uniform in the type of starch grain which they possess. Compound starch grains are characteristic of most Festucoideae, the Chloridoid-Eragrostoid complex, the Arundineae, Oryzeae, and probably Bambuseae. Simple starch grains are found almost throughout the Panicoideae, as well as in the *Hordeae, Brachypodium,* and *Bromus* among the Festucoideae.

Third, there has been marked differentiation in respect to the cells surrounding the vascular bundles of the leaves (W. V. Brown). This is relatively little developed in the Bambusoid, Danthonoid, and Festucoid groups, but in both the Panicoideae and the Chloridoid-Eragrostoid group, as well as in some of the smaller groups, there has been extreme specialization in respect to both the parenchyma sheath cells and the chloroplasts which they contain. The connections between these anatomical features and the functions of photosynthesis, food storage, and food transport in the leaves have not yet been established, but certainly deserve attention.

Finally recent work (Al-Aish, 1956) has shown that grasses differ greatly in their response to a weed-killing chemical, isopropyl-*N*-phenyl carbamate (IPC). The Festucoideae, Danthonieae, and Stipeae are all easily killed as germinating seedlings by weak doses of this chemical, while the other groups tested, Panicoideae, Chloridoid-Eragrostoid group, Oryzeae, *Aristida,* and *Streptochaeta,* are strongly resistant to it, to such an extent that in weak doses IPC may stimulate germination. This difference is associated with the ability of the IPC-resistant species to carry on respiration in nearly anaerobic conditions. These latter species, furthermore, are mostly tropical or subtropical in distribution, while the grasses which are susceptible to IPC occur exclusively in temperate regions. Here is a connection between physiological divergence and geographic distribution, which, when further analyzed, may throw much additional light on the evolution of the grass family.

This discussion of the new classification of grasses and its bearing on evolution leads to the following conclusions. The new system of classification will not lighten the burden of the taxonomists who are charged with the task of identifying and naming the thousands of grass specimens which are collected each year. In fact, the wiser course for such work may be to retain the artificial keys constructed on the basis of the traditional system, since they are known to work reasonably well, and many of the more newly discovered diagnostic characteristics are rather hard to determine on the basis of the usual dried specimens. On the other hand, recognition of the newer characteristics and their bearing on evolutionary relationships will undoubtedly lead to a far better understanding of the nature and direction of evolution in this remarkable family. Furthermore, it has practical significance. It can give the grass breeder a clearer idea of the extent of the "gene pool" from which he can "borrow" genetic material by hybridization, with which to enrich the store of genetic material in an economically valuable species. Furthermore, the physiologist who is seeking herbicidal chemicals which will distinguish selectively between valuable grasses and noxious ones will be helped much more by applying the newer system, with its emphasis on physiological and cytological characteristics, than by judging relationships in the traditional manner, solely on the basis of gross external morphology.

THE ROLE OF POLYPLOIDY IN THE EVOLUTION OF GRASSES

Recent studies of grass evolution have shown that the doubling of the entire chromosome number, or polyploidy, has played an unusually large role in the evolution of this family. Nearly all genera of grasses contain species with chromosome numbers which are multiples of the original basic number. In wheat and oats the various species contain 14, 28, and 42 chromosomes in their body cells; in the panic grasses (*Panicum*) the numbers are 18, 36, 54, and 72; while in the beard grasses (*Andropogon*) somatic numbers of 20, 40, 50, 60, 80, 120, and up to 180 have been found.

If those species are considered polyploid which possess multiples of chromosome numbers which are known or can reasonably be inferred to exist in their genera, then about 70 per cent of the species of grasses investigated cytologically are polyploids. Since the percentage of polyploid species in the flowering plants in general is about 30 to 35 per cent (Stebbins, 1950), grasses have more than twice as many polyploids as the average for the flowering plants. Furthermore, there is much evidence that the basic, or x, number of many grass genera was itself derived by polyploidy in the remote past, which suggests that the percentage of species with a record of polyploidy somewhere in their evolutionary history is even greater.

The geographic distribution of polyploid grasses does not favor either the hypothesis of Tischler, that polyploidy is favored by cold climates, or that of Hagerup, that dryness promotes polyploidy. To be sure, the frequency of polyploids and the degree of polyploidy in many genera of the Northern Hemisphere, such as *Poa, Calamagrostis,* and *Bouteloua,* become higher as one goes northward. But this tendency can be explained on another basis, namely, that the northern lands were not long ago occupied by a great ice sheet which changed completely their topography and soil conditions. Polyploids, being better adapted to new ecological niches, were better equipped than their diploid relatives for the invasion of these lands as the ice retreated. In respect to tolerance of drought the data are meager, since few grass genera dominant in arid regions have been subjected to intensive cytogenetic study. A survey of these data suggests, however, that polyploids have been equally successful in both moist and arid regions.

The most valid generalization which can be made about the relative distribution of diploids and polyploids is that polyploids usually occupy areas which are newer geologically than those of their diploid ancestors (Stebbins, 1950, pp. 348–350). Polyploidy, as a means of altering the genetic nature of plants, is more likely to reduce than to improve their adaptation to the environment in which the original diploid species belongs and is well adapted. This tendency has become clear from the results of many experiments with artificially produced autopolyploids of various species of grasses and cereals, all of which have turned out to be less well adapted to the original habitat than their diploid progenitors. On the other hand, the radical change caused by polyploidy can often promote the adaptation of the new types to entirely different habitats from those occupied by their diploid ancestors. This is particularly true when polyploidy is combined with hybridization, as usually happens. The most common pattern of distribution and morphological variability which we find among genera of grasses and other plants containing polyploidy is consequently represented by the polyploid complex. Such complexes typically contain two or more diploid species or subspecies, each with a distinctive set of morphological characteristics and a well-defined range of geographical and ecological distribution. As a rule, however, these diploids represent only a small portion of the complex and are far outnumbered by the polyploids. The latter may include a few types which are hardly distinguishable in outward appearance from their diploid ancestors, but a much larger portion of the polyploids are easily recognized by their outward appearance. They are, however, usually devoid of distinctive morphological characteristics not found in the diploids. On the other hand, they usually contain various recombinations of the characteristics of the diploid species. Furthermore, the polyploid members of such complexes are usually more widespread in their geographic distribution than their diploid ancestors, and instead of having neatly defined ranges of ecological tolerance often are adapted to a great variety of habitats. Abundant evidence, some of which will be presented below, shows that this wide range of ecological tolerance possessed by natural polyploids has two causes. First, the polyploid representatives of a complex include a greater variety of closely interrelated genotypes than the diploids, and second, many of the individual genotypes themselves can tolerate a wide range of different conditions.

The polyploid complex thus emerges as a group of plants with a distinctive evolutionary history, dominated by the processes of hybridization and chromosome doubling. Successful polyploid complexes apparently arise from recombination through hybridization between genetic types adapted to radically different environments or possessing different modes of adaptation to the same environment. This genetic recombination builds up mechanisms of adaptation to entirely new environments, to which none of the diploids are adapted. Chromosome doubling may serve one or both of two purposes. Species hybrids which are sterile because of differences in chromosomal patterning of their parental species may be turned into fertile amphiploids, or hybrid polyploids, which breed true to their new, intermediate condition. Fertile hybrids between races or subspecies of the same species can, by doubling their chromosome number, become "buffered" against too rapid dissipation of their intermediate genotypes by genetic segregation, since at the tetraploid level segregation is much more complex and each gene has a smaller effect on variation than it does at the diploid level.

On the other hand, the larger number of genes or alleles present in polyploids tends to reduce the effectiveness of new gene changes or mutations, and consequently progressive evolution in the direction of entirely new mechanisms of adaptation is slower in polyploids than in diploids. For this reason, polyploid complexes may pass through a series of stages. The complexes of most recent origin contain diploid species which are common and successful at least in some regions, while the polyploids may or may not exceed the diploids in their range of distribution. Somewhat older polyploid complexes exist in which the diploids, although containing among them all the extremes of morphological variation and ecological adaptation found in the complex, are nevertheless far less common than the polyploids and tend to be narrow endemics. In still older complexes, nearly all the diploid species have become extinct and new cycles of polyploidy have arisen, based on hybridization and chromosome doubling of species which behave like diploids but which have chromosome numbers of ancient polyploid derivation. Finally, there exist monotypic genera containing a single species with a very high chromosome number but which has no close relatives. These probably represent ancient polyploid complexes, of which all but one of the representative species has become extinct. Examples of each of these types of polyploid complexes will be discussed in turn.

An example of a recent polyploid complex is the goat grass genus, *Aegilops*, a group of annual grasses native to the Mediterranean region. These grasses have been intensively studied because of their close relationship to wheat, at least one and probably two or more species of the genus having figured in the ancestry of the bread wheats. The following account is based chiefly on the recent discussion of the group by Kihara (1954).

Nine diploid species exist, which on the basis of genetic affinity can be arranged into five groups. They constitute a phylogenetic series in the degree of specialization of their fruiting spikelets. In the external morphology of its spikelets the most primitive of these, *A. mutica,* is not strikingly different from species of the larger and ancestral genus *Agropyron*. On the other hand the most advanced species, *A. squarrosa, A. caudata,* and *A. umbellulata,* have separately evolved complex and distinctive fruiting spikes, which constitute highly efficient methods of seed dispersal. At the same time, their chromosomes have been greatly altered by means of reciprocal translocations which have changed the positions of the centromeres and the relative sizes of the different chromosomes of a set. These diploids have given rise by hybridization and polyploidy to 10 different tetraploid species, all of which are amphiploids, combining the characteristics of two different diploid species. The most successful amphiploids have been derived from the most specialized diploid species, *A. squarrosa*, *A. umbellulata* and *A. caudata*.

Experiments of artificial hybridization and chromosome doubling carried

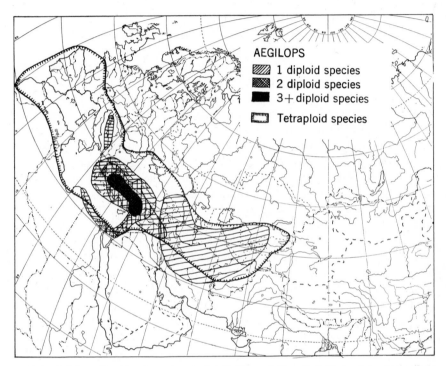

FIG. 5. Map showing the natural distribution of the diploid species of *Aegilops* and the limits of the natural distribution of the tetraploids. Areas into which the genus has been introduced by man in historical time are not included. (*From Kihara, 1954.*)

out by Sears and Kihara have synthesized counterparts of some of the natural tetraploid species, thus reproducing under observation an important part of the evolution of these grasses.

The areas of geographic distribution of the diploids are smaller than those of the tetraploids and occupy the center of the distributional area of the complex as a whole (fig. 5). From two to four diploid species occur together in parts of Asia Minor and western Iran, and the range of *A. umbellulata*, the diploid which has entered into the ancestry of the largest number of tetraploid species, overlaps that of most of the other diploid species. The formation of new hybrids and amphiploids involving these species is, therefore, still possible. On the other hand, the diploid ancestors of some of the amphiploids now occur in widely separated areas, so that their geographic ranges must have been different when the hybridization and polyploidy occurred.

This distributional pattern most probably reflects a recent origin of the complex. The species of *Aegilops* are weeds, which grow best on the edges of cultivated fields and in overgrazed pastures. They have followed agricultural and pastoral man in his wanderings, wherever the climate has been suitable for them. Two of the amphiploids, *A. triuncialis* and *A. cylindrica*, have spread rapidly through parts of the central and western United States during the present century. For this reason the writer is inclined to believe with Kihara that the more recent of the amphiploids were formed in early Neolithic times, when previously uncommon and geographically separated diploid species may have been brought together and hybridized naturally in the cultivated fields and grazed pastures which men were beginning to create in the Middle East at that time. Their subsequent spread throughout the Mediterranean region accompanied the expansion of agriculture and grazing in that region. By observations on the growth of the plants as cultivated in the climate of Japan, Kihara has shown that the amphiploids are far more tolerant of climatic diversity than their ancestral diploids. This fact, along with their efficient means of seed dispersal, accounts for their rapid spread.

On the other hand, the oldest of the amphiploids probably dates from the Pleistocene epoch, since altered distributions necessary for the hybridization of *A. squarrosa* and *A. comosa,* leading to the formation of the amphiploids *A. ventricosa* and *A. crassa,* are most easily explained by changed climatic conditions which existed during the pluvial period of the great ice age. The polyploid complex of *Aegilops,* therefore, has evolved relatively recently. It owes its success partly to the opening up of new ecological niches by climatic changes which accompanied the ice age, but even more to the changes in the earth's vegetation brought about by man's activity.

A somewhat older type of polyploid complex is represented by the genus *Dactylis,* or orchard grass. This genus consists of perennials native to the Mediterranean region and adjacent parts of Europe and Asia. Its best-known representative, the common orchard grass of central and northern Europe, was once regarded as a classical example of an autotetraploid derived from a single diploid type, which is represented by *D. aschersoniana,* found in the forests of the same region. More recently, however, Myers (1948) and Zohary (1955) have found that typical *D. glomerata* is intermediate in morphological characteristics between *D. aschersoniana* and another very different diploid type native to the steppes of northeastern Iran and adjacent Turkmenistan, *D. woronowii.* Zohary and the present writer, furthermore, have found eight other different diploid types. These diploids are mostly distributed around the periphery of the natural geographic range of *Dactylis* as a whole, and with the exception of *D. aschersoniana* and its close counterpart in south central Asia, they occupy very limited areas. Each diploid type is markedly distinct from other diploids in outward appearance and is rather constant. Some of them differ widely from each other in their climatic preferences, and together they represent all the types of climatic tolerance found in *Dactylis*. In addition to the forest-loving *D. aschersoniana*,

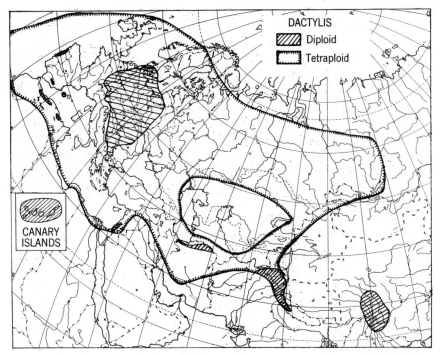

FIG. 6. Map showing the natural distribution of the diploid subspecies of *Dactylis* and the probable limits of the tetraploids before they became spread throughout the temperate regions of the world by man.

which has a close diploid counterpart in the forests of the Himalaya and western China, and the steppe-inhabiting *D. woronowii,* the known diploids include three native to restricted areas in the Mediterranean region, with its mild wet winters and dry, hot summers; one found in the equable climate of the Atlantic coast of Portugal; one adapted to high montane or subalpine conditions in the Sierra Nevada of southern Spain; and finally a peculiar diploid, *D. smithii,* endemic to the Canary Islands, where it grows in the subtropical belt, in the zone of banana cultivation (fig. 6).

Although these diploids are sharply distinct morphologically, they are closely related genetically. They are easily intercrossed, and with a few exceptions the artificial hybrids between them are vigorous, fertile, and have perfect chromosome pairing. But they constitute only a small fraction of the genus. Over the great bulk of its geographical distribution *Dactylis* is represented only by tetraploid strains. These tetraploids are abundant, aggressive, and highly variable. In external morphology and ecological adaptation they are mostly intermediate between various ones of the diploids, but some of them are very hard to distinguish from certain diploids in outward appearance. They have, nevertheless, the cytological and genetic characteristics of autopolyploids, which is to be expected if they are derived from diploid hybrids similar to the ones made artificially between the existing diploid types.

Dactylis, therefore, has a pattern of morphological variation typical of that found in many polyploid complexes, and one which is very confusing to taxonomists working on such groups. If only the diploids existed, we would have a series of constant, well-differentiated species, each occupying its own well-defined habitat and geographic area. But the tetraploids, in addition to simulating some of the diploids so closely that they cannot be distinguished from each other except by counting the chromosome number, also form a continuous network of intergrading forms, connecting all the diploids with each other in such a way that no clear lines of distinction can be drawn between them. For this reason, Zohary and the present writer believe that all the diploids and tetraploids together should be grouped as the numerous subspecies of a single highly variable species.

The evidence from geographic distribution indicates that the polyploid complex of *Dactylis* is considerably older than that of *Aegilops*. The forest-loving *aschersoniana* type of diploid, with a disjunct pattern of distribution in central Europe, the Himalaya, and western China, is probably a relic of the Tertiary period, when a continuous zone of forest stretched across Eurasia. Another probable relic is *D. smithii,* since the flora of its native home, the Canary Islands, contains many woody species which have close counterparts in the later Tertiary fossil flora of Europe. Furthermore, tetraploid forms of *Dactylis* having a few unmistakable characteristics of *D. smithii* exist along the Atlantic coast of Portugal, southern Spain, and North Africa. This phytogeographic evidence that the diploids of *Dactylis* formerly occupied wider areas than at present is matched by genetic evidence, since the intermediate characteristics of most of the tetraploids indicate that their formation was accompanied by extensive hybridization between different diploids. Such hybridization would be impossible at present, because the areas of the diploids do not overlap.

We can thus reconstruct three phases of the evolutionary history of the polyploid complex of *Dactylis*. The first phase occurred during the Tertiary period. It involved the divergence of the diploids from each other and their establishment as relatively homogeneous populations inhabiting different ecological niches in the widely divergent climatic zones. The second phase was brought about by the climatic changes which accompanied the Pleistocene ice age and permitted types with different climatic preferences to come together and hybridize. The products of this hybridization advanced into new habitats made available by the effect of the periods of warm, dry climate which followed the pluvial periods, and for reasons which are not completely clear but which could be interpreted on a genetic basis, these hybrid derivatives were more successful after they had doubled their chromosome number to become tetraploids. The third phase of evolution was associated with human activity, since *Dactylis* seeds can be transported by domestic animals and the plants spring up readily in cut-over and burned-over forests and brushlands. The tetraploids which spread as a result of this type of habitat alteration came in contact with additional diploids, with which they could sometimes hybridize. As Müntzing (1937) has shown, the triploids resulting from such hybridization are by no means completely sterile and can give rise to many vigorous and fertile tetraploid offspring.

As an example of a polyploid complex which, in spite of a long and complex evolutionary history, still preserves intact most or all of its original genetic types, *Dactylis* illustrates very well the accompanying factors which have made evolution by polyploidy highly successful in the higher plants. These are principally the origin of new adaptive types through hybridization between diploids adapted to widely different ecological conditions and the availability of new ecological niches which can be occupied by these polyploid hybrid derivatives.

Many genera of grasses contain polyploid complexes which have reached a more advanced stage of maturity and in which many diploid species have become extinct. An example is *Bromus*. This genus is predominantly Eurasian and American, with a few species in Africa. Because of its unspecialized spikelets, it is generally regarded as one of the most primitive genera of the Festucoid series. A closely related and hardly distinct genus endemic to the Juan Fernández Islands off the coast of Chile possesses the unusual and primitive characteristic of three stigmas on the ovary. The evidence from both external morphology and geographic distribution suggests that *Bromus* is relatively old. On the other hand, the distribution and aggressiveness of many of its species indicate that the genus is still in an active state of evolution.

Bromus is divided into five clearly marked sections. These are, nevertheless, related closely enough to each other so that intersectional hybrids can be made, though with difficulty, between nearly all of them. Some of the sections are rather young, and others are much more ancient, as is evident from their morphology, geographic distribution, as well as the nature of their polyploidy.

The two sections *Eubromus* and *Bromium* contain annual species native to Eurasia, concentrated chiefly in the Mediterranean region and the Near East, but which have recently been carried by man and his livestock throughout the world as weeds. Both sections are highly developed polyploid complexes, with many diploid and tetraploid species, plus some hexaploids and octoploids. So far as is known, all the polyploids behave like amphiploids, and they probably have arisen from interspecific hybrids. At least one of them, *B. arenarius,* contains chromosomes of different sizes and, judging from its external morphology, is probably derived from an intersectional hybrid. Although the intricate interrelationships between the species of these polyploid complexes have been only partly analyzed, the evidence at hand suggests that they are nearly as recent in origin as *Aegilops* and have had a similar evolutionary history.

The third and largest section, *Bromopsis,* is highly developed on all three continents. It consists of perennials, mostly bunch grasses, but includes one of our most valuable sod-forming pasture species, *B. inermis,* the familiar "brome grass" of our middle western states. Although they occupy a great variety of habitats in the Temperate Zone, the majority of the species of this section grow in forested or shady areas and prefer good soil. The interrelationships of the species of *Bromopsis* are imperfectly known, but their chromosome numbers, which range from diploid (14) to octoploid (56), suggest that highly developed polyploid complexes exist in this section, particularly in Eurasia.

The final two sections of *Bromus, Ceratochloa,* and *Neobromus* consist entirely of polyploids and appear to represent the relics of polyploid complexes which were formerly more extensive. *Ceratochloa* contains three or four species which are hexaploid ($2n = 42$) and endemic to South America, plus about four octoploids ($2n = 56$) distributed primarily in North America, and one 12-ploid species ($2n = 84$) found in the southwestern United States.

The hexaploid South American species are all closely related to each other and are typified by "rescue grass" (*B. catharticus*), a lush pasture grass of subtropical regions which "rescues" livestock by its fine growth in winter. They have no living relatives with chromosome numbers lower than 42. They are not descended from diploids or tetraploids of the *Bromopsis* section, as is evident from the relatively primitive structure of their fertile scales (lemmas) and fruits (caryopses), plus their considerably smaller chromosomes which in several different artificial hybrids have been shown to be completely non-homologous to those of sect. *Bromopsis.* The cycle of polyploidy which built up their numbers probably occurred in the early or middle part of the Tertiary period, involving diploid and tetraploid species which are now completely extinct.

The later evolution of sect. *Ceratochloa* came about through hybridization between hexaploids of the rescue grass type and species belonging to other sections of *Bromus* (fig. 7). The manner of chromosome pairing in hybrids has shown that the octoploids of North America, which include the well-known mountain brome (*B. morginatus*) and California brome (*B. carinatus*) of our western states, contain 42 chromosomes essentially the same as those in the hexaploids, plus 14 chromosomes derived from diploid species of the sect. *Bromopsis*. They have probably originated as amphiploids from ancient intersectional hybrids. This new cycle of amphiploidy met with great success, since the species concerned are among the commonest grasses of western

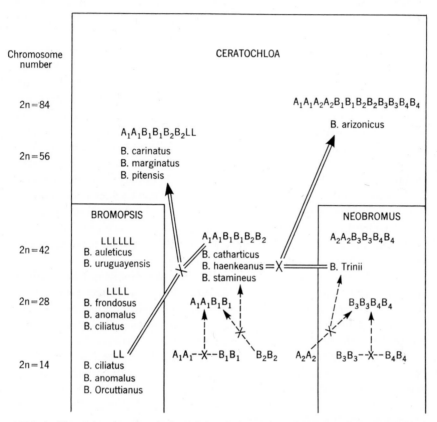

FIG. 7. Chart showing the phylogenetic relationships among New World polyploid species of *Bromus*. The broken lines indicate hypothetical connections between extinct species; continuous double lines indicate connections between living species which have been verified by experiments.

North America. Finally the species of sect. *Ceratochloa* with 84 chromosomes (*B. arizonicus*) has been shown to be the product of hybridization and amphiploidy between a species of the rescue grass type and the sole surviving species of another ancient polyploid complex, the hexaploid *B. trinii* of sect. *Neobromus*. The success of *B. arizonicus*, which is a common weed in much of its area of distribution, shows that two waning polyploid complexes can receive new life through pooling their genic resources via an intersectional hybrid and amphiploid.

The evolution of *Bromus* shows how successive cycles of polyploidy can build up high chromosome numbers and can elaborate a network of evolutionary relationships by bringing together genes derived from widely divergent evolutionary lines. Less complete studies of other genera and groups of genera, particularly the blue grasses (*Poa*), beard grasses (*Andropogon*), and sugar cane (*Saccharum* and related genera), indicate that these groups have had a similar evolutionary history.

CONCLUSION. The picture of grass evolution which emerges from these studies can be summarized about as follows. Early in the history of the family, the major groupings, or tribes, became separated from each other partly through adaptation to different climatic zones and partly through the establishment of subtle differences in anatomy and in the structure of the reproductive parts, the adaptive significance of which is not obvious. The later evolution of most of the tribes consisted largely of reduction and simplification of the parts of the inflorescence and was marked by parallel trends in several different evolutionary lines. In addition, many lines developed highly specialized fruits, of which the inflorescence scales, or bracts (glumes and lemmas), became variously modified to assist in seed dispersal. These major trends were accompanied by a series of cycles of divergent and convergent or reticulate evolution, the latter being brought about by hybridization and chromosome doubling, or amphiploidy.

The high frequency of amphiploidy in the grass family can be attributed to several causes. In the first place, different species of grasses grow together in large numbers, giving ample opportunities for hybridization. Second, they have light, wind-borne pollen, which can be carried long distances, and many species are self-incompatible, so that they must be fertilized by pollen from another individual of a different genetic type. Third, the individuals of many species are very long-lived and have efficient methods of vegetative reproduction. This means that interspecific hybrids and newly originated polyploids, many of which are highly sterile, can persist in spite of this reduced fertility and produce many offspring, some of which will have an increased fertility. Grasses can therefore pass relatively easily through the "bottlenecks" of partial sterility which necessarily accompany evolution by polyploidy. Finally, most grasses are by their very nature adapted to a role as pioneer colonizers of newly available ecological niches. The processes of hybridization and polyploidy, acting together, aid them greatly in this role.

The research of the past twenty-five years has, therefore, given us a reasonably clear picture of the evolutionary forces which have molded the grass family into its present form. Plant breeders are now making use of this information to evolve new types of grasses and cereals better suited to human needs. The progress of such research is inevitably slow, since even if we are able to speed up the natural processes of evolution a hundred times, the production of new, valuable types will require scores of years. Nevertheless, increasingly rapid progress in this direction is being made in several different laboratories, and the goal is in sight.

LITERATURE CITED

AL-AISH, M. 1956. The effect of isopropyl-*N*-phenyl carbamate on the germination of grass seeds and the bearing upon systematics of the Gramineae. Ph.D. thesis. Univ. of Texas. Austin, Tex.

ARBER, A. 1934. The Gramineae—A study of cereal, bamboo, and grass. 440 pp. Cambridge Univ. Press. New York.

AVDULOV, N. P. 1931. Karyo-systematische Untersuchungen der Familie Gramineen. Bull. Appl. Bot. Suppl. vol. 44, 428 pp. Russian with German summary.

BEWS, J. W. 1929. The world's grasses—Their differentiation, distribution, economics, and geology. 408 pp. Longmans, Green Co. New York.

CLAPHAM, A. R., F. T. TUTIN, AND E. F. WARBURG. 1952. Flora of the British Isles. 1591 pp. Cambridge Univ. Press. New York.

DE WET, J. M. J. 1954. The genus *Danthonia* in grass phylogeny. Amer. Jour. Bot. 41:204–211.

———. 1956. Leaf anatomy and phylogeny in the tribe Danthonieae. Amer. Jour. Bot. 43:175–182.

HITCHCOCK, A. S., AND AGNES CHASE. 1950. Manual of the grasses of the United States. 2d ed. U.S. Dept. Agric. Misc. Publ. 200. 1071 pp.

HUBBARD, C. E. 1948. The genera of British grasses. *In* J. HUTCHINSON, British Flowering Plants, pp. 284–348.

KIHARA, H. 1954. Considerations on the evolution and distribution of *Aegilops* species based on the analyser method. Cytologia 19:336–357.

MÜNTZING, A. 1937. The effects of chromosomal variation in *Dactylis*. Hereditas 23:113–235.

MYERS, W. M. 1948. Studies on the origin of *Dactylis glomerata* L. (Abstr.) Genetics 33:117.

PILGER, R. 1954. Das System der Gramineae. Bot. Jahrb. 76:281–384.

PRAT, H. 1936. La systématique des graminées. Ann. Sci. Nat. Sér. Bot. X, 18:165–258.

REEDER, JOHN R. 1953. Affinities of the grass genus *Beckmannia* Host. Bull. Torrey Bot. Club 80:187–196.

——— AND KRAFT VON MALTZAHN. 1953. Taxonomic significance of root-hair development in the Gramineae. Proc. National Acad. Sci. (U.S.) 39:593–598.

ROW, H. CLARK, AND JOHN R. REEDER. 1957. Root-hair development as evidence of relationships among genera of Gramineae. Amer. Jour. Bot. 44:596–601.

SPORNE, K. R. 1956. The phylogenetic classification of the angiosperms. Biological Rev. 31:1–29.

STEBBINS, G. L. 1950. Variation and evolution in plants. 643 pp. Columbia Univ. Press. New York.

ZOHARY, D. 1955. Cytogenetic studies in the polyploid complex of *Dactylis glomerata* L. Ph.D. thesis. Univ. California. Berkeley, Calif.

12

TAXONOMY OF THE HIGHER PLANTS

Reed C. Rollins

For man, the most significant idea having its origins in taxonomy is the idea of evolution. As we contemplate a celebration of the centennial of Darwin's *Origin of Species* in 1959, we are moved to reflect on the far-reaching ramifications of the idea of evolution outside of biology. There is scarcely an area of learning that has not embraced it in one form or another. And within biology, by the turn of the last century, organic evolution had become a focal point of much research. Even today, various aspects of evolution are very much in the central stream of research activity in biology. As with many, perhaps most, great ideas, the emergence of the theory of evolution was inevitable, made so by the gradual accumulation and organization of facts regarding the living world. It is a significant and special characteristic of taxonomy that this branch of biology is concerned with the accumulation and organization of knowledge concerning plants and animals, whatever they may be or wherever they may occur.

It is not trite to say that taxonomy starts and ends the inquiry about a particular organism. The first biological question asked is: What is it? This was also the pristine question of man. Once answered today, one possesses an open sesame to the accumulated wisdom and knowledge of our civilization concerning a particular species. Important as it is to be able to open the door, it is of far greater significance for taxonomy that it also stands at the end of the line to profit from any and all inquiries that may be directed toward a given organism. The numerous modes of research represented by the various branches of botany, ranging from physiology to palynology, produce a mass of data about given plants that is not only significant for its own sake, but often is very pertinent for the systematist. In other words, the field of taxonomy in a way epitomizes the work of all other branches of biology centered on the organism itself and brings the varied factual information from them to bear on the problems of interrelationship, classification, and evolution.

Thus taxonomy, as has been aptly remarked, is at once the alpha and omega of biology.

What has happened in plant taxonomy, the oldest of the botanical disciplines, during the past fifty years, the lifetime of the Botanical Society of America? It matters little whether we call it the new systematics, biosystematics, or the new taxonomy, we cannot fail to recognize that there have been significant changes during this period. Perhaps the rise of genetics, with its important impact on taxonomy, has had the most far-reaching influence, but there have been other changes within the subject itself. In the following essay, I propose to point up some of the characteristics of the taxonomic field and its relationship to other branches of botany and to stress some of the changes during the past fifty years that seem significant.

At the outset, it should be made clear that certain aspects of plant taxonomy are concerned ultimately with the individual plant. And the finite life of every individual plant, whether it be a small, ephemeral herb that completes its life cycle from seed to maturity in a few weeks or a giant redwood that lives for a thousand years, is tied into a line of descent. Within each descent line are contained and propagated the determinants and strictures of the total nature of each individual. And there is a certain permanency about each such descent line even though constancy is not a necessary feature. The degree of constancy and of permanency is dependent on a large number of factors and differs widely from one line of descent to another.

The number of relatively discrete present-day end points of descent lines of plants on the earth's surface presumably corresponds somewhat to the number of species. However, these lines are of an extremely complex origin, often formed by the fusing of two or several different lines. For this reason, the picture of the evolutionary relationships of our modern species of plants takes the form of a reticulum with anastomosing descent lines reaching far into the past. The very difficult task of the taxonomist is that of discovering these end points, their origins and connections, together with the presentation and codification of information concerning them. The genetical interrelationships of living individuals within a population, of populations of individuals within a given taxon,[1] and of the members of different taxa are primary considerations.

One of the most dynamic aspects of taxonomy is the study of populations of living plants to establish the variation patterns present. This type of study provides a rich source of understanding of a given taxon, and when these patterns are properly evaluated, in terms of their repetition and geographical spread, they are at the base of the taxon's proper definition. Thus variation

[1] The word taxon has come into general use in a very short time. It is used to refer to any taxonomic category or group without specifying which one. For example, species, genera, families, etc., are all taxa.

patterns, arising from genetical sources within and between populations, set the stage for the development of discontinuities upon which taxonomic systems may be founded. The development of taxonomy in relation to population sampling is interesting in itself. During the early historical period, a single sample [specimen] of a species was deemed to be adequate for study. Only gradually was variation within species recognized and appreciated. With this appreciation came the realization that adequate samples are required to assure a factual assessment of the genetically controlled variation within a species. This point of view for taxonomy is relatively recent but is now firmly established.

Learning the numerous characteristics and organizational vagaries of hundreds of different kinds of plants as part of his "stock-in-trade" has usually been the lot of the taxonomist. In order to be accomplished at spot identifications, he has often acquired a broad, sometimes rather superficial, acquaintanceship with a vast array of plant groups. To aid him in performing this function for those who wish to know, as well as for his own ends, the taxonomist collects and assembles samples. This has been going on for over three hundred years, and the number of specimens now in herbaria throughout the world is well over one hundred million. In the beginning, many specimens were collected and treated as curios. As serious study displaced curiosity, specimens began to be assembled, not only for their novelty, but for the purpose of providing the data for a critical understanding of the taxa they represented. The modern herbarium possesses samples of a given flora in space and, in a modest way, in time. Not only is the sample thus preserved the source of the data, but it may be a voucher through which observations and information about more ephemeral aspects of a plant may be solidly tied into a given species. It may be remarked that specimens are no longer studied only visually with a dry hand lens, as Darlington (1956) would have us believe, but instead provide material for thoroughgoing microscopic studies. The value of specimens as vouchers of research is perhaps most appreciated by taxonomists, but the need is no less great in many aspects of cytology, genetics, ecology, and physiology. The number of chromosome studies and published records based on misidentified material, with no chance of rectification because voucher specimens were not preserved, is next to scandalous. The need for specimens, in the extensive experimental work with clones of plants grown in different environments, was demonstrated most vividly by Clausen, Keck, and Hiesey (1940). Some further pertinent words on the uses of specimens are given by Marsden-Jones et al. (1931).

If the sampling of the earth's plants was at first erratic, this was only to be expected, for geographical exploration itself was erratic. But with the increased tempo of exploration came a parallel increasing interest in the plants of the world for their own sake, until now we have in herbaria a minimum number of samples of perhaps more than 80 per cent of the existing species of vascular plants. True, many species are represented by a single collection and some by a single specimen. On the other hand, many species have been studied in great detail and the assembled specimens of them number in the hundreds, representing every known part of their geographical ranges.

In modern taxonomic research, the specimens assembled over the years, together with the published literature, form the starting point for a given investigation. From the leads readily established from these two sources, the student knows pretty well what the critical problems are and where he has to go to find the material for their solution. His next step is into the field to learn from the living plants. Here he comes to grips with variations of every sort. The ephemeral, environmentally induced variations must be sorted out from those of a more permanent nature that are of genetical origin. The latter become the object of study from as many angles as possible. Gradually, through intensive study, the taxonomist is able to discern constellations of character combinations that run through his material. Some of these may consist of variation patterns, others of characteristics without much variation, or still other constellations may combine characters that display neat variation patterns and characters that are uniform.

It matters little whether one studies species of plants, their constituent parts, or genera and higher taxa, for the ultimate source of information is the individual. And the individual must be studied as part of a dynamic population of the same species which is forever changing because of the operation of the particular genetic potential of that species. However, in spite of these changes, it still retains the essential features that persist to distinguish it from the nearest related species. Thus, we come full circle, returning to the problem of the sampling of a population and of a taxon. It is not a simple matter to sample something of which we do not know the size, either as to the numbers of individuals or the exact geographical extent. But this is the situation with most plant taxa. For that matter, the definition of a population is extremely difficult, if not impossible, even when certain restrictions are imposed. Does a population consist of all the living individuals of a given species? If one takes the affirmative view, he has to consider the fact that many species have highly disrupted geographical ranges, with groups separated from each other by hundreds or even thousands of miles. Neither the species with a disrupted range nor even those with a continuous range are, to my mind, a single population. Rather we tend to think of a population as being composed of reasonably closely associated individuals, where interbreeding is freely possible. I am aware that such a definition is subject to criticism and that the tropical botanist will point to the rather wide spacing of individuals of a given species in a tropical forest. However, these spaced individuals are often closely associated in terms of interbreeding because of the pollinating mechanism involved. They share in a common gene pool.

LOCAL POPULATION SAMPLING

Real advances have been made in taxonomy in recent years by the development and use of the technique of mass sampling of wild populations. This is done by systematically collecting a large number of specimens in a set pattern over a population. The specimens may consist of whole plants, or in most instances they will be critical portions of plants selected because of a prior knowledge of the type of data these portions will yield. Part of the data for a population analysis will often be taken in the field. Items such as flower-color variation, insect visitation, and other aspects of a given study must be undertaken on the spot. And there are those who believe that the data for a full analysis of a population should be gathered only in the field. However, such a procedure has limitations. In the field, one cannot bring into full play the aid provided by good microscopic equipment. Also of importance are human limitations in the field. It is scarcely possible to assemble a full complement of the kinds of variation data important in taxonomy from the field alone. The most elite implications of variation patterns often are perceived only after many comparisons of actual specimens, including critical parts such as trichomes, pollen, stomata, cell structure, etc., and this can best be done in the laboratory.

Critical studies of living populations of plants and of mass samples from them are now becoming a widespread procedure in taxonomic work. From this type of study is emerging an ever-clearer picture of the complete nature of plant species. Furthermore, deviations from expected patterns of variation are showing up in increasing numbers. These are often traceable to the involvement of special mechanisms of reproduction or, in many instances, to natural interspecific hybridization. As the work proceeds, we may expect a greater insight into the nature and extent of natural hybridization between species and of such specialized reproductive mechanisms as those involved in apomixis.

NATURAL INTERSPECIFIC HYBRIDIZATION

The impact of interspecific hybridization on classification, and particularly upon the course of evolution, is only now coming into full view. Among other things, the evidence calls for a recasting of ideas concerning the singularity of the species as a key point in evolutionary differentiation. The consequence of reuniting once-separated evolutionary lines through hybridization is at once evident.

The fact that hybridization does occur naturally among plant species has been widely recognized in plant taxonomy for many years, but there remains much to be learned about this subject. The early and to some extent the continuing emphasis of taxonomists and evolutionists generally is upon the discontinuities found between different taxa. Separations of relatively similar types are easier by the use of discontinuities than by the use of the correlated characteristics of each type. Hence it is only natural that discontinuity should receive first attention in arriving at a classification. Certainly, the idea of discontinuity between species is firmly fixed in the biologist's mind. Discontinuities are of a variety of sorts ranging from spatial or geographical separation to genetic incompatibility. But it is the latter that has gotten in the way of a full appreciation of interspecific hybridization. The belief is widespread that one of the obvious characteristics of a species is that it does not and cannot hybridize and exchange genes to any degree with related species. Yet the number of known cases is steadily increasing where different species do hybridize, and the resulting hybrids show but little indication of incompatibility between themselves or with their parental species. Even where incompatibility is present, it may not be all or none but a degree of incompatibility that will permit some gene exchange between species, with important consequences to the species involved. Thus, the introgression of some of the genetic materials of one species into another may occur, in spite of the presence of genetic incompatibility between them. Reproductive isolation in such a case is not complete.

The real point to be made here is that taxonomic studies dealing with hybridization are very much in the forefront of the field and bid fair to contribute sizably to a fuller understanding of the interrelationships of many plant groups and to an understanding of their evolutionary history. We no longer think of an evolutionary pattern for plants in terms of a dendritic, ever-diverging arrangement. Rather, we recognize the numerous possibilities for anastomosing lines, once separated, into an interlocking network.

GENETICAL VS. ENVIRONMENTALLY CONTROLLED CHARACTERISTICS

Some of the fundamental tenets of taxonomic botany and of genetics were seriously challenged by the published work of Gaston Bonnier (1920), which received a rather wide hearing among biologists generally. Bonnier claimed to have converted a number of lowland species into different but related high-altitude species by transplanting them from their low-elevation stations to the same habitat with similar and presumably related species at high elevations. The changes said to be induced by the changed environment were presumed to be permanent. Stimulated by Bonnier's findings, F. E. Clements conducted transplant experiments on Pikes Peak in Colorado and made claims similar to those of Bonnier. These experiments of Bonnier have since been shown to be erratic and unreliable, and the claims of Clements remain unsubstantiated by any reliable subsequent work. The early work of Kerner

(1891) and the more recent work of Clausen, Keck, and Hiesey (1940) have forcefully shown the fallacy of these attempts to demonstrate that the environment can provide the causal factors required to produce the far-reaching changes that would make one well-recognized species become identical with another. However, the modifications of plants by the environment can be rather great. Environmental modifications are as numerous and varied as the combinations of factors that produce them. The taxonomist early learns to be wary of placing any reliance upon such modifications for purposes of classification. Indeed, one of his first tasks in any detailed study of species is to find out which part of the phenotypic variation he is dealing with is correlated with the environment and which part is under direct genetical control. The complicated interplay of genetical and environmental factors in producing the ultimate phenotype makes the distinguishing of these forces a task of large proportions. It calls for experimental procedures that are so expensive in time, effort, and money that for many plant groups the kinds of information needed will be exceedingly slow in coming, if at all.

Fortunately, men like Hall (1932), Turesson (1922), Clausen, Keck, and Hiesey (1940), and Marsden-Jones and Turrill (1931) have pointed the way by developing methods of differentiating between environmental modifications and hereditary differences. Each such study adds immensely to our understanding of the plant group that is so studied. But one point in this connection should be reemphasized. It would take a millennium of hard work by many more botanists than are now active to produce the kind of study for all plants we now have as models from the work of Clausen, Keck, and Hiesey. Fortunately, too, a wide general experience with growing plants will often permit an investigator to short-cut to a sound position with respect to the variation in a given group, without resorting to exhaustive experimentation. For example, an experienced taxonomist quickly learns the nature of a whole constellation of phenotypic effects that are produced by bringing a wild plant into cultivation, where abundant fertilizer and water are supplied. He knows what modifications to expect, when shade plants are found in the sun, and vice versa. In fact, he is always wary of quantitative characters associated with vegetative growth up to a point, and unless the differences are considerable, he will not use them for the purpose of trying to distinguish between taxa. Even after he feels confident of quantitative information he must remain wary of chimeras, sucker shoots, and the like. His aim is to discern the characters, the variations of which are genetically controlled, for it is those characters that reflect phylogenetic and evolutionary relationships, which in turn make up the framework of a sound taxonomical system.

CYTOGENETICS IN RELATION TO TAXONOMY

Much of the work in taxonomy is founded on the concept that the pheno-type, if sufficiently and accurately studied, can be relied upon to reflect the nature of the genotype. This requires the elimination from consideration of the effects of the environment upon the phenotype, as suggested above. Basi-cally, what we are saying is that the phenotype is the product of the genotype, except for the modifications produced by the environment. This is the same postulate, underlying the genetical principles of Mendel, that has proved to be so fruitful for the field of genetics. Today, we include microscopic char-acteristics as well as ultimate physiological reactions and characteristics of the individual as features of the phenotype. A half century ago, the phenotype was thought of pretty much in macroscopic terms with no thought of bio-chemical or similar characters as a part of it.

The establishment of the chromosomes, as bodies upon which discrete units of heredity, the genes, are carried from one generation to the next, was a sig-nificant step for taxonomy as well as genetics. It is only natural that out of this basic discovery of the importance of the chromosomes should come a tremendous emphasis upon the karyotype for its own sake and for its role in relation to heredity, development, and evolution. The question for taxonomy, aside from those related to heredity and evolution, has been: What added information will the chromosomes provide? How significant are differences in chromosome numbers in assessing the characteristics of different taxa? What can be done with chromosome morphology from the taxonomical point of view? These and other questions have been repeatedly asked in connection with different plant groups, and we are now beginning to get at an evaluation of chromosome studies in so far as taxonomy is concerned.

Ordinarily, the same chromosome number prevails throughout a species. However, there are exceptions, and it is unsafe to assume on slender evidence that no chromosome-number differences exist within a species. It has often been maintained that either aneuploid or polyploid chromosome difference between two plants is sufficient evidence to establish them as separate species. Now, we know that diploid and polyploid plants may and do occur within the same species rather frequently. Aneuploid plants may also exist within the same species, but cases of this kind are apparently less frequent. Certainly, it should not be taken for granted that a single, accurate chromosome count establishes the count irrefutably for a given species, nor should an investigator be too surprised to discover that a given species has more than one chromo-some number, particularly where a polyploid relationship is revealed. We do not know at present how much the preconception that different chromosome numbers are not allowable within a species has affected chromosome-number reports, especially in cases where the chromosomes are excessively small, numerous, or difficult to handle. However, caution in interpreting the significance of chromosome counts is fully justified.

The work on chromosome morphology is tedious and difficult in many plants, and in many others there is little or no morphological differentiation within the chromosome complement of a given species. In difficult groups, it has often not been profitable to attempt to work with chromosome morphology for taxonomical purposes. However, in some plant groups, where the chromosomes are sizable and dissimilar and there are karyotypic differences between species, marked results have been achieved. We may confidently cite the major role played by chromosome work, in the monographic studies of *Crepis* by Babcock (1947) and his coworkers, to demonstrate this fact. Here, chromosome morphology combined with chromosome number was of considerable importance both in the genetical and in the taxonomical phases of the study. Another major work in which chromosome studies played an important role is that of Goodspeed (1954) and his collaborators on the genus *Nicotiana*. Of classical interest in this connection is the work of Sakamura (1918) on *Triticum*, who greatly aided in clarifying the taxonomy of the wheats through chromosome studies.

We feel impelled, by the numerous overstatements of Darlington (1956) as to the importance of the chromosomes for all phases of botanical study, to suggest that the key to all the truths regarding plants does not lie in the karyotype. Here, as in other features, the facts one finds are most likely to show their greatest importance when properly intermeshed with many other facts from various sources. To the taxonomist above all others it is essential that the total evidence regarding a given plant be admitted and evaluated.

THE ROLE OF EXPERIMENT

The early work in taxonomy was observational and descriptive. But as the science of botany developed, there was a long succession of taxonomists who manipulated their plants to discover new facts. This was especially true in research connected with reproduction and the functioning of the floral mechanism. These botanists were the forerunners of the experimentalists who developed some of the present-day botanical disciplines where experimental procedures are preeminent. As the subjects of plant physiology and genetics developed, taxonomy was for a time diverted away from experimental areas of botany. However, it has not remained so, and the trend during recent years has been toward the utilization of experiment along with other procedures in elucidating the facts of relationship and classification. Experimental taxonomy has indeed become an increasingly important aspect of the work in taxonomy as a whole.

The type of experimentation differs, depending upon the objectives. The most frequent are undoubtedly those associated with genetics and cytology, in which the reproductive process or the level of polyploidy is under investigation. The most effective experimental approaches in taxonomy have combined work in the herbarium and field with studies in the greenhouse and experimental plot.

Another area of experimentation that impinges directly on our subject is that concerned with gene ecology. It is not only essential that genetical vs. environmental influences on the phenotype be well understood, but the reactions of the genetically controlled characteristics to varying ecological situations are also pertinent to an understanding of the taxonomy of a given group. Real progress in this area of investigative work was touched off by the contributions of Turesson (1922), which have been followed up by numerous investigations. The most notable and sustained experiments are those of Clausen, Keck, and Hiesey (l.c.), beginning with the setup developed by Hall (1932) and extending over a period of more than thirty years. Aside from the information concerning phenotypic responses of different genotypes under different climatic and edaphic conditions, this work has highlighted the tremendous genetical, physiological, and taxonomical complexity present in plant species. A new dimension of appreciation of this complexity is certainly one of the major lessons for botanists provided by this area of research.

One of the many segments of taxonomy where a job remains to be done by experiment is that having to do with the variability of different types of plant characters. The assessment of characters that are of taxonomic importance, using the actual variation present in a given taxon under a controlled set of conditions as a base for determining the potential variation under the same and different patterns of conditions, must be done by experiment. We need to know definitely which characters of plants deviate the most under changed conditions and in what way.

It may be that information of this kind will always have to be somewhat limited in its application and will have to be determined anew in every plant group. On the other hand, it is hoped that a quantity of data will eventually provide the basis for certain generalizations helpful to the taxonomist. The point may be recognized that the ultimate strength of a classification is dependent upon the accuracy of evaluation of the characters used in developing that classification. Furthermore, it is important that the widest possible assortment of characters be evaluated and used.

THE PROBLEM OF COMMUNICATION

Plant names are basic to accurate communication in botany. Like the terms of description and designation in science generally, each of them carries a precise meaning if properly used. Also, like terms, their precise meaning may be devalued by improper use and altered completely by misapplication to the wrong plant. It has been difficult to develop a foolproof system by which the proper application of a name can always be determined with precision. When the binomial system first came into use, the problem of application was not fully recognized. In fact, it was not until the present century that adequate attention was given to the devising of a method for ensuring the precise application of a plant name. The type method was partly borrowed from Zoology and partly developed anew to provide a mechanism whereby this need might be fulfilled. The type method does provide this possibility and is now in effective use. Unfortunately, it is not fully understood by some botanists (cf. Darlington, 1956, p. 31).

A particular nomenclatural type is that element of the taxon with which the name is permanently associated. In practice, the element of a taxon referred to is usually a particular specimen. Thus, a species name is always to be associated with a specimen, and the application of that name can be readily determined by the study of that specimen. The commonest mistake made concerning the type is to assume that it is typical of the species. Thus, it is often assumed that the type specimen represents the biological type, which is not intended. The type specimen is not necessarily the most typical or representative element of a species. It may be, but if so, that is coincidental to the prescribed function, which is that of providing the point of reference within the species where the name is associated. Stretching the type concept beyond this leads to confusion.

Because the question as to "what the plants are, around the world" is the concern of taxonomy, the correlated matter of nomenclature also lies within its province. There have been periods during the long history of our subject when nomenclatural matters have received a disproportionate amount of attention. However, the trend in the present era has been away from considerations of nomenclature for their own sake. This is a fortunate trend. But the problem of nomenclature remains as "a thorn in the flesh" and to some extent cannot be ignored. There are many instances of competing names for the same plant, which have arisen over the years. These competing names have come about in a variety of ways. During the early period of botanical activity, several names for the same species were often proposed by different workers, often because of ignorance of each other's published papers. Communication among scientists was difficult, often nonexistent, and publication of botanical names often occurred in obscure, unnoticed places. Furthermore, there was nothing to prevent anyone who chose to do so from providing a species with a botanical name. And some botanists did choose to reject names, for one reason or another or sometimes on mere whim, and to provide their own totally different names.

The major problem that grew out of this seventeenth- and eighteenth-century confusion was how to devise a system of selecting from among competing names those that would be accepted by subsequent generations of botanists. It was well understood that the names were the key to communication about plants and that stability of names was essential if that key was not to become the weak link in the communication chain.

Along with all of science and the world of learning, there has always been a strong desire in botany to recognize the work of the pioneers and to give credit to original discovery. Thus the principle of priority was settled upon as the basis for determining which of the competing names was to be accepted for a given taxon. Priority of publication has worked well when applied to most fields of learning, and some sense of justice has dominated the recognition given to the discoverers of the laws and principles of each discipline. This is in general true despite attempts to alter priority considerations by nationalistic propaganda. However, the application of priority to discovery involving a relatively few items such as facts, laws, principles, geographical areas, and the like is not overly complex. On the other hand, applying priority to the names of organisms, where discovery is at a relatively high rate and the total number is great, is far more difficult and complex.

A real complication arises from applying strict priority because many names, especially those of Old World plants, had an obscure beginning. Nevertheless, there was a movement in the late eighteen hundreds and the early part of the present century, led by certain American and German botanists, to make absolute priority the basis for the application of plant names. The utter impossibility of untangling the dates of sixteenth-, seventeenth-, and early eighteenth-century literature, or even finding much of it, was early recognized. As a result, limited priority has been adopted as a working principle and agreements have been reached on starting dates before which priority is not operative.

Out of such problems of communication, involving as they do truly international questions, international congresses of botany have developed an International Code of Botanical Nomenclature, which is now universally accepted. All the work of international cooperation along these lines has not been done, but great strides in this direction have been made during the last half century. The earlier attempts of a small group of American botanists to establish an American Code of Botanical Nomenclature were doomed to failure because strictly nationalistic actions seldom prevail in matters of universal concern. Fortunately, through compromise, all botanists have been won over to the support of the International Code, which combines many of the best features of both previous codes. Competing codes of nomenclature have thus been eliminated.

Taxonomists have developed a unique technique of communication that is of some importance, though not generally known outside of the field. I refer to the use of sets of exsiccatae. The procedure is to collect a number of specimens of a single species at a single location. This set of exsiccatae is then studied in conjunction with other material of the species it represents. When finally labeled and distributed, these specimens provide a roughly comparable reference point for anyone who has access to a specimen of the set. By this technique, many taxonomists at places remote from one another may be provided with written information plus samples to verify it. A refinement of this procedure is to collect a large number of specimens with the uniformity of the specimens in mind. When these are distributed, more or less comparable samples are in the hands of the recipients.

STRUCTURAL CHARACTERISTICS

Developmental processes are no more important to the ultimate under-standing of plants than the structures that culminate these processes, although in these days we are often told otherwise. At least up to the present, it is no mere happenstance that taxonomy has concerned itself to a large extent with structural features of plants. For the most part, these have provided fruitful and reliable bases for systems of classification and evidences of rela-tionship, while developmental modes and processes have been elusive and difficult to assess in these connections. Furthermore, the tremendous mass of available morphological and anatomical information has made it a practical necessity to utilize these data for taxonomical purposes. The major depend-ency of taxonomy upon structure is not a new development. The interdepend-ency of taxonomy, morphology, and anatomy stretches back to their begin-nings. The intricate threads of phylogenetical connections among the major plant groups seem only amenable to elucidation through structural studies. Genetical methodology is not adaptable above the generic level, and the data from physiology and biochemistry are much too sparse to be of any great value at the present time. This is at least true for vascular plants. In some of the lower plant groups, a very large amount of potentially useful chemical information is being accumulated, and in some instances this has been brought to bear on taxonomical problems.

A knowledge of the structural features of plants is so obviously a prerequi-site to any serious taxonomical work that these two aspects of botany are and ought to be inseparable. Therefore it leads to redundancy to try to de-velop any idea of a system of interrelationship between taxonomy on the one hand and the subjects dealing with structure on the other. Taxonomy is utterly dependent on morphological and anatomical information, and tax-onomists have been major contributors to these fields over the years.

Perhaps the most significant new approaches arise from the careful, pains-taking evaluation of anatomical and morphological data in relation to pre-sumed phylogenetic sequences. In the work of Bailey (1954) and his asso-ciates and students, dealing with the so-called Ranalean complex, is found an excellent model showing what can be done to clarify structures and relation-ships. It is interesting to observe that refined techniques have played a sig-nificant role in the development of critical evaluations of structural features for taxonomical purposes. In many instances a reevaluation of previously worked families and genera has yielded extremely valuable information. And one point stands out above all others. It is important to assess the data obtained from all parts of the plant in a combined way. The vulnerability of conclusions drawn from the overemphasis of data from a single structure or feature of a group of plants has been so clearly demonstrated that no one should fall into such a trap today.

The rather large accumulation of a wide range of information over the past five decades has not been fully exploited for the purpose of producing a system of classification of the higher plants. Various attempts during this period have resulted in improvements over the older systems, but none have met with universal acceptance. It would be entirely out of place here for me to attempt to evaluate the different systems now "on the books." Perhaps it will suffice to point out that the growth of paleobotany and the contributions of this subject to a better understanding of major plant groups are notable. Furthermore, the influence on future systems should be considerable. This, combined with the more searching studies in comparative anatomy and morphology concerned with phylogenetical relationships, should provide a better basis for a sound taxonomical system than has been available heretofore. We look confidently to the future.

MONOGRAPHS AND FLORAS

Much of the research in taxonomy is ultimately published in the form of monographs concerned with particular plant groups or in the form of floras concerned with plants of a given area. There are, of course, many other types of publication, and seemingly there is an increasing tendency toward short papers. Pressure to publish short definitive papers dealing with a single problem comes from at least three sources. One is the demand by administrators for activity in research on the part of faculty or staff. This is symbolized by publication and a large bibliography. Second is the attempt by editors and managers of journals to satisfy the ever-increasing demand for more and more costly journal space by keeping the papers as short as possible. Thirdly, there is the ever-present tendency in science to reduce the reporting to symbolism. Most sciences do not suffer too much by these pressures toward brevity because an adequate job of reporting can be done in a limited space. However, taxonomy does suffer publication-space limitation because of the very nature of the subject. In a first-rate taxonomical monograph, there are elements of history, geology, geography, climatology, pedology, and sometimes chemistry, in addition to the numerous aspects of botany previously stressed. The synthesis of information from such diverse sources requires considerable publication space.

There is at present a steady flow of new monographic treatments of different plant groups, but a large number of genera have never been studied monographically and many more have not been so studied for fifty years or more. The continued accretion of new species and new knowledge about the known species makes these older publications very much out of date. But in many cases we are still dependent upon them for they are the only sources available.

When one examines the situation with respect to floras, the need for additional taxonomical work stands out very clearly. Vast areas of the earth have not so far received a definitive treatment of the flora. This is the case in large areas of Africa, South America, China, and southeastern Asia, to say nothing of parts of Canada, the United States, most of Mexico, much of Central America, and the West Indies. The detailed study of the flora of a sizable land area is no small task. Often many years of highly concentrated research are required. Today, more than an ordinary amount of devotion is necessary to ensure the successful conclusion of a sizable floristic work. Many taxonomists do not undertake such studies because the rewards are not great. However, floristic studies stand at the base of many types of practical work involving the plants of a given area, ranging from forestry and range management on the one hand to conservation and flood control on the other. Encouragement and financial help should be given to those willing to undertake the preparation of a flora, and the achievement of publishing such a work merits wide recognition.

LOOKING AHEAD

Because it is the oldest of the botanical disciplines, taxonomy is frequently held to be a finished area of our knowledge of plants, a closed book. Nothing is further from the truth. Perhaps such a misconception, which seems to be rather general, has been in part responsible for the tremendous gaps that seem to persist in our knowledge of the taxonomy of plants. Certainly new researchers are not attracted to a subject that is purported to be all through, as far as new knowledge is concerned.

To my way of thinking, the most obvious needs in the field center on studies in comparative systematics. Thoroughgoing comparative studies of species are wanted that not only uncover new facts but in addition bring together facts from diverse sources telling us what the natures of the plants are; where they occur today; where they came from; and what their relationships are to each other. We need correlated genetical and morphological studies to evaluate taxonomical characters; comparative studies of cytological characteristics ranging widely through the plant kingdom; detailed analyses of pollinating mechanisms and reproductive patterns in relation to population characteristics both within and between species; meaningful work on geographical distributions; searching studies on species survival and persistence in relation to geomorphic processes; and perhaps most important of all, the synthesis of data from all these diverse sources into a whole picture of particular plant groups and the present-day plant cover of the earth's surface. Thus, the entire world of plants is our bailiwick and the manifold ramifications of their evolutionary relationships are the guide lines of our activities.

But I am sure that all taxonomists will not agree as to the relative need for research in the various areas of study within the field. Some might point to the many bizarre new plants being discovered and recorded for the first time from the Amazon basin of South America or similar remote areas of the world and suggest that plant exploration needs much attention; and I would agree. To find new plants, one need not go far afield. Who would have suggested five years ago that there were four undescribed species of any genus of plants east of the Mississippi River in the United States? Yet, I have recently described four new species of *Lesquerella* (1952, 1955) from Tennessee and Alabama. These are not species already represented in the collections but only now recognized. They are species not even seen by Payson (1922), the most recent monographer of the genus, and not known to anyone except the most recent collectors. Indeed, we do need plant exploration, and not only in remote places.

The taxonomy of cultivated plants has been much neglected, and many groups of tremendous importance to man's economy are in dire need of study. There are many reasons why cultivated plants offer excellent opportunities as objects of study from both scientific and practical points of view. Some of these reasons have been given by Anderson (1952), along with a left-handed dressing down of taxonomists for not having previously put their subject in order by concentrating attention on plants of the fields and wastes.

There is a very large amount of information about plants that is essentially lost because it is so scattered. Some suggestions to help this situation were made at the last International Botanical Congress by Just (1954), Lanjouw (1954), and myself (1954). In essence, the proposals were for the preparation of an encyclopedia of plants or a "genera plantarum" by taxonomists under some world-wide scheme. Such a compendium is badly needed and is something that should be worked toward.

The number of unsolved problems and the amount of needed research in the taxonomical field are staggering. As pointed out above, not only are there hundreds of groups of the vascular plants that remain without any definitive treatment, but many areas of the world have no book available that will tell about the plants that are present there. Our hope and concern is that as we move along developing new techniques, new areas of discovery, and new ways of looking at old information, the plants of the world will continue to become invested with an ever-greater mantle of man's learning as a result of our efforts. Furthermore, we hope that in the search for truths about plants

it will be the concern of all botanists to produce a rounded whole, not leaving
dark places and unexplored areas to mar the final picture.

LITERATURE CITED

ANDERSON, EDGAR. 1952. Plants, man and life. 245 pp. Little, Brown. Boston.

BABCOCK, E. B. 1947. The genus *Crepis*. Part 2. The taxonomy, phylogeny, distribution and evolution of *Crepis*. 197 pp. Univ. Calif. Press. Berkeley, Calif.

BAILEY, I. W. 1954. Contributions to plant anatomy. Chronica Bot. 15:1–262.

BONNIER, G. 1920. Nouvelles observations sur les cultures expérimentales à diverses
altitudes. Rev. Gén. Bot. 32:305–326.

CLAUSEN, JENS, DAVID D. KECK, AND WILLIAM M. HIESEY. 1940. Experimental
studies on the nature of species. Carnegie Inst., Washington, Publ. 520:1–452.

DARLINGTON, C. D. 1956. Chromosome botany. 186 pp. Allen and Unwin. London.

GOODSPEED, T. H. 1954. The genus *Nicotiana*. Chronica Bot. 16:1–536.

HALL, H. M. 1932. Heredity and environment—as illustrated by transplant experiments. Sci. Monthly 35:289–302.

JUST, TH. 1954. Generic synopses and their role in modern botanical research.
Taxon 3:201–202.

KERNER, ANTON. 1891. Pflanzenleben. Vol. 2, pp. 1–896. Bibliog. Inst. Leipzig and
Vienna.

LANJOUW, J. 1954. Index nominum genericorum and genera plantarum. Taxon
3:207–208.

MARSDEN-JONES, E. M., V. S. SUMMERHAYES, AND W. B. TURRILL. 1931. Special
herbaria as adjuncts to modern botanical research. Jour. Ecol. 18:379–383.

———— AND W. B. TURRILL. 1931. Report on the transplant experiments of the
British ecological society at Potterne, Wilts. Jour. Ecol. 18:352–378.

PAYSON, E. B. 1922. A monograph of the genus *Lesquerella*. Ann. Missouri Bot.
Gard. 8:103–236.

ROLLINS, R. C. 1952. Some Cruciferae of the Nashville Basin, Tennessee. Rhodora
54:182–192.

————. 1954. An encyclopedia of plants. Taxon 3:203–205.

————. 1955. The auriculate-leaved species of *Lesquerella* (Cruciferae). Rhodora
57:241–264.

SAKAMURA, T. 1918. Kurze Mitteilung über die Chromosomenzahlen und die Ver-
wandtschaftsverhältnisse der *Triticum*-Arten. Bot. Mag. Tokyo 32:150–153.

TURESSON, G. 1922. The genotypical response of the plant species to the habitat.
Hereditas 3:211–350.

13

HIGHLIGHTS OF BOTANICAL EXPLORATION IN THE NEW WORLD

Bassett Maguire

Much of the past thirty years of my life had been spent in botanical exploration. So, when I was invited to write on the subject of exploration, subconsciously acknowledging my own comprehension of the field, I accepted the invitation with more spontaneous alacrity than thoughtful consideration. Difficulties of presentation immediately appeared as I began to frame my piece. Most shocking to me was my inability to answer the primary question, what is exploration?

When Lewis and Clark, and Nuttall traversed the New Land; when St.-Hilaire pushed into the upland plateau of central Brazil; when Schomburgk crossed Guayana from the Atlantic seaboard to the Orinoco and Amazon; certainly these exploits obviously and gloriously represented exploration in the epic and heroic sense. But what of the work and journeys, great and small, of the multitude of men and women whose botanical collections constitute the matrix from which the great body of information about natural vegetation comes? Are not their accomplishments to be placed under that somewhat illusive and romantic term "exploration"? Most assuredly so! This paper, then, undertakes to show some of the many facets of exploration rather than to present a roster of explorers or a history of exploration of our time.

The closing decades of the nineteenth century brought to an end that long period of classic exploration in which the two continents of the Western Hemisphere had been circumscribed, probed, and traversed. Exploration had opened up geography, subdued or pushed aside native peoples, introduced commerce, and, as chief by-product, brought vast quantities of plant specimens from virgin territories to the botanical centers of Europe and America. From the materials of historic exploration and the accumulation of innumerable lesser collections, there were compiled the plant records for the great pioneer floras of country-wide or continental scope.

The twentieth century, essentially the life span of the Botanical Society of America, ushered in a new era of field botany characterized by a diminution in exploration on the grand scale and an intensification in regional and local field activity. The necessity for natural-resource inventory, the reactivated and more exacting requirements of phytogeography, the more critical demands of ecology and cytogenetics, the implications of paleobotany and structural and historical geology have compelled more precise attention to details of distribution, habitat, abundance, and morphologic variation as they obtain among individuals and populations in the field.

If the term exploration brought to the minds of our predecessors of the nineteenth century the idea of expedition in the grand manner, the concept must now be expanded to include not only field excursion over long periods of months to remote places, but also to field operation involving narrower special interests and the more intensive study of restricted and not necessarily remote areas. It is in this more general sense that the term exploration is used in this paper.

It will perhaps be useful to present this account of the highlights of contemporary exploration in the Western Hemisphere in geographical sequence, beginning first at the north.

I. BOREAL AMERICA

The early great voyages and epic explorations of boreal America, beginning with the visit to Alaska of Steller in 1741, had been concluded by the middle of the nineteenth century. Hooker in the *Flora Boreali-Americana* (1829–1840) had brought together and organized the collections of the pioneer British field botanists John Richardson, David Douglas, and Thomas Drummond. Ledebour in the *Flora Rossica* (1841–1853) had recorded the American collections of Chamisso, Eschscholtz, Wormskjold, and their compatriots.

During the succeeding half century, many collectors contributed to the body of materials and records of the floras of Canada, Alaska, and Greenland. The collation of this newer body of material, combined with the historical record, was published over a period of two decades (1888–1902) in the *Catalogue of Canadian Plants* by John Macoun, Botanist of the Geological Survey of Canada. This work brought to a close the first hundred and fifty years of boreal American field work.

Eric Hultén, eminent student of arctic botany and author of the Floras of Kamchatka, the Aleutian Islands, and Alaska and the Yukon Territory, has prepared an interesting and thoroughly documented account of the history of botanical exploration (*Botan. Notiser*, 289–346) in Alaska and Yukon. He lists more than two hundred collectors who have worked in this region before 1940. Hultén himself during the year 1925, together with his assistant J. E. Eyerdam, in a visit to the Aleutian Islands collected some 3800 numbers of flowering plants. Duplicate specimens are widely deposited in herbaria in the United States and in Europe.

The late J. P. Anderson, long-time resident and devoted amateur student of the rich Alaskan flora, brought together the largest botanical collection ever made by one individual in that immense region. Largely from his own collections Anderson published many papers on the flora of his beloved territory, and from them compiled his *Flora of Alaska.* Tragically, his personal herbarium of specimens collected before 1924 was destroyed by fire. His later herbarium is on deposit at the Iowa State College. Large series of duplicates are on file at New York and Washington, and in Europe at Lund, Stockholm, Gothenberg, and elsewhere.

Before World War II, governmental field activities were carried on chiefly by the U.S. Biological Survey. During the war military construction and operation confronted new problems related to drainage in frozen ground. A solution of these problems and those related to the requirements of men living in the arctic led the Armed Forces to develop a broad program of research dealing with the many phases of biological and physical phenomena of the arctic. The resulting effort stands as a fine example of achievement to be derived from broad, comprehensive, integrated field study. William S. Benninghoff, Chief, Alaskan Terrain and Permafrost Section, has very generously provided me with information concerning field exploration which I condense as follows:

In 1948 botanical investigations were integrated with the terrain and permafrost program of the U.S. Geological Survey. Botanists were attached to all field parties. They not only studied the effects of vegetation on frozen ground, but broadened investigations to include the study of related geologic processes such as the mass movement of soils. They developed criteria for interpreting ground conditions from plant composition and physiognomy, derived from rapid reconnaissance and aerial photography. In the progress of these studies, together with detailed geographic and ecological notes, extensive collections of plants totaling more than 20,000 numbers were taken. This great amount of plant material is at this time, for the most part, housed at the Geological Survey in Washington. The first set is to be deposited at the National Herbarium. Duplicate material will be distributed elsewhere.

During this program, now in progress for nearly a decade, extensive regions in Alaska have been studied.

Robert S. Sigafoos in the three field seasons of 1948–1950 investigated the vegetation of the Seward Peninsula. In 1952 R. S. Sigafoos and M. D. Sigafoos made botanical reconnaissance in the Kobuk River Valley, investigating geomorphic processes of rivers and sand dunes in relation to vegetation. And in 1953 they studied the vegetation in relation to erosion in the vicinity of Healy. They have collected some 7000 numbers of plants.

William S. Benninghoff in 1948 made reconnaissance of the vegetation of the Yukon Flats in the vicinity of the Hadweenzic and Hodzana Rivers. In 1949 Benninghoff, accompanied by William C. Steere, collected on St. Lawrence Island in the vicinities of Mount Sevuokuk, Savoonga, Mount Tamnik, and Tam-nik Lagoon. During 1950 and 1951 Benninghoff made reconnaissance of the lowland and west side of the Kenai Peninsula, collecting in addition to some 3000 vascular plants and cryptogams, peat samples for pollen analysis. (In 1953, assisted by Herbert C. Robbins, he made ecological reconnaissance of the area between Petowik Glacier and Olrik's Fjord in northwestern Greenland.) And, finally, in 1955 and 1956 Benninghoff mapped the vegetation north of the Alaska Range between the Delta and Gerstle Rivers.

In all, Doctor Benninghoff has amassed a large collection of some 7300 numbers.

In 1949 William C. Steere investigated the moss flora of selected sites in central and western Alaska and made extensive collections from local areas. He has completed the taxonomic study of most of these collections and is in the process of distributing duplicates to appropriate herbaria. Some results of the investigations have appeared in short papers, and others have been incorporated in larger studies that Steere has made more recently under the sponsorship of the Office of Naval Research.

In 1949 and 1950 William H. Drury made a botanical survey and joint investigation with geomorphologists in the upper Kuskokwim region in the vicinity of McGrath and Farewell. He collected approximately 4000 numbers of vascular plants, mosses, and lichens, of which the vascular plants were studied at and are now filed in the Gray Herbarium.

During four field seasons, 1949–1952, Ernest H. Muller, geologist, assisted by Karl Raup and Arthur Lachenbruch, made small but critical collections in the lowlands surrounding Kvichak and Nushagak Bays in southwestern Alaska. These collections, totaling about 800 numbers, are now deposited in the National Herbarium.

Four vegetation maps at 1:25,000 have been prepared for restricted areas by Benninghoff, and a vegetation map of northwestern North America at a scale of 1:2,500,000 has been prepared by R. S. Sigafoos. A few suggestive titles of the many publications already made emphasize the scope and significance of this most important integrated research program: "Frost Action and Vegetation Patterns on Seward Peninsula, Alaska" and "Frost Action as a Primary Physical Factor in Tundra Plant Communities," both by R. S. Sigafoos; "Interaction of Vegetation and Soil Frost Phenomena" by W. S. Benninghoff; and "Bog Flats and Physiographic Processes in the Upper Kuskokwim River Region, Alaska" by W. H. Drury. The taxonomic results to be derived from the undertaking for the most part await publication.

Ira L. Wiggins from September, 1949, to the summer of 1956 carried on investigation in the field to provide the basis of a taxonomic treatment of the vascular plants of arctic Alaska north of the Brooks Range, under the auspices of the Arctic Research Laboratory. He was assisted in the field by John H. Thomas and Henry J. Thompson in 1950, Kenton Chambers in 1951, George H. Ward and George E. Lindsay in 1952. Field investigations covered the area in the immediate vicinity of Point Barrow very thoroughly, and other areas north of the crest of the Brooks Range and west of the mouth of the Colville River less thoroughly. Howard Crum did especial collecting at Cape Lisburne, and Lloyd Spetzman provided data on somewhat more than 400 species and subspecies of vascular plants which he has collected or noted north of the Brooks Range in his work for the Arctic Institute of North America. The large numbers of plants collected and experience gained in the field, together with arctic Alaskan specimens on file in the major herbaria of the United States, form the basis of a taxonomic treatment of the "Flora of Arctic Alaska," the draft manuscript of which was completed by Professor Wiggins in 1956.

In recent or contemporary time, field investigation in Canada has been most active. After the productive eras of the Macouns, M. O. Malte, Chief Botanist at the National Herbarium of Canada, 1921–1933, carried on extensive botanical exploration in all the provinces of the country. His large collections are for the most part in the National Herbarium. He published very little and made no major contribution to the Canadian botanical literature.

For the past thirty years A. E. Porsild, presently Chief Botanist, National Herbarium of Canada, has been the outstanding field investigator of boreal American vegetation. He has led no fewer than sixteen major expeditions to various and remote parts of Canada and unquestionably has contributed more to the botany of boreal America than any other botanist now living. After early work in west Greenland, he began floristic and phytogeographic studies in arctic and boreal northwest America, where he spent seventeen summers and seven winters. In 1926, after working through the spring and early summer in central Alaska, he traveled down the Yukon to the coast, where he spent the summer and autumn around the Norton Sound and Seward Peninsula and Kotzebue Sound region. The following winter he continued by dog sledge along the north coast of Alaska to the Mackenzie River, where the succeeding two years were spent exploring the arctic coast and hinterlands lying between the Mackenzie and Coppermine Rivers and the Great Bear Lakes area, the region traversed with such privation and tragedy by Richardson and his party nearly a hundred years earlier. The summer of 1929 he went to James Bay, and in 1930 explored the Kazan River area of central Keewatin and the west coast of Hudson Bay between Churchill and

Eskimo Points. In 1931, after a few months in Alaska, he returned to the Mackenzie Delta, where during the next four years he traveled extensively along the arctic coast between Anderson River and Herschel Island. In 1937 he was a member of Captain Bob Bartlett's expedition to Labrador and west Greenland, and during the war years 1940–1943, while Canadian Consul to Greenland, did considerable botanical collecting along the west coast of Greenland. In 1944 he conducted a botanical survey in southeastern Yukon along the Alaska Highway and the Canol Road, and in 1945 commenced a botanical exploration of the southern Canadian Rocky Mountains, which has been continued during the summers of 1945, 1951, and 1956. The summer of 1947 was spent on the Mackenzie River between Slave Lake and the Delta. In 1949 he went to Great Bear Lake and the western islands of the western Canadian Arctic Archipelago. In 1953 he made a short visit to Axel Heiberg Island in the eastern Arctic Archipelago.

Porsild's extensive collections are chiefly at Ottawa. Duplicates are widely distributed. Some eighty-odd titles, mainly on arctic botany, geography, and zoology, have resulted from his long period of field activity. Many of these are of major revisionary, monographic, and floristic scope. Illustrative of the latter are "Botany of Southeastern Yukon Adjacent to the Canol Road," "The Vascular Plants of the Western Canadian Arctic Archipelago," and *Illustrated Flora of the Canadian Arctic Archipelago*. Doctor Porsild is now in the process of writing a Flora of the Canadian Rocky Mountain Parks extending from Waterton Lake to Jasper and is preparing botanical maps for a new atlas of Canada.

Hugh M. Raup, Director of Harvard Forest at Harvard University, is another outstanding contributor to the botany of Canada. He served as field botanist for the Canadian National Museum during the summers of 1928–1930 and led successive expeditions to the Peace River District, Wood Buffalo Park, and Lake Athabaska in the Mackenzie River Basin, 1926–1930, 1932, 1935, and 1939 and expeditions along the Alcan Highway where he was consultant to the U.S. Army in 1943 and 1944. In 1948 he conducted an expedition to the southwest Yukon.

There has resulted from Professor Raup's many years of exploration in northwestern Canada a vast amount of collected materials, approximately 15,000 field numbers, the first set of which is deposited at Gray Herbarium. Major contributions to the literature of Canada are his "Phytogeographic Studies in the Peace and Upper Liard River Regions," "Botanical Investigations in Wood Buffalo Park," "Phytogeographic Studies in the Athabaska–Great Slave Region," and "Botany of Southwestern Mackenzie." Raup is a practicing and vocal exponent of field operation, which seeks not only to make plant inventory of the region traversed, but to combine an interpretation of plant identity and kind with over-all ecology and phytogeography, particularly as they relate to the overriding requirements of effective and conservative land utilization. His contribution to the broader aspect of vegetation study in Canada has been very great.

H. G. Simmons, late professor at the University of Uppsala, was a member of the Sverdrup's Second Norwegian Expedition to the American Arctic Archipelago. He spent four years on Ellesmere Island, where he obtained extensive materials of vascular plants, mosses, and lichens. Simmons made the most significant contribution to the knowledge of the distribution of American arctic plants since the work of Hooker in his *Vascular Plants in the Flora of Ellesmere Land* and *A Survey of the Phytogeography of the Arctic American Archipelago.*

M. L. Fernald, in a long series of expeditions, 1904–1926, visited many times the maritime provinces of eastern Canada, Gaspé, Nova Scotia, and Newfoundland. His most frequent companion was K. M. Wiegand, with whom he collaborated in numerous taxonomic studies. A coterie of friends and assistants at various times accompanied him, prominent among them Ludlow Griscom, John M. Fogg, Harold St. John, Bayard Long, and A. S. Pease. Fernald's boreal field activity extended botanical investigation to new areas. His contribution to phytogeography was considerable, and perhaps no single paper has more stimulated contemporary thought and inquiry on the subject than Fernald's "Persistence of Plants in Unglaciated Areas of Boreal America."

Encouraged by the work of Fernald, Frère Marie-Victorin began a series of botanical surveys in Quebec centering about the Gulf and estuary of the St. Lawrence, the St. John River, and the Ottawa Valley. Work in the field formed the basis of his *Flore Laurentienne.* His influence has been largely responsible for the present upsurge in botanical activity in the province of Quebec, which has been carried on by many of his students. In Porsild's opinion, the appearance of the *Flore Laurentienne* represents a turning point in the history of Canadian botany.

In the vast reaches of Canada there still remain great areas in the less populated arctic and interior regions in which there is opportunity for original exploration. Many field men are now actively at work in these regions.

H. R. Senn and his cohorts at the Department of Agriculture in Ottawa have opened up an extensive program of exploration, chiefly that of J. A. Calder and W. J. Cody in the Arctic Archipelago and the Franklin District, N.W.T.

Homer J. Scroggan of the National Museum has prepared his *Flora of Manitoba,* which is based on extensive field work carried out during the years 1948–1953. He is at present gathering material for a flora of maritime eastern Canada. Professor Soper is conducting extensive floristic studies in southern Ontario. T. M. C. Taylor and R. C. Hosie have carried on intensive botanical exploration along the north shore of Lake Superior. E. C. Smith and A. E. Rolland have made major contributions in their investigation of the flora of Nova Scotia. Ernst C. Abbe has conducted expeditions to the Labrador and Hudson Bay regions, including the Ungava Peninsula and the Richmond Gulf.

II. TEMPERATE NORTH AMERICA

In temperate North America, for convenience here the United States, the turn of the century introduced an era of concentrated investigation and evaluation of localized segments of the country's vegetation.

Watson and Robinson had finally (1895) brought to a close Gray's *Synoptical Flora of North America,* which superseded the Torrey and Gray *Flora of North America* (1838–1843). The monumental work of the *Synoptical Flora* was enriched and, indeed, made possible as a result of the numerous great western and transcontinental expeditions of the mid-century: Fremont, *Exploring Expedition to the Rocky Mountains* (1845); Charles Wright, *Plantae Wrightianae Texano-Neomexicanae* (1852); *Botany of the Pacific Railroad Survey* (1857–1860), collections made by James A. Snyder, E. G. Beckwith, M. Creutzfeldt, J. W. Gunnison; Charles Wilkes, *Expedition to the Pacific Coast of North America* (1862–1874); *Botany of the Mexican Boundary Survey* (1859), collections made by C. C. Parry; Clarence King, *Geological Exploration of the Fortieth Parallel* (1871), collections made by Sereno Watson; *U.S. Geographical Surveys West of the One Hundredth Meridian* (1878), collections by J. T. Rothrock; and the Whitney *Geological Survey of California* (1876–1880), collections made mostly by W. H. Brewer and H. N. Bolander.

In the west the pioneer Floras, in California, Green's *Flora Franciscana* (1891), in Oregon, Howell's *A Flora of Northwest America* (1897–1903), in Colorado, Porter's and Coulter's *Synopsis of the Flora of Colorado* (1874), and Coulter's *New Manual of Botany of the Central Rocky Mountains* (1885) had set the stage for more mature works. The same effect had been accomplished by Chapman's *Flora of the Southern United States* (1860, 1883), and in the east by the successive six editions of *Gray's Manual.* And, finally, in 1896, Britton and Brown brought out their three-volume *Illustrated Flora of the Northern United States, Canada, and the British Possessions,* which in form and concept set a new pattern, one which was to have strong influence on North American botany for the succeeding half century.

Perhaps no botanist of our time has more influenced the taxonomy of America than the late Merritt Lyndon Fernald. He became assistant in botany at Harvard University in 1891 and continued his labors at the Gray Herbarium for more than half a century. He struck a rare balance between field activity and herbarium study. No one had become more familiar in the field with the plants of the Atlantic states from Maine to Virginia than

Fernald. Comment has already been made about his numerous expeditions to the maritime provinces of Canada, Nova Scotia, and Newfoundland. Field activity took him not only to the Atlantic seaboard region of the *Gray's Manual* range, but also as far south as Virginia, where from 1933 to 1945 he made some thirty-three field trips. By 1940, at the conclusion of thirty trips, he had been able to "collect 650 [species] of flowering plants not recorded as definitely growing in the state." Companions on his southern journeys were Ludlow Griscom and Bayard Long, both of whom had been with him in the north.

Fernald, with B. L. Robinson, had compiled and issued in 1908 the seventh edition of *Gray's New Manual of Botany,* which has been one of the standard texts for nearly fifty years. In 1950, at the end of his long and full career, he completed the eighth edition of *Gray's Manual of Botany.* This great work was wholly his own and stands as a monument to his own field industry and individual critical herbarium study.

From 1896 to 1952 the *Illustrated Flora of the Northern United States, Canada, and the British Possessions* by N. L. Britton and Addison Brown shared prominence and influence with *Gray's Manual.* This work, which has set a standard for later illustrated floras, was completed by Britton while he was still professor of botany at Columbia University. Britton had been active in the field as a student of the flora of the northeastern states, but after he founded and became director of The New York Botanical Garden, he became most widely known as a field man by his numerous expeditions to the West Indies.

The *New Britton and Brown Illustrated Flora of the Northeastern United States and Adjacent Canada* (1952) is entirely a completely rewritten and re-illustrated work. It bears wholly the point of view and interpretation of H. A. Gleason (except for portions contributed by collaborators), who himself was first a field man and student of ecology in the middle west. This work of Gleason's is a well-balanced book, reflecting clearly the influence of his insight into modern phytogeographic, geologic, and genetic concepts. It will remain the standard work on the northeast flora for many years.

John Kunkel Small, who for nearly forty years was attached to the staff of The New York Botanical Garden, was a dominant figure in the study of the southeastern flora. In a succession of more than a hundred field trips throughout the southeast from Virginia to Florida (more than thirty-five to Florida alone) and Texas, he accumulated the mass of material which was to provide the basis for his *Flora of the Southeastern United States* (1903) and the second edition (1913), and the *Manual of the Southeastern Flora* (1933). Edward J. Alexander, long an associate of Dr. Small's, was primarily instrumental in the final assembling of the *Manual,* which was published shortly after Small's death.

Roland M. Harper, who today has the greatest store of field experience of any living botanist of the southeast, was wholly contemporaneous with Dr. Small.

One of the most comprehensive programs of study for any sectional part of the United States has been organized at the Gray Herbarium. Under the sponsorship and leadership of George R. Cooley, the Gray Herbarium and Arnold Arboretum have projected a long-term study of the flora of the southeastern states, which will utilize the efforts of the Harvard taxonomic staffs and draw on the collaboration of many prominent resident southern botanists, among them Wilbur Duncan in Georgia, A. E. Radford and his associates in North Carolina, A. J. Sharp in Tennessee, James D. Ray in Mississippi, John A. Moore in northern Louisiana, and D. M. Moore in Arkansas. This well-conceived operation, to be based on thorough new field exploration, has as its objective the ultimate publication of three manuals treating the flora of the southeast, viz., (1) a study of the genera of the southeast, (2) the production of a conventional-type manual, and (3) a manual of cultivated plants.

Per Axel Rydberg, of gentle, modest disposition, has never had an adequate or sympathetic biographer. Ewan (*Rocky Mountain Naturalists*, 1950) wrote: "No single botanist is more critically involved in the history of the study of the Rocky Mountain flora than Rydberg." Indeed, as an explorer and a writer, the productivity of no other student of western botany can compare with that of Rydberg.

First of all a field man, Rydberg collected widely from 1891 until nearly 1930, earlier in the Rocky Mountain area from Montana to New Mexico and Utah and later in the Great Plains states. His field excursions, despite his lameness, reached into remote and difficult places, many of them not since effectively botanized. Numerically his collections were prodigious. Unfortunately, there is no adequate tabulation of his field operations. In addition to numerous critical taxonomic studies, he became the most prolific writer of major floras of his generation, all of which were based most importantly on his own collections. Successively he wrote the *Flora of Montana and Yellowstone Park* (1900), *Flora of Colorado* (1906), *Flora of the Rocky Mountains and Adjacent Plains* (1917), and *Flora of the Prairies and Plains of Central North America* (1932, published posthumously).

Aven Nelson, contemporary of Rydberg's, whose life span as an active field botanist exceeds that of all other outstanding western botanists, collected extensively in Montana, Wyoming, Colorado, Utah, Nevada, and Arizona. He remained tireless in the field. I cherish the memory of a week's collecting in the Baboquivari Mountains in southern Arizona with Nelson, his able student and colleague N. L. Goodding, and my old professor, K. M. Wiegand. Nelson, at the age of eighty years, visited (with Ruth Ashton Nelson) Mount McKinley, Alaska, in 1939, where he proposed to collect materials upon which to base a flora of the Mount McKinley National Park.

Willis Linn Jepson has influenced west coast botany during our time perhaps more than any other of the large school of contemporary Pacific Coast botanists. The impact and importance of his major floras is well known. Perhaps less emphasized in the evaluation of his work has been his effectiveness and thoroughness as a field student of California plants. His large private herbarium, the core of which is composed of plants of his own collecting, served as the chief body from which he drew material for his *Manual,* his *Silva,* and his *Flora.*

During the past few decades, numerous state and local floras have been written. It is perhaps accurate to state that not one of these has been successfully accomplished without a thorough preparation of field investigation, as is pointed up by the following:

In the collation of material for his excellent *Flora of Indiana* (1940), Charles C. Deam collected for a period of forty years, and since 1914, by his own reckoning, has collected over 59,000 numbers, and in travel, covered over 125,000 miles.

George Neville Jones and George Damon Fuller spent a preparatory period of "more than a dozen years" of field activity in gathering record and data for their *Vascular Plants of Illinois* (1955).

For an *Illustrated Manual of California Shrubs* (1957), Harold E. McMinn spent twenty years collecting exsiccatae and living material from all parts of California. Three hundred of the eight hundred species admitted to his manual had been transplanted to his trial garden at Mills College and there observed for structural variation.

At the present time six major floristic works are in progress, all of them supported by intensive new exploration. In New York, Stanley J. Smith and his colleagues in the office of the State Botanist have been conducting a county-by-county survey in the preparation of a new flora of the state. C. R. Lundell and D. S. Correll and their colleagues at the Texas Research Foundation are carrying out field exploration which will form the basis of a flora of Texas. Julian A. Steyermark, with the extraordinary energy he has always shown in the field, has completed the field activity and the preparation of manuscript for his *Flora of Missouri.* P. A. Munz and D. D. Keck have put together their independently gained long field experience and that of researches of the Carnegie Institution at Stanford to write a new flora of California. This work is approaching completion. C. L. Hitchcock, Arthur Cronquist, Marion Ownbey, and J. W. Thompson have under preparation a flora of the *Vascular Plants of the Pacific Northwest.* Ira L. Wiggins has essentially completed his flora of the Sonoran Desert. All these projects have involved an extensive program of plant exploration. I shall comment on the field activity of the last two.

Preparatory work for the new *Vascular Plants of the Pacific Northwest* has been under way some fifteen years. Its collaborators combine a wide range of talent and experience. The senior author, C. L. Hitchcock, has collected widely throughout the Rocky Mountain, Intermontane, and Pacific West, and particularly during the past number of years has concentrated field excursion in the geographical area of their flora. His extensive collections combined with the still larger lifetime collections of J. W. Thompson form the backbone of the working herbarium at the University of Washington. At Washington State College, Pullman, are the important collections of Piper, Cusick, and St. John and the enormous herbarium of some 30,000 sheets of W. N. Suksdorf. All these collections have been made in the region of the northwest flora. In addition, the writers have had available the herbarium of M. E. Peck at Willamette University, which houses the approximately 30,000 numbers collected by Peck during his long life of plant exploration throughout the state of Oregon. Cronquist has conducted field exploration in Idaho, Washington, Montana, and Oregon from 1939 to 1955, during which time he has accumulated a total of 4800 numbers yielding some 38,000 sheets. The first set is at The New York Botanical Garden; the numerous duplicates are widely distributed.

J. H. Christ, formerly in government service, amassed a large personal herbarium of about 18,000 specimens, mostly unicate numbers, collected between the years 1921 and 1953 in all parts of Idaho. This collection is now incorporated in the herbarium at The New York Botanical Garden.

It is therefore obvious that the *Vascular Plants of the Pacific Northwest* (Part V, "Compositae," by Cronquist, released in 1955) will be one of the most thoroughly documented of any modern and comparable flora.

Field work to collect material for a flora of the Sonoran Desert was begun by Ira L. Wiggins in the fall of 1932. Thirteen extensive field trips, including explorations of the full length of the Peninsula of Baja California, have been accomplished by Wiggins and his colleagues, Forrest Shreve, J. R. McMurphy, R. C. Rollins, and others. The desert parts of Arizona, southeastern California, lower California, and Sonora have been effectively covered. Approximately 7000 numbers of vascular plants have been collected in sets of six to twelve specimens. The first set is deposited at the Dudley Herbarium; duplicates are widely distributed.

This program has had the collaboration of an experienced taxonomist and a competent ecologist who has devoted a lifetime to the study of the ecology of the American desert flora.

Shreve has already completed a book dealing with the ecological and geographical aspects of the Sonoran vegetation (*Carnegie Inst. Wash. Pub.* No. 591, 1951). The taxonomic treatment by Wiggins is nearing completion.

From 1931 to 1954 Bassett Maguire and his many students and associates collected extensively in the western United States from Washington, Idaho, and Montana to southern California, Arizona, and New Mexico. Most intensive field exploration was carried out in the high western intermontane plateaus to underlie the preparation of a flora of the Intermontane Region. Approximately 20,000 field numbers were assembled during this period of exploration. Principal sets are at Logan, New York, Cornell, and Gray. In 1942 Arthur H. Holmgren, now curator of the Intermountain Herbarium at Logan, Utah, joined the program.

Perhaps the larger part of the plant material which forms the great body of specimens in the herbaria of the country has been collected by individual explorers independently of any formalized program or institutional support. Oftentimes the work has been carried on at great personal sacrifice, as was that of Pringle, Suksdorf, Marcus E. Jones, Howell, Clokey, and many others. Of this innumerable host of first-rate field investigators I shall comment only on the work of an immediate contemporary, Rupert C. Barneby.

For eighteen consecutive years, 1939–1956 (with the exception of 1952), R. C. Barneby and H. D. Ripley, or Barneby alone, spent much or all of the collecting season in western America. Each year they had carefully selected objectives which their experience in the field and knowledge of the literature indicated would yield interesting and profitable collecting. During this period of eighteen years they amassed a total of 10,959 collection numbers. The more complete sets are deposited at the California Academy of Sciences and The New York Botanical Garden. Other specimens have been distributed variously in America and chiefly at Kew in Europe.

Consistently the selection of specimens has been done with discrimination, to the end that essentially all the material is of taxonomic or geographic significance. Barneby has acquired a rare faculty for discovering novelties in regions that have been traversed over and again by professional botanists. From the Barneby-Ripley western collections there have been described sixty new taxa, of which only ten are subspecific. As was to be expected, because of special interest in the genus, a large percentage of the new species, in fact more than half, belong to the genus *Astragalus,* perhaps taxonomically the most complex of western genera. Barneby is today the outstanding student of American *Astragalus.*

III. TROPICAL AMERICA [1]

Thirty-eight years before the first permanent English settlement was established at Jamestown, Francisco Hernández in 1570 sailed from Spain to begin a seven-year botanical exploration of New Spain. More than two hundred years were to elapse before the advent of the next famous Spanish expedition to Mexico, that of Martín Sessé y Lacasta in 1788–1804 (for a detailed account see "The Royal Botanical Expedition to New Spain" by

[1] It was intended to extend this paper to an account of exploration in temperate South America. At this writing, however, that cannot be done.

H. W. Rickett, *Chron. Bot.* Vol. 11, No. 1, 1947), at the same time when
Ruiz and Pavón were sent to Peru. Sessé and his associates, chief among
them Mociño, after seventeen years in Mexico and the regions to the south,
returned to Madrid, where the fruitful results of their labors met the same
fate that had befallen the works of Hernández, that of being ignored by
authorities without publication. Finally, 274 species of plants from New Spain
were described by de Candolle from drawings made from the paintings of the
Sessé-Mociño expedition. The original herbarium of some 4000 sheets is at
Madrid.

During the last year of the Sessé expedition, von Humboldt arrived in
Mexico with the botanist Bonpland. From Bonpland's industrious field exploration, nearly 1000 collections were made, of which many represented new species
that were described by Kunth. Botanical progress for nearly the succeeding
one hundred years was summarized in the work of Hemsley (1879–1888).
J. D. Smith published extensively on his own collections (Guatemala and
Costa Rica, more than 3500 numbers) made in 1889–1906, and those of
H. von Türckheim (Guatemala, about 3000 numbers) made in 1877–1908. The
last half century witnessed a great upsurge in field investigation and preparation of floristic writings dealing with the large and complex floras of Central
America and Mexico.

In contemporary time, the Mexican botanists C. Conzatti (*Géneros vege-
tales Mexicanos,* 1903–1905, and *Flora taxonómica Mexicana,* 1936–1947),
F. Miranda (*La vegetacion de Chiapas,* 1952–1953), E. Matuda, and E. Hernández X. have been most active in field exploration. Many Europeans and
North Americans have recently contributed to the field botany of Mexico,
the more conspicuous among them being G. B. Hinton, who amassed some
10,000 collection numbers in large series mostly from the states of México
and Guerrero; C. G. Pringle (1888–1906) with nearly 10,000 collections
chiefly from Coahuila, Nuevo León, Hidalgo, Nayarit, Jalisco; and E. Palmer
(1886–1910) with considerably more than 2000 numbers from Chihuahua,
Coahuila, Durango, and San Luis Potosí.

In 1924 (*Proc. Cal. Acad.* Vol. 12) I. M. Johnston reported on the expedition of the California Academy of Sciences to the Gulf of California of
1921, during which the islands of the gulf and mainland of Sonora and
Baja California were visited. The work of this expedition was an important
precursor to that of the later expeditions of Wiggins (q.v.).

In addition to the effective work of contemporary resident Mexican
botanists, A. J. Sharp of the University of Tennessee continues with his
program of taxonomic, ecologic, and phytogeographic studies in Tamaulipas
and San Luis Potosí; and Rogers McVaugh continues his more extended
floristic activity over many parts of the country. The well-known *Trees and
Shrubs of Mexico* (1920–1926) by Paul C. Standley was, as stated by the

author, based primarily on the large collection of Mexican plants housed at the U.S. National Herbarium.

In southern Mexico and neighboring Guatemala and British Honduras, numerous collectors, of whom the more prominent have been Millspaugh, Schipp, Lundell, Stevenson, Bartlett, Gentle, Gentry, Paul H. Allen, and L. O. Williams, were active in the field, mostly between 1895 and 1940.

At the turn of the century in 1895, C. F. Millspaugh collected in Yucatán. The botanical report, under the title "Contribution to the Flora of Yucatán," was issued as *Field Columbian Mus. Pub*. Nos. 4, 15, 25, 69, and 92, 1895–1904.

Under the stimulus and leadership of H. H. Bartlett and C. L. Lundell, a series of botanical explorations into parts of the Yucatán Peninsula, northern Honduras, and adjacent Mexico, undertaken chiefly during the years 1928–1936, has been published upon in a series of botanical papers under the title "Botany of the Maya Area" (*Carnegie Inst. Wash. Pub*. No. 461, 1936; No. 522, 1940); "Vegetation of Petén," C. L. Lundell (*Carnegie Inst. Wash. Pub*. No. 478, 1937). H. S. Gentry collected in the valley of the Mayo River, Sonora, 1933–1939, spending a total of more than twenty-seven months in the field collecting "3200 numbers, representing 1276 species and varieties, of which 90 have already been detected as new," published in his "Río Mayo Plants" (*Carnegie Inst. Wash. Pub*. No. 527, 1942).

No field men have been more vigorously active in Central America than P. C. Standley (7500 field numbers in the Canal region alone) and his associate and successor in the field, Julian A. Steyermark. The numbers of collections made by these two men exceed by far those obtained by any other American botanist. From 1923 to 1950 Standley carried on intensive field work in Panama, Costa Rica, Honduras, Guatemala, El Salvador, and Nicaragua. He returned to Honduras in 1950, where he is now pleasantly and comfortably living out the later years of his life.

Account of the natural history of the region of the Isthmus reaches farther back into history than that for any other part of the New World (see introduction, *Flora of the Panama Canal Zone*, P. C. Standley, 1928). Oviedo, who between 1513 and 1529 spent much time in Panama, wrote extensively about the natural wealth of Central America in his *Historia general y natural de las Indias*, finally published in Madrid in 1851–1855.

Significant early contributions to the flora of the region were made by Barclay and Sinclair (1837), who were attached to the British ship *Sulphur;* and Seemann who was naturalist on the British ship *Herald*. Seemann's plants (1848–1849), deposited at Kew, are the most important of the early collections from the general region of Panama. Fendler, who earlier collected in the southwestern United States and later in Venezuela, made valuable Panama collections in 1849–1850.

Collectors of our time who have contributed largely to the flora of Panama are those resulting from a series of explorations sent out by The New York Botanical Garden, J. F. Cowell in 1905, M. A. Howe in 1909–1910, and the important collections of R. S. Williams made in 1908; J. Francis Macbride and J. N. Rose in 1918; E. P. Killip in 1917–1918 and 1922; C. V. Piper in 1923; and W. R. Maxon in 1911 and 1923. Henri Pittier, after his work in Costa Rica, Mexico, and Colombia, went to the Canal Zone in 1910, and in 1914–1915 amassed there a collection of 4175 numbers. During 1935–1943 Steyermark actively collected in Panama and Guatemala.

From the enormous work of these indefatigable workers, there has resulted Standley's flora of the Panama Canal Zone, flora of Costa Rica, and the flora of Guatemala by Standley and Steyermark and collaborators.

Standley's "Flora of Costa Rica" (*Field Mus. Nat. Hist.* Vol. 18, Pts. 1–4, 1937–1938) is one of the best-documented floras of any part of Central America. Standley himself made two expeditions to Costa Rica, 1923–1924 and 1925–1926, during which he collected some 15,000 numbers of vascular plants. In addition to his own and historical materials, Standley had available the rich collections of the resident botanists, Pittier, Tonduz, Biolley, Wercklé, Brenes, and the Brade brothers, whose carefully planned and executed expeditions netted some 18,000 numbers. Henri Pittier had lived in Costa Rica 1887–1903, and during this time had separately made about 5000 collections. Alberto M. Brenes, according to Standley, assembled the largest set of Costa Rican plants, some 20,000 numbers, collected by any one individual. Sets of his specimens are at Chicago, New York, Harvard, Washington, and probably elsewhere. His personal herbarium is deposited at New York.

The *Flora of Guatemala* by P. C. Standley and Julian A. Steyermark, issued in parts, with the collaboration of other authors, not yet completed, has been issued as *Fieldiana*, Vols. 24–25, 1949–1955. Volume 25, 1949, comprises the *Mosses of Guatemala* by Edwin B. Bartram; Vol. 24, Part 2, 1955, the *Grasses of Guatemala* by Jason R. Swallen, with the *Bamboos* by F. A. McClure; and Vol. 26, Part 1, 1952, and Part 2, 1953, the *Orchids of Guatemala* by Oakes Ames and D. V. Correll.

At the Escuela Agrícola Panamericana, near Tegucigalpa, Honduras, founded by Dr. Wilson Popenoe with the support of the United Fruit Company, over the past decade an effective herbarium of Central American plants (and supporting library) has been developed chiefly from the field industry of Louis O. Williams, Paul H. Allen, and their associates, Sr. Molina and others. Having established a well-coordinated organization for the collation of taxonomic, economic, and agricultural information, *Ceiba, A Scientific Journal* was begun by Drs. Popenoe and Williams and their colleagues, in 1950 (Vol. 1, No. 1, June 23; and it had reached Vol. 5, No. 4, by January, 1957).

Based on a series of continuing field explorations begun in 1935, organized and led by R. E. Woodson, Jr., and assisted variously in the field by R. J. Seibert, Paul Allen, R. W. Schery, and others, new material has been collected to contribute to a Flora of Panama. The Flora is a well-documented, fully descriptive work, released in parts, at this time having progressed into the third volume ("Flora of Panama" by Robert E. Woodson, Jr., and Robert W. Schery and collaborators, *Ann. Mo. Bot. Gard.* Vol. 30, Nos. 1–2, 1943; Vol. 31, No. 1, 1944; Vol. 32, No. 1, 1945; Vol. 33, Nos. 1, 4, 1946; Vol. 35, No. 1, 1948; Vol. 36, Nos. 1, 2, 1949; Vol. 37, No. 1, 1950).

Early history of botany in the West Indies is associated with the pre-Linnaean field work and publication of Hans Sloane, who spent fifteen months in Jamaica during the years 1687–1689, with Patrick Browne's floristic writings on Jamaica (1756), Plumier's works (1693–1760), Jacquin's visits (1754–1759) to Jamaica, St. Kitt's, St. Vincent, and Granada, from which resulted his important *Historia Selectarum Stirpium Americanarum* (1780), and Swartz' field work in Jamaica, Haiti, and some of the lesser Antilles in 1784–1789, resulting in his *Flora Indiae Occidentalis* (1797–1806). This long era of the early history was brought to a close by the preparation of the *Flora of the British West Indian Islands* by Grisebach (1859–1864). Grisebach provides a short sketch of the history of the West Indian Islands, particularly those of the British West Indies, in the preface to his *Flora*. Ignatius Urban in the introduction to his *Symbolae Antillanae seu Fundamenta Florae Indiae Occidentalis* (1898–1928) and his *Geschichte des Königlichen Botanischen Museums zu Berlin-Dahlem* (1815–1913), published in 1916, has provided extensive historical material.

From the turn of the century, two field operations on the grand scale were carried on in the West Indian area, the first and more extensive by N. L. Britton and his numerous colleagues in the field, chief of whom were Percy Wilson, C. F. Millspaugh, L. M. Underwood, W. R. Maxon, J. K. Small, G. V. Nash, and N. Taylor. During a period of more than twenty years they amassed a large body of material (some 97,121 specimens!), which is deposited at The New York Botanical Garden and which became the basis of the *Flora of Bermuda* by N. L. Britton (1918); *The Bahama Flora* by N. L. Britton and C. F. Millspaugh (1920); and "Botany of Puerto Rico and the Virgin Islands," N. L. Britton and Percy Wilson (1923–1930). In Cuba, Britton carried out extensive field explorations with his collaborators and in conjunction with Hermano León of the Colegio de La Salle. A manuscript of "A Flora of Cuba," based on these and the extensive historical collections of C. Wright and others, was prepared and is on file in the library of The New York Botanical Garden. Unfortunately, because of Britton's death, it was never published. This manuscript and materials from the collections of more than 22,000 numbers of Hermano León and later those of Hermano Alain are the sources upon which the present *Flora de Cuba*, by

Hermano León (J. S. Sauget y Barbier) and Hermano Alain (E. E. Liogier), are based.

Britton and his colleagues carried on intermittent but extensive field exploration in Trinidad and had prepared from them the undated typescript provisional list of the spermatophyta of the Trinidad flora (deposited in the library of The New York Botanical Garden). The *Flora of Trinidad and Tobago,* initiated by R. O. Williams, Vol. 1, 1928, an outgrowth of the Britton preliminary work, has been issued irregularly since and is presently in progress through the efforts of numerous contributors.

The second great program was that initiated by Urban to provide new materials for the preparation of his *Symbolae Antillanae.* The Swedish botanist E. L. Ekman, on behalf of Urban and the Berlin Botanical Garden, was sent to Cuba in 1914 and later to Hispaniola. He finally took up permanent residence in the Dominican Republic and died there a comparatively young man in 1931. R. A. Howard, contemporary student of the West Indian flora, has written as follows (*Bull. Torrey Club* 79:84, 1952):

"Ekman's contribution to the knowledge of the Caribbean flora is the greatest of any single collector. His work covered 17 continuous years in the field and resulted in collections of over 35,000 numbers, 19,000 from Cuba and over 16,000 from Hispaniola. His collections added 2,000 new species to the known flora of the area. At least six new genera of plants bear his name, and innumerable new species of plants, birds, and snails bearing his name, reflect his contribution. His specimens will form the basis of study of any future works on the vegetation of the Greater Antilles and the only regret anyone has is that he did not collect more duplicates.

"Ekman's specimens were sent to Urban for study and the majority of the types are now in the Riksmuseum in Stockholm. Unfortunately many of the types were kept in Berlin and were destroyed during the war. Ekman's publications on the Caribbean were few for he intended to write later. However his letters and complete notes preserved in Stockholm will supply the field observations of an outstanding taxonomist and ecologist for future research on Caribbean flora."

For twenty-one years, William Fawcett, Director of Public Gardens and Plantations in Jamaica, gave especial attention to botanical exploration of the island, which resulted in more than 13,000 collection numbers. From 1910 to 1926 Fawcett and Rendle published five volumes of their *Flora of Jamaica.* The work of this Flora had a rich botanical history, beginning with the collections and publications of Hans Sloane, Patrick Browne, Joseph Banks, Olof Swartz, and others. Perhaps the most extensive series of modern collections (17,480 specimens) of the island is that made by N. L. Britton and his colleagues, which is deposited at The New York Botanical Garden. Recently field study in Jamaica has been re-activated by William T. Stearn of the British Museum (Natural History) and the resident botanist George

R. Proctor, who has collected intensively in Jamaica since 1950. The completion of the *Flora of Jamaica* is now under progress by Stearn.

The field work of H. Stehlé and his collaborators on the French islands adjacent to and including Martinique and Guadeloupe has resulted in his *Flore de la Guadeloupe et dépendances*, Vol. 1, *Essai d'écologie et de géographie botanique*, 1935; Vol. 2, *Catalogue des phanérogames et fougères*, the latter by H. and M. Stehlé and L. Quentin, 1937–1949. Additional recent studies in the West Indies are as follows: A. Questel, *The Flora of the Island of St. Bartholomew* (1941); the important work of W. H. and B. T. Hodge on the Island of Dominica, which has resulted so far in the collection of some 4000 numbers and the publication of *Flora of Dominica* (parts, 1937, 1938, 1940); the work of John and Pamela Beard (1943–1944) in the forests of the Lesser Antilles, *Natural Vegetation of the Windward and Leeward Islands;* and the work of R. N. Moscoso in compiling the *Catalogus Florae Domingensis* (1942).

For the past fifteen years Richard A. Howard, director at the Arnold Arboretum, and E. S. Howard have conducted explorations in the Bahamas, Jamaica, and the islands of the Greater and Lesser Antilles. Their continuing extensive field investigations anticipate descriptive publication in the future.

Many investigators have taken part both in early times and our own in the exploration of coastal regions and the vast interior of tropical South America. Even yet the complex and enormous flora of no part of the area can be considered sufficiently known to prepare a descriptive treatise which could satisfy the standards of contemporary demand.

No comprehensive summation of the tropical American floras has been made, or indeed could have been made, since the prodigious accomplishment of Martius' *Flora Brasiliensis*. Its writing occupied a period of sixty-six years (1840–1906) in the preparation of fifteen folio volumes of one to six parts each, contributed by the outstanding botanists of the period. Into it went the records and study of the collections of the great explorers of the time, stretching over nearly a century, resulting in the description of 2253 genera, 22,767 species (5689 new, 19,629 Brazilian, 3138 extra-Brazilian) and 6246 illustrations. It is today useful for all the region of the hylean rain forest of South America.

VENEZUELA. The earliest botanical collector in Venezuela (for a history of the botanical exploration of Venezuela see the introduction to *Las plantas usuales de Venezuela*, 1926, by H. Pittier) was Peter Loefling, a student of Linnaeus and a member of Solano's geographical explorations. Loefling in the year 1754 collected in the vicinity of Cumaná, Barcelona, and the lower Caroní. Before 1800, short visits were made to Venezuela by Jacquin, Bredemeyer, and Schücht.

On July 16, 1799, Alexander von Humboldt, the great geographer and man of letters, arrived at Cumaná, Venezuela, with his companion Aimé

Bonpland, the botanist of the expedition for the ensuing five years. From Cumaná and Caracas explorations were made in northern Venezuela until the party on March 27, 1800, arrived at San Fernando de Apure, some miles up the river from its junction with the Orinoco. From there the explorers pressed up the Orinoco River to the town of San Fernando on the Atabapo, near the confluence of that river with the Orinoco. Along the common commercial route of the time to the upper Río Negro, they traveled up the Río Atabapo to Yavita, across the short pleasant portage to Pimichín, and thence on the Río Guainía to the point where its union with the Casiquiare marks the beginning of the Río Negro. The Humboldt party proceeded up the Río Casiquiare back into the Río Orinoco, and thence on to the savannas of Esmeralda, lying at the foot of the majestic sandstone mountain of Duida, on May 21, 1800. There Bonpland made the first botanical collections from a region that since has become legendary in its botanical interest, and there Humboldt became the first European to witness the preparation of curare. On November 24, 1800, Humboldt and Bonpland sailed from Nueva Barcelona for Cuba, thus completing a visit of some sixteen months, during which time Bonpland had collected the great mass of Venezuelan material that was to become in large part the subject of C. S. Kunth's report in the sevenvolume *Nova Genera et Species Plantarum*, 1815–1825, one of the most important writings on the early botany of America.

Subsequent to the historic expedition of von Humboldt and Bonpland, during the nineteenth century there followed a number of resident botanists and visitors who collected variously in the country. A few of the more prominent were J. M. Vargas; J. W. K. Moritz, who collected at Colonia Tovar in the region of Caracas and in the Andes of Mérida and Trujillo; Robert and Richard Schomburgk (1838–1842), who collected in the Gran Sabana region; J. J. Linden in 1844; L. J. Schlim and N. Funk in 1845; Hermann Karsten in 1843, when he visited the states of Carabobo and Miranda, returning in 1847 and finally in 1852 to continue with his principal work in Colombia; August Fendler, who earlier made botanical collections in New Mexico, Panama, and Trinidad, came to Venezuela in 1853 and established himself at Colonia Tovar; Richard Spruce, who from January, 1852, until November, 1854, collected in large series 1813 numbers of vascular plants in the Río Negro and Alto Orinoco basins. Field activities of the 1800's came to a close in Venezuela with the visit of H. H. Rusby and Roy W. Squires to the lower Orinoco in 1896. The first set of their collection of 444 numbers is deposited at The New York Botanical Garden.

Henri Pittier, whose thirty years of botanical activity in Venezuela ended at the mid-century, dominated the botany of that country in our time. By 1918 he had accumulated 5000 collection numbers, the principal sets of which are deposited at Caracas and Washington. He founded the National Herbarium and as a result of his own efforts built the collections to 30,000 specimens.

Pittier and his successsor, Tobías Lasser, and their various colleagues, Felix Cardona, Leandro S. Aristeguieta, L. Schnee, Zoraida Luces de Febres, V. Badillo, and Vareschi, have continued with vigorous field investigation.

During 1901 and again in 1903, visits were made to the Island of Margarita by J. R. Johnston. Between 3000 and 4000 collection numbers were obtained on each visit, the first sets of which are deposited at the Gray Herbarium. Johnston's studies were published in the "Flora of the Islands of Margarita and Coche, Venezuela" (*Contr. Gray Herb.* n.s. 37, 1909). Alfredo Jahn, 1887–1922, collected widely in Venezuela along the Alto Orinoco and the Río Negro, in the Andes of Trujillo, Mérida, and Táchira and in the states of Lara and Zulia, and finally around the Lake of Maracaibo. His collections of more than 1300 numbers are deposited at Caracas and Washington. In 1917, Hugh M. Curran collected in the coastal regions of Venezuela, and in recent years, attached to the *Forestal*, he has collected widely in the forest areas throughout the country. Most of his specimens are at Caracas and New York.

In more recent years, North American botanists have contributed materially to exploration in Venezuela. Llewelyn Williams from February to May, 1939, on behalf of the Servicio Botánico conducted a botanical exploration of the lower and middle Caura River in the state of Bolívar. His extensive collections are at Caracas, Chicago, and elsewhere. Later he collected in the region of the Ríos Atabapo, Guainía, Casiquiare, and Alto Orinoco in Amazonian Venezuela.

Perhaps the most significant of all the recent field work done generally in Venezuela is that of Julian A. Steyermark, where from December, 1943, to September, 1944, he explored portions of the Venezuelan Andes, the coastal range, Cerro Duida, and Mount Roraima for the United States government in connection with the *Cinchona* Survey. From October to December of 1944 he made the initial exploration of Ptari-tepuí and its outlying regions under the auspices of the Chicago Natural History Museum. And from February to June, 1945, sponsored by the Servicio Botánico, he explored certain areas in the states of Sucre, Anzoátegui, and Monagas. Altogether he assembled the large total of 8550 collection numbers divided as follows: the Andes, 2048; eastern part of the Cordillera de la Costa, in the states of Sucre, Anzoátegui, and Monagas, 1947; western and central part of the Cordillera de la Costa, 1261; Ptari-tepuí and vicinity, 1644; Roraima and vicinity, 841; Duida and vicinity, 809. The first sets are at Chicago; duplicate sets are at Caracas, New York, Washington, and elsewhere. Botanical reports on the collections of these explorations are to be found in *Contributions to the Flora of Venezuela, Fieldiana,* Vol. 28, Parts 1–4, 1951–1957.

King Leopold of Belgium in 1951 collected in the Alto Orinoco region. His plants are at this time being studied at New York.

In the Guayana Highland since 1925 The New York Botanical Garden has actively conducted floristic and field studies. Chiefly involved in the field have been G. H. H. Tate, and Bassett Maguire and J. J. Wurdack and their associates. The work of the program will be discussed later in this paper.

BRITISH GUIANA. Aublet's botanical activity in French Guiana during the years 1762–1764 (*Histoire des plantes de la Guiane Françoise*, 1775, J. B. C. Fusée Aublet) may be considered the effective starting point for botany in the Guiana coastal region. Two fairly good sets of Aublet's plants are still in existence, the fuller set at the British Museum, a complementary one at Paris.

In British Guiana, among the early important collectors were Robert Schomburgk (1835–1843) and Richard Schomburgk (1840–1844), whose collections of nearly 2500 numbers were, for the most part, studied by Bentham; C. F. Appun; E. F. im Thurn; F. N. McConnell and J. S. Quelch; all of whose collections were made on and in the vicinity of Mount Roraima, the original materials of which are at Kew.

More recently George S. Jenman, from 1903 to 1929 Government Botanist at Georgetown, conducted extensive explorations in British Guiana and collected on the Kaieteur Escarpment, obtaining altogether more than 5000 numbers which are widely distributed in the herbaria of the world. The original set is at Kew.

R. A. Altson, Assistant Government Botanist and mycologist from 1923 to 1927, made two excursions into the Pakaraima region. His collections are chiefly in the Jenman Herbarium at Georgetown and at Kew.

H. A. Gleason made important collections (940 numbers) in the Potaro River Gorge in 1934. His specimens are at New York. De la Cruz, employed by Dr. Gleason, independently made collections of some 3000 numbers.

N. Y. Sandwith in 1929 and again in 1937 collected in the region of the Moraballi Creek and the Kaieteur Plateau. The first set of his collections of more than 1300 numbers is at Kew.

In 1920 A. S. Hitchcock made general collections (about 1250 numbers) with chief emphasis on the grass flora. These specimens are at Washington and New York.

From about 1930 to the present time, various members of the Forest Department at Georgetown have made collections, in various parts of British Guiana, which now total more than 7000, the first set of which was submitted to Kew. The chief duplicate set is at New York. T. A. W. Davis from 1932 to 1936, followed by D. B. Fanshawe, who served in the colony for fourteen years and became the principal student and collector of its flora, have made an outstanding contribution to the knowledge of botany in British Guiana.

In 1933 T. G. Tutin, on behalf of the Oxford Expedition, made collections on the Kaieteur Plateau, the first set deposited at the British Museum.

A. C. Smith in 1937–1938 obtained more than 1600 numbers as a member of the Terry-Holden expedition to the Kanuku and Akarai Mountains, the original material being at New York.

In 1948 Frère Wilson-Brown obtained more than 600 collections in the Kanuku Mountains. The original set is at New York.

Nicholas Guppy, from September through November, 1952, visited the Akarai Mountains along the British Guiana–Brazilian frontier. He collected 679 numbers of vascular plants which are being studied at New York.

In a series of expeditions, Bassett Maguire, with D. B. Fanshawe in 1944 and 1951–1952, with R. S. Cowan in 1954–1955, and with W. M. C. Bagshaw and C. K. Maguire in 1955, collected variously in British Guiana. The first sets of more than 2250 numbers are at New York.

SURINAME. Among the many early collectors in Suriname were F. Allamand (1756–1771), specimens at the Linnean Herbarium; F. W. Hostmann and A. Kappler, separately and together during the period 1824–1840, who made extensive collections which are widely distributed in herbaria; the collections of H. C. Focke (1835–1850) are chiefly at Utrecht; F. L. Splitberger (1837–1838), whose original collection is at Leiden; C. Weigelt (1827–1828), whose collections are widely distributed; and H. R. Wullschlaegel (1849–1855), whose original collections are at Brussels.

The most important body of material recently collected in Suriname has come from officers of the Forest Bureau, who have amassed nearly 10,000 specimens, the original set of which is at Utrecht. Individual collectors who have contributed most significantly are A. A. Pulle (1903–1904, 1920), whose original sets are at Utrecht. His expedition in 1903–1904 was the impetus for the further preoccupation during his life with the flora of Suriname. He wrote the "Enumeration of the Vascular Plants Known from Surinam," 1906, and organized and edited the earlier parts of the new *Flora of Suriname*, initiated in 1932. J. Lanjouw, who has visited Suriname frequently since 1933, is presently editor-in-chief of the continuing *Flora*, and himself has in the field collected large series of plants, the original sets of which are at Utrecht. Gerold Stahel, who was director of the Agricultural Experiment Station in Paramaribo from 1914 to 1939, and his associate, D. C. Geijskes, made various expeditions into the hinterland. Their collections are largely at Utrecht. More recently, J. S. Lindeman, F. P. Jonker, and A. M. E. Jonker have studied chiefly the Araceae and other monocotyledons in coastal Suriname. Their collections are at Utrecht.

In April and later from June to October, 1944, Bassett Maguire collected with Gerold Stahel in the coastal regions, and independently in the interior on the Saramacca River and Tafelberg. The first set of more than 1600 numbers is at New York.

In 1954–1955, R. S. Cowan and J. C. Lindeman, and Bassett Maguire collected nearly 400 numbers on Nassau Mountain and in the vicinity of Moengo. The materials are at New York and Utrecht.

FRENCH GUIANA. Subsequent to the activities of Aublet were the collections of L. C. M. Richard (1781–1785), J. B. Leprieur (1830–1836), A. Poiteau

(1817–1822), M. Mélinon (1840–1862), and P. A. Sagot (1854–1878), whose original materials are at Paris. These specimens still constitute the chief body of material collected in French Guiana. The original specimens of J. Martin, some 1172 sheets, are at the British Museum.

Unfortunately, contemporary exsiccatae from French Guiana are few. W. E. Broadway's collections of 1020 numbers are at New York. R. Benoist in 1913–1914 made floristic and ecological studies in the coastal regions from which he derived 2765 collection numbers, often in large duplicate series, all of which are yet at Paris. At the present time, P. Bena and M. Lamoine, with the assistance of Mr. Hook, have been actively engaged in reconnaissance in various parts of French Guiana. Their specimens are being submitted to Paris, Utrecht, and New York. In 1955 R. S. Cowan collected 310 numbers in the vicinity of Cayenne, Montagne de Kaw, and St. Laurent, the first set of which is at New York.

AMAPÁ, BRAZIL. Recently, botanical activity in Brazilian Guiana has occupied the attention of J. M. Pires and his colleagues at the Instituto Agronômico do Norte at Belém: R. L. Fróes in 1950 and 1951 collected a total of 822 specimen numbers, and George Black in 1949, 1951, 1954, and 1955 a total of 798 numbers. In 1955 R. S. Cowan (in small part with Bassett Maguire) obtained nearly 600 numbers from the Serra do Navío and from the vicinity of Oyapock on the Amapá–French Guiana border.

COLOMBIA. In Colombia the earliest collections of note were made by J. C. Mutis (1760–1808) in his many years' residence at Bogotá. Mutis amassed a large herbarium of more than 6000 specimens which, with the well-known beautiful paintings done under Mutis' direction, are at Madrid. Subsequent collectors of especial note were H. Karsten (1846), whose original collection of more than 2000 sheets (deposited at Leningrad) formed the basis for his excellently illustrated *Florae Colombiae*, 1858–1869, in two folio volumes; J. J. Triana (1854–1892), whose original collection of more than 5000 sheets is at Paris; E. André (1875–1876), who made a large collection of over 14,000 numbers, the first set of which is deposited at Kew; F. C. Lehmann (1880–1899), who collected chiefly in Colombia, gathered more than 7000 collections of which the first set is at Kew; and J. J. Linden (1841–1843), whose collection of more than 2000 numbers is at Gent.

Many botanists have recently contributed to contemporary work on the rich and diversified flora of Colombia. Under the leadership of A. Dugand, E. P. Arbeláez and the present director of the Instituto Nacional de Ciencias, Lorenzo Uribe-Uribe, Colombian botanists, notably Hernándo García-Barriga and Jesús Idrobo, have contributed importantly. Numerous non-Colombians have been very active in the study of the Colombian flora.

Unquestionably the first-ranking contemporary student of the flora of Colombia is José Cuatrecasas, who over a period of seventeen years collected the enormous total of 24,661 numbers of plants, often in duplicate series.

His most important and contributive program has been as follows: his first expedition of 1932, sponsored by the University and Botanical Garden of Madrid, was conducted in the region of the Río Magdalena and Valle del Cauca, yielding 1500 numbers which are chiefly at Madrid; the second expedition of 1938, sponsored by the University and Botanical Garden of Madrid, to the regions of Cundinamarca, Boyacá, Soatá-Cocuy, and the llanos of the Meta, resulted in the collection of 3500 numbers which are chiefly at Madrid; during the third period, 1939–1942, as Professor of Botany at the Universidad Nacional, Bogotá, he made excursions chiefly to the llanos and rain forests of Meta, Vichada, Vaupés and Amazonas, the East Cordillera, the Central Cordillera, and the West Cordillera, and parts of the lower Magdalena Valley and Cauca Valley, from which 8861 numbers were obtained and are chiefly at Bogotá; during the fourth period, 1942–1947, as Professor of the Agronomic Faculty of El Valle and Director of the Comisión Botánica del Valle, he made expeditions to the West Cordillera on both slopes and their highest peaks, the rain forest of the Pacific Coast, the mangrove areas of the west coastal range, the Central Cordillera, and the plains of the Cauca Valley and Popayán, resulting in 11,000 collections which are chiefly at Cali. Collaborators in the field with Dr. Cuatrecasas have been H. García-Barriga, R. Jarmillo, Pérez Arbeláez, R. E. Schultes, E. Smith, R. Metcalf, and E. P. Killip (with his own enumeration). Large sets of Cuatrecasas' plants are at Chicago and Washington.

Cuatrecasas' numerous writings have clearly made his the outstanding present-day contributions to the literature of the botany of Colombia.

E. P. Killip, in association with a number of associates, has made three major expeditions and several shorter visits in Colombia. On the first expedition in 1922, in the company of F. W. Pennell and T. E. Hazen, he collected extensively about Buenaventura Bay and in the luxuriant forests at the base of the western cordillera and the páramo of Sta. Isabel. On the second, 1926–1927, E. P. Killip and A. C. Smith in five months carried on exploration in the region of Cartagena and Calamar on the Magdalena River, vicinity of Turbaco, Arjona, and Puerto Wilches. With Bucaramanga as headquarters, they collected in this region and elsewhere on the western slopes of the Eastern Cordillera near Piedecuesta, Mesa de los Santos, Las Vegas, and northward in the vicinities of Suratá, San Antonio, La Baja, and Charta and visited the páramos at Santurbán, Vetas, Rico, Los Colorados; Mutistua, páramo de Santurbán, Pamplona, Toledo, and Norte de Santander; Cúcuta and Maracaibo. A total of some 7000 numbers yielding approximately 25,000 specimens were obtained by these effective field men. Killip on his third Colombian expedition in 1939 visited Gorgona Island; explored the region from Bogotá to Villavicencio (with A. H. G. Alston) in the western cordillera and visited the interior of Chocó. Much of this period was spent with H. García-Barriga. Approximately 2700 numbers yielding 11,000 specimens were obtained. The more complete sets derived from these expeditions are at Washington, New York, and the Gray Herbarium.

F. W. Pennell made extensive exploration in 1917 with H. H. Rusby (the first set of approximately 4791 specimens is at New York), and later with Killip, as noted above, in 1922 and in 1925. The first set obtained on the last expedition is at the Philadelphia Academy of Sciences.

During the periods 1941–1946 and 1949–1953, R. E. Schultes collected extensively in Colombian Amazonas. Comment on his activities will be made later.

ECUADOR. During the period 1735–1747, the ill-fated Joseph de Jussieu was botanist of the scientific expedition to Ecuador headed by Charles-Marie de La Condamine. The years 1755–1771 were spent on the same mission in Peru. A considerable part of Jussieu's material was lost during the long period of his residence in America. His remaining collections are at Paris.

Richard Spruce, after serving five years in the field in the valley of the Amazon and Rio Negro, was despatched to Ecuador where for ten years (1855–1864) he supervised the gathering of seed and seedlings of *Cinchona* to be sent to the British East Indies. During this long period he continued diligently to collect his beloved cryptogams and much new vascular plant material, of which he accumulated a total in Ecuador and Peru of approximately 2683 numbers.

From 1876 to 1908, Luis Sodiro assiduously gathered a collection of some 6000 numbers. The first set is in Budapest.

Bonpland in 1802 continued in Ecuador with the botanical part of the von Humboldt expedition.

M. Acosta-Solís has in recent years led resident botanists in the botanical exploration of Ecuador.

During the period of a year and a half in 1944–1945, while a member of the Misión de Cinchona del Ecuador, for the last six months of this period representing The New York Botanical Garden, Wendell H. Camp made extensive collections of 6523 numbers. Camp's collections are particularly impressive in the excellence of the field data accompanying them and the large series representing most collection numbers.

PERU. Weberbauer in *El mundo vegetal de los Andes Peruanos*, 1945, wrote a thorough account of the botanical history of Peru, dating from the period of Pedro de Osma in 1568 to the contemporary time of 1940. The following brief has been extracted largely from his account.

The most important of the early explorations of Peru was made from April, 1778, to April, 1788, ten years lacking seven days, by Hippólito Ruiz, José Pavón, and J. Dombey (*Travels of Ruiz, Pavón and Dombey in Peru and Chile, 1777–1788*, by Hippólito Ruiz, translation by B. E. Dahlgren, *Field Mus. Nat. Hist.* Vol. 21, 1940). Their collections are widespread, the principal existing set of approximately 2000 sheets is deposited at Florence. Dombey's original set is at Paris. Their *Flora Peruviana et Chilensis* in three volumes, 1798–1802, is the beginning point of the important literature dealing with plants of Peru.

Over the next hundred years, numerous botanists visited and collected in Peru, among the notable being Bonpland (with von Humboldt) in 1802. E. F. Poeppig arrived in Peru in May of 1829, where he collected until he crossed the Brazilian frontier in August, 1831, after which he departed from Pará in October, 1832. His herbarium representing approximately 2000 species is at Vienna; duplicates are widespread. Andrew Mathews from 1833 to 1841 collected in various parts of Peru, assembling some 10,000 numbers; the more complete set is at Kew. Antonio Raimondi traveled through the entire country, 1851–1859, collecting a great mass of 13,000 numbers which was studied at Berlin. Raimondi was the first of the Peruvian botanists to make a contribution of consequence to his country. In acknowledgment of his great services, Weberbauer dedicated his own *El mundo vegetal de los Andes Peruanos* to Raimondi. Richard Spruce in the years 1855–1857, while engaged on his *Cinchona* program, collected numerously in Peru; Ernst Ule from August, 1902, to April, 1903, collected in eastern Peru near Yurimaguas, and especially in the vicinity of Tarapoto.

The very important work of Weberbauer began in the autumn of 1901 and continued until the spring of 1940. During this period of nearly forty years, Weberbauer was absent on trips to Europe on two occasions, from September, 1905, to September, 1908, and from December, 1929, to June, 1930. To support his extensive ecological and phytogeographic studies, Weberbauer collected some 8100 numbers which were deposited chiefly at Berlin; duplicate collections are at Breslau, Geneva, Chicago, Gray Herbarium, Washington, and the School of Agriculture in Lima.

From 1922 over a period of eleven years, Fortunato L. Herrera collected some 3800 numbers, which were deposited in part in Berlin, Washington, New York, Chicago, and Gray Herbarium. J. Francis Macbride carried out two expeditions, the first in 1922, in which he collected approximately 18,000 specimens and upon which he laid the basis of his great work *The Flora of Peru*. Beginning in 1936, many parts have been issued; the work continues in preparation. Gunther Tessman, ethnologist, in 1926 amassed a collection of 6000 numbers, the first set of which was deposited at Berlin. Francis W. Pennell in 1925 collected in Peru and Chile, obtaining 2617 numbers, of which the first set is at New York. In 1927 Carlos Schunke collected for the Field Museum in Chicago. In 1929 E. P. Killip and A. C. Smith collected in a considerable part of eastern Peru. Llewelyn Williams in 1929–1930, chiefly in Amazonian Peru, collected a large series of 8252 numbers and 2500 wood specimens, the first set of which is at Chicago. G. Klug, a nationalized Peruvian, collected chiefly in the year 1929 in northeast Peru, obtaining 4403 collection numbers, the original set of which is at New York. In 1931 and later in 1935–1952,

T. H. Goodspeed and his large contingent of assistants collected in Peru, Bolivia, Chile, and Argentina in their search for living and exsiccatae material of the genus *Nicotiana*. They assembled a total of 13,673 collection numbers, the first set of which is at Berkeley. In 1940 Erik Asplund made large collections, the first set of which is deposited at Stockholm.

Dr. Ramón Ferreyra, Professor of Systematic Botany and Plant Geography at the University of San Marcos and Curator at the Museo de Historia Natural, has kindly supplied me with detailed information concerning plant exploration in Peru subsequent to the account of Weberbauer. Extracts from his notes are as follows:

Christopher Sandeman, June-September, 1938, made collections in the coastal and Andean regions; his specimens, mostly in small series, are at Kew. F. Pennell and R. Ferreyra explored in central and northern Peru during 1948 chiefly for Scrophulariaceae, Polygalaceae, and Compositae; in 1948 F. R. Fosberg collected *Rubiaceae* in central and northern Peru; his material is stored at Chicago. In 1948 C. Rick spent several months in Peru collecting chiefly *Lycopersicon*. In 1952 P. Hutchinson and R. Ferreyra made collections in central Peru for the University of California. In 1953 P. Hjertig and E. Petersen of the faculty of Agronomy at Tucumán made exploration in central and southern Peru and Bolivia, with especial interest in *Solanum*. In 1954 E. E. Smith of the Bureau of Plant Introduction, Beltsville, Maryland, made general collections of economic plants in central and southern Peru and in Bolivia. W. Rauh and F. Monheim of Heidelberg University made collections in the Peruvian and Ecuadorian Andes. Large parts of this collection are being studied at New York. Lincoln Constance in 1954 collected for several months in the cordillera of Chile and central Peru (Departments of Lima and Junín). In 1955 A. Krapovickas and R. Ferreyra collected in central Peru. E. Cerrate, assistant in botany at the University of San Marcos, has since 1950 explored chiefly in the province of Bolognesi, collecting approximately 2500 field numbers. Professor O. Tovar of the University of San Marcos since 1950 has botanized in the Department of Huancavelica, where he has acquired some 3000 numbers. Ferreyra has collected widely in Peru since 1946 and has assembled a large collection of more than 12,000 numbers yielding more than 30,000 specimens. In addition, he has collected in Argentina, Chile, and the United States. He has published more than thirty papers, chiefly on the flora of Peru, dealing especially with the genera *Onocerus, Monnina,* and *Chaetanthera*. He has inscribed a new genus of the Mutisieae, *Weberbauerella* (ined.), to the great student of Peruvian botany.

BOLIVIA. Martín Cárdenas, Director, Facultad de Ciencias, Cochabamba, has for many years been the outstanding student of the flora of Bolivia. The more prominent of the field botanists of the nineteenth century who worked in the highly diversified and rich flora of Bolivia were H. A. Weddell (1845–1847, 1851), whose original set is at Paris; G. Mandon (1863–1883), whose materials are widely distributed in the principal herbaria; Otto Buchtien, whose collections exceeded 1000 numbers; M. Bang (1890–1895), whose materials are widely distributed, the first set of which, some 3002 sheets, is at New York; and more recently J. Steinbach (1915–1929), who collected some 8992 numbers that are widely distributed, with large sets at New York and Kew.

H. H. Rusby in 1885, a year after his graduation from medical college, was sent by Parke, Davis & Company to Bolivia to conduct explorations (1885–1886) chiefly in the interest of obtaining plants with potential drug value. In 1921, at sixty-six years of age, he returned to Bolivia as leader of the Mulford Biological Exploration of the Amazon Valley (1921–1922). Rusby obtained 3196 collection numbers on the first expedition, 2629 on the Mulford Expedition, and with Pennell in Colombia in 1917 some 4791. The original sets are at New York.

BRAZIL. I. Urban presents an excellent history of the early complicated history of exploration of Brazil in Part 1 of the first volume of the *Flora Brasiliensis,* offering detailed accounts of the itineraries of the principal plant collectors who have done field work in Brazil up to 1904. Prominent among them were C. F. P. von Martius (1817–1820), whose original set of more than 1500 numbers is at Munich (Martius' personal herbarium is at Brussels); F. Sellow (1814–1831) collected some 13,219 numbers, the original set of which was at Berlin, but duplicates are widely distributed; A. von Chamisso (1815–1816) collected perhaps 12,000 numbers on his world voyage, the earlier from Santa Catarina, the original set at Leningrad; A. F. C. P. de St.-Hilaire (1816–1822), collections numbering nearly 7600, original set at Paris; G. H. von Langsdorff (1813–1829), original set at Leningrad; J. F. Pohl (1817–1821), original set at Vienna; H. W. Schott (1817–1821), original set at Vienna; J. S. Blanchet (1828–1856), a collection of some 4000 numbers, widely distributed; W. J. Burchell (1825–1830), collection of some 11,765 numbers, including 52,000 specimens and 7022 species, original set at Kew; Johann Lhotsky (1830–1832), original collections at Vienna; Charles Gaudichaud-Beaupré (1832–1833, 1836), original collections at Paris; P. Claussen (1834–1843), specimens widely distributed; George Gardner (1836–1841), over 7000 numbers widely distributed, original sets at British Museum and Oxford; E. Poeppig (1831–1832), original set at Vienna; A. F. Regnell, long-time resident physician in Brazil (1841–1874), original set at Stockholm; L. Riedel (1821–1836), original set of more than 7000 numbers at Leningrad; R. Spruce (1849–1855), nearly 10,000 collection numbers, original set at Kew; A. F. M. Glaziou (1861–1895), some 22,770 numbers, original set on deposit at Kew, specimens widely distributed.

Martius himself during four years of exploration (with the zoologist J. B. von Spix) from 1817 to 1820 collected chiefly in eastern Brazil. The last eight months were occupied by his magnificent trip from Manáos up the Rio Negro and its tributary the Caquetá as far as the sandstone Serra do Araracuara (in Amazonian Colombia).

The important collections of George Gardner, made over a period of five years in the field, exceeded more than 7000 numbers. He traversed the interior regions north of Rio de Janeiro and westward over the high plateaus of Goyaz and Matto Grosso and across eastern Brazil to Aracaty, near the present-day city of Fortaleza in the state of Ceará.

Perhaps the largest of the earlier collections was made by Glaziou, who over a period of thirty-five years obtained nearly 23,000 field numbers mostly in eastern Brazil.

Overwhelmingly the most important collections of Amazonian materials were made by Richard Spruce during the fifteen years of his heroic exploration of the Amazon River and its tributaries, the Trombetes, Negro, Uaupés, Casiquiare, and Pacimoni Rivers, regions of the upper Orinoco in Venezuela, and finally of Peru and Ecuador during the last nine years. His collections of nearly 10,000 field numbers are widely distributed in the herbaria of the world, of which 6544 numbers are of vascular plants. The first set of the latter, studied by Bentham, is on deposit at Kew. Spruce made the taxonomic study of his moss and liverwort collections.

Since 1900 the outstanding figure in Amazonian botany has been Adolpho Ducke. There is available at this time no detailed account of his long years of exploration throughout the Amazon Basin, nor has a collation been made of the numerous written contributions that he has made to the flora of Hylea. It is unquestionably accurate to say that he has collected more plant material of the finest quality from the Amazonian region than has any other man in the entire history of American tropical botany. His important collections are widely distributed in the world herbaria, the principal sets being at Rio de Janeiro, Belém (in the Museu Goeldi and Instituto Agronômico do Norte), Washington, and New York. At present, Ducke, in his eighty-first year, is engaged in a field study of the flora of the state of Ceará. He is in residence in the city of Fortaleza.

For a number of years J. Huber, who died in 1914, was in charge of the botanical collections at the Museu Goeldi at Belém. The most complete set of his collections and the most complete set extant of the important Brazilian collections of E. Ule, together with many of the earlier of A. Ducke and their contemporaries of the period, are at the Museu Goeldi.

P. F. von Luetzelberg in 1911 became head gardener at the botanical garden in Rio de Janeiro. From there until 1922, serving with the Brazilian government in various capacities, he traveled widely throughout eastern Brazil. By 1920 he had accumulated 12,000 herbarium specimens, which in 1922 he took with him to Munich. On his return to Brazil in 1924, he continued in government service, joining the frontier commission under General Rondon in 1927. From 1927 until 1929, while on the frontier commission, he took part in the exploration of the Rios Tacutú and Uraricuera, visited Mount Roraima, and along the Colombian frontier traveled up the Rio Negro to the Rio Uaupés. From these explorations 2000 herbarium specimens were sent to Munich. During the years 1935–1937 he again traveled in eastern Brazil.

Ernst Heinrich Ule was one of the great productive explorers of Brazil, whose extensive travels in Brazil occupied much of his life between 1883 and 1912. Three extended return visits to Germany, in 1898–1899, 1903–1906, and 1908, interrupted this long period of field activity. The early part of his work centered in the south of Brazil, chiefly in the states of Santa Catarina, Rio Grande do Sul, and Rio de Janeiro. Later he spent much time in Minas Gerais, Goyaz, and Piauí. In 1900 he became active in the study of the vast forest floras of the Amazon Basin, working in the basins of the Juruá and Marary during that year. In 1902 and 1903 he conducted extensive work in the upper Amazon basin from Manáos to the regions of Tarapoto and Iquitos in Peru, returning after nearly a year and a half to Manáos in late 1903. After his return from his last visit to Berlin, he was again in Manáos and took up residence in Boa Vista on the upper Río Branco from October, 1908, until February, 1910. During this period he was much assailed by fever and tropical sores and had to return to Manáos at least once for hospitalization. From Boa Vista he conducted an excursion of some seven weeks to Mount Roraima, which he ascended on four separate occasions. From Manáos in November, 1910, he began the last of his long journeys, progressing up the Rios Purús and Acre to the region of the Bolivian frontier, reaching Manáos in February, 1912, after nearly a year and a half's absence. He returned to Berlin the last time in April, 1912, and remained there working on his materials. He never fully recovered from the ravages of fever and tropical sores and died July 15, 1915, at the age of sixty-one.

The enormous effort of his field activity yielded approximately 17,000 field numbers, of which more than 10,000 were vascular plants. Unfortunately, most of the original set was destroyed in Berlin during the war. The most complete duplicate sets that now exist are at the Museu Goeldi at Belém and at Leiden. Substantial bodies of his material are at the British Museum and elsewhere.

During the years 1931–1936, B. A. Krukoff conducted five expeditions to the Amazon Basin, during which he amassed a total of about 10,000 numbers. In addition, he had prepared 40,000 wood hand samples, for which voucher specimens were represented in the exsiccatae. R. L. Fróes for the most part was Krukoff's chief assistant and collected independently for him in 1939–1941. The original sets of the very important Krukoff collections are at New York; duplicates are widely distributed in world herbaria. A résumé of the regions of the five expeditions is as follows (the first and second expeditions were respectively to Africa and the Far East):

Third Expedition, 1931–1932; collection numbers 1700–2024; Rio Tapajóz, Edo. Pará, Rio Solimões, Edo. Amazonas, and Rio Madeira, Edos. Amazonas and Matto Grosso. Fróes under Krukoff's direction in 1932–1933 collected in the Basin of the Rio Maracassumé, Maranhão.

Fourth Expedition, 1933; collection numbers 2228–5959; basins of the Rios Grajahú and Tocantins, Edos. Maranhão and Goyaz; the Rios Purús, Ituri, and Juruá, Edo. Amazonas and Terr. Acre.

Fifth Expedition, 1934–1935; collection numbers 6034–7314; Rio Madeira, Edo. Amazonas.

Sixth Expedition, 1935–1936; collection numbers 7501–7910; Edos. Amazonas and Pará.

Seventh Expedition, 1936–1937; collection numbers 7911–9124; basins of the Rios Negro and Solimões, Edo. Amazonas.

Eighth Expedition, 1939; collection numbers 10,001–11,805; Bolivia.

For the last two decades botanists at the Instituto Agronômico do Norte at Belém, under the direction of J. Murça Pires, have undertaken extensive exploration throughout the Amazon Basin. During the period 1945–1947, Pires (with G. A. Black) assembled 1668 collection numbers in the Amazon Basin from Belém to Iquitos in Peru. In subsequent years he has continued his field work independently and with his colleagues, extending his work as far as the upper Rio Negro. George A. Black, 1946–1955, particularly in the states of Pará, Ceará, Amazonas, and the territories of Amapá, Rio Branco, and Guaporé, has collected 18,817 numbers. In Brazil he has collected also in the states of Maranhão, São Paulo, Minas Gerais, Rio de Janeiro, and Bahia. In addition, he has collected in Colombia, Peru, Bolivia, Ecuador, French Guiana, Argentina, Mexico, and the United States. The original sets are at the Instituto in Belém; duplicate material is largely at New York and Washington.

R. L. Fróes from 1942 to 1953 collected 10,732 numbers principally as follows: the states of Amazonas, Pará, Bahia, Maranhão, and the territories of Rio Branco and Amapá. The original sets are at the Instituto; duplicates are at New York, Washington, and elsewhere.

Consideration of botanists of southern Brazil would perhaps better be relegated to a final section. But, that lacking, some brief comments are made here.

Contemporaneous with Ducke, two other luminaries over a period of nearly five decades, but with their center of operation in southern Brazil, have contributed much to the field botany of the country. J. G. Kuhlmann terminated his long career as director of the Botanical Garden at Rio de Janeiro; F. C. Hoehne as director at São Paulo.

Hoehne served as botanist on a number of the expeditions of the frontier commission in the Amazon Valley led by Brazil's most famous field geographer, Coronel (later General) Rondon (Chefe da Commissão Brasileira). Hoehne accompanied the well-known expedition of which Theodore Roosevelt and his party were members, called by the courtesy of the Brazilian government the Roosevelt-Rondon Expedition. More recently (1940–1955) his botanical efforts have been directed toward the editing and writing of the *Flora Brasílica,* his own contribution being chiefly the completion of the treatment of the family of his greatest interest, the *Orchidaceae.*

During recent years, Belo Horizonte in Minas Gerais has become the center of considerable botanical field activity. A. Macedo, independent collector, has distributed extensive series of exsiccatae.

In the state of Santa Catarina, Padre P. Paulino Reitz, director of the Herbário Barbosa Rodrigues at Itajaí, with his colleague Padre Balduino Rambo, has undertaken the preparation of a flora for Santa Catarina. Extensive field investigation has gone into the undertaking. Assistance of numerous collaborators has been invited, chiefly of Lyman B. Smith of the U.S. National Herbarium, who at this writing is in the field in southern Brazil.

In 1928–1929, Smith visited classic localities in the vicinity of Rio de Janeiro to obtain topotypes and to effect general collecting. His field efforts were made chiefly in Niteroi, Teresópolis, Petrópolis, and Mount Itatiaia in Rio de Janeiro state; the Federal District; and São Paulo, Alto da Serra, and Santos in São Paulo state. The original set is at Gray Herbarium. In 1952 he visited the coastal slope of Santa Catarina and adjacent Paraná and Rio Grande do Sul. The original set is at Washington.

Contemporary exploration of large scale, as in the past, more often is motivated by multiple interest. Its execution is generally accomplished by the collaboration of several individuals and institutions. Its costly support of necessity must be sustained by government, industrial organizations, larger institutions, and interested friends of substance. Its accomplishments are usually diversified and manifold. The work of five such large-scale operations of current interest and activity, already referred to in the preceding pages, is amplified to some extent in the following paragraphs. Attention has earlier been called to comparable projects that have recently been completed or are at this time under way in the study of boreal and temperate American botany.

THE U.S. NATIONAL HERBARIUM ANDEAN PROGRAM. Over a period of twelve years, an effective collaborative program for exploration in the vast flora of Andean South America was carried on by the Smithsonian Institution, The New York Botanical Garden, and Harvard University. The program was initiated in 1917 by the trip to Colombia of F. W. Pennell and H. H. Rusby, both then associated with the staff of The New York Botanical Garden. The second expedition was conducted by Pennell, Killip, and Hazen in 1922. The third and culminating expedition to Colombia under the collaborative program was conducted by E. P. Killip of the Smithsonian and A. C. Smith of New York, who were in that country from October, 1926, to April, 1927. In 1929

Killip and Smith continued their association in their expedition to Peru, collecting in the field from the beginning of April until October. Killip independently made several additional trips to Colombia.

These four expeditions yielded more than 20,000 collection numbers, including a total of some 70,000 sheets, a remarkable accomplishment that could only have been made by the combined resources of several institutions and a number of efficient field operators. As a result of these activities, and those of Schultes, Idrobo, and García-Barriga, and the materials of the Cinchona Mission, the collections of the National Herbarium are now especially rich in plants of Colombia, Ecuador, and Peru.

UNIVERSITY OF CALIFORNIA BOTANICAL GARDEN EXPEDITIONS TO THE ANDES (1935–1952). For a period of fifty years, T. H. Goodspeed, W. A. Setchell, who initiated the program, and numerous collaborators brought to focus the several techniques of exploration, geography, taxonomy, experimental culture, anatomy, morphology, and cytology upon the study of a single genus, *Nicotiana*. Goodspeed's monographic treatment, *The Genus Nicotiana*, 1954, resulting from the concentrated application of so many interrelated disciplines of botanical science, is an outstanding example of results to be achieved by concert in research.

Of particular interest here is the field program. Between 1935 and 1952, five expeditions were sent into the field to Mexico, El Salvador, Costa Rica, Nicaragua, Honduras, Colombia, Ecuador, Peru, Chile, Bolivia, and Argentina. Besides Goodspeed, some nineteen botanists took part at one time or another in the field operation of the five expeditions. A total of 13,673 collections was obtained; principal sets are at the University of California.

In greater part, these collections were not directly related to the primary project, the study of *Nicotiana*. In the future, as they become incorporated in the taxonomic and geographic studies of the Central and South American Cordillera, accessory and subordinate material results of the expeditions will continuously become of more evident importance. Professor Goodspeed wrote: "It might be noted that the floras in general of the regions traversed were collected and mapped with the result that the University of California Botanical Garden Expeditions to the Andes have made not an inconsiderable contribution to knowledge of the composition and distribution of the vegetation of western South America."

THE "CINCHONA" PROGRAM. As a result of the exclusion of the United States and its allies from the source of raw materials in the Far East by the outbreak of the war with Japan, an emergency program dealing with the procurement and study of native American species of *Cinchona* was inaugurated by the Federal government. In 1942 and 1943 the formative stages of the program to obtain cinchona-bark for the emergency production of quinine were initiated by the U.S. Board of Economic Warfare. The program was officially terminated in April, 1945.

William C. Steere was the first botanist to reach the field, having been engaged in exploration for *Cinchona* in Colombia since November, 1942. He was transferred to Ecuador in July, 1943, to organize operations in that country. As the program proceeded, he was joined successively by Julian A. Steyermark, William B. Drew, F. Marion Ownbey, W. H. Camp, Gerald W. Prescott, Ira L. Wiggins, F. B. Wallace, and M. Acosta-Solís. Steyermark in the spring of 1943 was sent to Venezuela to extend the procurement program into that region.

F. R. Fosberg, who in November, 1942, likewise became engaged in the project in Colombia, remained in Colombia to direct field operations after the departure of L. R. Holdridge in February, 1943. Botanists and foresters who were thereafter associated with operations in Colombia were Donald Winters, William Silcocks, E. L. Core, Henry Kernan, A. L. McComb, Chapin Jones, E. L. Little, Jr., F. J. Hermann, Norman Fassett, M. L. Grant, Harold St. John, and Joseph Ewan.

Thus, no fewer than twenty-two plant taxonomists of experience were placed in the field in search for sources of cinchona-bark, to discover and map the range and abundance of *Cinchona* populations within the areas of survey and to collect data and material preparatory to taxonomic studies of the genus *Cinchona* and related groups.

No record is available concerning the enormous amount of material that must have been collected for the *Cinchona* study alone. In addition to that, as Steere has indicated, there were opportunity and encouragement for participating botanists to collect material of their own particular interest; for example, Steere collected materials of the Rubiaceae and Bryophyta, Prescott of the Algae, Drew of the Orchidaceae, Camp of the Ericaceae and *Lycopodium*, Steyermark of the general flora, and Wiggins of the Pteridophyta. Urgent as was the initial *Cinchona* activity during the war, as a result of the perfection of synthetic anti-malarials the immediate practical urgency soon became inconsequential. There remained, however, the value of the scientific, chemical, phytogeographic, and taxonomic studies on *Cinchona*. And of further significance, there will emerge as by-product contributions to the greater knowledge of the Andean flora.

The work of W. H. Camp may serve as an example of this sort of by-product. During the period of the *Cinchona* program and for six months after its termination, Camp with his assistants Francisco Prieto, Henning Jorgensen, and Manuel Giler collected most vigorously in some of the more remote areas of Ecuador, essentially through the period April, 1944, to October, 1945, amassing a total of 6523 collection numbers, usually in large series and consistently provided with good field data. This large collection, which is the most valuable of contemporary material to have come from Ecuador, is at New York.

The official collections of the various members of the program have been submitted to the U.S. National Herbarium. Personal collections of the many participants are at many botanical institutions of this country.

THE RUBBER PROGRAM. During the war period, because rubber supply from the Far East had been cut off, a comprehensive program was pursued by the Division of Rubber Plant Investigation, Bureau of Plant Industry, at Washington, to locate in the field and obtain material for the selection of high-yield and disease-resistance strains and to obtain data and specimens for the taxonomic study of *Hevea* and related genera.

Prominently concerned in the field program were John T. Baldwin, R. J. Seibert (1940–1946), and Richard E. Schultes, who did field work in the Amazon Basin almost continuously from 1941 to 1953.

In addition to specimens collected for the specific purposes of the program, including those for detailed taxonomic study of *Hevea, Micrandra,* etc., an enormous amount of general material was collected which, now that the urgency of the rubber program has receded, may in all probability come to be the most important result of the undertaking.

In his thirteen years in the hylean region of the Amazon Basin (1941–1942, under the auspices of the National Research Council, 1943–1953, for the U.S.D.A.), Schultes obtained approximately 23,000 collection numbers mostly of vascular plants as follows: 1941–1946, in Colombian Amazonas; 1947–1948, in Brazilian Amazonas (three months in 1945 in Peruvian Amazonas); and 1948–1953, again in Colombian Amazonas. The first set of these important collections is at Washington.

Schultes has thus spent a longer period of time in the hylean region than did his illustrious predecessor and mentor Richard Spruce. He has collected again many of the species known only from Spruce specimens and has himself discovered large numbers of "new" species. He has especially contributed important materials and geographical data pertaining to the region of the Roraima sandstone sediments of Colombian Amazonas.

THE GUAYANA HIGHLAND PROGRAM OF THE NEW YORK BOTANICAL GARDEN. This long-term project, supported in part by the National Science Foundation, unlike the preceding four, has been carried on primarily by the staff of a single institution. The New York Botanical Garden since 1928 has been concerned with the exploration and floristic study of the Guayana Highland of southern Venezuela and contiguous British Guiana and Brazil. This is a region characterized topographically by great and small, lofty, more or less isolated sandstone, tabular mountains, separated, except in the Gran Sabana in Venezuela and parts of Colombian Amazonas, by valleys and river-drainage basins supporting low-altitude rain forest. Geologically, these tabular mountains are the erosion remnants of a series of sand and volcanic sediments collectively known as the Roraima Formation and presumably were laid down in Cretaceous time.

Historically, botanical exploration of the Guayana Highland began with the original visits of Robert H. Schomburgk and Richard Schomburgk, 1838–1842, during which period Robert "discovered" Mount Roraima, the highest of the eastern block-mountains, at the tricorners of Venezuela, British Guiana, and Brazil. In fairly rapid sequence Roraima was visited by Appun (1864), im Thurn (1884), McConnell and Quelch (1894 and 1898), and by Ule (1909–1910). The primary materials of these explorations (except Ule's) are at Kew and the British Museum.

The second phase of exploration of the region of the Roraima sediments was occupied by the three remarkable expeditions of George H. H. Tate, of the American Museum of Natural History, to Mount Roraima in 1927–1928, the initial exploration of Cerro Duida in 1928–1929, and finally of Auyán-tepuí on the Gran Sabana in 1937–1938. The plants of these expeditions were studied by H. A. Gleason at The New York Botanical Garden, where the original sets are preserved.

The third and contemporary phase of exploration of Guayana has been carried on chiefly by Bassett Maguire and John J. Wurdack and their associates Richard S. Cowan, D. B. Fanshawe, L. Politi, W. M. C. Bagshaw, and others. Since 1944 eighteen expeditions to some twenty-five strategically located tabular mountains or otherwise prominent regions have been accomplished. Separately, Julian A. Steyermark in 1944, in the employ of the Cinchona Mission, visited Mount Roraima and Cerro Duida. The following year, for the Chicago Natural History Museum, he made the initial exploration of Ptari-tepuí on the Gran Sabana. In 1953 Wurdack and Steyermark separately visited opposite sides of Chimantá-tepuí, and in January of 1955 The New York Botanical Garden and Chicago Museum combined forces, sending Steyermark and Wurdack back for a joint exploration of Chimantá-tepuí. In the current season of 1957–1958, Maguire and Wurdack expect again to be in the field in Amazonian Guayana.

During the past decade and a half, Captain Felix Cardona, for the government of Venezuela, has traveled widely in Guayana doing geographical survey. As a part of his activity Cardona has made many collections of plants which add greatly to the floristic record of the region. Tobías Lasser and his colleagues from the Servicio Botánico, actively engaged in botanical exploration throughout Venezuela, have sent several expeditions to Guayana, the last being that of Vareschi to Auyán-tepuí, completed in 1956. The original sets of the Maguire and Wurdack collections are at New York; those of Steyermark are at Chicago; and the recently acquired materials of the Servicio Botánico are at Caracas and New York.

Over a period of years, William H. Phelps, Jr., of Caracas, has carried on ornithological exploration in Guayana. Kathleen D. Phelps (Mrs. William H. Phelps, Jr.), often with Charles B. Hitchcock, director at the American Geographical Society, served as botanist of the expeditions, collecting important series of plants which are on deposit in New York and Caracas.

There have been obtained during this program approximately 22,000 collection numbers in large series collected by Maguire and Wurdack and associates and an additional 2500 by Tate and the Phelps expeditions.

The objectives of these expeditions have been twofold: first, to make inventory and floristic study in the remarkable, strongly holopatric, highly endemic flora of Guayana; and secondly, to consider this flora in the light of problems of origin, dispersal, and geographic arrangement of primary floras in tropical South America.

As indicated by the contents of this paper, it is conclusively evident that exploration is the precursor of and is inevitably to be associated with floristic, phytogeographic, ecologic, and biosystematic investigation and of plant-resource inventory and effective land utilization. Exploration historically has been associated with the development of descriptive botany. It continues, now, to be adjunct to the most refined plant census in the preparation of the most modernly designed manual or flora. Exploration remains, therefore, an essential part of biotaxonomic and floristic procedure today. It will be essential for a long time to come.

14

NATURAL HISTORY, STATISTICS, AND APPLIED MATHEMATICS

Edgar Anderson

One February afternoon about twenty years ago, I was conducting a field trip in Natural History for a class of intelligent amateurs varying widely in age, social status, and scientific sophistication. One had his master's degree in botany and was then a manufacturer dealing with polymerized molecules. Another, a wholesale grocer of much native intelligence, had had no formal education since the time he left high school to help support his widowed mother. There were two high-school biology teachers, a bored investment banker, and the gracious, gray-haired president of the city's most exclusive garden club. Conducting such a class through the winter woods is a real challenge. Problems must be put on such a fundamental level that the most advanced students will be bored, yet in such simple terms that the beginners are not overwhelmed.

Finally, I hit upon an exercise so effective that I used it year after year, first with these night-school classes and then with college students. Eventually I exposed graduate students to it with such uniformly excellent results that now I use it in discussions with fellow scholars: biologists, mathematicians, social scientists.

On that February afternoon I selected a big white oak tree and, leaning against it, addressed the class somewhat as follows: "It is just over a hundred years since this hillside was first taken title to by pioneers from Virginia. In that time many things have happened on this site. There are certainly hundreds of ways you can find your way to analyzing the main factors in what has taken place here. There is one very easy way, that I know of for certain. It is probably not the only easy one, but most of the other methods are difficult and indirect and time-consuming. Now your assignment for the next hour is to find what were the main steps in vegetational change on this site in the last century. You can all solve the problem with no more technical equipment and no more botanical training than you now have. We'll take this tree as the center of a hundred-foot circle. What has happened here in a century? Don't neglect any kind of evidence, just because it seems trivial. The world is full of easy keys to important problems; only once in a while does a genius come along and label these trivial keys as significant evidence. I warn you there is such a key here, and most of you will ignore it—though it is in plain sight and requires no book learning to interpret correctly. Any one of you could solve this problem given a day or two; several of you I know will work it out laboriously this afternoon; is there anybody here who can find the easy way in the first five minutes?"

There wasn't. In twenty years I have had just two students who had the wit to notice that all the time I was talking to them my left hand was playing idly with a scrap of barbed wire which sticks out an inch or so from a scar on the big oak. Off to the left about thirty feet is another tree with a similar scar, though without any barbed wire, and way off to the right in more or less of the same straight line is another oak with two such horizontal scars, one about a foot above the other. There had, you see, been a wire fence strung through the woods, using the trees as posts. When the land on both sides of it was acquired for an arboretum, the barbed wire was mostly removed, but it had stayed in place so long that some of the trees had buried it in their bark. This was more than just a fence row; it was a section line, the boundary between two farms which had been differently managed. One had been cut over and fairly heavily grazed; the other family had only taken out a tree here and there. If one figures out where the fence once ran and then comes and stands on the fence line and faces first toward one farm and then turns round about and faces away from it, he sees two different landscapes. On one side there are few large trees, no big oak, and a good number of vigorous young trees in groups of two or three, showing where an old stump had sprouted. There are plants which indicate a former pasture, a few surviving grasses, and one prairie rose not too happy in the shaded woodland. There are a number of dead red cedars, red cedars being planted everywhere thereabouts by the birds but able to survive only in the sunlight. In the other direction there are big oaks, little underbrush, no stump sprouts, no cedars, and scattered dogwoods. Facing west, one looks into a typical first-growth white-oak–sugar-maple woodland; facing east into vigorous second-growth woods. If he looks up and down the old fence line he can see how, for some decades, the woodland trees sent husky branches out sidewise toward the sunlight of a brushy pasture, branches which are just now beginning to die in the heavier shade of the maturing second growth.

The greatest delight I ever had as a teacher was when at last one alert student glanced at the barbed wire I had been handling, looked back and forth along the line of old trees for further scars, stood on the former fence line looking first due east and then straight west, then gave me a wink and went and lay under the big oak until his fellow students solved the problem by their own slower-witted techniques. He is today a highly successful professional rose breeder, but as I follow the careers of my other students I note that they all profit by the methodology of Natural History, though there is only one of them who really works in that field. I note in particular that it is used in their everyday thinking by two or three who, when they were graduate students, had no great gifts in that direction or had, by their undergraduate mentors, been taught to despise such methods. Yet there is no better way for getting to grips with the fundamentals of a big problem than the method of Natural History. The problem is at first a set of unrelated facts; as the trained naturalist examines it, he perceives groups of facts organized into patterns, patterns recognized because they repeat their essential features time after time.

One of the outstanding points about Natural History is the large extent to which it deals with pattern data, rather than with pointer readings, lengths, widths, densities, weights, etc. To be specific, in the problem I set my class, the barbed-wire scars were a significant pattern, the trees coming up in groups of two or three as stump sprouts were another, the dead and dying branches which once extended out from the uncut forest to the cutover pasture were still another. An experienced observer could use one set of patterns to set up a hypothesis, then figure out the logical consequences of this hypothesis and check with other data to confirm it.

One reasoned something as follows: fence scars in a line, and one of them has a piece of barbed wire; this must be a boundary between two fields. Ah yes, the stump sprouts are all on the east side, and there are none on the west. If the east side was cut over, then the trees along the fence should have sent out branches sideways into the light and there should be either the scars of such branches or the branches themselves more or less dying off in the reduced light. A quick glance confirmed this hypothesis; a checkup on the one-sided distribution of light-loving plants, pasture roses, red cedars gave added support. One was almost as certain as if one had been present that this was indeed an old fence line between two fields, one of which had been cut over and the other not. One's mind and eye worked back and forth from data to hypotheses, then back again to data. Inductive and deductive reasoning tripped so closely on one another's heels that they were one simultaneous process.

Confronted with any large and complex problem, in any field, the scientist who has had effective training in Natural History knows more or less instinctively what to do. Everything looks chaotic at first, but we do not live in a chaotic universe. There may be confusion in our minds, but there is no chaos in the way the world is running. Faced with such a problem, the properly trained scholar looks around for significant repeatable patterns in the data and reasons back and forth from observation to hypothesis until he has found his way into it. The finicky pointer-reading data, single sense impressions, lengths, widths, weights, so useful for precise analysis, are best deferred until we know what kind of a problem we are up against.

Pattern data have a broader observational basis than pointer-reading data, as Minot pointed out (1911) half a century ago in his pioneer attempt to fit growth curves. Therefore they are invaluable in the early stages of any complex problem. Before we have some notion of what we are about, pointer readings by themselves are little help. Lengths, densities, weights, though accurately determined, merely allow us to phrase our ignorance more elegantly. Precision has little advantage until we have enough understanding to use precise analysis. In the early stages of a problem, accurate, unrelated data, if collected in big enough quantities by many people and scattered through numerous papers, may actually obscure the problem and hinder its solution. Platoons of busy workers may share their data so expertly that only a gifted few realize the fundamental obscurity of the problem. I remember with a shudder the lectures and the seminars on growth tropisms I endured before the Wents (following Darwin's lead) cracked the whole problem wide open by an elegant combination of pattern data (curvature of *Avena* coleoptiles) and pointer readings (analysis of the growth substances concentrated in the agar blocks).

The most rapid scientific advances come when some genius recognizes a pattern which is diagnostic, which can be used with precision, and which orders up whole pages of pointer readings. Such was the recognition of the periodic system, such was Mendel's lighting upon the Mendelian factor as a hereditary unit. He noted that with the round versus the wrinkled peas, with the tall versus the short and fasciated plants, he had significant patterns which behaved as units in their transmission from generation to generation. We do not yet know the precise relationship between these unit patterns and the germ plasms of which they are a part, but the recognition that they were more or less the same sort of thing and that they were significant patterns with which to analyze problems of inheritance has made Genetics one of the most fertile fields in biology during the past fifty years.

Those who have not actually participated in such routine genetic chores as the making of linkage maps seldom realize how qualitative the basic data of Genetics can be. It is a simple point, but worth emphasizing. Genetics advanced so rapidly because it was using pattern data with their broad observational basis, but using them with great precision. Take the eye mutants in *Drosophila* for instance. In an experiment with several marker genes involving eye color, one could catalogue them and their various recombinations efficiently only when he had learned to recognize as significant patterns various little differences in color, texture, size, and aging. Imagine trying to separate two wing mutants of *Drosophila* on a truly objective, statistical basis! It would be as difficult as separating two closely related species statistically.

The basic data of classical Genetics and of classical Taxonomy are much more alike than has been generally realized. I have myself collected and determined tradescantias from Texas roadsides where two or three species were growing intermingled. I have also scored *Primula sinensis* crosses segregating simultaneously for "oak," "fern," and "tongue," three mutants which affect leaf shape. The two experiences (identifying tradescantias and scoring primrose genes) were all of a piece. One was cataloguing patterns in both cases. The initial judgments were quite as qualitative for the one as for the other. However, after the tradescantias had been identified, one could only catalogue them as *Tradescantia gigantea, T. occidentalis,* and *T. humilis* and a host of unclassifiable intermediates. With the primulas one had such a precise understanding of the patterns that the results were set out in neat mathematical symbolism OOTTyy, OottYY, etc. [Parenthetically, it is some satisfaction to realize that if I went back today to that same Texas roadside, I could now, with the method of Pictorialized Scatter Diagrams (1954), born out of my struggles with the *Tradescantia* problem, catalogue the puzzling intermediate and the parental species, with almost the precision of an experiment in Genetics!]

Though pattern data are more widely used in Natural History than in other disciplines they are by no means confined to it or to Biology. The periodic system (Physics) has already been referred to. Other examples with the fields to which they belong are cold fronts (Meteorology); terminal moraines (Glacial Geology); the equation of a straight line (Mathematics); electron photographs (Physical Chemistry); X-ray diffraction patterns (Physics); the bending of *Avena* coleoptiles (Biology); a continental shelf (Physiography).

Yet of all the disciplines, Natural History is the most richly endowed with pattern data. For that reason alone, if for no other, it needs to be kept in the science-training curriculum. It is the one method so broadly based that with it you can always discover something you were not looking for. We can nowadays replace many of the functions of the human mind with a properly designed machine. Yet you cannot design a machine, to find something you do not yet know you are looking for, a machine, to take a specific example, which could examine contaminated agar plates, *in advance of any knowledge of antibiotics,* and discover penicillin. Natural History trains one to think in terms of hypotheses about the phenomena; to postpone mathematical models until one has at least a rough idea of what kind of a model will be needed. These are healthy attitudes for a scholar in any field. If, however, we are to bring Natural History to its full stature as a science, we need to learn how to use its pattern data with greater precision; need even more to learn how to think about them analytically. Greater precision is no great benefit unless it leads to a sharper analysis.

Let us therefore examine pattern data on as simple a level as possible. In

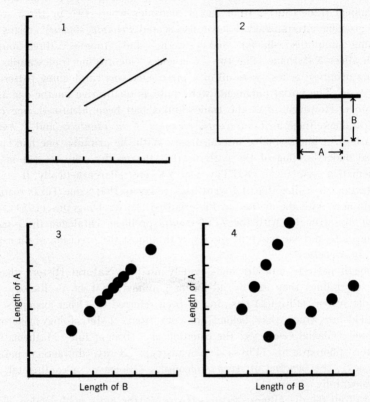

Fig. 1–4.—Fig. 1. Pattern data reduced to their mathematically simplest form. The two lines differ in (1) length, (2) position on the grid, (3) slope.—Fig. 2. A simple example of a machine which could produce pattern data such as those in fig. 1. The large square represents sheets of plastic which are being cut by a right-angled cutting bar, to produce small squares of plastic in which A equals B. Further explanation in the text.—Fig. 3. A plotted against B when the machine in fig. 2 is in proper adjustment.—Fig. 4. A plotted against B for five samples each from two days' run when the machine was not being properly set up by the supervisor. Further discussion in the text. Note that straight lines drawn through the two series of dots would produce a figure essentially like the theoretical one of fig. 1.

mathematical terms the simplest patterns I can imagine are the two straight lines in fig. 1. They differ in their length, the angle of their slope, and their position on the descartian grid. To make the problem easier to think about, let us invent a ridiculously simple example which could yield two such lines. Therefore (as a basis for discussion) let us imagine a big punch press which cuts squares out of sheets of plastic. For the purposes of our problems we will suppose that the cutting edge has a right-angled bend in it, that one square is cut from each sheet of plastic, and that the machine is oriented at the corner of the plastic sheet as in fig. 2. Furthermore, let us suppose that at the beginning of the day's run the press is set up by a supervisor using precision equipment so that A is exactly equal to B. We will also suppose that so long as A equals B and the punched corners are square, there is no need in this particular process for any great precision and that the operator merely uses his eye and turns out a set of squares of somewhere near the same size. If we examine the squares from a day's run and actually measure A and B on each, we will find that a scatter diagram of them looks something like fig. 3. Having been set up with precision equipment, on the scale of our measurement they vary in size but not appreciably in shape.

Now, consider what will happen when something goes wrong with the precise setting up of the machine. It may be that the supervisor is having trouble with his wife and stops for a couple of drinks on his way to work. Under these conditions he will set up the press some mornings so that A is much shorter than B and on others so that it is longer. The press of course is oriented on the corner of the plastic sheets so that it will turn out a series of rectangles of varying size, all of them somewhat wider than high in the first case and somewhat higher than wide in the other. If we take a few samples from a series of runs on two different days and plot A against B, we will get a scatter diagram something like that of fig. 4.

This diagram is the nub of the argument. Given the facts as shown on this diagram, what are the chances that the two sets of squares were punched on different days? What would be the odds if you knew about the machine but not about the supervisor's home life; what would they be if you understood the supervisor and the operator as well as the machine? What would your opinion be if you knew nothing about the machine but had merely had considerable experience with pattern data? Or to ask the question a more significant way: under each of these conditions how many of the punched-out rectangles would you want to measure before you could be reasonably certain that they were produced on different days? The actual answers to these questions by scientists with different backgrounds are illuminating. One research physicist replied immediately, "Well, if you know that the punch is oriented on the corner, then the line through the measurements for each day must go through the origin. You'll need only one sample from each day's run." Other physicists thought about the problem in the same way but wanted two samples from each run to be reasonably certain. One of my former students, familiar with various kinds of pattern data, said that he would want three to four from each. Two samples each would establish the two straight lines, one more each would confirm that hypothesis, and a fourth would make doubly sure.

There is of course no one right answer to such a problem as this. It is a problem in applied mathematics. We are not dealing with a neat, circumscribed, made-up universe with simple rules and yes-or-no answers. We are dealing with the actual world around us, imperfectly understood at best, in which answers are matters of judgment.

For all their efficiency, pattern data need rigorous mathematical thinking for maximum scientific usefulness. Here we immediately reach an impasse. The kinds of minds which deal effectively with both pattern data and mathematical symbols are rare indeed, so rare that the connections of pattern data to mathematics have scarcely been touched upon in print. Apparently the fact that multiple-sense-impression data (i.e., pattern data) require (and deserve) to be analyzed by appropriate and efficient methods was not pointed out until 1954 (Anderson, 1954) and then only in connection with one specialized problem. Yet (as was then demonstrated) the same methods of statistical analysis which deal so effectively with pointer readings—weights, yields, frequencies—can be inefficient, if not positively misleading, when applied to pattern-data problems.

The fundamental reason is not far to seek. The chief branch of applied mathematics which has turned its attention to such problems is Statistics. As its name suggests, Statistics grew out of the state's need to keep (and eventually to analyze) its records: births, deaths, incomes, marriages; exports; and the like. Note that these are all single-sense-impression data. Each separate statistic is a number and nothing more; none of them are pattern data. To analyze these data, statisticians eventually got help from Probability, from notions derived ultimately from relatively simple games of chance (simple, that is, by comparison with chess or basketball). Probability's basic ideas were first worked out either by gamblers of some mathematical competence or by mathematicians who for one reason or another (friendship with a gambler seems to have been the commonest) took an interest in the operation of gaming tables. Randomness and chance are therefore central concepts of Statistics. To illustrate how basic such ideas are to statistical thinking, I shall quote and comment briefly from a recent inaugural address (de Loor, 1954) by a prominent statistician, B. de Loor of the University of Pretoria. He outlines the increasing role of Statistics in many fields of science and then turns to generalizations about the basic problems of Statistics and (by implication) of science.

"Statistics," says de Loor, "is not interested in the individual." This is certainly true of most statisticians of my acquaintance. Perhaps there is no inherent reason why it should continue to be true for Statistics. Certainly applied mathematicians are interested in the significant individual. Whether such problems belong in another field of Applied Mathematics and must forever be excluded from the domain of Statistics is a relatively trivial quibble. It is a fact that in many kinds of scientific work and even when dealing with precise mathematically analyzed data, an individual may be highly significant. A single electron track on a photographic plate (Physics), a single erratic boulder (Glacial Geology), a single crossover between two closely linked genes (Genetics) are examples from three fields of science of individuals which might be the decisive evidence in critical experiments.

"In many cases individuals behave at random," says de Loor. Most certainly not. We do not live in that kind of a world. In our ignorance, in our imperfect understanding of some factors (and our complete ignorance of even the possibility of knowing about others), it may seem to us as if individuals—plants, molecules, insects, or microscopic particles, as the case may be—are behaving at random. The better we understand any particular problem, the less do we have to assign random behavior to any of the factors in it.

"Certainties barely exist for him," says de Loor, speaking of the statistician. With efficient pattern data, efficiently analyzed, the scientist may be as certain as it is possible to be. In the example of the former fence line in the woods, I am as certain as if I had been there that one property was cut over a considerable number of years ago and the other was not. Furthermore, any competent naturalist given the same assignment would come to the same conclusion. How certain can you get? Remember what Thoreau said about circumstantial evidence? "Sometimes," he said (and let me remind you that Thoreau was accustomed to using pattern data and to pondering deeply over it), "circumstantial data can be very convincing, as when you find a minnow in the can of milk!"

In the introduction to his inaugural address de Loor pointed out the ever-increasing role of Statistics in modern science. He said (and here I agree with him wholeheartedly), "Its development has been phenomenal, especially during the last two decades. To express it in terms of modern physics, a chain reaction has been set up and is making its influence felt in nearly every sphere of human activity." He then cites examples from nuclear physics, agricultural research, meteorology, medicine, social sciences, quality control, operations research, economics, and even from philology. In all the examples of which I have some knowledge, where Statistics has been an unqualified success, it has been with problems dealing with numbers (single-sense-impression data), usually pointer readings. In Agronomy it has revolutionized comparative-yield tests, even more in the way they are laid out than in the way in which the data are organized after they have been gathered. In Genetics it has simplified and codified the calculation of linkage data. (It should specifically be pointed out that the outstanding contributions of Sewall Wright to the fields of developmental and of population genetics owe little to conventional Statistics. His own method of path coefficients is a semi-graphical method for exploring factor interaction. It is in part a device for making pattern data out of pointer readings.) In Ecology, Cytology, and Haemocytology where Statistics has dealt with frequencies of occurrence using Poisson techniques, it has been effective though scarcely revolutionary. With pattern data, in all the fields with which I am personally conversant, it has always been inefficient and sometimes positively misleading.

In my own work I have spent the last thirty years in an attempt to measure evolution-in-progress directly from its results, that is, from the variation in living populations of plants and animals. Early in this attempt I worked directly with one of the world's greatest statisticians, Sir Ronald Fisher. I went to him with data on variation in populations of wild irises. He took a lively interest in the problem; with his facile mind he worked out an extension of some of his other techniques which could be applied to such problems, pointed out the kind of data which would be decisive for such a problem, and encouraged me in getting them. When I turned them over to him he worked out his multiple-discriminant function, using them as an illustration (1936), and in his gracious way gave me more credit than I deserved.

Working with Fisher was a stimulating experience. He cleared many cobwebs out of my thinking. He would say, "Now what do you mean by this statement? *If* you mean so-and-so then obviously such-and-such follows, but if on the other hand you mean thus-and-so, why then just as obviously this-and-that should follow." On the other hand, he did not in the end sell me on using his methods for my problems. I had been too strongly influenced by E. M. East and his insistence on the exhaustive examination of the phenomenon itself. I was muddleheaded compared to Fisher, but my ideas were soundly set on a broad observational base; though I was greatly impressed, I was not bowled over. After all, as Whitehead remarked (Price, 1954), sometimes "muddleheadedness is a condition precedent to independent thought, may actually be independent thought in its first stage." Eventually I worked out a simple graphical method for analyzing my iris data. It showed virtually everything I could have gotten out of the problem by analysis-of-variance methods and some things I could not have. A decade later, after various trial-and-error attempts, I originated the pictorialized scatter diagram (1954), a simple, precise, semi-graphical, semi-mathematical way of dealing with multiple-sense-impression problems. It has been rapidly adopted by various workers in my own field, soundly damned as heresy by a few agronomo-statisticians, and roundly praised by a few mathematicians. These experiences have led me to examine critically the relationships between pattern data on the one hand and statistics and applied mathematics on the other.

The point of view exemplified by de Loor's generalizations is common to nearly all the statisticians I have dealt with. It is not shared by the applied mathematicians of my acquaintance. It has, however, when applied to number data, produced results of such theoretical and practical importance that most thoughtful statisticians have been caught up in the busy burgeoning of their own discipline. Few statisticians indeed have, in the last few decades, had quiet moments in which to inquire into the limitations imposed upon their techniques by their own attitudes. They have been too busy with new disciples. ("God," as Renan remarked about St. Peter, "tests his saints by sending them disciples.")

So widespread has been the use and misuse of modern Statistics in biology and agriculture that it would be a simple matter to find illustrations of its inefficiency with pattern data in almost any journal in those fields. Competent statisticians are well aware that their beautifully precise methods are continually misapplied by scholars who learned them by rote and only halfway understand them. What I am concerned about, however, is a far graver matter; it is a basic maladjustment between natural history and mathematics. I am therefore deliberately choosing an example from the work of one of the ablest scholars in the field of Maize Genetics in his generation. Given the initial assumption (which would be concurred in by most American agronomists and by many able statisticians) that modern statistical methods are appropriate for pattern data (multiple-sense-impression problems), his facts were recorded with precision and the calculations were carried out with professional circumspection. Nor is it strange that E. W. Lindstrom, from one of whose minor investigations I am drawing my final example, should have been led astray in this initial assumption. Partly as the result of his own efforts (he was department head, vice-dean of the graduate school, influential as teacher, scholar, and administrator), several of his ablest colleagues were either first-rate statisticians or facile in the use of Statistics. He was simultaneously a maize geneticist and a successful corn breeder (the inbred lines he developed made a real contribution to modern hybrid corn). Both in Genetics and Plant Breeding he had seen the revolutionary effects of Statistics properly applied to number data. He and his statistically trained colleagues were far too busy with neophytes to sit down and conduct a searching inquiry as to the proper limits of the new techniques they were teaching.

But the point remains that like anyone, eminent or obscure, who applies traditional statistical methods to good pattern data, he was making a mistake. At the very least, such methods are inefficient for such problems. At the worst, as in this instance, they give the wrong answer, yet give it with such an air of objective precision and professional competence that the world as a whole is fooled. If such a man can make such a mistake, is it not time for a rigorous examination of the field between Natural History, Statistics, and Applied Mathematics?

This illustration is from one (1940) of Lindstrom's minor investigations

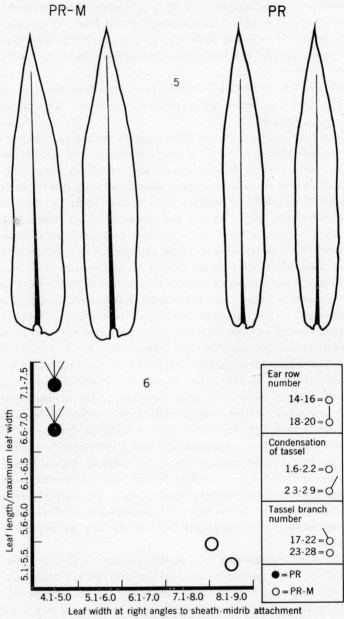

FIG. 5–6.—FIG. 5. Comparable leaves from two plants of Lindstrom's mutant inbred PR-M compared with two from plants of the inbred PR. From greatly reduced tracings of herbarium specimens collected from Lindstrom's experimental plot.—FIG. 6. The four specimen leaves of fig. 5 analyzed efficiently by a pictorialized scatter diagram. The leaf measurements used on the X and Y axes were de-

with maize inbreds. An inbred line known as PR gave rise to a mutant line PR-M with fewer rows of kernels to the ear. It also had shorter, broader kernels, a tassel with a thicker central spike, yet in hybrids and backcrosses with the parental line it behaved like a single gene difference. It seemed to Lindstrom that the leaves were wider, but to be certain he made careful statistical tests of this point. He measured leaf width at the midpoint for each leaf from many plants of PR and of PR-M, analyzed the results by chi-square methods, and came to the conclusion that differences of this order could have been due to chance alone. Using such methods the segregation of the differences between the two lines (PR and PR-M) became difficult to follow in subsequent generations, and he eventually discontinued active work with the problem.

At about this time I visited his experimental plot and collected herbarium specimens of both PR and PR-M. In making the specimens I noted a difference in the leaves and spoke to Professor Lindstrom about it. He replied that he had thought there was such a difference but that statistical tests had shown that "it was not significant." I then took the leaf just below the upper ear on the first five plants from a row of PR and from a row of PR-M and laid them down on the earth between the corn rows. It was immediately apparent that this was a problem with pattern data (fig. 5). The leaves differed in shape. Random sets collected from each line might or might not differ in median diameter, but *any* of the upper leaves of either line could immediately be distinguished from *any* of the upper leaves of the other, if one used the pattern of the whole leaf for his comparisons. To demonstrate this point, I turned my back on the plot and, using the two sets of specimen leaves as a reference, correctly identified all the leaves of PR or of PR-M which were brought to me. You see they were really different, *different for a categorically higher kind of difference* than two sets of widths could ever achieve.

Note from fig. 5 and 6 that in distinguishing between leaves of PR and PR-M we are dealing with multiple-sense-impression data. Using methods appropriate for such pattern data, one could demonstrate the differences with samples of 10 to 20 leaves and even establish it objectively.

Admittedly, this was one trivial statistical test, made by a busy and productive scholar. However, it gave him the wrong answer, and what is worse, it gave the wrong direction to his thoughts about a desperately important

---

rived directly from the tracings. The data on ear row number, tassel condensation, and tassel branch number were either taken in the field or are from tassel specimens made at the same time.

Note that this makes an objective record of five kinds of differences. It reinforces the impression derived from the tracings that PR and PR-M are two quite different things and that *the more one focuses his attention on all the differences,* the more evident is the discontinuity between them.

genetical question, the analysis of quantitative inheritance, a field in which
he was a leader. One of the reasons that this science is in the doldrums is
that at the present time anyone who goes into it gets a thorough training
in Statistics which in few cases known to me is accompanied by an equally
sound training in mathematics. The pattern data which could be so efficient
in solving some of the basic problems in this field are consequently ignored,
or are inefficiently turned into number data. Yet this is only one of many
fields where the brilliant successes of statistical methods with number data
have blinded all but a few scholars to:

1. Their inefficiency in dealing with patterns.

2. The various dangers of using concepts based on randomness in what is
obviously a very non-random universe.

3. The peculiar advantages of Natural History in dealing with pattern
data.

4. The need for the development of logical basic procedures in fields where
Natural History, Statistics, and Applied Mathematics come together.

LITERATURE CITED

ANDERSON, E. 1954. Efficient and inefficient methods of measuring specific differ-
    ences. Statistics and mathematics in biology. Iowa State College Press. Ames,
    Iowa.
DE LOOR, B. 1954. Statistics and statisticans. South African Jour. Sci. 51:49–53.
FISHER, R. A. 1936. The use of multiple measurements in taxonomic problems. Ann.
    Eug. 7:179–188.
LINDSTROM, E. W. 1940. Fifth annual report, Iowa Corn Research Institute. Pp.
    1–80.
MINOT, C. S. 1911. The method of science. Science 33:128.
PRICE, L. 1954. Dialogues of Alfred North Whitehead. P. 46. Little, Brown. Boston.

15

APPLICATION OF SOME PHYTOSOCIOLOGICAL TECHNIQUES TO BRAZILIAN RAIN FOREST [1]

Stanley A. Cain, Gustavus M. de Oliveira Castro, J. Murça Pires,
and Nilo Tomâs da Silva

PART I. FOREST COMPOSITION OF ARAPARÍ ISLAND, PARÁ [2]

Although taxonomic studies of the woody flora of the Amazonian rain forest have made known a considerable portion of the thousands of species,[3] there have been very few studies of the composition and structure of the

[1] At the time of these studies the senior author was a member of the United Nations Technical Assistance Mission to Brazil employed by UNESCO as Expert in Ecology. After his initial project had been carried as far as possible an arrangement was made between UNESCO, the Serviço Nacional de Malaria, and the Conselho Nacional de Pesquisas for work on a *Manual of Vegetation Analysis* to be prepared by Doctors Cain and de Oliveira Castro. In connection with this project, field work was done in the Territory of Amapá and the states of Pará, Minas Gerais, Paraná, Rio Grande do Sul, and the Federal District. The present paper is in a sense a by-product of this field work, in which we attempted the application to tropical vegetation of phytosociological concepts and methods originated in studies of temperate vegetation.

The senior author of this paper had accepted the invitation of the Editor of the *American Journal of Botany* to prepare a review of recent advances in phytosociology. Time did not permit fulfillment, so this original work was offered in its place. The studies are presented in three parts with designation of specific authorship at the appropriate points. Deep appreciation of the cordial cooperation of Brazilian scientists and their institutions is a pleasure to express.

[2] Gustavus M. de Oliveira Castro, Stanley A. Cain, and Nilo Tomâs da Silva.

[3] For example, for one family alone, Ducke and Black (1953) state that 846 species of Leguminosae are known from the Amazon region, with 206 species known from the neighborhood of Belém, Pará.

forest. In the Belém region Black et al. (1950) found 87 species of trees on a 1-hectare sample plot of *terra firme* rain forest and 60 species on a similar plot of *igapó* rain forest, all 1 dm. or more in diameter. On a 2-hectare sample plot at Mucambo, which we will report on in some detail, Murça Pires found 173 species of trees.

In January, 1956, the authors found it possible to visit Araparí Island, a few hours by launch south of Belém, through the courtesy of the Brazilian Malaria and Public Health services. The island lies approximately at 1° 40″ S. Lat. and 48° 30″ W. Long., where it is part of the complicated system of rivers and channels of the Belém region southeast of Ilha do Marajó, which is the principal island of the delta region of the Amazon. The rivers and channels are subject to the influence of the Atlantic tides, and all of Araparí island lies in the flood plain subject to the annual high-water periods.

About 3⅓ million acres of the Amazon basin, the hylaea, are covered by rain forest that is divided into two principal types. The *mata da terra firme* is the non-flooded upland. The *mata da varzea* is essentially the flood plain. It varies in width up to about 160 km. and in depth and duration of its annual inundation. Some intermediate strips of land that are occasionally but not regularly inundated are called *restinga,* and any small channel or basin where the soil never dries out is called an *igapó.* Locally, as at Araparí Island, shallow basins that stay wet from rain water are also called *igapós.* As seen from the boat, Araparí Island shows no topographic relief. One sees an even wall of forest with scattered emergent trees such as *Ceiba pentandra.* Internally, however, the island is threaded by channels that carry tidal water and the flood waters of the main rivers. There are numerous shallow, muddy basins kept moist by the almost daily rains which accumulate to more than 100 inches a year.

Along the muddy banks of rivers and channels that are subject to tides, there occurs a very common community dominated by Aninga, *Montrichardia arborescens.* This is a peculiar member of the Araceae that forms dense clans by vegetative reproduction of stout rhizomes, with a pigmy forest of trunks rising from a few to several feet, according to the fluctuation in tide levels, topped by tufts of broad, arrow-shaped leaves. One afternoon a rather rough sampling of this community was attempted from a rowboat. Ten units of this shore-line community were examined for the presence of different species, and for which coverage estimates were made. Each unit was approximately 30 m. (100 feet) long. Because the banks are typically steep, the community usually has a depth of about 5 m., so it was possible to locate all species and, when the identification was uncertain, collect them from the boat. The dominance of the species was estimated according to six coverage classes: (*) covering less than 1 per cent, (1) 1–5 per cent, (2) 6–25 per cent, (3) 26–50 per cent, (4) 51–75 per cent, and (5) 76–100 per cent. Table 1 shows the

Table 1. *Presence and coverage of species of the Montrichardia zone,*
Arapari Island, Pará

Species	Pres-ence	Cover-age
MICROPHANEROPHYTES: 2–8 m. tall		
Aninga—*Montrichardia arborescens* Schott	10	3–5
Veronica sp.	3	2–4
Mamorana—*Bombax aquaticum* (Aubl.) K. Sch.	2	1–2
Mututi—*Pterocarpus amazonicus* Huber	2	*–2
Unha de gato—*Bignonia* ? *unguis-cati* L.	2	*–1
Janau—*Tricanthera gigantea* HBK.	2	*–1
Tabebuia aquatilis (E. Mey.) Sprague & Sandwith	2	*–1
Ioioca—Gen. sp.?	2	*
Aturiá—*Machaerium* ? *lunatum* (Mey.) Ducke	1	1
Paliteira—*Clitoria racemosa* Sessé & Moc.	1	*
Carucaa—*Cordia multispicata* Cham.	1	*
Assaí—*Euterpe oleracea* Mart.	1	*
Cestrum latifolium var. *tenuiflorum* (HBK.) O. E. Schulz	1	*
Peperomia magnoliaefolia (Jacq.) A. Dietr.	1	*
NANOPHANEROPHYTES: 0.25–2 m. tall		
Juquirí—*Mimosa pigra* L.	3	*–1
Berreria latifolia Aubl.	3	*–1
Kyllinga sp.? (epiphytic on stems of *Montrichardia*)	1	*
LIANAS		
Parreira—*Cissus erosa* Rich.	5	*–2
Mucuna altissima DC.	3	*–1
Guapui—*Martinella obovata* (HBK.) C & S.	3	*
Cestrum sp.?	3	*
Ipomoea tiliacea (Willd.) Choisy	3	*
Stigmaphyllon sp.?	3	*
Mikania micrantha HBK.	2	*–2
Anomospermum sp.?	2	*–1
Hiraea sp.?	2	*
Menora flavida (DC.) Bur. & K. Sch.	1	1
Parreira (Puci)—*Cissus sicyoides* L.	1	*
Mucuná—*Dioclea glabra* Benth.	1	*
Manihot sp.?	1	*
Trichomanes sp.?	1	*

results of this sample. The only species regularly present in the sub-samples was *Montrichardia*. It also had the highest coverage, ranging in the ten units from class 3 to class 5. The dominance of the community by this species is apparent. Woody lianas are almost as abundant as phanerophytes of shrub and tree form. The denseness of the vegetation and the steepness of the muddy banks make landing difficult any place along the shore where the *Montrichardia* community occurs.

When viewed from the water there appears to be a second zone behind the *Montrichardia* that has some characteristic species and often is dominated by Assaí, *Euterpe oleracea*. Our examination of the island forest, however, failed to establish any significant stream and channel-bank forest type at Araparí Island. When first visiting the island we cruised up the Araparizinho channel as far as possible at the current water stage. Then we returned, rounded the end of the island, and cruised the opposite side. Six stations were selected for study, as follows:

    I. Araparizinho channel, afternoon of Jan. 23, 1956.
   II. Araparizinho channel, morning of Jan. 24, 1956.
  III. Araparizinho channel, afternoon of Jan. 24, 1956.
  IV. Carnapicho River, morning of Jan. 25, 1956.
   V. Carnapicho River, morning of Jan. 25, 1956.
  VI. Arauaia River, afternoon of Jan. 25, 1956.

In the Amazon, generally, homesteads are all located on water, and this is completely true of Araparí Island, where isolated families live in small houses of various construction in small clearings in the forest at the water's edge. Livelihood is based on fishing and hunting and gathering. The principal sources of income are from tapping rubber trees, *Hevea brasiliensis,* gathering for the market coco fruits, *Theobroma cacao,* the oil nut Andiroba, *Carapa guianensis,* Assaí for the fruits from which a drink is made, *Euterpe oleracea,* etc. Some of the clearings are large enough for planting of a few trees of banana and a small garden, mostly Mandioca, *Manihot utilissima.* As a consequence of his way of life, the *caboclo* often is something of a *mateiro,* or woodsman. Our stations were spaced around the island and also selected where there was a *caboclo* familiar with the adjacent woods who could act as guide and help in the identification of trees. Our major dependence for field identification, however, was on one of the authors of this paper, Sr. Nilo da Silva. In critical cases material was collected for later identification in the herbarium of the Instituto Agronômico do Norte, Belém. Time being drastically limited, we were able to spend only two to three hours at a station. We walked the trails of the *seringueiro,* or rubber gatherer, which wind around mostly on higher ground, examining all trees encountered until at least fifty species were added to the list for a station. Although time and

Table 2. Phanerophytes of the varzea of Araparí Island, Pará, arranged according to the life-form classes of Raunkiaer

Species	Presence at 6 stations					
	I	II	III	IV	V	VI

MEGAPHANEROPHYTES: taller than 30 m.

Emergent

Species	I	II	III	IV	V	VI
Sumaúma—*Ceiba pentandra* (L.) Gaertn.	x	x	x	x	x	x
Meriti—*Mauritia flexuosa* L.f.	–	–	x	–	–	–

Not emergent

Species	I	II	III	IV	V	VI
Seringueira—*Hevea brasiliensis* (HBK.) Muell. Arg.	x	x	x	x	x	x
Andiroba—*Carapa guianensis* Aubl.	x	x	x	x	x	x
Iperana—*Crudia bracteata* Benth.	x	x	x	x	x	x
Tanimbuca—*Terminalia guyanensis* Eichl.	x	x	x	x	x	x
Jatobá—*Hymenaea courbaril* var. *subsessilis* Ducke ..	x	x	x	x	–	x
Patacheiro—*Dimorphandra* sp.?	x	x	x	x	–	x
Ucuuba—*Virola surinamensis* Warb.	x	x	–	x	x	x
Taperebá—*Spondias mombim* L.	–	x	x	x	x	x
Cabeça de macaco—*Pouteria* aff. *paraensis* (Standl.) Baehni	–	x	x	x	x	x
Paracuuba—*Mora paraensis* Ducke	–	x	x	x	x	x
Guajará—*Chrysophyllum* sp.?	–	x	x	x	x	x
Matamata giboia—*Eschweilera subglandulosa* (Steud.) Miers	x	–	–	x	x	x
Matamata commun—*Eschweilera odora* (Poepp.) Miers	x	x	–	x	–	x
Faveiro—*Vantanea guianensis* Aubl.	x	x	x	–	–	x
Rim de paca—*Crudia oblonga* Benth.	–	x	x	x	x	–
Tacacazeiro—*Sterculia elata* Ducke	–	x	x	x	x	–
Apuí—*Ficus* sp.?	–	–	x	x	x	x
Tatapiririca—*Tapirira guianensis* Aubl.	x	–	x	x	–	–
Parapará—*Jacaranda copaia* (Aubl.) D. Don	x	x	–	x	–	–
Jutairana—*Cynometra bauhiniaefolia* Benth.	x	–	–	–	x	x
Açacu—*Hura crepitans* L.	x	–	–	–	x	x
Envira pe d'anta—*Sterculia pruriens* (Aubl.) K. Sch.	–	–	–	x	x	x
Comida de pombo—*Citharexylon poeppigi* Walp.	x	–	x	–	–	–
Cajú acu—*Anacardium giganteum* Engl.	–	x	–	x	–	–
Caxinguba—*Ficus radula* Willd.	–	x	–	x	–	–
Cedra—*Cedrela odorata* L.	–	–	–	x	x	–
Buiuçu—*Ormosia coutinhoi* Ducke	x	–	–	–	–	–
Macaranduba—*Manilkara huberi* (Ducke) Standley	x	–	–	–	–	–
Pitaicá—*Swartzia acuminata* Willd.	x	–	–	–	–	–

Table 2. Phanerophytes of the varzea of Araparí Island, Pará, arranged according to the life-form classes of Raunkiaer (Cont.)

Species	Presence at 6 stations					
	I	II	III	IV	V	VI
Parimarí—*Parinarium rudolphi* Huber	x	–	–	–	–	–
Sapucaia—*Lecythis paraensis* (Huber) Ducke	x	–	–	–	–	–
Pajurá—*Couepia bracteosa* Benth.	–	x	–	–	–	–
Mutamba—*Guazuma ulmifolia* Lam.	–	–	x	–	–	–
Guaruba bacuri—*Qualea albiflora* Warm.	–	–	x	–	–	–
Mamorana—*Bombax spruceanum* (Decne.) Ducke	–	–	–	x	–	–
Tauarí—*Couratari pulchra* Sandwith	–	–	–	–	x	–
Nectandra pichurim Mez.	–	–	–	–	x	–
Anani—*Symphonia globulifera* L.f.	–	–	–	–	x	–
Munguba—*Bombax munguba* Mart. & Zucc.	–	–	–	–	x	–
Maparajuba—*Manilkara amazonica* (Huber) Standley	–	–	–	–	–	x

MESOPHANEROPHYTES: Group A, 20–30 m.

Species	I	II	III	IV	V	VI
Mututí—*Pterocarpus amazonicus* Huber	x	x	x	x	x	x
Jatuaúba—*Guarea guedesii* C. DC.	x	x	x	x	x	x
Inga nobilis Willd.	x	x	x	x	x	x
Pracaxi—*Pentaclethra macroloba* (Willd.) O. Ktze.	x	x	x	–	x	x
Ipê—*Macrolobium angustifolium* (Benth.) Cowan	x	–	x	x	x	x
Maúba—*Licaria mahuba* (Samp.) Kosterm.	x	x	x	x	–	x
Cupurana—*Matisia paraensis* Huber	–	x	x	x	x	x
Areuareu—*Protium* sp.?	x	x	–	x	–	x
Ingá-açu—*Inga cinnamomea* Spruce	x	–	–	x	x	x
Marupá—*Simaruba amara* Aubl.	x	x	x	–	–	x
Ingá cipó—*Inga edulis* Mart.	–	x	x	x	–	x
Ventosa—*Hernandia guianensis* Aubl.	–	x	–	x	x	x
Aroeirá—*Licania macrophylla* Benth.	x	–	–	–	x	x
Cumarúrana—*Taralea oppositifolia* Aubl.	x	x	–	x	–	–
Pente de macaco—*Apeiba burchellii* Sprague	–	x	x	–	x	–
Imbaúba branca—*Cecropia leucocoma* Miq.	–	x	–	x	x	–
Jutaí pororoca—*Dialium guianense* (Aubl.) Sandwith	–	–	–	x	x	x
Bacaba—*Oenocarpus bacaba* Mart.	x	–	x	–	–	–
Patauá—*Oenocarpus bataua* Mart.	x	x	–	–	–	–
Uchirana—*Saccoglottis guianensis* Mart.	–	x	–	–	x	–
Açacurana—*Erythrina glauca* Willd.	–	x	x	–	–	–
Taxirana—*Coccoloba latifolia* Lam.	–	–	–	x	–	x
Jacareuba—*Calophyllum* aff. *brasiliense* Camb.	–	x	–	–	–	–
Cordia nodosa Lam.	–	x	–	–	–	–
Paliteira—*Clitoria racemosa* Benth.	–	–	x	–	–	–

Table 2. Phanerophytes of the varzea of Araparí Island, Pará, arranged according to the life-form classes of Raunkiaer (Cont.)

Species	Presence at 6 stations					
	I	II	III	IV	V	VI
Chapeu de sol—*Cordia tetrandra* Aubl.	–	–	x	–	–	–
Helicostylis pedunculata R. Ben.	–	–	–	x	–	–
Mucucú—*Licania heteromorpha* Benth.	–	–	–	–	x	–
Caneleira do igapo—*Toulicia* sp.?	–	–	–	–	x	–
Cordia exaltata Lam.	–	–	–	–	x	–
Pouteria sp.?	–	–	–	–	–	x

MESOPHANEROPHYTES: Group B, 8–20 m.

Mututí duro—*Swartzia racemosa* Benth.	x	x	x	x	x	x
Breu—*Protium pinesii* Swart.	x	x	x	x	x	x
Assaí—*Euterpe oleracea* Mart.	x	x	x	x	x	x
Geniparana—*Gustavia calycaris* Miers	x	x	x	x	x	x
Bacurirana—*Rheedia macrophylla* (Mart.) Planch. & Triana	x	x	x	x	x	x
Ingárana—*Pithecolobium huberi* Ducke	x	x	x	x	–	x
Murumuru—*Astrocaryum murumuru* Mart.	x	x	x	x	x	–
Inajárana—*Quararibea guianensis* Aubl.	–	x	x	x	x	x
Cupuí—*Theobroma subincana* Mart.	x	x	–	x	–	x
Ubuçu—*Manicaria* sp.?	x	x	–	–	x	x
Cacauí—*Theobroma speciosa* Spreng.	x	–	x	x	–	x
Paxiuba—*Iriartea exorrhiza* Mart.	–	x	x	x	x	–
Meraúba—*Mourira grandiflora* DC.	–	x	–	x	x	x
Trichilia paraensis C. DC.	–	x	x	x	–	x
Canela de garca—*Rinorea martini* (Turcz.) Blake	–	–	x	x	–	x
Janaú—*Trichanthera multijuga* Rich.	x	–	–	–	x	x
Inaja—*Maximiliana regia* Mart.	–	–	x	–	x	x
Tamaquaré—*Caraipa grandifolia* Mart.	x	–	–	–	–	x
Mamorana—*Bombax aquaticum* (Aubl.) K. Sch.	x	–	x	–	–	–
Urucurí—*Attalea excelsa* Mart.	–	–	x	–	x	–
Mangarana—*Tovomita stigmatosa* Planch. & Triana	x	–	–	–	–	–
Jupatí—*Rhaphia taedigera* Mart.	x	–	–	–	–	–
Guadua glomerata Munro	–	x	–	–	–	–
Envira preta—*Guatteria atra* Sandwith	–	x	–	–	–	–
Cassia multijuga Rich.	–	–	x	–	–	–
Marajá—*Bactris* sp.?	–	–	–	–	x	–
Caripê—*Couepia* sp.?	–	–	–	–	–	x
Mouriria sagotiana Triana	–	–	–	–	–	x

Table 2. Phanerophytes of the varzea of Araparí Island, Pará, arranged according to the life-form classes of Raunkiaer (Cont.)

Species	Presence at 6 stations					
	I	II	III	IV	V	VI
MICROPHANEROPHYTES: 2–8 m.						
Cacau—*Theobroma cacao* L.	x	x	x	x	x	x
Ubim—*Geonoma* sp.?	x	–	–	–	–	–
Sororoca—*Ravenala guyanesis* Petersen	x	–	–	–	–	–
Seringarana—*Elvasia elvasioides* (Planch.) Gilg	x	–	–	–	–	–
Pitomba—Gen. sp.?	x	–	–	–	–	–
Capitiú—*Siparuna guianensis* Aubl.	–	–	x	–	–	–
Tabernaemontana angulata Muell. Arg.	–	–	–	x	–	–
Heisteria sessilis Ducke	–	–	–	–	–	x
Summary by stations and total for Araparí:						
Megaphanerophytes (42)	21	20	20	24	22	20
Mesophanerophytes (59)	28	33	30	29	30	34
Microphanerophytes (8)	5	1	2	2	1	2
Total (109)	54	54	52	55	53	56

distance were not controlled and equivalent, 1 to 2 km. of trail were examined in each case. The results are set down in table 2, pages 265 ff.

Table 2 shows the presence at each station of each species. The arrangement of species in the table is first by Raunkiaer's phanerophytic life-form classes, except that the mesophanerophytes are subdivided into two height groups. Within these divisions the species are arranged according to their presence class, from those present at all stations to those encountered at only one station. It should be noted that these lists are complete for the areas examined but that the areas are small. Further search at any one station would certainly have turned up additional species and increased the presence of the species listed. It would also have revealed still more species of low presence.

On a basis of these data it is seen that on the average any one station list contains about half the species of the combined lists. Fourteen species had a presence of 6/6, five of them megaphanerophytes, eight mesophanerophytes, and one microphanerophyte. At the other end of the scale, 39 of the 109 species were encountered only once, as shown in table 3, page 269.

As to life form, 42 species were megaphanerophytes, exceeding 30 m. high, 59 were mesophanerophytes, from 8 to 30 m. high, and only eight were microphanerophytes, less than 8 m. high. We made no effort to determine the nanophanerophytes or other members of the forest community, such as the lianas and epiphytes. Terrestrial herbs were almost completely absent, but tree reproduction was sometimes very dense in the ground layer.

A certain amount of layering in the forest is readily apparent. As noted before, the emergent Sumaúma, *Ceiba pentandra,* often extends 10 m. or

Table 3. *Summary table of presence and life form of phanerophytes of the mata da varzea, Araparí Island, Pará*

| Presence class | Number of species in each presence class | | | |
	Mega-phanerophytes	Meso-phanerophytes	Micro-phanerophytes	Total
6/6	5	8	1	14
5/6	7	7	. .	14
4/6	6	11	. .	17
3/6	5	8	. .	13
2/6	4	8	. .	12
1/6	15	17	7	39
Total	42	59	8	109

more above the general canopy of megaphanerophytes at the level of about 35 m. A layer below the general canopy is sometimes well marked by a local abundance of *Euterpe oleracea* at about 15 to 20 m. A still lower layer at about 5 to 8 m. is well marked by *Theobroma cacao.* Strata within the general mesophanerophytic level are not apparent. The ground is generally crowded by tree reproduction and nanophanerophytic shrubs intermixed at levels from about 1 to 3 m. except in the wetter *igapós* where the soil is bare or with a jumble of plank-like roots or snake-coiled masses of superficial cylindrical roots and pneumatophores.

PART II. COMPOSITION AND STRUCTURE OF *TERRA FIRME* RAIN FOREST AT MUCAMBO, BELÉM, PARÁ [4]

Mucambo is a rather extensive tract of apparently primeval *terra firme* rain forest on the grounds of the Instituto Agronômico do Norte on the eastern side of Belém, Pará, at about 1° 27″ S. Lat. and 48° 27″ W. Long. Mucambo lies at a slight elevation above the *varzea* (flood plain) between Igarapé Calu and Igarapé Agua Preta, which connect with the Rio Guamá.

In an easily accessible portion of the forest about a kilometer from one of the Instituto service roads Dr. Murça Pires laid out a sample plot of 2

[4] Stanley A. Cain, Gustavus M. de Oliveira Castro, and J. Murça Pires.

Table 4. *Flora of a 2-hectare sample plot of tropical rain forest (terra firme) Mucambo, Belém, Pará. Primary arrangement of the species is by Raunkiaerian life-form classes with secondary arrangement by leaf-size classes.*

Species	Family	Leaf complexity	Leaf area, sq. cm.
MEGAPHANEROPHYTES (height over 30 m.)			
Macrophyll			
1. *Didymopanax morototoni* (Aubl.) Decne. & Planch.	Araliaceae	Palmate	368
Mesophyll			
2. *Manilkara huberi* (Ducke) Standley	Sapotaceae	Simple	100
3. *Iryanthera juruensis* Warb.	Myristicaceae	Simple	42
4. *Vouacapoua americana* Aubl.	Leguminosae	Pinnate	29
5. *Eschweilera odora* (Poepp.) Miers	Lecythidaceae	Simple	57
6. *Licaria camara* (Rob. Schomb.) Kosterm.	Lauraceae	Simple	68
7. *Vantanea guianensis* Aubl.	Humiriaceae	Simple	74
8. *Tachigalea myrmecophila* (Ducke) Ducke	Leguminosae	Pinnate	56
9. *Carapa guianensis* Aubl.	Lecythidaceae	Simple	112
10. *Vochysia guianensis* (Aubl.) Poir.	Vochysiaceae	Simple	40
11. *Trattinickia rhoifolia* Willd.	Burseraceae	Simple	70
12. *Hevea brasiliensis* (HBK.) Muell. Arg.	Euphorbiaceae	Trifoliate	72
13. *Symphonia globulifera* L.f.	Guttiferae	Simple	32
14. *Sterculia pruriens* (Aubl.) K. Sch.	Sterculiaceae	Simple	112
15. *Helicostylis peduncula ta* R. Ben.	Moraceae	Simple	139
16. *Aspidospermum alba* (Vahl.) R. Ben.	Apocynaceae	Simple	21
17. *Couratari pulchra* Sandwith	Lecythidaceae	Simple	54
18. *Micropholis guyanensis* (A. DC.) Pierre	Sapotaceae	Simple	50

19. *Vantanea cupularis* Huber	Humiriaceae	Simple	26
20. *Anacardium giganteum* Engl.	Anacardiaceae	Simple	140
21. *Thyrsodium paraense* Huber	Anacardiaceae	Simple	95
22. *Caryocar villosum* (Aubl.) Pers.	Caryocaraceae	Trifoliate	85
23. *Aniba burchellii* Kosterm.	Lauraceae	Simple	68
24. *Osteophloeum platyspermum* (Poepp.) Warb.	Myristicaceae	Simple	36
25. *Eschweilera blanchetiana* (Berg.) Miers	Lecythidaceae	Simple	23
26. *Ocotea rubra* Mez.	Lauraceae	Simple	74
27. *Caryocar microcarpum* Ducke	Caryocaraceae	Trifoliate	36
28. *Minquartia guianensis* Aubl.	Olacaceae	Simple	57
29. *Aspidosperma verruculosum* Muell. Arg.	Apocynaceae	Simple	40
30. *Laetia procera* (Poepp. & Endl.) Eichl.	Flacourtiaceae	Simple	40
31. *Hymenaea oblongifolia* Huber	Leguminosae	Bifoliate	68
32. *Andira retusa* HBK.	Leguminosae	Pinnate	21
33. *Tapirira guianensis* Aubl.	Anacardiaceae	Pinnate	30
34. *Ormosia paraensis* Ducke	Leguminosae	Pinnate	23
35. *Parahancornia amapa* Ducke	Apocynaceae	Simple	27
36. *Coumarouna odorata* Aubl.	Leguminosae	Pinnate	40
37. *Lecythis ocitata*	Lecythidaceae	Simple	48
38. *Pouteria robusta var. longifolia* Eyma	Sapotaceae	Simple	56
Microphyll			
39. *Inga gracilifolia* Ducke	Leguminosae	Pinnate	3.5
40. *Goupia glabra* Aubl.	Celestraceae	Simple	12
41. *Dialium guianense* (Aubl.) Sandwith	Leguminosae	Pinnate	14
42. *Terminalia amazonia* (Gmel.) Excell	Combretaceae	Simple	16
43. *Qualea albiflora* Warm.	Vochysiaceae	Simple	14
44. *Crudia oblonga* Benth.	Leguminosae	Pinnate	8

Table 4. Flora of a 2-hectare sample plot of tropical rain forest (terra firme) Mucambo, Belém, Pará. Primary arrangement of the species is by Raunkiaerian life-form classes with secondary arrangement by leaf-size classes (Cont.)

Species	Family	Leaf complexity	Leaf area, sq. cm.
45. *Ocotea guianensis* Aubl.	Lauraceae	Simple	16
46. *Pithecolobium jupunba* (Willd.) Urban	Leguminosae	Bipinnate	2.8
Nanophyll			
47. *Parkia gigantocarpa* Ducke	Leguminosae	Bipinnate	1.2
Leptophyll			
48. *Parkia pendula* Benth.	Leguminosae	Bipinnate	0.05
49. *Piptadenia suaveolens* (DC.) Benth.	Leguminosae	Bipinnate	0.08
MESOPHANEROPHYTES (8–30 m. high)			
Macrophyll			
1. *Licania macrophylla* Benth.	Rosaceae	Simple	200
2. *Licania longistyla* (Hook. f.) Fritsch	Rosaceae	Simple	208
3. *Theobroma subincana* Mart.	Sterculiaceae	Simple	241
4. *Pourouma myrmecophila* Ducke	Moraceae	Palmate	486
5. *Protium poeppigianum* Swart.	Burseraceae	Simple	260
6. *Pouteria,* aff. *paraensis* (Standl.) Baehni	Sapotaceae	Simple	242
7. *Ormosia nobilis* Tul.	Leguminosae	Pinnate	280 [a]
8. *Iriartea exorrhiza* Mart.	Palmaceae	Pinnate	450
9. *Cecropia obtusa* Trecul.	Moraceae	Palmate	307
10. *Theobroma speciosa* Spreng.	Sterculiaceae	Simple	186

Mesophyll

11. *Protium polybotryum* (Turcz.) Engl.	Burseraceae	Pinnate	29
12. *Trichilia lecointei* Ducke	Meliaceae	Pinnate	26
13. *Chimarrhis turbinata* DC.	Rubiaceae	Simple	90
14. *Vitex triflora* Vahl	Verbenaceae	Simple	52
15. *Licania paniculata* Fanshawe & Maguire	Rosaceae	Simple	60
16. *Eschweilera krukovii* A. C. Smith	Lecythidaceae	Simple	75
17. *Mouriria huberi* Cogn.	Melastomaceae	Simple	32
18. *Swartzia racemosa* Benth.	Leguminosae	Simple	50
19. *Sloanea guianensis* (Aubl.) Benth.	Elaeocarpaceae	Simple	27
20. *Tapura singularis* Ducke	Dichapetalaceae	Simple	36
21. *Saccoglottis guianensis* Benth.	Humiriaceae	Simple	33
22. *Couepia hoffmanniana* Kl.	Rosaceae	Simple	29
23. *Protium trifoliolatum* Engl.	Burseraceae	Pinnate	30
24. *Dendrobangia boliviana* Rusby	Icacinaceae	Simple	89
25. *Protium nodulosum* Swart.	Burseraceae	Pinnate	43
26. *Inga brachystachys* (Ducke) Ducke	Leguminosae	Pinnate	43
27. *Elvasia elvasioides* (Planch.) Gilg	Ochnaceae	Simple	96
28. *Tovomita stigmatosa* Planch. & Triana	Guttiferae	Simple	96
29. *Apeiba echinata* var. *macropetala* Ducke	Tiliaceae	Simple	56
30. *Sagotia racemosa* Baill.	Euphorbiaceae	Simple	60
31. *Iryanthera paraensis* Huber	Myristicaceae	Simple	149
32. *Protium polybotryum* var. *blackii* Swart.	Burseraceae	Pinnate	24
33. *Swartzia macrocarpa* Spruce	Leguminosae	Simple	48
34. *Pogonophora schomburgkiana* Miers	Euphorbiaceae	Simple	44
35. *Pouteria guianensis* Aubl.	Sapotaceae	Simple	74
36. *Protium carnosum* A. C. Smith	Burseraceae	Pinnate	28
37. *Micropholis acutangula* (Ducke) Eyma	Sapotaceae	Simple	60

273

Table 4. Flora of a 2-hectare sample plot of tropical rain forest (terra firme) Mucambo, Belém, Pará. Primary arrangement of the species is by Raunkiaerian life-form classes with secondary arrangement by leaf-size classes (Cont.)

Species	Family	Leaf complexity	Leaf area, sq. cm.
38. *Protium divaricatum* var. *intermedium* Swart.	Burseraceae	Pinnate	24
39. *Pouteria engleri* Eyma	Sapotaceae	Simple	66
40. *Cordia scabrida* Mart.	Boragniaceae	Simple	95
41. *Amaioua guianensis* Aubl.	Rubiaceae	Simple	82
42. *Fusaea longifolia* (Aubl.) Safford	Anonaceae	Simple	112
43. *Saccoglottis cuspidata* (Benth.) Urban	Humiriaceae	Simple	30
44. *Emmotum acuminatum* Miers	Icacinaceae	Simple	56
45. *Trichilia acariaeantha* Harms	Meliaceae	Simple	21
46. *Licania guianensis* (Aubl.) O. Ktze.	Rosaceae	Simple	43
47. *Mouriria sagotiana* Triana	Melastomaceae	Simple	24
48. *Poraqueiba guianensis* Aubl.	Icacinaceae	Simple	120
49. *Ambelania acida* Aubl.	Apocynaceae	Simple	84
50. *Hebepetalum humiriifolium* (Planch.) Jackson	Linaceae	Simple	84
51. *Brosimum paraense* Huber	Moraceae	Simple	27
52. *Aparisthmium cordatum* (Juss.) Baill.	Euphorbiaceae	Simple	100
53. *Sloanea brevipes* Benth.	Elaeocarpaceae	Simple	162
54. *Protium aracouchli* (Aubl.) March.	Burseraceae	Pinnate	27
55. *Lacmellea aculeata* (Ducke) Monachino	Apocynaceae	Simple	64
56. *Diospyros melinoni* (Hiern.) A. C. Smith	Ebenaceae	Simple	29
57. *Swartzia brachyrachis* var. *snethlageae* Ducke	Leguminosae	Simple	48
58. *Inga disticha* Benth.	Leguminosae	Pinnate	27
59. *Pourouma velutina* Mart.	Moraceae	Simple	86

274

	Family	Leaf	
60. *Paypayrola grandiflora* Tul.	Violaceae	Simple	84
61. *Gustavia hexapetala* (Aubl.) Smith	Lecythidaceae	Simple	68
62. *Pouteria*, aff. *scytalophora* Eyma	Sapotaceae	Simple	90
63. *Inga marginata* Willd.	Leguminosae	Pinnate	56
64. *Protium sagotianum* March.	Burseraceae	Pinnate	72
65. *Calyptranthes speciosa* Sagot	Myrtaceae	Simple	168
66. *Licania micrantha* Miq.	Rosaceae	Simple	48
67. *Protium neglectum* Swart.	Burseraceae	Pinnate	40
68. *Rinorea passura* (Aubl.) O. Ktze.	Violaceae	Simple	60
69. *Rheedia brasiliensis* Planch. & Triana	Guttiferae	Simple	30
70. *Adenostephanus guyanensis* Meissn.	Proteacaea	Pinnate	36
71. *Pouteria glomerata* Radlk.	Sapotaceae	Simple	46
72. *Chrysophyllum prieurei* A. DC.	Sapotaceae	Simple	52
73. *Licania grisea* Kleinh.	Rosaceae	Simple	72

Microphyll

	Family	Leaf	
74. *Ptychopetalum olacoides* Benth.	Olacaceae	Simple	10
75. *Protium pilosissimum* Engl.	Burseraceae	Pinnate	15
76. *Miconia cuspidata* Naud.	Melastomaceae	Simple	8
77. *Sideroxylon callophylloides* (Pierre) Engl.		Simple	6
78. *Hirtella caudata* Kleinh.	Apocynaceae	Simple	16
79. *Protium bangii* Swart.	Burseraceae	Pinnate	20
80. *Licania imene* Aubl.	Rosaceae	Simple	14
81. *Maprounea guianensis* Aubl.	Euphorbiaceae	Simple	12

Leptophyll

	Family	Leaf	
82. *Pentaclethra macroloba* O. Ktze.	Leguminosae	Bifoliate	0.12
83. *Enterolobium schomburgkii* Benth.	Leguminosae	Bipinnate	0.02

275

Table 4. Flora of a 2-hectare sample plot of tropical rain forest (terra firme) Mucambo, Belém, Pará. Primary arrangement of the species is by Raunkiaerian life-form classes with secondary arrangement by leaf-size classes (Cont.)

Species	Family	Leaf complexity	Leaf area, sq. cm.
MICROPHANEROPHYTES (2–8 m. high)			
Macrophyll			
1. *Tabernaemontana angulata* Muell. Arg.	Apocynaceae	Pinnate	216
Mesophyll			
2. Coll. 73, gen. sp.	Palmaceae	Pinnate	74
3. *Coccoloba latifolia* Lam.	Myrtaceae	Simple	27
NANOPHANEROPHYTES (25 cm.–2 m. high)			
Macrophyll			
1. *Ischnosiphon obliquus* (Rudge) Koern.	Marantaceae	Simple	340
2. *Calathea* sp., Coll. 60	Marantaceae	Simple	194
Mesophyll			
3. *Maieta guianensis* Aubl.	Melastomaceae	Simple	101
4. *Sabicea* sp., Coll. 4	Rubiaceae	Simple	50
5. *Palicourea guianensis* Aubl.	Rubiaceae	Simple	132
6. *Piper hostmannianum* (Miq.) C. DC.	Piperaceae	Simple	46
7. *Piper* sp., Coll. 11	Piperaceae	Simple	146
8. *Dichorisandra* sp., Coll. 18	Commelinaceae	Simple	32
9. *Cephaelis bicolor*	Rubiaceae	Simple	84
10. *Brunfelsia guianensis* Benth.	Solanaceae	Simple	48

276

	Family		
11. *Ischnosiphon arouma* (Aubl.) Koern.	Marantaceae	Simple	86
12. *Psychotria* sp.	Rubiaceae	Simple	23
13. *Bactris* sp.	Palmaceae	Pinnate	120
14. *Geonoma* sp. #1	Palmaceae	Pinnate	144
15. *Geonoma* sp. #2, Coll. 37	Palmaceae	Pinnate	41
16. *Potalia amara* Aubl.	Loganiaceae	Simple	111
17. *Piper* sp., Coll. 58	Piperaceae	Simple	80
18. *Piper* sp., Coll. 59	Piperaceae	Simple	82
19. *Costus* sp., Coll. 75	Zinziberaceae	Simple	34

Microphyll

20. *Psychotria rubra* (Willd.) Muell. Arg.	Rubiaceae	Simple	18
21. *Piper* sp., Coll. 9	Piperaceae	Simple	13
22. Fam. gen. sp., Coll. 72		Simple	10

LIANAS

Macrophyll

1. *Monstera milleriana* Schott	Araceae	Simple	430
2. *Carludovica* sp., Coll. 26	Cyclanthaceae	Bifid	382
3. *Coccoloba latifolia* Lam.			

Mesophyll

4. *Smilax schomburgkiana* Kunth	Liliaceae	Simple	70
5. *Bauhinia cuspidata*	Leguminosae	Bifid	
6. *Bauhinia rutilans* Benth.	Leguminosae	Bifid	
7. *Arrabidaea tuberculata* DC.			
8. Gen. sp., Coll. 3	Araceae	Simple	56
9. Gen. sp., Coll. 8	Araceae	Simple	88
10. Gen. sp., Coll. 14	Araceae	Simple	45
11. *Heteropsis* sp., Coll. 15 (Cipotitica)		Simple	64

Table 4. Flora of a 2-hectare sample plot of tropical rain forest (terra firme) Mucambo, Belém, Pará. Primary arrangement of the species is by Raunkiaerian life-form classes with secondary arrangement by leaf-size classes (Cont.)

Species	Family	Leaf complexity	Leaf area, sq. cm.
12. *Cyclanthus* sp., Coll. 32	Cyclanthaceae	Bifid	112
13. Fam. gen. sp., Coll. 27			92
14. Gen. sp., Coll. 34	Polypodiaceae	Pinnate	84
15. *Syngonium* sp., Coll. 38			164
16. *Gurania* sp., Coll. 40	Cucurbitaceae	Simple	50
17. *Noranthea guianensis* Aubl.		Simple	168
18. Gen. sp., Coll. 49	Piperaceae	Simple	70
19. *Abuta imene* Eichl.	Menospermaceae	Simple	36
20. *Mikania*, aff. *hirsutissima* DC.	Compositae	Simple	168
21. Gen. sp., Coll. 57	Malpighiaceae	Simple	56
22. Fam. gen. sp., Coll. 69			85
23. Fam. gen. sp., Coll. 84			67
24. Fam. gen. sp., Coll. 84			84
Microphyll			
25. *Dioscorea* sp., Coll. 16	Dioscoreaceae	Simple	16
26. *Prestonia* sp., Coll. 64			6
27. *Vanilla* sp., Coll. 86	Orchidaceae	Simple	9
28. Fam. gen. sp., Coll. 10		Simple	10
29. Fam. gen. sp., Coll. 68		Simple	3
Nanophyll			
30. *Securidaca* sp., Coll. 41	Polygalaceae	Pinnate	1.6

Megaphyll

#	Species	Family		Value
1.	*Monstera* sp., Coll. 74	Araceae	Simple	2400

Macrophyll

2.	*Asplenium*, aff. *serratum* L., Coll. 36	Polypodiaceae	Simple	358
3.	*Aechmea*, aff. *setigera* Mart. Coll. 42	Bromeliaceae	Simple	570
4.	*Vriesia amazonica* (Baker) Mez	Bromeliaceae	Simple	212
5.	*Philodendron* sp., Coll. 51	Araceae	Simple	700

Mesophyll

6.	Gen. sp., Coll. 52	Orchidaceae	Simple	80
7.	*Anthurium* sp., Coll. 46	Araceae	Simple	72
8.	*Piper* sp., Coll. 87	Piperaceae	Simple	163

Microphyll

9.	*Tillandsia* sp., Coll. 43	Bromeliaceae	Simple	18
10.	*Tillandsia anceps* Lodd.	Bromeliaceae	Simple	12
11.	*Tillandsia pulchella* Hook.	Bromeliaceae	Simple	4
12.	*Tillandsia monadelpha* Baker, Coll. 78	Bromeliaceae	Simple	10
13.	*Scuticaria steelii* Lindl.	Orchidaceae	Simple	3.6
14.	*Polypodium ciliatum* Willd.	Polypodiaceae	Simple	2.8
15.	*Peperomia* sp., Coll. 65	Piperaceae	Simple	2.3

Nanophyll

16.	*Trichomanes reptans* Sw.	Hymenophyllaceae	Simple	0.15
17.	*Peperomia* sp., Coll. 88	Piperaceae	Simple	0.21
18.	*Hecistopteris pumila* (Spr.) J. Sm.	Polypodiaceae	Simple	0.4
19.	*Polypodium duale* Maxon	Polypodiaceae	Simple	0.5

279

Table 4. Flora of a 2-hectare sample plot of tropical rain forest (terra firme) Mucambo, Belém, Pará. Primary arrangement of the species is by Raunkiaerian life-form classes with secondary arrangement by leaf-size classes (Cont.)

Species	Family	Leaf complexity	Leaf area, sq. cm.
CHAMAEPHYTES (Buds above the soil and below 0.25 m.)			
Mesophyll			
1. *Maranta* sp., Coll. 89	Marantaceae	Simple	56
Leptophyll			
2. *Selaginella stellata* Spring	Selaginellaceae	Simple	0.02
HEMICRYTOPHYTES (Buds at the soil surface)			
Macrophyll			
1. *Trichomanes vittaria* DC.	Hymenophyllaceae	Simple	403
Mesophyll			
2. *Olyra.* sp., Coll. 80	Gramineae	Simple	53
3. *Dryopteris* sp., Coll. 66	Polypodiaceae	Bipinnatifid	22
Microphyll			
4. *Trichomanes pinnatum* Hedw.	Hymenophyllaceae	Pinnate	4.2
Nanophyll			
5. *Nephrolepis exaltata* (L.) Schott	Polypodiaceae	Pinnate	2.0
6. *Lindsaya lancea* (L.) Bedd.		Bipinnate	1.4

280

GEOPHYTES (CRYPTOPHYTES) (Buds buried in the soil).

Macrophyll

1. *Heliconia psittacorum* L.f. .... Musaceae | Simple | 486

Mesophyll

2. *Pariana radiciflora* Sagot ex Doell, Coll. 24 .... Gramineae | Simple | 53

THEROPHYTES (Annuals, living over only in seeds)

None

---

[a] *Ormosia nobilis* is a mesophanerophyte with pinnate leaves, the leaflets of which are about 280 sq. cm. As a young tree in the microphanerophytic size class, the leaflets commonly are about 700 sq. cm.

Plants known from the Mucambo plot but for which leaf-size classification is not presently available include the following:

Megaphanerophytes: *Eschweilera* sp., ? *Nectandra*, *Trattinikia* sp., *Vantanea* sp., *Aspidosperma* sp.
Mesophanerophytes: *Vouacapoua guianensis*, *Pouteria* sp., *Pseudolmedia* sp., *Protium* sp. *"Breu mescla," Protium divaricatum* Engl. v. *lutea*, Sapotaceae, Gen. sp. ? #3, Sapotaceae, Gen. sp. ? #4, *Oenocarpus* sp., *Pouteria* sp. #5, "Mata mata sapeiro," Sapotaceae, Gen. sp. ? #6, Myrtaceae, Gen. sp., *Neea* sp., *Gustavia licanoida*, Rosaceae, Gen. sp., *Guatteria longicuspis* R. E. Fries. Nanophanerophytes: *Syagrus* sp., Coll. 29. Lianas: *Hippocratea* sp. *Syagrus* (*Cocos*) sp., *Ormosia flava*, *Sloanea* sp.

hectares, divided into 20 strips each 10 × 100 m. When we first visited the Instituto in September, 1955, we were taken to the plot by Dr. G. A. Black, as Dr. Pires was at that time working in the United States. It was immediately apparent that the plot offered a fine opportunity for concentrated study of a small tract of equatorial rain forest, as each tree of the 20 strips had been numbered by a metal tag and careful identifications by personnel of the Instituto were nearly completed. Also, most of the tree species were represented by collections from Mucambo in the Instituto herbarium. Contact was made with Dr. Pires, and we returned to Belém to study the plot in January, 1956.

The original lists of Dr. Pires consisted of trees on the plot that were about 1 dm. d.b.h. or more, divided into two size classes, those under and those over 40 cm. d.b.h. As the trees were numbered consecutively in each strip, it was possible to go onto the plot and determine from the tags which stems were in each 10 × 10 m. quadrat. It was thus possible to use the data for density and frequency studies. We also went back over the plot and determined the exact diameter of each stem by use of a steel tape, which allowed us to compute basal area for each species and for the plot as a whole. Determination of the maximum height of each species allowed assignment to Raunkiaerian life-form classes. Each of the 200 quadrats was searched for non-arboreal species, and collections were made for determination and leaf-size classification as well as for life-form classification. These various aspects of the composition and structure of the forest on the sample plot will be discussed separately, but first the total known flora is presented in table 4. Primary arrangement of the species in this table is by Raunkiaerian life-form classes, and within them, by Raunkiaerian leaf-size classes. To save repetition this table also shows whether the leaf is simple or compound and gives the blade or leaflet area in square centimeters. Common names are not used, as in most cases we can provide a Latin name. Because there is no manual of the flora of the region, we have added name authorities and family names. Some material that has not been named is nevertheless used for life-form and leaf-size study since the more complete the flora the more valuable the spectra.

DENSITY OF TREES. Table 5 shows the density of stems on sub-plots of different sizes formed by combinations of contiguous 10 × 10 m. quadrats. This table shows the number of sub-plots in each size group that contains a given number of stems 1 dm. or larger in diameter. For example, in the 10 × 10 m. series, 7 quadrats had only 2 stems, 14 plots had 3 stems, 32 plots had 4 stems, etc. The total sample of 2 hectares contains 1,188 trees whose stems are approximately 1 dm. d.b.h. or over, which is an average of 16.8 sq. m. per stem. In order to have some measure of the reliability of the density data, table 6 was developed. Using the smallest subdivisions of the 20,000 sq. m. plot, the 200 10 × 10 m. quadrats, it was found that the

Table 5. Density of trees 1 dm. or more in diameter in equatorial rain forest at Mucambo, arranged according to sub-plots of different sizes and based on original data by Murça Pires for a 2-hectare plot

10 × 10		10 × 20		20 × 20		10 × 100		40 × 40	
Density	Number	Density	Number	Density	Number	Density	Number	Density	Number
2	7	5	1	14	1	41	1	76	1
3	14	6	3	16	1	50	1	79	1
4	32	7	5	18	4	51	2	80	1
5	38	8	5	19	5	52	1	84	1
6	36	9	9	20	3	53	1	91	1
7	33	10	13	21	4	54	2	97	1
8	17	11	12	22	3	56	2	98	2
9	7	12	13	23	5	61	1	101	1
10	11	13	7	24	2	62	2	116	1
11	4	14	12	25	5	65	2		
14	1	15	7	26	6	67	1		
		16	4	27	1	68	1		
		17	5	29	2	72	1		
		18	1	30	2	73	1		
		20	3	31	1	75	1		
				32	4				
				33	1				
Plots 200		100		50		20		10	
Trees 1188		1188		1188		1188		920	

283

Table 6. Density variability of trees on a 2-hectare sample plot of equatorial rain forest at Mucambo, Belém. The plots of larger size are recombinations of contiguous 10 × 10 m. sub-plots, with only the largest size not utilizing the entire plot

Number of sub-plots	Plot size, m.	Average density	Standard deviation,[a] ±	Coefficient of variation
200	10 × 10	5.94	2.00	33.7%
100	10 × 20	11.88	3.22	27.1%
50	20 × 20	23.76	4.63	19.5%
20	10 × 100	59.40	8.79	14.8%
10	40 × 40	92.00	11.74	12.7%

[a] All standard deviations were computed on the basis of the square root of the sum of deviations squared divided by the number of sub-plots except for the 10 largest plots where $n - 1$ was used in addition to give the following results: standard deviation, 12.42; coefficient of variation, 13.5 per cent.

average density per plot is 5.94 ± 2.0, with a coefficient of variation of 33.7 per cent. By combining the quadrats in contiguous pairs we obtained 100 sub-plots of 10 × 20 m. size that have an average density of 11.88 ± 3.22 trees per plot and a coefficient of variation of 27.1 per cent. For the 50 sub-plots of 20 × 20 m. and the 20 sub-plots (original strips) of 10 × 100 m. the coefficient of variation fell to 19.5 per cent and 14.8 per cent, respectively. The largest size sub-plot available in the present sample was 10 plots each 40 × 40 m. for which the coefficient of variation (using $n - 1$ in the standard-deviation formula because of the small value of n) was 13.5 per cent, or little different from the value for the strips. This study shows that small plots commonly employed in series in many phytosociological studies are not suitable for the rather heterogeneous equatorial rain forest, at least in the numbers used here.

SIZE OF TREES. Although very large trees occur in equatorial rain forest, both in *terra firme* and *varzea,* the impression one gets of the forest is more that of moderate to small trunks with long unbranched boles and relatively small crowns—a columnar forest. The large trees which usually are emergent rise above the canopy at Mucambo at about 35 to 40 m. and are usually widely scattered. This impression of relatively small stature of trees, even in primeval rain forest, is substantiated by the data from the Mucambo plot. Our re-measurement of the trees on the plot, using a steel tape at the constant height of 4.5 ft. above the ground, revealed only one tree with a diameter in the 150 to 159 cm. class. Only six trees had a diameter of 1 m. or more, and only 69 trees had a diameter of 0.5 m. or more, while 1,101 of the stems were smaller than 0.5 m. The size classes were as follows: 150 to

159 cm., 1; 130 to 149 cm., 1; 110 to 129 cm., 3; 90 to 109 cm., 7; 70 to 89 cm., 25; 50 to 69 cm., 32; and 10 to 49 cm., 1,101 stems, from a total of 1,170 trees. This number of re-measured stems differs from the original number because of trees that had died in the interval and ones that proved not to be as large as 1 dm.

No counts were made of smaller trees than 10 cm. d.b.h., but there is no doubt that most of the density and coverage in the lower strata of the forest, including the ground layer occupied by herbs in temperate forests, is formed by reproduction of trees capable of attaining the forest canopy. As will be shown later in the life-form study, rain forest is overwhelmingly phanerophytic.

Coverage is commonly taken as a measure of dominance. Cover is the combined foliage measured as proportion of ground area shaded when the canopy is assumed to be projected vertically onto the ground, as if there were a direct overhead source of light. In forests generally it is difficult to estimate the coverage of species of trees, and in rain forest this is impossible because the density of the crown and the multiple layers prevent one making accurate observations. It is, therefore, common practice to determine dominance not by means of coverage, as for herbs, but by means of basal area. The basal area of a species of tree in a forest is the sum of the cross-section areas of the stems of trees of the species, measured at the standard height of 4.5 ft. above the ground. Having exact measurements of all the stems on the plot, it was easy to compute the basal areas.

For the entire plot the combined basal area was 65.2 sq. m. for trees 10 cm. d.b.h. or over. This is equivalent to 32.6 sq. m. (350.8 sq. ft.) per hectare and 13.04 sq. m. (140.3 sq. ft.) per acre. *Vochysia guianensis*, with 981.2 sq. dm. of basal area on the plot, was the leading species. *Goupia glabra* was second, with 704 sq. dm. and 10.8 per cent. The first five species in importance, according to basal area, had a total of 40.65 per cent of the basal area. Altogether there were only 25 species with individual basal areas of 1 per cent or more of the total, and together they made up 71.6 per cent of the total basal area. This leaves nearly 150 species to make up the remaining 28.36 per cent. There is, then, in this type of forest no approach to dominance by one or a small number of species as the concept is customarily used to apply to temperate forests by foresters and plant sociologists alike.

FREQUENCY. Frequency is the phytosociological concept concerned with pattern of occurrence of members of a species population within a community. It is determined on a basis of presence or absence of plants of a species on sub-samples taken within a stand of a community. It is commonly expressed as percentage of sub-samples containing the species in relation to the total series of sub-samples. Frequency data have an obvious relationship to size of sub-sample inasmuch as the larger the sample area the greater the chance a species has of being included in it.

At Mucambo the tree flora is so rich in species and the density of most of them is so low that it is obvious that sample plots of small area would not discriminate among the frequencies of the various species. In other words, nearly all species would have low percentages. For this reason we have calculated frequency of the species on a basis of the 20 sub-plots that are 10 × 100 m. and the 10 sub-plots of 20 × 100 m. Since the number of frequency

Table 7. The occurrence of tree species in Raunkiaerian frequency classes in equatorial rain forest at Mucambo

	20 sub-plots each 10 × 100 m.		10 sub-plots each 20 × 100 m.	
Frequency classes	Species	Per cent	Species	Per cent
Class A (0–20%)	131	75.8	122	70.5
Class B (21–40%)	16	9.2	18	10.4
Class C (41–60%)	17	9.8	15	8.7
Class D (61–80%)	5	2.9	10	5.8
Class E (81–100%)	4	2.3	8	4.6
Only trees 1 dm. d.b.h. or over	173		173	

classes is as great as the number of sub-samples, it is customary to use a limited number of classes. We follow the system of Raunkiaer (1934) and use five even-sized classes as shown in table 7. On a basis of the 10 × 100 m. sub-samples, only four species attained class E (81 to 100 per cent) frequency: *Eschweilera odora, Protium trifoliolatum, Eschweilera krukovii,* and *Protium* sp. ? ("Breu mescla"). With the sample size doubled in area, four additional species attained this class: *Tovomita stigmatosa, Vochysia guianensis, Iryanthera juruensis,* and *Theobroma subincana.* Also with relatively high frequency, class D (61 to 80 per cent), were five additional species for the smaller plots and 10 for the larger ones. At the other end of the scale is found the vast majority of the species which have low frequencies (75.8 and 70.5 per cent of the total species in the two sizes of sample areas) and are encountered only occasionally in the forest.

RELATIVE MEASURES. Tables 8, 9, and 10 have been prepared to give some of the specific data that have already been mentioned and also to show the relative positions of the leading species according to each of the measures. Relative density (table 8) is the per cent which the density of a species (on the total sample) is of the total density of all species. In the same way relative basal area (dominance) (table 9) is the per cent that the basal area of a given species is of the total basal area on the plot, and relative frequency is the per cent the frequency of a given species is of the sum of the frequencies

Table 8. Tree species having the greatest density on a sample plot of equatorial rain forest at Mucambo, including only those 10 cm. and over d.b.h.

Species	Density,[a] trees on 2 hectares	Relative density, per cent of total
Echweilera odora	101	11.26
Protium trifoliolatum	69	7.69
Eschweilera krukovii	58	6.47
Vochysia guianensis	49	5.46
Protium sp.? "Breu mescla"	39	4.35
Tovomita stigmatosa	27	3.01
Iryanthera juruensis	26	2.90
Protium nodulosum	22	2.45
Goupia glabra	21	2.34
Vouacapoua americana	17	1.89
Protium carnosum	17	1.89
Theobroma subincana	16	1.78
Sapotaceae, Gen. sp.?	14	1.56
Micropholis acutangula	14	1.56
Vantanea cupularis	12	1.34
Protium polybotryum v. *blackii*	11	1.23
Protium puncticulatum	11	1.23
Poraqueiba guianensis	11	1.23
Piptadenia suaveolens	13	1.45
Sterculia pruriens	11	1.23
Tapura singularis	10	1.11
Iryanthera paraensis	9	1.00
Helicostylis pedunculata	9	1.00
Osteophloeum platyspermum	9	1.00
Echweilera blanchetiana	9	1.00

[a] Densities were calculated two ways. The first employed the original lists of Dr. Pires, giving a total of 1,188 trees, and the second—used in this table and in the summary table 11—is based on our re-measurements and the elimination of trees nearly but not quite 1 dm. d.d.h., and a few that died in the interval between the two measurements. The latter gave a total of 897 stems on 2 hectares.

Table 9. Tree species having the largest basal area on a sample plot of equatorial rain forest at Mucambo

Species	Basal area, sq. dm.	Relative basal area, per cent of total
Vochysia guianensis	981.2	15.05
Goupia glabra	704.0	10.80
Echweilera odora	437.7	6.71
Trattinikia sp.? "Sucuruba"	309.5	4.75
Eschweilera krukovii	217.8	3.34
Parkia pendula	207.7	3.18
Anacardium giganteum	175.6	2.69
Vantanea cupularis	155.4	2.38
Protium sp.? "Breu mescla"	139.3	2.13
Chimarrhis turbinata	135.4	2.08
Caryocar microcarpum	119.9	1.84
Protium trifoliolatum	114.3	1.75
Pourouma myrmecophila	94.0	1.44
Piptadenia suaveolens	88.9	1.36
Protium nodulosum	87.3	1.34
Sterculia pruriens	74.6	1.14
Vouacapoua americana	73.5	1.13
Pithecolobium jupunba	72.0	1.10
Protium carnosum	72.1	1.10
Qualea albiflora	70.3	1.08
Neea sp.?	70.2	1.08
Enterlobium schomburgkii	69.3	1.06
Trattinikia rhoifolia	68.9	1.06
Caryocar villosum	68.0	1.04
Sapotaceae, Gen. sp.?	64.9	1.00

of all species (table 10). By the use of relative measures it becomes possible to add up the otherwise disparate data of number (density), basal area (dominance), and occurrence (frequency). Although calculations have been made for all the species on the 2-hectare plot, these tables show in each case only the relatively small number of leading species. Only 25 species have a relative density of more than 1 per cent and a relative basal area of more than 1 per cent. Only 18 species have frequencies in classes D and E and exceed relative frequencies of about 1.25 per cent.

Table 10. Tree species having Raunkiaerian class D and E frequencies on a sample plot of equatorial rain forest at Mucambo

| Species | Frequency percentages | | Relative frequency, per cent of total frequency |
	20 plots 10 × 100 m.	10 plots 20 × 100 m.	
Class E frequency			
Eschweilera odora	100	100	3.64
Protium trifoliolatum	100	100	3.64
Echweilera krukovii	95	100	3.09
Tovomita stigmatosa	80	100	2.91
Vochysia guianensis	80	100	2.91
Protium sp.? "Breu mescla"	85	90	2.91
Iryanthera juruensis	75	90	2.73
Theobroma subincana	65	90	2.18
Class D frequency			
Protium nodulosum	70	80	2.54
Protium carnosum	60	80	2.00
Vantanea cupularis	50	80	1.82
Protium puncticulatum	55	70	1.64
Micropholis acutangula	55	70	1.82
Osteophloeum platyspermum	50	70	1.64
Sterculia pruriens	45	70	1.64
Sapotaceae, Gen. sp.?	45	70	1.64
Helicostylis pedunculata	40	70	1.45
Thyrsodium paraensis	35	70	1.27

COMBINATION OF DATA. On a basis of the relative measures it is possible to combine the different quantitative data available for the trees of the Mucambo plot. The sum of the relative density, relative dominance, and relative frequency of a species may be referred to as the *importance value index* (Curtis and McIntosh, 1951). Since these are percentage data, the sum of all indexes would be 300.

Table 11 gives the importance value index for each species that attains a value of 1 per cent or more in any of the series: density, dominance, or frequency. There are only 44 of them, or about one-fourth of the total species present on the plot. The leading species of the forest, by this combined measure, is found to be *Vochysia guianensis,* with an index of 23.42. This is the sum of 5.46 per cent relative density, 15.05 per cent relative dominance, and 2.91 per cent relative frequency. In this case it is seen that basal area

Table 11. The leading tree species on a sample plot of equatorial rain forest at Mucambo, arranged according to their "importance value indices," or the sum of relative densities, frequencies, and dominances

	Family	Importance value index
Vochysia guianensis	Vochysiaceae	23.42
Eschweilera odora	Lecythidaceae	21.61
Goupia glabra	Celastraceae	15.14
Protium trifoliolatum	Burseraceae	13.08
Echweilera krukovii	Lecythidaceae	12.90
Protium sp.? "Breu mescla"	Burseraceae	9.29
Tovomita stigmatosa	Guttiferae	6.45
Iryanthera juruensis	Myristicaceae	6.38
Protium nodulosum	Burseraceae	6.33
Trattinikia sp.?	Burseraceae	5.62
Vantanea cupularis	Humiriaceae	5.54
Anacardium giganteum	Anacardiaceae	5.03
Protium carnosum	Burseraceae	5.00
Vouacapoua americana	Leguminosae	4.67
Theobroma subincana	Sterculiaceae	4.63
Piptadenia suaveolens	Leguminosae	4.26
Sapotaceae, Gen. sp.?	Sapotaceae	4.20
Parkia pendula	Leguminosae	4.05
Micropholis acutangula	Sapotaceae	4.04
Sterculia pruriens	Sterculiaceae	4.01
Osteophloeum platyspermum	Myristicaceae	3.40
Protium polybotryum v. blackii	Burseraceae	3.30
Chimarrhis turbinata	Rubiaceae	3.29
Protium puncticulatum	Burseraceae	3.27
Eschweilera blanchetiana	Lecythidaceae	3.26
Pourouma myrmecophila	Moraceae	3.24
Poraqueiba guianensis	Icacinaceae	3.17
Pithecolobium jupunba	Leguminosae	3.15
Helicostylis pedunculata	Moraceae	3.11
Tapura singularis	Dichapetalaceae	2.90
Caryocar microcarpum	Caryocaraceae	2.82
Thyrsodium paraensis	Anacardiaceae	2.72
Qualea albiflora	Vochysiaceae	2.66
Ptychopetalum olacoides	Olacaceae	2.63
Couepia hoffmanniana	Rosaceae	2.61

Table 11. The leading tree species on a sample plot of equatorial rain forest at Mucambo, arranged according to their "importance value indices," or the sum of relative densities, frequencies, and dominances (Cont.)

	Family	Importance value index
Pouteria caimito	Sapotaceae	2.52
Iryanthera paraensis	Myristicaceae	2.46
Manilkara huberi	Sapotaceae	2.43
Dendrobangia boliviana	Icacinaceae	2.31
Pouteria sp.?	Sapotaceae	2.06
Trattinickia rhoifolia	Burseraceae	1.93
Caryocar villosum	Caryocaraceae	1.91
Neea sp.?	Nyctaginaceae	1.37
Enterolobium schomburgkii	Leguminosae	1.35

plays an important role in giving the species its high rank. *Eschweilera odora,* the second ranking species, has an index of 21.61. This is made up of 11.26 per cent relative density, 6.71 per cent relative basal area, and 3.64 per cent relative frequency, in which density plays the most important role.

The combined indexes of all species total 300. The five leading species (table 11) together have 86.15 points, and the 44 species together have 229 of the 300 points. The relative insignificance of the vast majority of the species is thus made clear.

FAMILY DOMINANCE. There are some types of vegetation in which no species or combination of a few species attains dominance in the community, but dominance occurs for the combined species of a family (Richards, 1952). This question was investigated for the forest at Mucambo, with the results shown in table 12. The Burseraceae is found to be the leading family, the sum of the index values of its eight species being 47.92. This family is followed by the Lecythidaceae, Vochysiaceae, and Leguminosae, each succeeding one being about 10 points less than the preceding family. Inasmuch as the Burseraceae with 47.9 points make up only about 18 per cent, there clearly is no family dominance in this community.

LIFE FORM AND LEAF SIZE. It is well known that there is some correlation between the physiognomy of vegetation and its environment. One of the most successful methods of investigating this relationship on an extensive scale is that of the life forms of Raunkiaer (1934). His limited classes, easy of determination and readily subject to statistical comparisons, have been widely used. Although only a few concrete data are available, it has long

Table 12. The leading tree species of equatorial rain forest at Mucambo arranged by families and the sums of the importance value indexes of the species

Family	Number of species	Importance value
Burseraceae	8	47.92
Lecythidaceae	3	37.77
Vochysiaceae	2	26.08
Leguminosae	5	17.48
Sapotaceae	5	15.25
Celastraceae	1	15.14
Myristicaceae	3	12.24
Sterculiaceae	2	8.64
Anacardiaceae	2	7.75
Guttiferae	1	6.45
Moraceae	2	6.35
Humiriaceae	1	5.54
Icacinaceae	2	5.48
Caryocaraceae	2	4.73
Rubiaceae	1	3.29
Dichapetalaceae	1	2.90
Olacaceae	1	2.63
Rosaceae	1	2.61
Nyctaginaceae	1	1.37
19 families	44	

been known that the vegetation of equatorial humid regions—the various types of rain forest—is predominantly woody, with many medium and tall trees. This is the vegetation of phanerophytic dominance that exists in Raunkiaer's "phanerophytic climate." Our analysis of the vegetation at Mucambo is given in table 15, where it is seen that 74.3 per cent of the known flora of the sample plot is made up of true phanerophytes. When the lianas and vascular epiphytes are distributed among the sub-classes of phanerophytes according to the maximum height they attain, the percentage of total phanerophytes jumps to 95.37 per cent. The sub-class of tall trees (exceeding 30 m.) contains 22.48 per cent of the flora; that of medium-sized trees (8 to 30 m.) contains 39.45 per cent; small trees (2 to 8 m.) make up only 1.38 per cent; and shrubs (0.25 to 2 m.) are 11.01 per cent. Lianas and epiphytes are fairly abundant, being 12.84 per cent and 8.25 per cent, respectively. The other classes in which the perennating buds receive progressively more protection are all so small as to be essentially insignificant, and annuals (therophytes) are completely missing from among the total of 218 species on the plot that have been analyzed for life form.

Raunkiaer's leaf-size classes have not been widely used, although they are equally amenable to statistical treatment as are the life-form classes. Table 15 shows both types of classification simultaneously, not only for the total flora of the sample plot, but also for the sub-classes. It is seen that the mesophyll leaf size is predominant, with 68.35 per cent of the species having leaves of that size range. Only about 11 per cent have larger leaves, while something over 20 per cent have smaller leaves. The leaf-size classes smaller than mesophyll are better represented in the higher strata of the forest than they are in the lower, as shown by the tallest trees (megaphanerophytes) having 4.08 per cent leptophyll, 2.04 per cent nanophyll, and 16.33 per cent microphyll leaves, whereas the medium-sized trees (mesophanerophytes) have 2.33, zero, and 10.46 per cent, respectively. There is further discussion of life-form and leaf-size classification in Part III of this paper.

DISCUSSION. Black et al. (1950) studied three 1-hectare plots of equatorial rain forest, two of which were in Pará near our study. On these plots they found 60 species among 564 trees of the *varzea* type near Belém, 87 species among 423 trees of the *terra firme* type, and 79 species among 230 trees of the *terra firme* type near Tefé Amazonas. From a study of their data they concluded that "only about half, or less than half, of the species of trees which exist in a given forest type in the region studied have been met with and recorded on our plots." In a later paper Pires et al. (1953) studied a 3.5-hectare plot at Castanhal, about 120 km. east of Belém. Here they found 179 species among 1,482 trees 10 cm. or more in diameter. Using the method of Preston (1948), they concluded that more than half the tree species of the local type had seen sampled and that all together the number was probably about 250 species.

In the present study at Mucambo, which is near the Belém plot mentioned above, we found 153 species of trees 10 cm. or more in diameter, among 897 trees. [5]

Figure 1 gives the species-area curves for the three *terra firme* plots from Pará. Curve *A* is for the 1950 study of Black et al., curve *B* for the Castanhal study, and curve *C* for our Mucambo analysis. In each case the plot was subdivided into 10 × 100 m. strips. The data for these curves are obtained by determining the "new species" added to a list as an additional strip is examined. All three studies can be compared at the 10,000 sq. m. area, which was the maximum size of the early Belém plot. As tested in this way, the floras differ in richness of tree species: 87, 108, and 144 species for the *A*, *B*, and *C* curves, respectively. Castanhal and Mucambo can be tested at the 20,000 sq. m. area where the difference is 149 and 173 species for the *B* and

[5] The original list of Dr. Pires contained some trees later dead and a number that did not quite measure 10 cm. diameter at 4.5 ft. above the ground by our steel tape. The earlier list had 173 species among 1188 trees.

C curves. The Castanhal sampling was continued to 3.5 hectares and 179 species. The three curves at the 1-hectare point and two of them at the 2-hectare point are running about 24 species apart, with the Mucambo flora

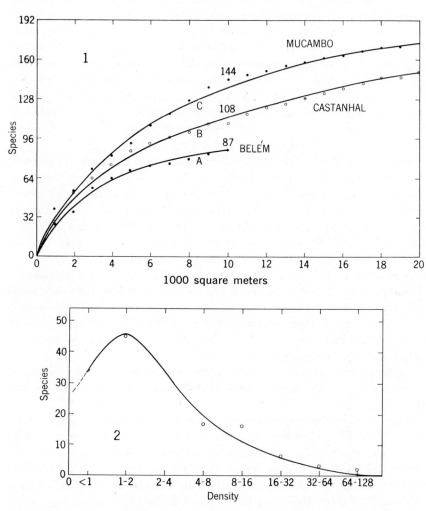

FIG. 1–2.—FIG. 1. Species-area curves for samples of *terra firme* rain forest in region of Belém, Pará.—FIG. 2. Frequency of species of given densities on a 2-hectare sample plot of *terra firme* rain forest at Mucambo, Belém, Pará.

the richest and the Castanhal flora intermediate. These appear to be parabolic curves and are not becoming asymptote, although there certainly is a finite number of species within a given forest type.

On the Mucambo plot we found (using our revised list of carefully measured trees) 153 species among 897 trees with the following distribution: 1 specimen only, 67 species; 2 specimens, 24 species; 3 specimens, 13 species, and so on: 4—9, 5—3, 6—3, 7—4, 8—5, 9—4, 10—1, 11—4, 12—1, 13—1, 14—2, 16—1, 17—2, 21—1, 22—1, 26—1, 27—1, 39—1, 49—1, 58—1, 69—1, and 101 stems, 1 species. Preston (1948) concluded that random samples of ecological assemblages indicate that the universes from which they are drawn have approximately the form of an ordinary Gaussian curve drawn upon a logarithmic base. Samples have the same form as the universe but are truncated at the left, a rather large number of rare species not being sampled. Preston approaches the problem by determining the number of species in each of a series of frequency classes of logarithmic nature, or octaves, as in the natural series of commonness: 1, 2, 4, 8, 16, 32, 64. . . . The octave 4–8, for example, would contain all the species represented by 5, 6, and 7 individuals in a sample, and half the species represented by 4 and 8 individuals. For our Mucambo study the octaves have the following values: <1—$33\frac{1}{2}$ (i.e., half the 67 species represented by a single specimen on the plot); 1–2—$45\frac{1}{2}$ species (half of the singles and half of the doubles); 2–4 —$29\frac{1}{2}$ species (half the doubles, all the species represented by three plants, and half those with four plants). Similarly, the remaining octaves are: 4–8 —17 species; 8–16—16 species; 16–32—$6\frac{1}{2}$ species; 32–64—3 species; and 64–128—2 species. These data are plotted in fig. 2. It is clear the model class is that of 1–2 specimens on this 2-hectare sample plot. This curve indicates that the total flora of the vicinity of this plot and within the particular forest type is probably in the neighborhood of 200 species of trees with diameters of 10 cm. or more. In other words, the 2-hectare plot sampled about three-fourths of the trees as defined here. Since we do not have density data for smaller trees, shrubs, etc., it is not possible to make a similar estimate of the total flora of the community.

Our data on frequency and basal area as a measure of dominance do not seem to need discussion. These and other phytosociological concepts are discussed in Braun-Blanquet (1932), Cain (1932), Oosting (1948) and in an extensive journal literature. The idea of combining data by the use of percentages, as in relative density, relative dominance, and relative frequency to form a sum known as the *importance value index* originated in the work of Curtis and his colleagues. Curtis and McIntosh (1951) modified the original method in a paper on the upland forest continuum in southwestern Wisconsin. They claim that this index is an excellent indication of the vegetational importance of a species within a stand. In temperate forests it is possible to estimate rather accurately the relative importance of the few species of trees, but the index permits a measurement and is a good device for comparisons of different stands. For the herbaceous layer of northern forests such estimation is difficult and the objective determination of the importance value index is an important device. In equatorial rain forests the flora is so rich, the densities of trees of a species so low, and the dominance so low and variable, that estimations of relative importance are nearly if not actually impossible. The use of the importance value index, how-

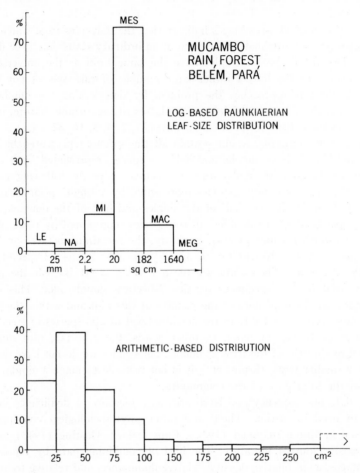

Fig. 3. Percentages of species of trees of *terra firme* rain forest at Mucambo, Belém, Pará, having leaves of different sizes. Plotting in the upper histogram is according to the leaf-size classes of Raunkiaer (see text) and in the lower diagram is according to equal-sized classes.

ever, permits the arrangement of *all* species in a linear series according to the values of their indexes. We believe that the introduction of this concept in phytosociological work in the tropics is very important.

Our data on life forms do not need discussion at this point, but there are certain points about the leaf-size study that should be exposed. In addition to a class for aphyllous species (not present in the Mucambo plot but occurring elsewhere in rain-forest vegetation in such plants as the epiphytic cactus, *Rhipsalis*), Raunkiaer established six leaf-size classes: leptophyll, up to 25 sq. mm.; nanophyll, with an upper limit of 9×25 sq. mm.; microphyll, $9^2 \times 25$ sq. mm.; mesophyll, $9^3 \times 25$ sq. mm.; macrophyll, $9^4 \times 25$ sq. mm.; and megaphyll, larger than the latter class. Figure 3 shows the distribution of the Mucambo species in these leaf-size classes. We also have distributed the leaves through a series of arithmetic classes, increasing by 25 sq. cm. units. Similar data were prepared for 150 tree species of the Castanhal rain-forest sample plot. On the basis of the Raunkiaerian leaf-size classes, which have a logarithmic base, the distribution is symmetrical about the modal mesophyll leaf-size class (table 13). When the distribution is made

Table 13. Frequency of species in Raunkiaerian leaf-size classes, terra firme rain forest, Pará

Class	Mucambo		Castanhal	
	Number	Per cent	Number	Per cent
Aphyllous	0		0	
Leptophyll	4	2.9	3	2.0
Nanophyll	1	0.7	2	1.3
Microphyll	17	12.3	20	13.3
Mesophyll	105	75.5	111	74.0
Macrophyll	12	8.6	13	8.7
Megaphyll	0		1	0.7
Total	139		150	

according to arithmetic classes, it is strongly skewed. It is completely unknown whether such a distribution of leaf sizes is abnormal for the world vegetation, as there is no "normal" distribution comparable with Raunkiaer's normal life-form spectrum, but it is undoubtedly characteristic of equatorial rain forest (table 14).

Further analysis of the leaves of trees available from the Castanhal study shows that 69.3 per cent are simple, 24.7 per cent are once-pinnate, 3.3 per cent are bi- or tri-pinnate, and 2.6 per cent are palmate divided or deeply lobed. At Mucambo we found 71.2 per cent to be simple, 18.7 per cent pinnate, 6.5 per cent bi- or tri-pinnate, and 3.6 per cent palmate. Also at Mucambo we found the proportion of compound leaves to increase with the height of the trees: megaphanerophytes were 33.3 per cent compound, mesophanerophytes were 21.0 per cent compound, and nanophanerophytes were 16.7 per cent compound. Microphanerophytes were too few in number for the percentage to be meaningful. Although the leaflets of compound leaves

Table 14. Frequency of species in arithmetic leaf-size classes, terra firme rain forest, Pará

Class, area in sq. cm.	Mucambo		Castanhal	
	Number	Per cent	Number	Per cent
0–25	32	23.0	32	21.3
26–50	43	30.9	42	28.0
51–75	28	20.1	31	20.6
76–100	14	10.1	17	11.3
101–125	5	3.6	4	2.7
126–150	3	2.2	7	4.7
151–175	2	1.4	3	2.0
176–200	2	1.4	1	0.7
201–225	1	0.7	3	2.0
226–250	2	1.4	4	2.7
Larger	7	5.0	6	4.0
Total	139		150	

may be as large as many of the simple leaves, there is some tendency for leaflets to average smaller than simple leaf blades in this vegetation.

One of the conspicuous features of the leaves of tropical trees is their predominantly entire margins and lack of lobing. Also acuminate leaf tips are very common. Among the Castanhal species we found 70.6 per cent with acuminate tips. Furthermore, 28.0 per cent of the 150 species studied had abruptly more or less long tips of the "drip-point" type. Leaf-tip analysis was not made of the Mucambo species, but it is our impression that drip points are very abundant on the leaves.

The degree of floristic relationship between the two samples of *terra firme* rain forest, Mucambo near Belém and Castanhal about 120 km. eastward, is not very great. There are 11 families found only in the Castanhal sample, 3 families only in the Mucambo sample, and 36 families common to the two. At the generic level there are 72 genera found only at Castanhal, 42 found only at Mucambo, and 58 genera common to both. Among species 133 were found only at Castanhal, 117 only at Mucambo, and 40 common to both. The degree of similarity can be expressed in this way: 72 per cent of the families are in common, 34 per cent of the genera, and only 14 per cent of the species. In making these calculations it was necessary, of course, to omit those taxa in which the specific or generic identities are unknown.

The vast majority of the genera are represented by a single species, and there are only a few large genera. *Protium* (Burseraceae) has 20 species in the combined lists, *Pouteria* (Sapotaceae) has 17 species, and *Licania* (Rosaceae) and *Inga* (Leguminosae) have 10 species each. Two genera have five species, five genera have four species, seven genera have three species, 28 genera have two species, and 102 genera have one species each. If it is assumed that the specimens not identified beyond the family are each monotypic in the flora, the latter number is increased to 126 entities.

CONCLUDING STATEMENT. We believe that this study of the Mucambo plot shows that certain phytosociological concepts and methods can be applied to the complex vegetation of the humid tropics much as they have commonly been employed in the study of temperate vegetation, with considerable improvement in understanding and description of such types as rain forest. Our work was greatly facilitated, in fact made possible in the short time at our disposal, by the help of local *mateiros,* for the richness of the flora presents problems of recognition and identification not common in temperate work. Furthermore, there are many parts of Brazil where such help could not have been received and where the flora is less well known.

PART III. LIFE-FORM AND LEAF-SIZE CLASSES OF THE BRAZILIAN RAIN FOREST [6]

In a long series of studies on statistical plant geography by Raunkiaer (brought together in English translation, 1934), considerable attention was given to life forms of plants in the analysis of floras and communities and as an approach to phytoclimate. Less attention was paid to leaf-size diagnosis, although a series of easily manipulated classes was developed. Raunkiaer's system of life-form classification met with considerable success as measured by its world-wide use since it was first introduced in 1904. The leaf-size classification, although equally amenable to statistical treatment, has been little used. A review of the world literature on life forms and phytoclimate was published by Cain (1950).

During the latter half of 1955 and early in 1956 the authors had an opportunity to travel considerably in Brazil in connection with the project mentioned in the introduction. Among the concepts and methods of plant sociology that we were able to test on Brazilian vegetation were Raunkiaer's systems of life-form and leaf-size classification. This paper gives the data we have on the rain forest (except for some studies of the temperate rain forest with an overstory of *Araucaria,* the Paraná pine). It cannot be said that our data are adequate for characterization of the life forms and leaf sizes of the Brazilian rain forest as a whole, but they come from widely scattered stations and are nearly complete for the flora of the sample plots studied. It seems to us that these fragmentary results are interesting and sufficiently

[6] Stanley A. Cain and Gustavus M. de Oliveira Castro.

significant to suggest the value of more extensive investigations along similar lines.

Our tables are so constructed as to present "spectra," or percentage arrays, not only for the life-form classification and leaf-size classification of the total floras of the sample plots, but also for the leaf sizes of each life-form class, and vice versa.

Raunkiaer employed three guiding rules in the selection of life-form characteristics: (*a*) the character must be structural and essential; it must represent an important morphological adaptation; (*b*) the character must be sufficiently obvious that one can easily see in nature to which life form a plant belongs; (*c*) all the life forms employed must be of such a nature that they constitute a homogeneous system; they must represent a single point of view or aspect of plants and thus enable a comparative statistical treatment of the flora of different regions or communities. On a basis of these principles Raunkiaer recognized five life-form classes, with suitable subdivisions, based on the kind and degree of protection afforded the perennating buds, which are the meristematic tissues responsible for renewal of growth after an unfavorable season. The classes, and the subdivisions we use in this study, are as follows:

PHANEROPHYTES. In these plants the perennating buds are elevated and exposed to the atmosphere during the unfavorable season. They are mostly woody trees and shrubs, although lianas, epiphytes, and some large perennial herbs can be classified here. Because the severity of conditions increases with height above the ground, as a general rule, the phanerophytes are subdivided into height classes, as follows:

Megaphanerophytes: With perennial parts, including buds higher than 30 m.

Mesophanerophytes: Between 8 and 30 m. tall

Microphanerophytes: Between 2 and 8 m. tall

Nanophanerophytes: Under 2 m. and over 25 cm. tall

These subclasses can be further divided according to whether the meristematic tissues are naked or protected by bud scales and the plants evergreen or deciduous.

Chamaephytes. Plants of this class are lower than 25 cm. but have their perennating buds definitely above the soil surface. During unfavorable conditions these plants may receive some protection from fallen leaves and in higher latitudes considerable protection from snow.

Hemicryptophytes. The third class has even more protection for its perennating buds, for they are located at the surface of the soil where litter, snow, etc., have the greatest chance of covering the buds during dormant periods.

Cryptophytes. These are the "hidden plants" in which all the aboveground parts die during the unfavorable season and the perennating buds survive under the surface of the substratum. The commonly used subclasses of hydrophytes and helophytes, aquatic and marsh plants, are not applicable to the present study, and the geophytes, with their buds buried in the soil, are scarcely represented in rain forests.

Therophytes. These are the annual plants in which all parts die except those that survive in seeds and fruits. The perennating bud is that of the embryo in the seed. No other meristematic tissues survive.

It is seen, then, that Raunkiaer's system meets the criteria set out: it is a unitary system, being based completely on the protection afforded the perennating buds. The characters are structural, essential, and adaptive. Furthermore, they provide a simple basis for statistical treatment. The array of percentages of the life-form classes of the flora of any area or the species composing any community is referred to as the biological spectrum. Because each class is given a percentage representation, different spectra can be compared directly.

The percentages of phanerophytes in different floras range from zero to over 90 per cent in tropical rain forests, the latter being characteristic of "phanerophytic climates." Deserts have been referred to as "therophytic climates" because the percentage of that class may reach more than 40. Relatively high percentages of chamaephytes often occur at high latitudes and altitudes, sometimes exceeding 50 per cent. Temperate forest vegetation, despite its domination by trees, often has high percentages of hemicryptophytes. Geophytes (cryptophytes) are relatively abundant in regions of Mediterranean climate and in the spring flora of broad-leaf-deciduous forests.

Because there are great variations among the biological spectra of different areas and there is no inherent "yardstick" or base line for comparisons, Raunkiaer devised a "normal spectrum" based on a sampling of the world flora using 1,000 entities. The question is unimportant whether the normal spectrum is representative of the world flora, for in any case it provides a base line from which departure of the percentage of any class for any flora can be ascertained. The normal spectrum has 46 per cent phanerophytes, 9 per cent chamaephytes, 26 per cent hemicryptophytes, 6 per cent cryptophytes, and 13 per cent therophytes. Many tables of comparison of biological spectra and discussions of their significance are to be found in the papers of Raunkiaer and in the review by Cain previously cited.

It is a general observation that leaves are larger the more favorable the conditions of growth, and smaller in dry or cold climates. Even on a single plant the more exposed leaves tend to be smaller than the protected ones. There are, however, very few data available on leaf sizes, especially as a characterization of a flora or community. As early as 1916 Raunkiaer published on the use of leaf size in biological plant geography, and although the system is relatively simple and amenable to statistical treatment of floras, little use has been made of it. Realizing the inherent variability of leaves of a single plant, Raunkiaer devised only a small number of size classes that increase geometrically, as follows:

Leptophyll: Leaves up to 25 sq. mm. area

Nanophyll: Leaves from 25 to 225 sq. mm. in area, the upper limit being 9×25 sq. mm.

Microphyll: Area from 225 to 2,025 sq. mm. (20.25 sq. cm.), or $9^2 \times 25$

Mesophyll: Area from 2,025 to 18,225 sq. mm. (182.25 sq. cm.), or $9^3 \times 25$

Macrophyll: Area from 18,225 to 164,025 sq. mm. (1,640.25 sq. cm.), or $9^4 \times 25$ sq. mm.

Megaphyll: Leaves larger than macrophyll, or 1,640.25 sq. cm.

Because of the range of the size classes and the variations among leaves, it seldom is necessary to make a highly accurate measurement of leaf area, for it usually is obvious to which class a leaf belongs. Raunkiaer presented a diagram of the class sizes that helps visual comparison and suggested that tracings could be cut out of paper, weighed, and compared with paper of known area and weight. The authors have devised a simpler system which uses a rule of thumb that the blade area is two-thirds of the rectangular area of length by width. This was found to be rapid and sufficiently accurate for Raunkiaerian leaf-size classification.

MUCAMBO, BELÉM, PARÁ. Our most extensive sample of rain forest for which we have both life-form and leaf-size classification of the total flora is at Mucambo. The property of the Instituto Agronômico do Norte lies at the eastern edge of the city of Belém, Pará, and includes an extensive tract of primeval rain forest of *terra firme* type of which Mucambo is a part. In an easily accessible part of this forest Dr. Murça Pires, of the Instituto staff, had surveyed a 2-hectare plot in 20 contiguous strips of 10×100 m. On each strip all trees of 1 dm. diameter or more were marked by metal tags bearing consecutive numbers. When the authors first visited the sample plot in September, 1955, identifications were still continuing and Dr. Pires was in the United States. We later obtained permission to carry on plant sociological work on the plot and revisited it in January, 1956. Part II of this paper gives the details, but the life-form and leaf-size work is summarized here (tables 15–17).

In table 15 we find that the total flora of the 2-hectare plot (table 4) contained 218 vascular species, of which true phanerophytes (trees and shrubs) were 162 (74 per cent). Therophytes were found to be absent, and chamaephytes, hemicryptophytes, and geophytes were of insignificant numbers. Table 16 is based on the same data but is organized so that the lianas (28 species, 12.8 per cent) and the epiphytes (18 species, 8.2 per cent) are distributed among the phanerophytic-height classes according to the maximum height at which each species was observed, except for two species the height of which we had not ascertained. On this basis, 206 (95.37 per cent) of the 216 species are phanerophytic. The largest sub-class is mesophanerophytic, although 49 species (22.69 per cent) are megaphanerophytic, exceeding 30 m. height. According to the initial lists of Murça Pires, the plot contained 173 species of trees that were 1 dm. or more in diameter. Our measurement of the trees of the plot reduced this number somewhat by elimination of trees that did not quite reach 1 dm. d.b.h. (diameter at 4.5 feet above the ground), but all of them do attain tree size elsewhere, if not on the plot. Such data not only show the reality of the phanerophytic dominance, taxonomically as well as physiognomically, but affirm Raunkiaer's designation of a phanerophytic climate for the constantly humid tropics. Although there is an impressive number of lianas (28 species, 12.84 per cent), *terra firme* rain forest of this type is not as rich in them as some other types. High forest is likewise not as rich in vascular (or for that matter, cryptogamic) epiphytes as are some other types, especially those of the coastal mountains. No climbing was done to obtain epiphytes from the forest crown, and many species may have been missed, but heavy storms had brought down many branches bearing epiphytes, so that our list is probably representative.

Turning now to leaf-size classes, we find a strong predominance in the mesophyll class (149 species, 68.35 per cent). Species with large leaves of the macrophyll class have a fair representation (24 species, 11 per cent), and the class of largest leaves, megaphylls, is completely missing. Comparing the two highest life-form classes, we find a consistent tendency for the leaves to be somewhat smaller in the megaphanerophytic class than in the mesophanerophytic class: leptophylls, 4.06 to 1.87 per cent; nanophylls, 2.03 to 0.93 per cent; microphylls, 16.35 to 14.02 per cent; mesophylls, 75.55 to 68.22 per cent. Consistently, the class with the largest leaves is smaller in the highest stratum: 2.03 to 14.95 per cent. Although the percentages are somewhat different when the lianas and epiphytes are not distributed according to phanerophytic sub-classes, the same relationship is clear (table 15).

The excellent book "The Tropical Rain Forest" by Richards (1952) shows the predominance of mesophyll leaves in rain forest. In the wet evergreen forest of the Shasta Reserve, Nigeria, 84 per cent of the leaves are mesophyll. In the evergreen seasonal forest of Trinidad the emergent trees are 86 per cent mesophyll and the trees of the lower story have 80 per cent in that class. Quoting from Brown (1919), in the Philippine Islands the dipterocarp tropical rain forest of Mt. Maquiling has 86 per cent mesophyll leaves; the submontane rain forest has 97 per cent; and the montane mossy rain forest has 50 per cent mesophyll leaves. The latter type has 50 per cent microphyll leaves. For the evergreen seasonal forest of Trinidad, Beard (1946; Richards, 1952) showed that the emergent trees have a higher percentage of species with mesophyll leaves than do the canopy species, while lower-story trees are intermediate.

Table 15. Occurrence in Raunkiaerian life-form and leaf-size classes of the species on a 2-hectare sample plot, Mucambo, Belém, Pará. Data by S. A. Cain and G. M. de Oliviera Castro

Life-form classes	Leaf-size classes					Total, per cent	Number
	Leptophyll	Nanophyll	Microphyll	Mesophyll	Macrophyll		
Total phanerophytes, lianas and epiphytes excluded	2.47	.62	12.35	75.92	8.64	74.31	162
Megaphanerophytes	4.08	2.04	16.33	75.51	2.04	22.48	49
Mesophanerophytes	2.33		10.46	75.58	11.63	39.45	86
Microphanerophytes				66.7	33.3	1.38	3
Nanophanerophytes			12.50	79.17	8.33	11.01	24
Lianas		3.58	17.85	67.85	10.72	12.84	28
Epiphytes		16.67	38.89	16.67	27.77	8.25	18
Chamaephytes	50.0			50.0		.92	2
Hemicryptophytes		33.33	16.67	33.33	16.67	2.75	6
Geophytes				50.0	50.0	.92	2
Therophytes						0	0
Total, per cent	2.29	3.21	15.14	68.35	11.01	100.00	
Number	5	7	33	149	24		218

Table 16. Occurrence in Raunkiaerian life-form and leaf-size classes of the species on a 2-hectare sample plot, Mucambo, Belém, Pará. Data by S. A. Cain and G. M. de Oliviera Castro. This table has Epiphytes and Lianas distributed according to phanerophytic height classes

Life-form classes	Leaf-size classes					Total, per cent	Number
	Leptophyll	Nanophyll	Microphyll	Mesophyll	Macrophyll		
Total phanerophytes	1.94	2.42	15.53	69.42	10.68	95.37	206
Megaphanerophytes	4.06	2.03	16.35	75.55	2.03	22.69	49
Mesophanerophytes	1.87	.93	14.02	68.22	14.95	49.54	107
Microphanerophytes			12.50	68.75	18.75	7.41	16
Nanophanerophytes		8.82	20.59	64.71	5.88	15.74	34
Chamaephytes	50.00			50.00		.92	2
Hemicryptophytes		33.33	16.67	33.33	16.67	2.78	6
Geophytes				50.00	50.00	.92	2
Therophytes							
Total, per cent	2.32	3.24	15.28	68.05	11.11		
Number	5	7	33	147	24		216

305

Table 17. Percentage of compound leaves in the height sub-classes of phanerophytes in the Mucambo flora

Life-form class	Simple leaves		Compound leaves	
	Number	Per cent	Number	Per cent
Megaphanerophytes	36	66.7	18	33.3
Mesophanerophytes	83	79.0	22	21.0
Microphanerophytes (only 3 spp.)				
Nanophanerophytes	20	83.3	4	16.7

Pires et al. (1953) published a list of trees observed on a 3.5-hectare plot in luxuriant, virginia *terra firme* rain forest near the village of Tres de Outubro, between Castanhal and the River Guamá, east of Belém, Pará. In 1955 the senior author of the present paper was able to study herbarium sheets of 150 of these species at the Instituto Agronômico do Norte, Belém, through the courtesy of Dr. G. A. Black, and computed the areas of typical leaves of mature trees. All the tree species of the Castanhal study were included in so far as they were represented in the herbarium, and where possible the Castanhal material was used. The result showed that 74 per cent of the species had leaves in the mesophyll-size class. It was not possible to separate the species into life-form classes, but the data allowed the distinction of species represented on the plot whose trunks were 40 cm. or more in diameter from the total that was 10 cm. or more in diameter. Comparing the larger trees with the total list, it was found that 16.6 per cent and 10.0 per cent were microphyll, 71.1 and 74.4 per cent were mesophyll, and 3.3 and 12.2 per cent were macrophyll. Very small percentages were in the other classes.

Further analysis of the leaves of trees in the Castanhal study showed that 69.3 per cent are simple, 24.7 per cent are once-pinnate, 3.3 per cent are bi- or tri-pinnate, and 2.6 per cent are palmate-lobed or divided. Considering only the 37 species that are pinnate, 24 (64.9 per cent) are of mesophyll leaf size, 11 species (29.7 per cent) are microphyll, and 2 (5.3 per cent) are macrophyll. In the determination of leaf-size class of compound leaves, the leaflet is taken as the unit, not the entire leaf, on the assumption that the leaflet is the physiological unit responding to the conditions of environment in correspondence with the simple-bladed leaf. Also in computing areas the petiole is ignored and only the blade is measured. Of the five species with decompound leaves, the leaflets were all small, three being leptophyll and two being nanophyll. The four species with palmate leaves had two with mesophyll leaflets and two with macrophyll leaflets.

In the present study of Mucambo there were found to be 46 species with compound leaves. On a basis of leaflet area, 4 species (8.7 per cent) were leptophyll, 1 species (2.2 per cent) nanophyll, 6 species (13 per cent) microphyll, 31 species (67.4 per cent) mesophyll, and 4 species (8.7 per cent) macrophyll. When arranged according to phanerophytic-height sub-classes (table 17), it is seen that compound leaves increase in proportion the higher the stratum. The fact that higher strata tend to have somewhat smaller leaf-blade areas is partly but not entirely a function of the fact that blades of leaflets tend to be smaller than blades of simple leaves.

For the Castanhal material an analysis of the leaf form was also made. The long-attenuate leaf tip, known as the drip point, is said to be character-istic of rain-forest tree species, or at least more abundant in this formation than in any other. It was found that only 29.4 per cent of the leaves were not acuminate. It is more or less arbitrary to classify some of the acuminate leaves as having drip points, but among the 70.6 per cent of the leaves with the acuminate tips, 28.0 per cent of the 150 species studied had abruptly more or less long tips of the drip-point type. Good examples from this com-munity of leaves with drip points include *Protium sagotianum* March., *Brosi-mum paranense* Huber, *Minquartia guianensis* Aubl., *Guatteria elongata* Benth., *Inga heterophylla* Willd., *Qualea albiflora* Warm., *Lacunaria crenata* (Tul.) A. C. Smith, and *Pouteria glomerate* Radlk. No statistics on the fre-quence of drip points in the Mucambo flora were made.

Table 4 contains the total vascular flora of the 2-hectare plot at Mucambo. In this list the species are arranged first according to life-form class, and within these classes are, second, arranged according to leaf-size class. The table excludes common names, but includes notation as to leaf form, whether simple or compound, and in the latter case the type of compounding. It is on a basis of these data that the foregoing statistics have been computed.

ALTO DO PALMITAL, FOZ DE IGUAÇU, PARANÁ.[7] The Falls of the Iguaçu are about 27 km. southeast of the town of Foz do Iguaçu near the junction of Argentina, Paraguay, and Paraná, Brazil, at about 25° 40″ S. Lat. and 54° 30″ W. Long. The excellent "Mapa Fitogeografico do Estado do Paraná" by Reinhard Maack (1950) shows the northwestern part of the state to be grassland *Campos limpos,* the southwestern part to be occupied by *Araucaria* forest, which has an understory of rain-forest trees, and the west central part to be occupied by sub-tropical rain forest ("Mata pluvial subtropical do 3° planalto, rich in Cyatheaceae, epiphytes, and lianas, and with the palms *Euterpe edulis* and *Cocos romanzoffiana*").

Table 18, which corresponds to table 15 for Mucambo, gives the per-centages of each of the life-form and leaf-size classes recognized. Only 66 species were collected and available for life-form and leaf-size study, although

---

[7] On our visit to the Falls area we were assisted in a sample-plot study by Sr. Aluiz Wichosky, Assistant Director of the National Park, and Sr. Romao Garcia and Sr. Ventura Orencis Margues, *mateiros.* We studied a plot of 2,800 sq. m. divided into sub-plots each 10 × 20 m.

Table 18. *Relationship between life-form classes and leaf-size classes, rain forest, Alto do Palmital, Foz de Iguaçu, Paraná*

Raunkiaerian life-form classes [a]	Aphyllous	Lepto-phyll	Nano-phyll	Micro-phyll	Meso-phyll	Macro-phyll	Total, per cent	Number
Total phanerophytes		5.4	2.7	32.4	59.4		56.1	37
Mesophanerophytes		6.3	3.1	34.4	56.2		48.5	32
Micro- and nanophanerophytes				20.0	80.0		7.6	5
Lianas				25.0	75.0		12.1	8
Epiphytes	12.5		12.5	25.0	25.0	25.0	12.1	8
Chamaephytes			50.0	25.0	25.0		6.1	4
Hemicryptophytes			14.3	14.3	71.4		10.6	7
Gryptophytes (geophytes)					50.0	50.0	3.0	2
Total, per cent	1.5	3.0	7.6	27.3	56.1	4.5		
Number	1	2	5	18	37	3		66

[a] Note the absence of the therophytic life-form class, and the megaphyll leaf-size class. Trees may occasionally exceed meso-phanerophytic height. When lianas and epiphytes are added to the phanerophytic-height classes they attain, the total for phanero-phytes becomes 80.3 per cent.

308

eight additional mesophanerophytes were observed on the plot: Palmeira de Coco, Paina, Marica, Cafezinho do Mato, Carne de Vaca, Urtiga, Sapuva, and Louro branco. Although this plot was only 2,800 sq. m., as opposed to 20,000 sq. m. for the Mucambo plot, the 72 species as to 218 show that the flora is distinctly less rich at Alto do Palmital than at Mucambo. Also, total phanerophytes, excluding lianas and epiphytes, are only 56 per cent in contrast to 74 per cent. With those classes included with trees and shrubs, the percentages are 80 and 95, respectively. Further comparison shows that the Alto do Palmital temperate rain forest differs from the Mucambo equatorial rain forest by having somewhat smaller leaves, somewhat more epiphytes, and lower stature of the tall trees. No species was observed to be a megaphanerophyte, although some undoubtedly are. The following are typical measurements of mesophanerophytes: Canjarana vermelha, 13.0 m. to branching and 19.4 m. to top of canopy; Canela preta, 6.0 m. to branching and 21.0 m. to top of canopy; Cedro, 10.2 m. to branching and 24.8 m. to top of canopy; Maria preta, 8.6 m. to branching and 28.0 m. to top of canopy; Guatambú, 27.7 m. to top of canopy; Palmito, 11.3 m. to base of leaves, 13.2 to top of canopy.

Later our collections from Alto do Palmital were examined by Padre Balduino Rambo, S.J., Porto Alegre, Rio Grande do Sul, who provided us with most of the technical names of the floristic list in table 19. This table is arranged by life-form and leaf-size classes.

The Mucambo plot has already been described in detail, but Alto do Palmital and the other plots have not, so a few additional descriptive data will be added for them. It has already been made clear that virgin temperate rain forest at Alto do Palmital is not unusually tall. Neither are the trees very large. Of the 193 trees measured on the plot we found 118 in the 10- to 19-cm. class (measured by diameter tape at 4.5 ft. above the ground), 33 in the 20- to 29-cm. class, 22 in the 30- to 39-cm. class, 12 in the 50- to 59-cm. class, 7 in the 50- to 59-cm. class, and 1 in the 60- to 69-cm. class. Of the trees 10 to 19 cm. in diameter the Palmito, *Euterpe edulis,* were 54, or 45.7 per cent of the total.

Basal area (cross-section area of the tree trunks at 4.5 ft. aboveground) totaled 851.96 sq. dm. on the 2,800 sq. m. plot. Table 20 shows that the greatest basal area was for Canjarana vermelha, *Cabralia oblongifolia,* with 10.2 per cent of the total. Seven other species had basal areas between 5 and 10 per cent, 20 species collectively made up 92.3 per cent of the basal area, and 19 species formed the remainder of 7.7 per cent. On a basis of this sample plot, similar timber would have 30.42 sq. m. (327 square feet) basal area on 1 hectare and 12.17 sq. m. (131 square feet) on 1 acre. This, incidentally, is slightly less than the average for virgin northern hardwood forest (temperate, broad-leaf deciduous forest) in the United States, as in northern Michigan.

Table 19. Floristic list of a 2,800 sq. m. sample plot of temperate rain forest at Alto do Palmital, Foz de Iguaçu, Paraná, arranged according to Raunkiaerian life-form and leaf-size classes

MESOPHANEROPHYTES (8–30 m. high)

Mesophyll

1. Palmito—*Euterpe edulis* Mart.	Palmae	Pinnate
2. Unknown #2—*Alchornea sidifolia* Muell. Arg.	Euphorbiaceae	Simple
3. Aguaí—*Chrysophyllum gonocarpum* (Mart. & Eichl.) Engl. (= *C. lucumifolium* Griseb.)	Sapotaceae	Simple
4. Paineira—*Chorisia insignis* HBK.	Bombacaceae	Palmate
5. Cincho, Rambincho—*Sorocea ilicifolia* Miq.	Moraceae	Simple
6. Guatambú—*Balfourodendron riedelianum* (Engl.) Engl.	Rutaceae	Simple
7. Guabiroba—*Campomanesia xanthocarpa* (Mart.) Berg	Myrtaceae	Simple
8. Jaracatiá—*Jaracatia dodecaphylla* A. DC.	Caricaceae	Palmate
9. Rabo mole—*Lonchocarpus muehlbergianus* Hassler	Leguminosae	Pinnate
10. Canjarana vermelha—*Cabralia oblongifolia* C. DC.	Meliaceae	Simple
11. Branquinho—*Banara tomentosa* Clos.	Flacourtiaceae	Simple
12. Amora—*Chlorophora tinctoria* (L.) Gaud.	Moraceae	Simple
13. Canela preta—?*Nectandra* sp.?	Lauraceae	Simple
14. Unknown #1—*Guarea* sp.?	Meliaceae	Pinnate
15. Cedro—*Cedrela* ?*fissilis* var. *macrocarpa* C. DC.	Meliaceae	Pinnate
16. Cabo de faca—*Seguieria* sp.?	Phytolaccaceae	Simple
17. Louro pardo—*Cordia* sp.?	Borraginaceae	Simple

Microphyll

18. Maria preta—*Diatenopteryx sorbifolia* Radlk.	Sapindaceae	Pinnate
19. Canela amarela—*Endlicheria hirsuta* (Schott.) Nees	Lauraceae	Simple
20. Marmeleiro—*Ruprechtia laxiflora* Meissn.	Polygonaceae	Simple
21. Esporão de galo—*Strychnos brasiliensis* (Spr.) Mart.	Loganiaceae	Simple

22. Peroba vermelha (rosa)—*Aspidosperma polyneuron* Muell. Arg.	Apocynaceae	Simple
23. Unknown #4—*Eugenia* sp.?	Myrtaceae	Simple
24. Catigua—*Trichilia catigua* A. Juss.	Meliaceae	Simple
25. Vapuriti—*Eugenia* sp.?	Myrtaceae	Simple
26. Vassourinha—*?Calyptranthes* sp.?	Myrtaceae	Simple
27. Farinha seca—*Machaerium* sp.?	Leguminosae	Pinnate
28. Amarelinha—*Dalbergia ?variabilis* Vog.	Leguminosae	Pinnate

Nanophyll

29. Maricá—Gen. sp.?	Leguminosae	Pinnate

Leptophyll

30. Anjico vermelha—*Piptodenia rigida* Benth. & Hook.	Leguminosae	Bipinnate
31. Anjiquinha—*Calliandra* sp.?	Leguminosae	Bipinnate

MICRO- and NANOPHANEROPHYTES

Mesophyll

1. *Inga marginata* Willd.	Leguminosae	Pinnate
2. *Psychotria* sp.?	Rubiaceae	Simple
3. *Miconia* sp.?	Melastomaceae	Simple
4. *Miconia ?hymenonervia* (Rad.) Cogn.	Melastomaceae	Simple

Microphyll

5. *Allophylus guaranitica* (St. Hil.) Niederl.	Sapindaceae	Trifoliate

LIANAS (reaching mesophanerophytic height)

Mesophyll

1. *Adenocalymna marginatum* DC.	Bignoniaceae	Bifoliate
2. Gen. sp.?	Bignoniaceae	Trifoliate
3. Gen. sp.?	Bignoniaceae	Trifoliate

Table 19. Floristic list of a 2,800 sq. m. sample plot of temperate rain forest at Alto do Palmital, Foz de Iguaçu, Paraná, arranged according to Raunkiaerian life-form and leaf-size classes (Cont.)

4. *Cissus* sp.?	Vitaceae	Simple
5. *Smilax* sp.?	Liliaceae	Simple
6. Fam. gen. sp.?		Simple
Microphyll		
7. *Bauhinia langsdorffiana* Bong. (= *B. microphylla* Vogl.)	Leguminosae	Simple
8. *Pyrstegia* sp.?	Bignoniaceae	Bifoliate
EPIPHYTES		
Macrophyll		
1. *Philodendron selloum* C. Koch.	Araceae	Simple
2. *?Diplazium* sp.?	Polypodiaceae	Simple
Mesophyll		
3. *Miltonia flavescens* Lindl.	Orchidaceae	Simple
4. *Aechmaea ?calyculata* (Morr.) Baker	Bromeliaceae	Simple
Microphyll		
5. *Billbergia nutans* Regel	Bromeliaceae	Simple
6. *Peperomia* sp.?	Piperaceae	Simple
Nanophyll		
7. *Peperomia nummularifolia* HBK.	Piperaceae	Simple
Aphyllous		
8. *Rhipsalis* sp.?	Cactaceae	

CHAMAEPHYTES

Mesophyll			
1. *Pharus glaber* HBK.		Gramineae	Simple
Microphyll			
2. Gen. sp.?		Polypodiaceae	Bipinnatifid
Nanophyll			
3. *Didymochlaena ?lunulata* Desv.		Polypodiaceae	Tripinnate
4. Gen. sp.?		Polypodiaceae	Tripinnate

HEMICRYPTOPHYTES

Mesophyll			
1. *Hydrocotyle callicephala* Cham.		Umbelliferae	Simple
2. *Calathea lindbergii* Peters		Marantaceae	Simple
3. *Doryopteris* sp.?		Polypodiaceae	Simple
4. *Doryopteris concolor* (Langsd. & Fisch.) Kuhn		Polypodiaceae	Pinnate
5. *Doryopteris stierii* Rosenst.		Polypodiaceae	Simple
Microphyll			
6. *Pteris denticulata* Sw.		Polypodiaceae	Pinnate
Nanophyll			
7. *Asplenium claussenii* Hieron.		Polypodiaceae	Pinnate

CRYPTOPHYTES (Geophytes)

Macrophyll			
1. *Asterostigma lividum* (Lodd.) Engl.		Araceae	Simple
Mesophyll			
2. *Ctenanthe casupoides* Petersen		Marantaceae	Simple

Table 20. Basal area of the trees of a 2,800 sq. m. sample plot of temperate rain forest at Alto do Palmital, Foz de Iguaçu, Paraná

Species	Basal area, sq. dm.	Per cent
Canjarana vermelha—*Cabralia oblongifolia*	87.32	10.2
Canela preta—*?Nectandra* sp.?	79.48	9.3
Guatambú—*Balfourodendron riedelianum*	72.00	8.5
Cedro—*Cedrela ?fissilis* var. *macrocarpa*	67.92	7.9
Aguaí—*Chrysophyllum gonocarpum*	58.76	6.9
Palmito—*Euterpe edulis*	57.59	6.8
Jaracatia—*Jaracatia dodecaphylla*	52.31	6.1
Alchornea sidifolia	43.58	5.1
Rabo mole—*Lonchocarpus muehlbergianus*	41.01	4.8
Louro branco—Not collected, hence not determined	40.97	4.8
Guarea sp.?	35.47	4.2
Maricá—Gen. sp.?, Leguminosae	35.76	4.2
Farinha seca—*Machaerium* sp.?	32.57	3.8
Guabiroba—*Campomanesia xanthocarpa*	21.90	2.6
Marmeleiro—*Ruprechtia laxiflora*	14.89	1.7
Paineira—*Chorisia insignis*	13.54	1.6
Paina—Not collected, hence not determined	12.12	1.4
Sapuva—Not collected, hence not determined	10.77	1.3
Cafezinho do mato—Not collected, hence not determined	9.42	1.1
19 additional species	64.58	7.7
Total on plot	851.96	100.0

As to density, Palmito was the most numerous species on the plot, with 54 stems. The only other species with more than five stems on the plot were Aguaí, *Chrysophyllum gonocarpum;* Canjarana vermelha, *Cabralia oblongifolia;* Canela preta, *Nectandra* sp.?; Cedro, *Cedrela fissilis;* and *Guarea* sp.?

Having tallied the 14 sub-plots separately, we can use them for frequency determination. Raunkiaerian frequency class A (1 to 20 per cent frequent) contained 21 species, or 53.9 per cent; class B (21 to 40 per cent) contained 13 species, or 33.3 per cent; class C (41 to 60 per cent) contained 3 species, or 7.7 per cent; and classes D (61 to 80 per cent) and E (81 to 100 per cent) each had one species. The two species of highest frequency are *Euterpe edulis* and *Chrysophyllum gonocarpum.*

CAIOBÁ, PARANÁ. This station is completely across the State of Paraná from Alto do Palmital near the seaside town of Caiobá just north of Baia de Guaratuba at about 25° 50″ S. Lat. and 48° 35″ W. Long. It is on the eastern, sea-facing slope of hills that are outliers of the Serra do Mar lying only a few hundred meters above sea level. Although there has been considerable disturbance of the forest in the region, the tract studied was said to be undisturbed original forest. The vegetation map by Maack (1950) shows the Serra do Mar to be covered by tropical, and this far south by sub-tropical, rain forest. As one moves southward along the coastal mountain rain forest there is no sharp break in type that is correlated with the Tropic of Capricorn. At this station we were assisted by Padre J. Mouré, S.J., of Curitiba. Time did not permit the study of a large plot, yet the species-area relationship of the six sub-plots, each 200 sq. m., indicated that we had a fairly satisfactory sample of the local type. Every vascular species observed on the plot was collected. Our data for trees are presented by common names of the species, and other entities determined as to life-form and leaf-size class are not listed, for we do not yet have technical identifications for the majority. This does not affect the central purpose of this paper, the comparative study of life-form and leaf-size class in various samples of rain forest.

Table 21 shows the distribution of the 90 species of the plot among the life-form and leaf-size classes. As at Alto do Palmital, megaphanerophytes are missing. The phanerophytic class as a whole has 53.2 per cent of the species, and with the addition of the lianas and epiphytes in the appropriate height classes, the total is 86.4 per cent. Lianas are seen to be relatively abundant, being twice the percentages at Mucambo and Alto do Palmital. Leaves average larger than at Alto do Palmital and about the same size as at Mucambo.

The plot held 66 trees with trunks 1 dm. or larger d.b.h. distributed among 21 species. Couvatán was found on all six sub-plots with 12 stems; Guamirim on five sub-plots with 10 stems; and Lucurana on four sub-plots with 10 stems. All other species were found on fewer plots and had one to four stems. Basal-area calculations showed Couvatán to be the leading species with 97.88 sq. dm. (23.3 per cent). Only two other species had significant percentages of basal area: Lucurana with 94.87 sq. dm. (22.6 per cent), and Guapiruvú with 59.63 sq. dm. (14.2 per cent). The fact that three species compose 60 per cent of the basal area is rather unusual in rain forest. On a basis of the sample plot this type of rain forest would have 35 sq. m. basal area (375 square feet) per hectare and 14 sq. m. (150 square feet) per acre (table 22).

Horto Botânico do Instituto Agronômico do Sul. In July, 1955, the senior author visited the Instituto Agronômico do Sul in connection with the *V Congresso Brasileiro de Ciencia do Solo* and was taken to the natural forest of the Horto Botânico by Dr. José da Costa Sacco, botanist of the Instituto. We returned to Pelotas, Rio Grande do Sul, later in the year and were materially assisted by Dr. da Costa Sacco in a study of the forest. Table 23 gives the percentages of the 140 species in each life-form and leaf-size class. Pelotas

Table 21. *Occurrence in Raunkiaerian life-form and leaf-size classes of the species on a small sample plot of rain forest, Caiobá, Paraná. Altitude 150 m. Distance from the sea 1 km. Data by S. A. Cain and Padre J. Mouré, S.J.*

Life-form classes [a]	Leaf-size classes					Total, per cent	Species
	Nanophyll	Microphyll	Mesophyll	Macrophyll	Megaphyll		
All phanerophytes	4.2	8.3	75.0	12.5	…	53.2	48
Mesophanerophytes	3.1	3.1	81.2	12.5	…	35.3	32
Microphanerophytes	…	30.0	60.0	10.0	…	11.1	10
Nanophanerophytes	16.7	…	66.7	16.7	…	6.6	6
Lianas	20.8	20.8	50.0	8.3	…	26.6	24
Epiphytes	16.7	16.7	50.0	16.7	…	6.6	6
Chamaephytes	…	33.3	33.3	16.6	16.6	6.6	6
Hemicryptophytes	…	33.3	66.7	…	…	3.3	3
Cryptophytes	…	…	100.0	…	…	3.3	3
Total, number	8	13	58	10	1	…	90
Per cent	8.8	14.4	64.4	11.1	1.1		

[a] Note the absence of megaphanerophytes and therophytes among life-form classes and the absence of aphyllous and leptophyll leaf-size classes. Thirty-one per cent of the species have compound leaves: assignment to leaf-size classes is on the basis of pinnules of compound leaves.

Table 22. Basal area of trees 1 dm. or over d.b.h. on a small plot of coastal mountain rain forest, Caiobá, Paraná. Distance from the sea about 1 km., elevation about 200 m. Data by S. A. Cain and Padre J. Mouré, S.J.

Species	Basal area, sq. dm. on 1,200 sq. m.	Per cent of total basal area
Covatãn	97.88	23.3
Lucurana	94.87	22.6
Guapiruvú	59.63	14.2
Rico de pato	24.37	5.8
Figara branca	23.95	5.7
Guamirim	16.96	4.0
Pinho do mato	16.77	4.0
Armesica	14.04	3.3
Ata	13.12	3.1
Guaçatunga	12.45	3.0
Caúna	10.96	2.7
Maria mole	10.01	2.4
Intaiá	8.33	2.0
Cafe bravo	6.13	1.5
Caiobá	4.52	1.1
Cambuí	2.36	0.6
Bacupari	0.94	0.2
Cereja	0.92	0.2
Guapurunga	0.66	0.1
Carvalho	0.66	0.1
Catigua	0.66	0.1
Total	420.19	(= 35.0 sq. m., or 375 sq. ft. per hectare, and 14.0 sq. m. and 150 sq. ft. per acre)

is at about 32° S. Lat. and 52° 30″ W. Long. In this region there is the southernmost attenuation of the coastal rain forest, and it is found as gallery forest along watercourses with grassland the dominant vegetation of the uplands.

The stature of the forest is low, but it is very dense with small evergreen trees casting a heavy shade. Megaphanerophytes are missing, and the mesophanerophytes are mostly about 20 m. high, although some species are emergent to about 25 m. Phanerophytes compose 51.4 per cent of the species and with the addition of the lianas and epiphytes, 70 per cent. The outstanding difference in this forest from those examined earlier lies in the increased im-

Table 23. Occurrence in Raunkiaerian life-form and leaf-size classes of the species of the natural forest of Horto Botânico do Instituto Agronômico do Sul, Pelotas, Rio Grande do Sul. Data by S. A. Cain, G. M. de Oliviera Castro, and José da Costa Sacco

Life-form classes	Aphyllous	Leaf-size classes					Total, per cent	Number
		Lepto-phyll	Nano-phyll	Micro-phyll	Meso-phyll	Macrophyll		
All phanerophytes	6.9	5.5	5.5	48.6	31.9	1.4	51.4	72
Mesophanerophytes				60.7	39.3		20.0	28
Microphanerophytes	6.7		6.7	66.7	20.0		10.7	15
Nanophanerophytes	13.8	13.8	10.3	27.6	31.0	3.7	20.7	29
Lianas		6.7	6.7	60.0	26.6		10.7	15
Epiphytes	27.3	9.1	9.1	36.4	18.2		7.9	11
Chamaephytes				80.0		20.0	3.6	5
Hemicryptophytes			26.1	60.9	13.0		16.4	23
Cryptophytes (Geo-)				71.4	28.6		5.0	7
Therophytes			28.6	71.4			5.0	7
Stem succulents [a]	(2)							
Total, per cent	5.7	4.3	10.0	54.3	24.3	1.4	100.0	
Number	8	6	14	76	34	2		140

[a] Stem succulents counted in their height classes.
Note the absence of the megaphanerophyte life-form class and the megaphyll leaf-size class.

318

portance of hemicryptophytes and the presence of some annuals, along with the reduced importance of phanerophytes. We find also that the mesophyll leaf-size class is no longer the dominant one and that the microphyll class composes 54.3 per cent of all species and 48.6 per cent of all trees and shrubs. There are a few aphyllous species, cacti among the epiphytes and micro-phanerophytes and species of *Baccharis* among the nanophanerophytes. No sample plots were laid out, and no basal-area measurements were taken. Coverage was estimated for natural strata as units, but not for individual species. The woods is penetrated by a rather close network of paths so that access to all parts of it was easy. Table 24 has the species arranged by strata and sub-groups according to relative importance of the species. Further arrangement is by leaf-size classes.

Table 24. Composition and structure of the natural forest of the Horto Botânico do Instituto Agronômico do Sul, Pelotas, Rio Grande do Sul. Species are arranged by strata, life-form,[a] and leaf-size classes,[b] with a distinction between those more and those less important. Basic data by Dr. José da Costa Sacco, with the assistance of the authors

	Life form	Leaf size
A. Tall tree stratum: 15–20 (25) m. Total coverage 50%		
More important species		
Luehea divaricata Mart. & Zucc. Tiliaceae	Ms	Ms
Arecastrum romanzoffianum (Cham.) Becc. Palmae	Ms	Ms
Sorocea illicifolia Miq. Moraceae	Ms	Ms
Patagonula americana L. Borraginaceae	Ms	Mi
Ficus subtriplinervia Mart. Moraceae	Ms	Mi
Allophylus edulis (St. Hil.) Radlk. Sapindaceae	Ms	Mi
Less important species		
Quillaja brasiliensis (St. Hil.) Mart. Rosaceae	Ms	Mi
Citharexylum montevidense (Spreng.) Moldenke Verbe-naceae	Ms	Mi
Xylosma salzmanni Eichl. Flacourtiaceae	Ms	Mi
Ocotea pulchella Mart. Lauraceae	Ms	Mi
Phyllocalix involucratus (DC). Berg. Myrtaceae	Ms	Mi
B. Intermediate tree stratum: (7) 8–10 m. Total coverage 70%		
More important species		
Pircunia dioica (L.) Moq. Phytolaccaceae	Ms	Ms
Myrsine umbellata Mart. Myrsinaceae	Ms	Ms
Pisonia nitida Mart. Nyctaginaceae	Ms	Ms
Trichilia catigua A. Juss. Meliaceae	Ms	Ms
Maba inconstans (Jacq.) Griseb. Ebenaceae	Ms	Mi

Table 24. Composition and structure of the natural forest of the Horto Botânico do Instituto Agronômico do Sul, Pelotas, Rio Grande do Sul. Species are arranged by strata, life-form,[a] *and leaf-size classes,*[b] *with a distinction between those more and those less important. Basic data by Dr. José da Costa Sacco, with the assistance of the authors (Cont.)*

	Life form	Leaf size
More important species		
Acanthosyris spinescens (Mart. & Eichl.) Griseb. Santala-ceae	Ms	Mi
Vitex montevidensis Cham. Verbenaceae	Ms	Mi
Actinostemon caribaeus Griseb. Euphorbiaceae	Ms	Mi
Cupania vernalis Cambess. Sapindaceae	Ms	Mi
Lithraea brasiliensis March. Anacardiaceae	Ms	Mi
Less important species		
Solanum swartzianum Roem. & Schult. Solanaceae	Ms	Ms
Myrsine ferruginea Spreng. Myrsinaceae	Ms	Ms
Trema micrantha (L.) Blume Ulmaceae	Ms	Ms
Campomanesia aurea Berg. Myrtaceae	Ms	Ms
Chuquiraga spinescens Baker Compositae	Ms	Mi
Fagara rhoifolia (Lam.) Engl. Rutaceae	Ms	Mi
Iodina rhombifolia Hook. & Arn. Santalaceae	Ms	Mi
Sebastiana klotzchiana Muell. Arg. Euphorbiaceae	Ms	?
C. *Low tree and high shrub stratum:* 3–5 m. Total coverage 40%		
More important species		
Myrcianthes gigantea Legrand. Myrtaceae	Mi	Ms
Basanacantha spinosa (Jacq.) K. Sch. Rubiaceae	Mi	Ms
Erythrina crista-galli L. Leguminosae	Mi	Ms
Celtis spinosa Spreng. Ulmaceae	Mi	Mi
Casearia silvestris Sw. Flacourtiaceae	Mi	Mi
Sambucus australis Cham. & Schlecht. Caprifoliaceae	Mi	Mi
Schinus polygamus (Cav.) Cabrera Anacardiaceae	Mi	Mi
Eugenia uniflora L. Myrtaceae	Mi	Mi
Fagara hiemalis (St. Hil.) Engl. Rutaceae	Mi	N
Cereus peruvianus (L.) Mill. Cactaceae	Mi	A
Less important species		
Scutia buxifolia Reiss. Rhamnaceae	Mi	Mi
Styrax leprosum Hook. & Arn. Styracaceae	Mi	Mi
Berberis laurina Thunb. Berberidaceae	Mi	Mi
Dodonaea viscosa Jacq. Sapindaceae	Mi	Mi
Cestrum parqui L'Herit. Solanaceae	Mi	Mi
Myrrhinium rubiflorum Berg. Myrtaceae	Mi	Mi

Table 24. Composition and structure of the natural forest of the Horto Botânico do Instituto Agronômico do Sul, Pelotas, Rio Grande do Sul. Species are arranged by strata, life-form,[a] *and leaf-size classes,*[b] *with a distinction between those more and those less important. Basic data by Dr. José da Costa Sacco, with the assistance of the authors (Cont.)*

	Life form	Leaf size
D. Low shrub stratum: 0.8–2.0 m. Total coverage 30–40%		
More important species		
Abutilon molle (Ort.) Sweet. Malvaceae	N	Ms
Daphnopsis racemosa Griseb. Thymelaeaceae	N	Ms
Dianthera nodosa Benth. & Hook. f. Acanthaceae	N	Ms
Solanum auriculatum Ait. Solanaceae	N	Ms
Baccharis spicata (Lam.) Baillon Compositae	N	Mi
Eupatorium buniifolium Hook. & Arn. Compositae	N	Mi
Pavonia communis St. Hil. Malvaceae	N	Mi
Baccharis dracunculifolia DC. Compositae	N	N
Baccharis articulata (Lam.) Pers. Compositae	N	Le
Calliandra tweedii Benth. Leguminosae	N	Le
Opuntia monacantha Haw. Cactaceae	N	A
Less important species		
Abutilon pauciflorum St. Hil. Malvaceae	N	Ma
Eupatorium inulaefolium HBK. Compositae	N	Ms
Lantana camara L. Verbenaceae	N	Ms
Buettneria urticifolia K. Sch. Sterculiaceae	N	Mi
Guadua trinii (Nees) Rupr. Gramineae	N	Mi
Guettarda uruquensis Cham. & Schlecht. Rubiaceae	N	Mi
Discaria longispina Miers Rhamnaceae	N	Le
E. Herb stratum: 0–0.8 m. Total coverage 80–90%		
Perennial plants, normally evergreen		
More important species		
Clidemia hirta (L.) D. Don Melastomaceae	N	Ms
Baccharis anomala DC. Compositae	N	Mi
Solanum gracile Dun. Solanaceae	N	Mi
Baccharis ochracea Spreng. Compositae	N	Le
Bromelia antiacantha Bertol. Bromeliaceae	Ch	Ma
Tradescantia fluminensis Vell. Commelinaceae	Ch	Mi
Oplismenus hirtellus (L.) Beauv. Gramineae	Ch	Mi
Chaptalia nutans (L.) Polak. Compositae	H	Ms
Elephantopus tomentosus L. Compositae	H	Mi
Paspalum inaequivale Raddi Gramineae	H	Mi
Paspalum paniculatum L. Gramineae	H	Mi
Paspalum mandiocanum Trin. Gramineae	H	Mi
Panicum helobium Mez. Gramineae	H	Mi

Table 24. Composition and structure of the natural forest of the Horto Botânico do Instituto Agronômico do Sul, Pelotas, Rio Grande do Sul. Species are arranged by strata, life-form,[a] and leaf-size classes,[b] with a distinction between those more and those less important. Basic data by Dr. José da Costa Sacco, with the assistance of the authors (Cont.)

	Life form	Leaf size
More important species		
Panicum missionum Ekman Gramineae	H	Mi
Panicum laxum Sw. Gramineae......................	H	Mi
Canna indica L. Cannaceae	G	Ms
Pharus glaber HBK. Gramineae	G	Ms
Oxalis sellowiana Zucc. Oxalidaceae	G	Mi
Solanum sisymbrifolium Lam. Solanaceae	?	Ms
Less important species		
Begonia semperflorens Link & Otto Begoniaceae	N	Ms
Solanum ciliatum Lam. Solonaceae	N	Ms
Heimia salicifolia (HBK.) Link & Otto Lythraceae	N	N
Solanum capsicastrum Link Solanaceae	N	N
Baccharis gaudichaudiana DC. Compositae	N	A
Baccharis sagittalis (Less.) DC. Compositae	N	A
Baccharisc trimera (Less.) DC. Compositae	N	A
Baccharis usterii Heering Compositae	Ch	Mi
Blechnum brasiliense Desv. Polypodiaceae	Ch	Mi
Doryopteris pedata (L.) Fee Polypodiaceae	H	Ms
Polygonum hydropiperoides Michx. Polygonaceae	H	Mi
Blechnum auriculatum Cav. Polypodiaceae	H	N
Plants normally dying back to the ground, or nearly so		
More important species		
Stipa megapotamica Spreng. Gramineae	H	Ms
Alternanthera pilosa Moq. Amaranthaceae	H	Mi
Urtica urens L. Urticaceae	H	Mi
Salpichroa origanifolia (Lam.) Thell. Solanaceae	H	N
Piptochaetium montevidense (Spreng.) Parodi Gramineae	H	N
Piptochaetium bicolor (Vahl.) E. Desv. Gramineae	H	N
Hyptis mutabilis (Rich.) Briq. Labiatae	G	Mi
Oenothera longiflora L. Onagraceae	G	Mi
Bidens pilosa L. Compositae	Th	Mi
Silene gallica L. Caryophyllaceae	Th	Mi
Senecio brasiliensis (Spreng.) Less. Compositae	Th	N
Sida rhombifolia L. Malvaceae	Th	N
Less important species		
Aristida altissima Arech. Gramineae	H	Mi
Conyza notobellidiastrum Griseb. Compositae	H	Mi

Table 24. Composition and structure of the natural forest of the Horto Botânico do Instituto Agronômico do Sul, Pelotas, Rio Grande do Sul. Species are arranged by strata, life-form,[a] and leaf-size classes,[b] with a distinction between those more and those less important. Basic data by Dr. José da Costa Sacco, with the assistance of the authors (Cont.)

	Life form	Leaf size
Less important species		
Paspalum plicatum (Michx.) Pers. Gramineae	H	Mi
Vernonia polyanthes Less. Compositae	H	Mi
Piptochaetium lasianthum Griseb. Gramineae	H	N
Stipa melanosperma J. Presl. Gramineae	H	N
Borreria centranthoides Cham. & Schlecht. Rubiaceae ..	G	Mi
Geranium albicans St. Hil. Geraniaceae	G	Mi
Briza subaristata Lam. Gramineae	Th	Mi
Bromus uruguayensis Arech. Gramineae	Th	Mi
Bromus unioloides HBK. Gramineae	Th	Mi
Verbena dissecta Willd. Verbenaceae	?	N
Iresine celosioides L. Amaranthaceae	?	Mi
Rivina humilis L. Phytolaccacae	?	Mi
Acanthospermum australe (Loefl.) O. Ktz. Compositae ..	?	?
Polycarpon tetraphyllum (L.) L. Caryophyllaceae	?	?
Jussieua fruticosa DC. Onagraceae	?	?
F. Lianas, listed according to the highest stratum attained, notation as above		
A stratum		
Passiflora suberosa L. Passifloraceae	Li	Ms
Passiflora elegans Mast. Passifloraceae	Li	Mi
Bignonia unguis-cati L. Bignoniaceae	Li	Mi
B stratum		
Pithecoctenium echinatum (Aubl.) K. Sch. Bignoniaceae	Li	Ms
Smilax campestris Griseb. Liliaceae	Li	Ms
C stratum		
Cissampelos pareira L. Menispermaceae	Li	Mi
Clematis bonariensis Juss. Ranunculaceae	Li	Mi
Canavalia bonariensis Lindl. Leguminosae	Li	Mi
Phaseolus adenanthus G.F.W. Mey. Leguminosae	Li	Mi
Orthosia aphylla (Vell.) Malme Asclepiadaceae	Li	Le
D stratum		
Passiflora caerulea L. Passifloraceae	Li	Ms
Janusia guaranitica (St. Hil.) A. Juss. Malpighiaceae	Li	Mi
Urvillea uniloba Radlk. Sapindaceae	Li	Mi
Muehlenbeckia sagittifolia Meissn. Polygonaceae	Li	Mi
Chymocarpus pentaphyllus (Lam.) D. Don Tropaeolaceae	Li	N
Solanum boerraviaefolium Sendt. Solanaceae	Li	?

Table 24. Composition and structure of the natural forest of the Horto Botânico do Instituto Agronômico do Sul, Pelotas, Rio Grande do Sul. Species are arranged by strata, life-form,[a] and leaf-size classes,[b] with a distinction between those more and those less important. Basic data by Dr. José da Costa Sacco, with the assistance of the authors (Cont.)

	Life form	Leaf size
G. Vascular epiphytes, listed according to the highest stratum attained		
A stratum		
Aechmea legrelliana Baker Bromeliaceae	E	Ms
Aechmea gamosepala Wittm. Bromeliaceae	E	Ms
Phoradendron sp. Loranthaceae (Hemiparasite)	E	Mi
Polypodium vacciniifolium Langsd. & Fisch. Polypodiaceae	E	Mi
Tillandsia aeranthos (Loisel) L. B. Smith Bromeliaceae ..	E	Mi
Tillandsia usneoides L. Bromeliaceae	E	Le
Rhipsalis aculeata Weber Cactaceae	E	A
Rhipsalis sarmentacea Otto & Dietr. Cactaceae	E	A
Rhipsalis saglionis Otto Cactaceae	E	A
B stratum		
Gen. sp. Orchidaceae	E	Mi
Peperomia deppeana Schlecht. & Cham. Piperaceae	E	N

[a] Symbols used for life-form classes: Ms—Mesophanerophyte; Mi—Microphanerophyte; N—Nanophanerophyte; Ch—Chamaephyte; H—Hemicryptophyte; G—Geophyte (Cryptophyte); Th—Therophyte; Li—Liana; E—Epiphyte (vascular).

[b] Symbols used for leaf-size classes: Ma—Macrophyll; Ms—Mesophyll; Mi—Microphyll; N—Nanophyll; Le—Leptophyll; A—Aphyllus.

Non-phanerophytic species are mostly associated with margins of the woods and openings or less thick places in it. We made no effort to prepare a list that was typical of the dense woods, but include the entire flora that is typical of the vegetation type as distinct from swamp woods or contiguous grassland. In doing this we believe that the life-form and leaf-size data are fairly comparable with those presented for the rain forest in its more typical forms northward.

DISCUSSION. In the classification of some species into life-form classes certain problems are encountered. Assignment to phanerophytic-height classes was always made on a basis of the height attained in the stand examined and not on a basis of greater height that might be attained elsewhere. There are some plants that start life as lianas but continue as epiphytes, losing contact with the soil, and others starting as epiphytes develop roots that make contact with the soil. In both cases it usually is more accurate to classify the plants as epiphytic. The greatest difficulty is in perennial herbs with evergreen aboveground parts. They often have stolons, rhizomes, or rootstocks and buds that would cause the plants to be classified as cryptophytes or hemi-cryptophytes if it weren't for the persistence of vegetative activity by aboveground parts. In temperate regions such plants die back to the ground, or under it, but in tropical vegetation it seems more accurate to classify such plants as chamaephytes or nanophanerophytes, even though not woody, for they do endure the environmental conditions their aerial parts are exposed to, and that is the crux of the Raunkiaerian system of life-form classification.

In the classification of plants according to leaf-size classes we have in all cases used the leaflet as the unit in the case of pinnate and palmate compound leaves. When leaves are deeply lobed some judgment is necessary as to whether the lobe is the physiological unit comparable to the blade of the simple leaf. In other words, we have not considered a leaf as simple, though in a strict morphological sense it is, if the divisions are so deep that the lobes have comparable exposure to leaflets. As explained earlier, leaf areas were determined as two-thirds of the length-breadth rectangle as a system of measurement sufficiently accurate in nearly all cases for classification into the Raunkiaerian units. At least any errors of classification made in individual cases, when areas are near the division line between classes, probably counterbalance one another. In all cases measurement is made of the blade, omitting the petiole, but attenuate leaf tips are included in the length measurement. Leaves of a species vary greatly in size in some cases, as between sun and shade forms. We have consistently tried to select representative leaves of the exposed type as the usually larger leaves of protected parts of the plants do not represent the correct relation between leaf size and general climate, but rather the more favorable microclimate of forest interior. This point applies, of course, only to transgressive plants that ultimately attain the canopy or an emergent position.

The absence of technical determination of the species does not affect the validity of the leaf-size and life-form classification of the taxa. We have, however, done our best to attach correct Latin names to the entities, although the Brazilian flora is extremely rich and imperfectly known. Most of the determinations have been made by comparison with herbarium materials in various Brazilian institutions, often with the assistance of local botanists, as indicated in the text. We do not know, however, that the Latin name used is the latest or most accurate. It is for that reason that we have added the name authorities in most cases. Family names are also added as a matter of convenience. There are several cases where further study and recourse to specialists would provide a technical name, but we have not thought that the nature of our study warrants the time and effort involved.

Table 25 summarizes the Brazilian rain-forest results as to life-form class according to Raunkiaer's five principal classes. In comparison with Raunkiaer's normal spectrum (which does not necessarily represent the world

Table 25. Summary table of life-form classes, comparing the Brazilian rain-forest results with Raunkiaer's normal spectrum and various phytoclimatic types

Type	Ph	Ch	H	Cr(G)	Th	Author
Raunkiaer's normal spectrum	46	9	26	6	13	Raunkiaer (1934)
Brazilian rain-forest spectra:						
Mucambo (Equatorial)	95	1	3	1	0	Cain and Castro
Caiobá (Coastal Temp.)	87	7	3	3	0	Cain and Castro
Alto do Palmital (Temp.)	80	6	11	3	0	Cain and Castro
Horto Botânico (Temp.)	70	4	16	5	5	Cain and Castro
Selected phytoclimates:						
Rain forest, Queensland	96	2	0	2	0	Cromer and Pryor (1942)
Subtropical evergreen, India	63	17	2	5	10	Bharucha and Ferreira (1941)
Temperate deciduous, Connecticut	15	2	49	22	12	Ennis (1928)
Mediterranean, Crete	9	13	27	10	38	Turrill (1929)
Desert, Transcaspian	11	7	27	14	41	Paulsen (1912)
Steppe, Colorado	0	19	58	8	15	Paulsen (1915)
Tundra, Spitzbergen	1	22	60	15	2	Raunkiaer (1934)

flora, but is useful as a base line for comparisons), lowland equatorial rain forest (Mucambo) is seen to be exceedingly high in phanerophytes. It is so high, in fact, that all other classes are of necessity negligible. The Mucambo situation is not unique, but is typical for the formation in low equatorial regions. As is well known, in Brazil the rain-forest formation extends far southward along the Serra do Mar. Our temperate station at Caiobá, about 26° S. Lat., is still strongly represented in the phanerophytic class (87 per cent), but this figure contains 33 per cent lianas and epiphytes in contrast to 21 per cent for Mucambo. Still farther south (32° S. Lat.), in fact at southern limits of the formation where it is found as gallery forest in a grassland region, the percentage of phanerophytes is 70 at Horto Botânico, including 18.6 per cent of lianas and epiphytes. This is still 24 per cent above that class in the normal spectrum, although a regional flora, including the grasslands and coastal vegetation of *praia* and *restinga*, would give quite different percentages. The interior, southwestern extension of rain forest, at Iguaçu (Alto do Palmital), lies beyond the *Araucaria* forest zone, which itself has a rain-forest understory. Both of these types are properly classified as temperate rain forest. Here we found 80 per cent phanerophytes, including 24 per cent lianas and epiphytes.

There is considerable difficulty in the classification of hemicryptophytes and geophytes in rain forest. This arises from the fact that many plants, although basically of these classes, are actually evergreen, perennating for several seasons without dying back to ground level or below. Not having year-around experience with the vegetation of the stations studied, we have had to use our best judgment in cases where local persons were unable to advise us.

There is no "normal spectrum" for leaf-size classes and, as pointed out earlier, very few data of any kind, so we merely present a summary table for the four rain-forest stations reported on here (table 26). With the stations

Table 26. Comparison of Raunkiaerian leaf-size classes in Brazilian rain forest

Class	Mucambo	Caiobá	Alto do Palmital	Horto Botânico
Aphyllous	0	0	1.5	5.7
Leptophyll	2.3	0	3.0	4.3
Nanophyll	3.2	8.8	7.6	10.0
Microphyll	15.1	14.4	27.3	54.3
Mesophyll	68.3	64.4	56.1	24.3
Macrophyll	11.0	11.1	4.5	1.4
Megaphyll	0	1.1	0	0

arranged in the same order as in table 25, we find that the three smaller leaf-size classes (and the aphyllous class) increase with departure from the central Amazonian station and that the three larger leaf-size classes diminish steadily in the same direction. There is no question of the validity of these shifts in leaf-size percentages.

Rain-forest phanerophytes are strongly mesophyll except at Horto Botânico, where the vegetation is strongly microphyll. There is some tendency for smaller leaf-size classes to have a higher percentage in taller strata than in lower ones. This shows up at Mucambo and Alto do Palmital.

SUMMARY

On a basis of sample plots, Brazilian rain forest has been studied in its equatorial form at Belém, Pará, in coastal mountain form at Caiobá, Paraná, as plateau, temperate forest at Foz de Iguaçu, Paraná, and as gallery forest in its southernmost extension at Pelotas, Rio Grande do Sul. Several concepts and methods of phytosociology that are commonly applied in studies of temperate vegetation have been employed in this study of tropical rain forest. These studies, although not extensive, show that the complex rain-forest vegetation can be analyzed by these methods and that often they bring out features that are not readily appreciated in non-quantitative studies.

LITERATURE CITED

BEARD, J. S. 1946. The natural vegetation of Trinidad. Oxford For. Mem. 20:1–155.

BHARUCHA, F. R., AND D. B. FERREIRA. 1941. The biological spectrum of the Madras flora. Jour. Univ. Bombay 9:93–100.

BLACK, G. A., T. DOBZHANSKY, AND C. PAVAN. 1950. Some attempts to estimate species diversity and population density of trees in Amazonian forests. Bot. Gaz. 111 (4):413–425.

BRAUN-BLANQUET, J. 1932. Plant sociology (Transl. Fuller and Conard). McGraw-Hill. New York.

BROWN, W. H. 1919. The vegetation of the Philippine mountains. Manila.

CAIN, S. A. 1932. Concerning certain phytosociological concepts. Ecol. Monogr. 2: 475–508.

———. 1950. Life-forms and phytoclimate. Bot. Rev. 16:1–32.

CROMER, D. A. N., AND L. D. PRYOR. 1942. A contribution to rain-forest ecology. Proc. Linn. Soc. New So. Wales. 67:249–268.

CURTIS, J. T., AND R. P. McINTOSH. 1951. An upland forest continuum in the prairie-forest border region of Wisconsin. Ecology 32:476–496.

DUCKE, A., AND G. A. BLACK. 1953. Phytogeographical notes on the Brazilian Amazon. Ann. Acad. Brasileira Ciencias 25:1–46.

ENNIS, B. 1928. The life forms of Connecticut plants and their significance in relation to climate. Conn. State Geol. Nat. Hist. Surv., Bull. 43:1–100.

LUIS, T., AND A. BERTELS. 1951. Horto Botânico do Instituto Agronômico do Sul (Pelotas): Guia dos visitantes. Pelotas, Brasil.

MAACK, R. 1950. Mapa fitogeografico do estado do Paraná. Inst. Nac. do Pinho. Curitiba, Brasil.

OOSTING, H. J. 1948. The study of plant communities. W. H. Freeman. San Francisco.

PAULSEN, O. 1912. The second Danish Pamir expedition. Studies on the vegetation of the Transcaspian lowland. Arbejder fra den bot. Have i Kobenhaven 90: 1–279.

———. 1915. Some remarks on the desert vegetation of America. Plant World 18:155–161.

PIRES, J. M., T. DOBZHANSKY, AND G. A. BLACK. 1953. An estimate of the number of species of trees in an Amazonian forest community. Bot. Gaz. 114:467–477.

PRESTON, F. W. 1948. The commonness and rarity of species. Ecology 29:254–283.

RAUNKIAER, C. 1934. The life forms of plants and statistical geography. Oxford Univ. Press. New York.

RICHARDS, P. W. 1952. The tropical rain forest. Cambridge Univ. Press. Cambridge.

TURRILL, W. B. 1929. The plant life of the Balkan Peninsula. A phytogeographic study. Oxford Univ. Press. New York.

16

THE DEVELOPMENT OF ASSOCIATION AND CLIMAX CONCEPTS

Their Use in Interpretation of the Deciduous Forest [1]

E. Lucy Braun

Ecology is defined as the study of life in relation to environment. It is concerned with what *is* and *why*. The ecological study of a single organism frequently meets with almost insurmountable obstacles because environment, if broken down into its component parts, is no longer environment. The ecological study of a complex piece of vegetation—a forest for example—presents innumerable problems, for the complexity of the environment—with its interacting factors—is multiplied by the complexity of the community; it does not yield to laboratory analysis. The methods of the physiologist fail.

Attempts at mathematical interpretation are for the most part static, and they often obscure rather than reveal the true picture of vegetation. Vegetation is dynamic—an ever-changing complex now appearing quiescent and in complete equilibrium with the habitat, now displaying obvious evidence of change. I believe that failure to recognize the dynamic aspects of vegetation is a primary cause of differing concepts. A dynamic approach is essential to interpretation of our eastern forests.

Observation of natural changes in vegetation long ago resulted in the concept of succession; recognition of quiescent phases led to the climax concept. The association concept arose from the need for designating so-called units of vegetation.

Concepts have changed through the years; they should change. As Cooper

[1] A paper delivered at Storrs, Conn., August 28, 1956, as part of the Ecological Society's symposium, "Approaches to Interpretation of the Eastern Forests of North America."

stated (1926), "a periodic inspection of foundations is most desirable." Concepts are bound to change with progress from local or intensive study to broad and extensive study. This is the reason for change with each individual worker; it has in part been the reason for change in concepts through the past 50 to 60 years of study of vegetation. Geographic location of studies also is a factor in the development of concepts.

Emphasis of the concepts of association, succession, and climax dates from the work of Henry C. Cowles around the beginning of the century (1899, 1901). Communities were recognized and at first called plant societies; later, plant associations. These were seen to be in equilibrium, more or less, with habitat; however, habitats change through the years, forcing change in vegetation. Changes were recognized as biotic, topographic, and climatic—the biotic due to reactions of the vegetation (and other accompanying life), the topographic to erosional and depositional forces, the climatic to the long-range variation in climate (Cowles, 1911; Clements, 1916, 1928). All groups of forces are at work everywhere, but locally one or another group may seem to determine the nature of vegetational change; all have been operative in determining regional vegetation.

Awareness of change led to the succession concept, for decades the guiding principle in ecological study and, I believe, the most fundamental of all concepts relating to the study of vegetation.

Succession is vegetational change—the *gradual* replacement of populations of species by other populations, i.e., of one community by another. The resulting plant succession (or sere) is not a series of steps or stages—no serious student of succession (a process) has ever claimed that a succession is made up of "discrete units." However, within any complete or partial sere there may be recognizable communities, communities sufficiently distinct from one another to justify naming them, usually for their dominants. Succession diagrams naming such "stages" place lines or sometimes arrows leading from one to another, which are intended to indicate gradual change. The whole sere is a continuously but gradually changing complex—the changes forced by biotic, topographic, or climatic factors. It is dynamic. It is a sequence in time, not in space, although spatial relations are often indicative of succession. Given time enough, the process of succession may lead to the establishment of a climax community, a community in which further change awaits major environmental change. It must be recognized that disruptive forces may prevent such progress, that although vegetational change is taking place, successions may be fragmentary and hardly recognizable.

Let us now apply these ideas to a concrete bit of forest vegetation—as the young student or the local worker must do. I select for this the primary forests of the Illinoian Till Plain of southwestern Ohio (Braun, 1936). Reconnaissance observation reveals a number of communities, among them those dominated by pin oak, by white oak, by beech. Each has certain characteristics and, according to the nomenclature so far suggested, may be called an association. Are they distinct and separate units, or are they related one to another? The primary pin oak association is normally an open forest of large trees occupying poorly drained areas wet or swampy in spring. Pin oak is an intolerant species—in spots between the large old trees may be seen younger individuals of this species, but in shady spots beneath the canopy formed by groups of pin oaks, other species occur, shagbark hickory and perhaps an occasional white oak or beech. As long as open spots remain, ecesis of pin oak is possible, but when the canopies of primary trees and older reproduction join, further ecesis of pin oak ceases. Gradually the older pin oak trees die out and the older individuals of other species of the understory replace them. Vegetational change is taking place, succession is in progress. Replacement takes place individual by individual—there is no jump from pin oak dominance to dominance by another species. Wherever a pin oak started in an open spot it may persist along with the new entrants which are changing the habitat by their deeper shade and their different leaf litter. After many forest generations and centuries of occupancy, a forest in which white oak is dominant may come into being. The old white oak forest, with trees 3 to 4 feet in diameter, again reveals evidence of change. Beech trees of various ages are interspersed, but white oak is absent from lower layers. Gradual dying out of white oak and growing to maturity of beech leads to the establishment of a beech forest. Beech, the most tolerant species of the area, is able to reproduce and perpetuate itself. Succession has been taking place because of biotic forces at work and has apparently ended in an unchanging or very slowly changing community—a climax of some sort.

Within any *single* forest tract the distribution of earlier and later developmental stages appears to be related to almost imperceptible topographic differences—depressions and swells differing but a few inches in elevation. But comparison with another tract may disclose that "earlier" stages are lacking and that "later" ones may occupy a greater variety of sites. The whole tract appears as a mixed forest, its unlike component communities often small in extent. It is a pattern of intergrading developmental and climax communities, not a climax pattern due to micro-relief (as suggested by Whittaker, 1953, p. 45). When analyzed by statistical methods of recent years, with quadrats laid out arbitrarily in a grid pattern (as has been done), with all trees above a certain diameter counted, and with basal areas determined, evidence of unlike communities within the tract is obscured and evidence of succession is lost. With this loss, the most fundamental concepts of vegetation are endangered.

Only after repeated field surveys of such tracts and only after the processes at work are thoroughly understood and the relationships of parts of the forest determined, could statistical methods be applied. Continuous transects, with vegetation related in so far as possible to environment, supply the most desirable method of study. Once the community relations have been determined, isolated samples of community types from other areas may be used to amplify concepts.

What are the concepts which can be illustrated by a dynamic approach to such a forest study as the above? (1) An association concept—for here are more or less well-defined communities, each with definite dominants and seemingly more or less in equilibrium with the habitat. (2) A succession concept, based on evidence of change, of lack of accord of canopy and understory, and of forces, here largely biotic, at work directing the changes. (3) A climax concept, for this succession appears to end in a self-perpetuating community. Will these concepts as first developed stand the test of application to other unlike sites in the geographic region and of application in other geographic regions? In part, yes; in part, no.

In unlike sites of the same geographic area, the communities are different, the causal factors of succession may be different, and topographic change rather than biotic direct the course of development. And still, communities are evident—let us for the present call them associations; succession is evident, and a climax is reached—but not a beech climax. At once we question our climax concept. The beech forest of our example is dependent on a particular site—an undissected plain in an immature topography. With the first development of drainage lines, changes begin again and development goes on. This beech forest is a physiographic climax. The climax of mature topographic sites is different and more enduring.

Soon we realize that no two pieces of vegetation are exactly alike, even though they may have the same dominants. Nichols (1923) realized this and proposed the association concrete (applied to a piece of vegetation) and the association abstract—the abstract concept gained by familiarity with many pieces of similar vegetation. Gleason (1926), recognizing unlikeness, suggested the individualistic concept.

In other geographic areas, we find again that concepts must be revised. The seemingly important associations of our local area are not found; a multiplicity of new ones occur. Succession may be less evident—not because succession is not or has not taken place, but because development of primary vegetation has progressed farther, or in some instances because development has been interrupted by frequent disturbance. Climax communities may be found which bear a marked resemblance to those of mature topography of our local area. Such climax communities begin to assume greater importance in our thoughts. We begin to understand Clements' views, which resulted from extensive work. We realize that our association concept is open to question, that there is a tremendous difference between the pin oak association, or the white oak association, or even the beech association, and the climax association which we find recurring again and again over a vast geographic area and as a result of many unlike lines of succession. Clements (1916) proposed the term *associes* for developmental units and retained *association* only for climax units. Even with this restriction, we must realize that all climax units are not equivalent, that there are different kinds of climaxes, chief of which are physiographic climaxes and regional climaxes.

Shall the term *association* be used only for regional climax communities or for all sorts of climax communities, physiographic and regional? Shall it be thus restricted, or shall it be used for all relatively stable communities even though developmental? Or shall the term be restricted to the abstract? The local worker usually shuns the restricted usage and prefers to designate all well-marked communities as associations. (I am not here concerned with division of associations or associes into consociations, consocies, etc.) Extensive work is sure to modify this view, for the great regional associations are not comparable to the local associations. If association is to be used for all, then the regional should be called major associations. In fact, such emphasis is often desirable even when a broad association concept is used.

The validity of an association concept (and of other community units) has been questioned (Whittaker, 1951). I believe everyone will agree that communities are recognizable in the field, that we do see patches of forest to which we can give names, because of dominants. The objection is based on the fact that communities do not have definite limits, but intergrade with one another; that the species which seem to characterize them extend into other communities, although probably in different proportions; that no two communities are exactly alike; that vegetation (barring abrupt site differences) is continuous though differing from place to place.

The climax concept, too, is questioned, perhaps because of rigidity of interpretation in some schools of thought (Whittaker, 1953). The monoclimax and polyclimax ideas do not help. To me, a monoclimax concept appears impossible (although I have been surprised to find that I am by some considered a supporter of the idea); equally, a polyclimax concept seems questionable. I adhere to the idea that there is more than one kind of climax. I do not refer to the complex Clementsian units—as serclimax, disclimax, postclimax, etc.—which I prefer not to recognize. Extensive investigation reveals the recurrence, on mesic although not exactly similar sites, of climax communities closely similar through wide geographic areas. Intensive or local studies usually reveal the existence of other climaxes, stable communities related to other, sometimes extreme, sites. The first group of communities are representative of what I prefer to call the regional climax—an abstract concept. The second are physiographic climaxes, or, if you prefer, topographic, or edaphic, climaxes. This should not be understood to imply that regional climaxes are not influenced by topography—environment operates on all. Regional climaxes are commonly, but not always correctly, referred to as climatic climaxes. The relative prominence of these climax groups and of the developmental communities in any region depends upon the age of the region (geologically speaking) and the degree of advancement of the erosion cycle. Much of the vegetation of old areas (or of mature topography), if undisturbed, has reached stability, and a mosaic or pattern of intergrading climax communities is seen. In young areas, areas of immature topography, succession is still active and much of the vegetation is not climax. Convergence of seres toward a regional climax is best illustrated in such areas. And it is in such areas that the possibility of further development or change is indicated; that is, the stability of the regional climax is open to question.

It should be realized that the terminology which has developed and the concepts implied are a result of the ecologist's need to classify (see Cooper, 1926). In the few areas where undisturbed forest of any extent still remains, patterns of vegetation can be determined and the relationships of communities can be investigated. Throughout almost all the Eastern Deciduous Forest, only small fragments of primary forest remain; no patterns are discernible. The need to classify remains, and the isolated sample must be assigned to a place in the system of classification, although it has no place in a concrete transect of vegetation. Such difficulties do not arise in local studies.

An understanding of the structure of our eastern forests is not dependent on agreement as to concepts. It is dependent on the recognition of development, of the existence of types of communities, and of climax; of climax as a long-term expression of regional factors, both climatic and local, stable as far as human life span is concerned, stable in relation to developmental communities of comparable life form, but nevertheless changing in accord with changes in regional factors.

Our forest vegetation has its roots in the early evolutionary history of angiosperms, their rise and their geographic spread as continental history permitted. The great deployment of deciduous forest (the eoclimax of Clements) came in Tertiary time. Related climaxes with the same general climatic features occur in widely separated geographic areas, in eastern America and eastern Asia, for example. These comprise a Clementsian panclimax, whose parts originated from the ancestral Tertiary forest. In America, that climax believed to be most like the ancestral Tertiary forest is the Mixed Mesophytic Forest climax. Its similarity to the mixed forest of China has been pointed out by Chaney, who has seen both the forests of China and the mixed mesophytic forests of the Cumberland Mountains, the area of best development of Mixed Mesophytic Forest.

Differentiation of the Deciduous Forest has resulted because of environmental changes related to progress of erosion cycles and to climatic changes. Awareness of and understanding of succession in its broadest aspects help to unravel the complex pattern of eastern forest vegetation.

Twenty years ago, in the Cumberland Mountains, great areas of the Kentucky slopes of Big Black Mountain and of the northwest slope of Pine Mountain were clothed with almost unbroken primary forest, affording, by the continuous transect method, opportunity to study the relationship of communities, and hence of community types (Braun, 1935a, 1940, 1942). Gradations related to altitude and to moisture (suggested by topographic position, insolation, etc.) as well as to substratum occurred. The whole displayed a multitude of segregates. The most mesic communities are the most highly mixed communities, including in the canopy a great number of tree species, some with wide ecological amplitude, which are species with many biotypes, and hence a variety of ecotypes, as Dr. Whittaker ably explained in a recent paper on the vegetation of the Great Smoky Mountains (1956). Partly because these very mesic mixed communities often contain a few red oak, white oak, and chestnut trees, Dr. Whittaker has compared them with transition forests of the Smokies, where *Castanea* is classed as "subxeric." However, in the Cumberland Mountains and on the Cumberland Plateau, *Castanea* has a greater variety of ecotypes and may be associated with river birch and sweet gum on river bottoms, with sweet gum, pin oak, and beech on swamp flats; that is, it varies from hydromesic to subxeric, but reaches greatest abundance in submesic and subxeric sites, where it may be codominant with sugar maple and tuliptree in the former, or with chestnut oak in the latter. Other species, also, have wider ecological amplitudes in the Cumberlands than in the Smokies.

To return briefly to concepts—all the mesic mixed communities have much in common, in species and in luxuriance and coverage of herbaceous vegetation. In a scheme of classification, all could be grouped under the broad term mixed mesophytic, that is, as belonging to the Mixed Mesophytic association. But because no two species are alike in physiological requirements, gradation in environment results in segregation of the mixture. For these interrelated similar communities the term association-segregate was proposed as a dynamic term suggesting response to environmental forces at work (Braun, 1935). It was apparent that gradations led from the mesic communities readily classified as belonging to the mixed mesophytic type to less mesic transitional types and finally to subxeric types on ridges. It was also apparent that a more or less distinct break could be found where influence of canopy (late leafing of oak and chestnut and slow decomposition of their leaf litter) was reflected in composition of undergrowth. This break occurs between what may be classed as mixed mesophytic communities and oak-chestnut communities.

In the Cumberland Mountains, mixed mesophytic communities occupy not only the coves but much of the slopes, except convexities and ridges. Nowhere else are such communities better developed. This I believe is because of (1) the long period of continued occupancy of an area of mature topography; (2) the very deep soils which can develop where underlying strata are horizontal or nearly so (in marked contrast to conditions in the Great Smoky Mountains and Blue Ridge); (3) the high annual precipitation, equably distributed and without the occurrence of summer droughts, such as the Southern Appalachians are subject to (see maps by Thornthwaite, 1941). It became apparent that here was the center of best development (not center of dispersal) of mixed mesophytic forest. Extensive travel disclosed the prevalence of mixed meso-phytic forest communities over a considerable geographic area, which I later designated as the Mixed Mesophytic Forest region. Beyond this region—in any direction—such communities are more limited in extent. Other climax types prevail. On the basis of prevalence of a particular climax type (and prominence of other community types) other forest regions were designated (Braun, 1950).

The prevalence of any particular climax type may be due to the control of climate; it may be related to the history of erosion cycles and past climates; it may be due to state of development of climax communities; or, more likely, to a combination of all.

Prevalence of a climax type should not be construed as uniformity of vegetation. Great diversity of vegetation is a characteristic of all areas of diverse topography. And each area may have its own peculiar vegetation types as well as some common to other areas of the region. In the intensive study of any local area, all community types should be distinguished, and the status (climax, developmental, primary, secondary) be determined. In an extensive approach, the need for classification is as evident as is the need for classifying species into genera and families—the number of community types would doubtless be in the thousands.

The scheme of classification most used by American ecologists in con-nection with the Eastern Deciduous Forest is division into what have been called climax associations. For many years a threefold concept prevailed which recognized three climax associations: beech-maple, oak-chestnut, and oak-hickory (Clements, 1916, 1928). In 1916, a fourth climax, mixed meso-phytic, was proposed for a mesic climax type with several dominants, among which beech was most important (Braun, 1916). Expansion of the concept became necessary, for beech is not always an important species, in fact is not always present. Two species, *Tilia heterophylla* and *Aesculus octandra,* are the most characteristic species of the mixed mesophytic association (Braun, 1947, 1950). This does not mean that other species cannot be thought of as characteristically present in mixed mesophytic communities, but that these two are essentially confined to such communities and do not occur in any other climax association than mixed mesophytic.

If the four major climax associations mentioned above are recognized, then a geographic region in which the mixed mesophytic association prevails can be distinguished as the Mixed Mesophytic Forest region; this occupies a central position. A region in which an oak-chestnut association prevails occupies a large area bordering it to the east and southeast and is called the Oak-Chestnut Forest region. Farther west, centering in the Ozarks, is the Oak-Hickory Forest region. The Beech-Maple Forest region lies to the north;

here a beech-maple or maple-beech climax prevails. In addition to these four climaxes, a maple-basswood is now generally recognized (Oosting, 1948; Braun, 1950).

The extent of these regions, and I believe the prevalence of the climaxes which characterize them, is a result of past history as well as present climate. That is why I like to think of these climaxes as regional rather than climatic. Evidence points to mid-Tertiary occupancy of much of the eastern half of the United States by mixed forest. Base leveling and climatic change curtailed its extent, leaving remnants, relics, in favorable sites, and giving advantage to less mesic types—just as moisture and slope differences in the Cumberland Mountains cause segregation into types. Glaciation further curtailed the mixed forest. Post-Wisconsin migrations have repopulated the glaciated area, including that part here designated as the Beech-Maple region. Here, more than anywhere else, the importance of succession is evident. Here also the question arises as to the permanence of this classic association. There is evidence that where dissection is beginning, beech-maple dominance is being broken by the entrance of additional mesic species (Braun, 1950, pp. 523, 527). Again, question is raised as to the climatic character of this regional climax.

The associations here distinguished are not concrete pieces of vegetation—they are abstract concepts to which communities and community types can be assigned. The species (or species populations) which make up these communities seldom have narrow habitat limits; mostly they are complex species or species made up of a number of ecotypes and hence may range through a number of different community types. A species which in one place may indicate subxeric conditions, in another may grow in hydromesic sites; hence conclusions reached in one intensive study cannot be carried over into another. Considering the four major associations, two are mesic, two submesic to subxeric. The area where the Mixed Mesophytic climax prevails is separated from the area where the Oak-Hickory climax prevails by a broad belt which I call the Western Mesophytic Forest region, characterized by a mosaic of climaxes including rich mixed mesophytic communities, various less mesic types, as beech-chestnut, white oak–black oak–tuliptree, and oak-hickory (of varying composition), pine communities, cedar barrens, and prairies. No existing gradient can account for the distribution of this motley assortment. Late Tertiary, Pleistocene, and post-Pleistocene climates, topography, and migrations must be considered. The distribution of mixed mesophytic communities in this region cannot be explained in relation to precipitation alone; rather, they appear to have persisted (with changes of course) from the more widespread mixed Tertiary forest, to have persisted where topography has been continuously favorable, and can and did, in drier times, partly compensate for reduced precipitation.

To summarize—I think of the Eastern Deciduous Forest (ignoring secondary forest) as made up of a vast number of intergrading communities. Some of the communities are developmental, others climax in nature, some are very local in occurrence and extent, others recur frequently over considerable geographic extent. The developmental communities give clues to trends. Those climax communities which are limited to specific sites, more or less extreme for their region, illustrate the great range of types possible in a region. Those climax types which recur again and again, represented by similar though individually different communities, are the ones which can be classified into the major associations of the Deciduous Forest and are the ones which best illustrate history and development of that forest through the long ages of its existence.

LITERATURE CITED

BRAUN, E. L. 1916. The physiographic ecology of the Cincinnati region. Ohio Biol. Surv. Bull. 7.

————. 1935. The undifferentiated deciduous forest climax and the association-segregate. Ecol. 16:514–519.

————. 1935a. The vegetation of Pine Mountain, Kentucky. Amer. Midl. Nat. 16:517–565.

————. 1936. Forests of the Illinoian till plain of southwestern Ohio. Ecol. Monog. 6:89–149.

————. 1940. An ecological transect of Black Mountain, Kentucky. Ecol. Monog. 10:193–241.

————. 1942. Forests of the Cumberland Mountains. Ecol. Monog. 12:413–447.

————. 1947. Development of the deciduous forests of eastern North America. Ecol. Monog. 17:211–219.

————. 1950. Deciduous forests of Eastern North America. Blakiston–McGraw-Hill. New York.

CLEMENTS, F. E. 1916. Plant succession. Carnegie Inst. Wash. Pub. 242.

————. 1928. Plant succession and indicators. H. W. Wilson. New York.

COOPER, W. S. 1926. The fundamentals of vegetational change. Ecol. 7:391–413.

COWLES, H. C. 1899. The ecological relations of the vegetation on the sand dunes of Lake Michigan. Bot. Gaz. 27:95–117, 167–202, 281–308, 361–391.

————. 1901. The physiographic ecology of Chicago and vicinity. Bot. Gaz. 31:73–108, 145–182.

————. 1911. The causes of vegetative cycles. Bot. Gaz. 51:161–183.

GLEASON, H. A. 1926. The individualistic concept of the plant association. Bull. Torrey Bot. Club 53:7–26.

NICHOLS, G. E. 1923. A working basis for the ecological classification of plant communities. Ecol. 4:11–23, 154–179.

OOSTING, H. J. 1948. The study of plant communities. W. H. Freeman. San Francisco.

THORNTHWAITE, C. W. 1941. Atlas of climatic types in the United States, 1900–1939. U.S. Dept. Agric. Soil Cons. Service Misc. Pub. 421.

WHITTAKER, R. H. 1951. A criticism of the plant association and climatic climax concepts. Northwest Science 25:17–31.

————. 1953. A consideration of climax theory: the climax as a population and pattern. Ecol. Monog. 23:41–78.

————. 1956. Vegetation of the Great Smoky Mountains. Ecol. Monog. 26:1–80.

17

RECENT EVOLUTION OF ECOLOGICAL CONCEPTS IN RELATION TO THE EASTERN FORESTS OF NORTH AMERICA[1]

R. H. Whittaker

INTRODUCTION: THE SYSTEM OF CLEMENTS. The eastern forests have always been the real homeland of American ecology. It is here that the largest number of American ecologists have lived and worked, the most extensive ecological research has been carried out. From study of the eastern forests have developed many of the concepts which ecologists have applied to interpretation of other areas. Results of ecological research in other areas have also influenced interpretation of the eastern forests; but the commerce of ecological ideas has been more one of export from than of import into the eastern forests. Of all the exports from the ecology of the eastern United States, the most widely influential was the system of vegetation interpretation designed by Clements. Discussion of changing views of ecological concepts, especially in relation to the eastern forests and Clements' system of interpretation, is the object of this paper.

The major unit of vegetation in Clements' system is the plant *formation*. The formation is a great regional unit of vegetation characterized by its dominant growth form, as the eastern forests are characterized by deciduous trees, the prairie where Clements did his early work by grasses. Every formation is a product of climate and is controlled and delimited by climate and climate alone; the formation occurs in a natural area of essential climatic unity and

[1] Based on the conclusion to a symposium on "Approaches to Interpretation of the Eastern Forests of North America," including also the cited papers of Braun (1956, published in this volume), Wang (1956), Raup (1956), and Bray (1956b), at the meetings of the American Institute of Biological Sciences, Storrs, Conn., August 28, 1956.

expresses the climate and its unity (Weaver and Clements, 1938, p. 89). The visible unity of the formation is due to its dominant species, for all these are of the same growth form and certain species and genera of dominants range widely through the formation and link together its various associations (Weaver and Clements, 1938, pp. 91, 489). The formation is not an abstraction or a mere unit of classification; it is a definite and concrete organic entity, covering a definite area marked by a climatic climax (Clements, 1928, p. 128). The formation is, in fact, a *complex organism,* and as such it arises, grows, matures, reproduces, and dies (Clements, 1928, p. 125).

The formation is the *climax* in its climatic region; the terms climax and formation are in fact synonymous (Weaver and Clements, 1938, pp. 91, 478). The climax is the final, mature, stable, self-maintaining, and self-reproducing state of vegetational development in a climatic unit. The climax formation is the adult organism, the fully developed community, of which all other communities are but stages of development (Clements, 1928, p. 126). Since climate alone determines the climax formation, there is but one true, or climatic, climax in a climatic region. Communities differing from the climax because of distinctive soils or other habitat characteristics are developmental. Relatively stabilized vegetation other than the climatic climax may occur in a region, however, because vegetation is held indefinitely in stages preceding the climax by factors other than climate (subclimaxes and serclimaxes), because local soils and topography offer conditions favorable to the climaxes of other regions (preclimax and postclimax), or because disturbance causes modification or replacement of the true climax (disclimax) (Weaver and Clements, 1938, pp. 81–86).

The formation, like other organisms, has an evolutionary history and arises from the modification of earlier formations; it has a *phylogeny.* The grouping of formations on different continents whose descent from a common ancestor is indicated by possession of similar dominant growth forms is a panclimax (Clements, 1936; Clements and Shelford, 1939, p. 243). Every climax formation consists of two or more subdivisions known as *associations,* each marked by one or more dominant species peculiar to it (Weaver and Clements, 1938, p. 93). Like the formation, the association is a regional vegetation unit; it is the climatic climax of a subclimate within the general climate of the formation. In the eastern forest formation, climatic influences have resulted in a threefold differentiation—into the maple-beech association in the northern, the oak-chestnut association in the eastern, and the oak-hickory association in the western part of the formation. Of these, the maple-beech is the typical association of the formation, because of the greater environmental requirements and smaller number of its dominants and its closer similarity to the European member of the panclimax (Weaver and Clements, 1938, p. 510). Each association is similar throughout its extent in physiognomy or outward appearance, in its ecological structure, and in general floristic composition (Weaver and Clements, 1938, p. 94). Differentiation of the association in relation to local habitats, however, requires the recognition of other units subordinate to it—the consociation, fasciation, lociation, etc.—and a parallel hierarchy of units exists for successional communities (Clements, 1936).

Each climax is the direct expression of its climate; the climate is the cause, the climax the effect, which, in turn, reacts upon the climate (Weaver and Clements, 1938, p. 479). Since the habitat is cause and the community effect, it is inevitable that the unit of the vegetative covering should correspond to the unit of the earth's surface, the habitat (Clements, 1905, p. 202; 1928, p. 119). During succession *dominant species* occupy the habitat, modify the habitat in ways unfavorable to themselves, and are replaced by other dominant species. Every succession ends in a climax when the occupation by and reactions of a dominant are such as to exclude the invasion of another dominant (Weaver and Clements, 1938, p. 237). The climax dominants are the species best adjusted to habitat and able to take possession of the habitat and hold it against all comers. The dominant receives the full impact of the environment and determines conditions of life for other species in the community both by effects on environment (reactions) and by relations to other species (coactions) (Clements and Shelford, 1939, p. 239). The dominant species characterize the community, express its environment, and indicate the actual or probable presence of other, associated species (Clements, 1928, p. 253). The dominant is the real basis of indicator study, so commanding is its role in the processes of vegetation (Clements, 1928, p. 236). Dominance, in fact, is one of the master keys to the understanding of vegetation, as successional process is another.

Such was Clements' system in essential features. Details which would too much lengthen the present paper have been omitted, but the abbreviated account makes clear one of the system's most significant characteristics—its coherence. Each of the preceding statements of the system has necessary logical interconnections with most of the other statements. Each major concept is defined, and seems explained through, other concepts; some of the concepts (climatic unit, formation, and climax; dominance, reaction, and community unit) are as strictly interdependent as the terms of an equation. Almost all there is about vegetation seems accounted for by the system and its complications (the various special climaxes, the subordinate vegetation units, etc.) introduced to accommodate it to the complexities of vegetation. It is a system which, in its orderliness, seems to imply the orderliness of vegetation. Clements' own role in creating this coherent and orderly system went far beyond the bringing together of inductive discoveries about vegetation from Warming, Cowles, Moss, and other predecessors and his own work. Influenced by the ideal of the deductive system represented in philosophy, mathematics, and physics, Clements fashioned from limited evidence and liberal assumption a coherent, and apparently inclusive, deductive system of vegetation interpretation.

The structure of the system began to appear early in the century (Clements, 1905), was developed in its major features in the monograph on plant succession (Clements, 1916, 1928) and textbook of plant ecology (Weaver and Clements, 1929, 1938), stated in definitive form in an essay on the climax (Clements, 1936, 1949), and soon thereafter applied to the study of natural communities through the plant-animal formation, or biome (Clements and Shelford, 1939). In its course of about half a century it has accumulated increasing criticism; although the most influential product of American ecology, its influence has declined in the last decades. In considering the meaning of this decline, the author has no desire to minimize the great contribution which Clements made or to criticize Clements or his system for the uncritical manner in which it was applied by some of his followers. The object is not to show that Clements was mistaken, or that time and experience have been unkind to his system, as they have been to others which were brilliant in their times. It is to show, with this system as background, how the climate of interpretation in a field of science has changed and seems to be changing today.

CHANGING VIEWS OF ECOLOGICAL CONCEPTS. One of Clements' central concepts is that of formation. Vegetation of the eastern United States seemed to support his view of formations as regional and climatic units, each distinct from others and unified within itself by a single dominant growth form. Three great formations are easily recognized in temperate eastern North America—the eastern deciduous broad-leaf forest, the grassland or prairie, and the northern evergreen needle-leaf forest, or taiga. These seem indeed distinct, natural, climatically determined units; there is only the problem of the mixed broad-leaf–needle-leaf forests of the Lake States, to be treated as either a transition between the first two or an additional formation. Experiences elsewhere in the world have not supported the view that formations are determined only by climate, that climatic regions and vegetation formations must always be identical. The tropical grasslands, or savannas, surely among the world's great plant formations, are thought to owe their existence to factors of both climate and soil (Beard, 1953). The formation is not simply a unit reflecting climate alone, but a grouping of communities which are of similar physiognomy and express a similar set of ecological conditions, of which climate is only one (Beadle and Costin, 1952). It seemed simple enough to recognize three major formations of temperate eastern North America by one character only—dominance of a single growth form. But in a broader view, many formations must be defined by mixtures of growth forms, and many others must be distinguished by differences of environments, not of growth-form dominance. Clements and others have been impressed by the discontinuity between grassland and forest in eastern North America;

but in a world view there is extensive continuity and intergradation among formations, as is especially evident in the tropics (Beard, 1955). This continuity is not easily reconciled with the view of the formation as a distinct entity comparable to an organism. All these observations contribute to a changed view of the formation as a vegetation unit. The formation seems not a distinct, concrete vegetation unit determined solely by climate, but an abstract grouping of communities of similar physiognomy and environmental relations, a grouping dependent in the end on man's choice of what constitutes sufficient similarity of physiognomy and environment.

The nature of the association has been more bitterly contested and is a problem many ecologists do not feel has been resolved. The essence of the concept lies in the association, i.e., occurrence together, of species populations to form community units which may be recognized by species composition. Since associations are thought to be "natural units," very often compared with species as units of classification, it has been natural to assume that they are distinct in the sense of being separated from one another by well-defined boundaries. The basis of the association concept was challenged by Ramensky (1924) with two propositions: (1) The principle of species individuality—each species responds uniquely to external factors and enters the community as an independent member; there are no two species which relate themselves to environments and communities in quite the same way. (2) The principle of community continuity—composition of the plant cover changes continuously in space; sharp boundaries between communities are special circumstances requiring special explanation. Ideas closely related to Ramensky's were expressed about the same time by Gleason (1926) and Lenoble (1926, 1928); they are most familiar to Americans as the former's "individualistic concept of the plant association" (Gleason, 1926, 1939).

If the association is a "natural unit" of species populations, its unity is presumably expressed in species distributions. Most, or at least some, of the associated species should have closely similar distributions. Recent studies in the eastern forests (Whittaker, 1951, 1952, 1956; Curtis and McIntosh, 1951; Brown and Curtis, 1952) have shown that, in fact, no two species are distributed alike, that species show the heterogeneity of distribution and lack of organization into distinct groups of associates which Ramensky's first principle asserts. Relations to other species must, to be sure, affect their distributions; species distributions cannot be "independent" in the sense that they are unaffected by competition and other interrelations. These interrelations, however, do not result in the organization of species into definite groups of associates; and species distributions are "individualistic" in the sense that each species is distributed according to its own way of relating to the range of total environmental circumstances, including effects of and interrelations with other species, which it encounters. Both continuity and discontinuity of vegetation have been very widely observed; but the same recent studies of the eastern forests support Ramensky's view that vegetational continuity is the more general, discontinuity the more special, condition (Whittaker, 1956). As discussed by Bray (1956b), these studies and some other current work (Goodall, 1954; Poore, 1955; Hale, 1955; Culberson, 1955; Bray, 1956a) are concerned less with associations than with ways of dealing effectively with vegetational continua.

The association thus ceases to be the clearly defined natural unit assumed by Clements. Two further difficulties are suggested in relation to Clements' associations. The first of these involves the dominance concept. The dominant trees of a forest strongly affect conditions of life for other species of the forest, but different tree species may affect the forest environment similarly. It is not the species of the dominant but the total environment in the forest which determines whether subordinate plant species can or cannot occur there. The principle of species individuality applies to relations of subordinate species to dominant species and total environmental complexes influenced by dominants. Dominants do not control the distribution of other species and organize them into well-defined groups of associates in the manner, or to the extent, assumed by Clements (Whittaker, 1956). Furthermore, as has been observed by European critics (Lippmaa, 1931; Braun-Blanquet, 1951, p. 560; Ellenberg, 1954), the dominant species are often very wide-ranging ones, occurring in most varied environments with most varied associates; the overemphasis of dominants by Clements and others is sometimes a rather crude and superficial approach to relations of whole communities to environments. Dominance cannot provide the simple, comfortable solution to many problems, the master key for the recognition and classification of communities, indication of community environments, and understanding of community function, assumed by Clements.

The other difficulty is in the treatment of associations as regional units. It is easily shown that geographically, as locally, no two species of an association have the same distribution (e.g., Billings, 1949). In consequence, the association as a particular combination of species is a localized phenomenon (Lippmaa, 1933; Bourne, 1934; Cain, 1947; Knapp, 1948; Ellenberg, 1954); and associations may be geographically, as locally, continuous with one another (Walter and Walter, 1953). Species are distributed in relation to total environmental complexes, not to climate alone; and species do not fit into sharply defined groups corresponding to climatic regions and regional associations. Approaches to generalization about geographic relations of species in communities are being developed in Europe (Böcher, 1938; Meusel, 1939, 1943; Walter, 1954b), but these provide no simple answers to the definition of associations and determination of their boundaries. The major concepts of such geographic treatment—species groups based on distributional relations, natural areas defined by species distributions, distributional centers—have no very close relation to the association concept or to Clements' regional vegetation units.

One direction in the modernization of Clements' association concept has been followed by Braun (1935, 1938, 1947, 1950, 1956) in her work on the eastern forests. Braun's associations are, in manner of definition, derived from Clements'; each is a large-scale, relatively heterogeneous unit which characterizes a geographic region as its climax. Clements' three-part division was shown by Braun to be unrealistic; and Braun recognizes six regional associations (not including the Lake Forest, the evergreen forest of the Gulf Coastal Plain, and the transitional Western Mesophytic Region). Of importance at least equal to this change of view is the immense complexity of detail in these forests described by Braun (1950). Because of this complexity, Braun's six associations are by no means all that an ecological splitter might choose to recognize. The association is a more or less arbitrary unit (Braun, 1947, 1950, p. 525); Braun's associations are no more than Clements' the unique and inescapable solution to division of the eastern forests. Braun's division is not simply true where Clements' was false; it is a better pattern of abstraction from the eastern forests because more realistic, more frankly cognizant of the underlying complexity in seeking that simplification from complexity which is necessary to any abstraction. Thus in Braun's work, retention of some of the essential form of Clementsian ecology is combined with a fundamental change in perspective.

Very different directions have been followed in Europe. In Braun-Blanquet's (1921, 1932, 1951) system, the one most widely applied by phytosociologists, communities are classified by character species—species, often rather obscure ones, which are centered in or largely confined to a given community type and which, hence, are more truly characteristic of it than wide-ranging dominants. An association is in general a vegetation unit of the lowest rank which can be defined by character species. For most areas, the approach through dominants is thought suitable only for preliminary and superficial work; but another vegetation unit, the sociation, is used in areas such as Scandinavia, where communities contain relatively few species. This unit is one of small scale, defined by dominants of the various strata, not of the uppermost stratum alone; and it is unrelated to Clements' regional associations. For neither the sociation nor the association is climax stability or regional prevalence required, as for the association of Clements. Although regional vegetation types are recognized there, the American association as such is used by no one in Europe. In contrast to Clements' view of formations and associations as "concrete" entities, most European authors emphasize that the association is an abstraction—the association first comes into being at the phytosociologist's desk (Klapp, 1949, p. 10). Increasingly detailed knowledge of the vegetation of Europe has led to increasing recognition of the limitations inherent in even this most successful definition of plant associations. Most communities are actually intermediate to associations (Klapp et al., 1954; Ellenberg, 1954); and (because of species individuality) the number of "good" character species becomes progressively smaller as knowledge of their distributional relations increases (Ellenberg, 1954).

In spite of its role in the work of Braun, the Clementsian association seems a concept of declining significance. Many American ecologists do not use it in current work, and it has little use outside this country. So far as the term *association* has an accepted international meaning, it is the meaning given it by Braun-Blanquet, recommended by the Botanical Congress of 1935 (Du Rietz, 1936), and accepted by much the largest number of students of vegetation around the world. The diversity of vegetation units, of which the formation, association, American association, and sociation are only a few, has a deeper significance in relation to Clements' system, however. It implies that there are many possible approaches to classification of vegetation, that nothing forces ecologists to choose one or another of these, and that none results in units really comparable to species. An association is not a concrete natural community; it is an abstraction from the unlimited complexity and intergradation of communities, a class produced by an ecologist's choice of a class concept or definition (Whittaker, 1956).

Clements' treatment of climax and succession seemed to imply three other assumptions about the orderliness of vegetation (although the difficulties were known to Clements and allowed for in his system): (1) Succession is an orderly growth process, leading from varied beginnings to the same maturity or climax. (2) The climax is determined only by climate; consequently climaxes and climatic regions must correspond. (3) Vegetation consists of climaxes and their successional communities, and the climax and successional conditions are clearly distinguishable. It is consistent with the "individuality" of species that they enter successions in the most varied ways; there appears also to be a strong element of chance, of accidents of dispersal and timing, affecting the composition and sequence of successional communities. The complex interrelations among these which result led Cooper (1926) to compare succession with a braided stream. Successional processes give an impression of relative irregularity and disorderliness in detail, together with a degree of orderliness in general pattern and trend (Whittaker, 1953).

The assertion that there is only one true, climatic climax in a climatic region—the monoclimax theory—has been one of the most frequently criticized parts of Clements' system. As the system was usually applied, only the regionally prevailing vegetation, that undisturbed vegetation occupying the largest part of the land surface, was regarded as truly climax. For undisturbed vegetation, climax stability, regional prevalence, and maximum mesophytism seemed to be identified with one another. Observations have been accumulating from all over the world which suggest that this identification is untenable, that many communities which are not regionally prevalent are as much stabilized, as much "climax," as the "climatic climax." Many ecologists have been led to a polyclimax view which defines climaxes by an essentially stabilized, or self-maintaining, condition, regardless of prevalence, and considers that a number of climaxes may exist in a given area. The differences of monoclimax and polyclimax approaches are in part semantic ones (Cain, 1947); for authors of the two viewpoints use different terms for the same observations, or the same terms for somewhat different conceptions. The essential difference seems one of relative emphasis. Monoclimax authors emphasize the essential unity of climax vegetation within a region, with allowance also for stabilized communities other than the climatic climax. Polyclimax authors emphasize the inherent complexity of climax vegetation, with allowance also for prevailing climax communities which characterize the vegetation of a region and express its relation to climate. This difference of emphasis is one of great importance, for it affects the manner in which evidence on natural communities is selected, treated, and interpreted; in a rather subtle and often unconscious way it may color and condition the ecologist's whole perspective in the interpretation of vegetation.

Braun's (1950) approach to the eastern forests follows Clements in recognition of climatic climaxes as regional units; other stabilized communities are subclimaxes which "only theoretically could be replaced by the climax." One region of the eastern forests, the Western Mesophytic Region, is characterized not by a monoclimax but by a mosaic of unlike climaxes and subclimaxes. In the present author's view, Braun's approach is primarily monoclimax both in its expression (Braun, 1950, pp. 12–13) and in the manner in which the description throughout the book is influenced by this conception. It is, however, quite different from the rather doctrinaire climate-climax-formation identification of Clements. Monoclimax conceptions far removed from Clements have recently been expressed also by Dansereau (1954) and Walter (1954a). Polyclimax, or climax-pattern, conceptions asserting that the climax state is determined by the environments of individual communities, not regional climate, have been stated by Schmithüsen (1950) and Whittaker (1953); the latter identifies the climax as a community steady state and substitutes "prevailing climax" for "climatic climax." The varied current interpretations of "climax" by the author and others suggest that none of these can claim exclusive truth or univocal determination by properties of vegetation.

Raup (1956) has discussed the role of hurricane winds in patchwise disturbance of New England forests at time intervals that are short in relation to the life cycles of trees. The eastern forests, like the prairies (Malin, 1956), are probably much less stable than the climax ideal has suggested to many ecologists. The more closely vegetational dynamics are observed, the less clear-cut becomes the distinction between climax and successional communities (Whittaker, 1953). Vegetation does not really consist of climaxes and successions leading toward them. In a long-range perspective, the vegetation of the earth's surface is in incessant flux; what we observe in the field are not simply successions and climaxes, but only different kinds and degrees of vegetational stability and instability, different kinds and rates of population change. Vegetation change does not consist of successions toward climaxes in quite the sense ecologists have implied. Rather than this, from the diversity of communities we observe, some can be arranged in meaningful sequences of temporal development; and thus we bring into order and comprehension some part, but never more than part, of the flux of populations in natural communities. Climaxes do not simply exist in nature; rather than this, ecologists must define the terms of relative vegetational stability by which their climaxes are to be recognized—or, in a sense, created.

The flux of populations and "braided" relation of communities bear also on community phylogeny. Common ancestry for the deciduous-forest formations of eastern North America, Europe, and eastern Asia is implied in Clements' concept of panclimax; and maple-beech was regarded as the "typical" association of the American deciduous forest. Braun's (1950) interpretation of eastern forest history leads to a very different view of the eastern-forest associations. The Mixed Mesophytic Association of the Appalachian plateaux is seen as the central, the oldest, and the most complex association of the Deciduous Forest Formation. From the mixed mesophytic, or its ancestral progenitor, the mixed Tertiary forest, all other climaxes of the deciduous forest have arisen (Braun, 1950, p. 39). Braun's treatment, too, suggests a "phylogeny" for these forest associations, though in a sense less literal than Clements'. A somewhat different, nonphylogenetic interpretation of eastern forest history has been discussed by Wang (1956).

As the relations of species in space and successional time are, in a limited sense, "free" so that they may combine and recombine in most varied ways, so, we may believe, are their relations in evolutionary time (Mason, 1947). Species of one association do not simply evolve together into a new association; the species may change their distributional relations in time, entering in varied ways into new "associations" with other species. Interrelations of communities in evolutionary time are consequently intricately reticulate. It cannot really be said that two modern communities are descended from one Tertiary one in the same sense as two modern species populations may be descended from one Tertiary one. Rather than a formal phylogeny, or descent in a strict sense, historical interrelation of community types must be based on judgments of floristic relation, of relative floristic continuity of a past and a present community vs. relative floristic divergence and dilution.

The historic data on which such judgments must be based are fragmentary, and to some extent ambiguous or indeterminate. The student of vegetational evolution must select from the available data that which is most relevant, provide the interpretation of its relevance, and fashion the interpreted data into a meaningful pattern according to his general perspective and chosen ecological concepts. Some conclusions of historians of man are pertinent, although the vegetational historian may be spared concern with influences of culture, personality, choice, and volition—except those affecting the historian. History is an imaginative reconstruction of the past which is scientific in its determinations but approaches the artistic in its formulation; and history is more genuinely scientific in spirit as it takes into account the inescapable limitations on its objectivity and rigor (Muller, 1954, p. 35). It is no criticism of Clements', Braun's, and Wang's interpretations of eastern forest history to observe that these are human conceptual reconstructions which cannot be simply inherent in, or uniquely determined by, the information which they bring into a pattern of interpretation. It is relevant to Clements' system, however, that vegetational evolution is not a phylogeny.

Natural communities are not organisms, except in Whitehead's sense in which "organism" is equivalent to "system." Their manner of function and organization, their interrelation and classification, their development and maturity, and their evolution present problems which are distinct from, and significantly different in character from, those of individual biological organisms. In Clements' system the complex organism became the central unifying theme, the background concept from which the meanings of other concepts were to be understood. The organismic analogy has been accepted by some authors (Phillips, 1934–1935; Tansley, 1920, 1935; Allee et al., 1949), rejected by many others (Gleason, 1917, 1926; Gams, 1918; Meusel, 1940; Schmid, 1942; Ellenberg, 1950, 1954); but in current writing it is not the central concept of vegetational understanding—it is seldom referred to. The treatment of environment as cause and community as effect has been criticized as a fundamental weakness of Clements' system (Egler, 1951); probably Clements would not have ventured the parallel statement: environment is the cause, and the plant is the result. The cause-and-effect view seems poorly suited to the manner in which the community and environment are interrelated; a "transactional" approach to the functional system formed by community and environment may be more appropriate (Whittaker, 1954). A central concept different from Clements' complex organism and its cause-and-effect relation to environment, and different from the kind of synthesis of plant-animal ecology attempted by Clements and Shelford (1939), appears in contemporary ecology. It is the concept of the functional whole formed by community and environment—the ecosystem.

CONCLUSION: A CHANGING OUTLOOK. Scarcely a major feature of Clements' system as an intellectual structure remains intact, in this author's view. To observe this alone, however, may be to underestimate both the lasting significance of Clements' contribution and the real significance of the change that has occurred. Taken all together, the changes in ecological conceptions discussed amount to a general re-orientation of viewpoint in a field of science.

The changes have usually been regarded piecemeal, as particular changes affecting particular concepts; but this conclusion will attempt a more general interpretation of their meaning.

One over-all feature of the change is the dissolution of a coherent, well-ordered, deductive system for the interpretation of vegetation, an attempt at deductive whole-knowledge of vegetation, and its replacement by less coherent and less interdependent, inductive part-knowledges of different vegetational problems. Implied in this is a change in the view of natural communities themselves. These seem no longer to form an area of clear-cut, well-ordered, simply defined, and neatly interdependent phenomena to which a deductive system like Clements' may be appropriate. Although the deductive system is an ideal of science, students of natural communities find themselves authors of an inductive science, with problems more akin to those of the social sciences than those of physics and geometry.

The lack of clear-cut orderliness in natural communities is a necessary consequence of the multiplicity of factors and complexity of interrelations with which the ecologist must deal. This complexity is as much a fundamental circumstance of the study of natural communities as of the study of man's communities. A basis of lack of simple orderliness may be found also in Ramensky's principle of species individuality. Species populations are distributed "individualistically," and they are not organized in terms of man's ecological concepts and classifications. Major problems of community classification, of succession and climax, and community evolution stem directly from this individuality of species distributions. Many ecologists view the implications of species individuality in a more conservative light than that of this paper; but to the author species individuality is one major theme of current changes in ecological concepts. A further aspect of the lack of simple orderliness is in substantial effects of chance, of largely unpredictable factors of dispersal and population interaction, on species distributions and communities (Palmgren, 1929; Egler, 1942; Whittaker, 1953). Species individuality, multiplicity of factors, and effects of chance all contribute to giving most statements about natural communities a quality of probability, not necessity, partial correlation, not strict interdependence, inductive generalization for which limitations and exceptions are granted, not exact prediction. And if one turns to Braun's description of the eastern forests with these things in mind, a view of these forests quite different from Clements' results. One is struck first by their immense, their almost overwhelming, complexity of pattern. If one seeks to view this complexity in perspective, in terms of species populations in space and successional and evolutionary change and without the intervention of man's ecological abstractions, then the view of the forest is not one of clear and orderly associations, successions, and phylogeny. It is one of a veritable shimmer of populations in space and time.

If this population shimmer is not simply and clearly orderly, it is also not devoid of order. It is neither well ordered as it seemed in Clements' system nor simply disorderly; the fundamental character of natural communities with which ecologists must deal might be described as *loosely ordered complexity*. In this, it is the task of the ecologist not to discover simple order inherent in his material, but to find such means of effective abstraction and generalization as the loosely ordered condition permits. In the author's view, it is the gradual coming to terms with this loosely ordered complexity, as it affected one ecological concept after another, that has characterized the changing climate of interpretation in synecology. The negative aspect of this change is a loss of the kind of uncritical faith in ecological concepts and systems which once prevailed. Ecological concepts, man's means of interpreting natural communities, were projected back into natural communities and seen as part of nature itself. They were hypostatized or reified and were directly identified with the natural communities from which they were abstractions. Not only were plant associations part of the order of nature (Conard, 1939; cf. Clements, 1916, 1928; Tansley, 1920; Du Rietz, 1921, 1929; Alechin, 1925); plant communities *were* formations and associations, vegetation *was* succession and the climax. More recent experiences have led to increasing wariness of such identification, and increasing awareness of the complexities which bedevil all ecological generalizations, the limitations affecting all ecological concepts. The positive aspect of the change has been the building of inductive knowledge and a more realistic understanding of the function of ecological concepts. Older concepts of continuing usefulness, like the climax and association, are seen in new lights, while newer concepts, like the ecosystem and continuum, share with them in the understanding of vegetation.

The changing view of the role of ecological concepts may be summarized in a few points:

1. All are necessarily abstractions; they are essentially human creations serving to order, interrelate, and interpret some of the information about natural communities available to us. None can be thought inherent in vegetation in the sense earlier authors assumed; none can be thought to represent the real, whole, ultimate truth about natural communities.

2. There is nothing in the nature of vegetation which compels us to adopt one or another of these concepts as the primary basis of vegetation interpretation in general—as Americans have often adopted succession and the school of Braun-Blanquet associations. Nothing in the nature of vegetation forces us to choose a particular way of defining a given concept. The various approaches and concepts have only different degrees of general usefulness and different appropriateness to particular circumstances and purposes.

3. There is in all these concepts a dependence on choice and assumption, an element of subjectivity and artistry, which can never be wholly escaped, even though it is an objective of science to minimize its influence. The best means of controlling subjectivity is through a recognition, as frank and clear-

sighted as possible, of its presence and its underlying sources and necessity.

4. All these concepts and approaches have a partial character; they bring into order and comprehension only a small fraction of the information available to us. No one of them, however exhaustively applied, nor all of them together, can ever bring into a pattern of understanding all the available information about natural communities.

5. Finally, these concepts are to some extent interdependent, since the definition of one may influence another; but they are not interdependent in any simple, direct, and necessary way. There is no necessary correspondence between climax stability and regional prevalence of vegetation, between climax regions and floristic natural areas, between limits of dominance and of community types, between associations in the international and associations in the American sense. Rather than assuming that such necessary correspondence exists, it may be best to pursue each approach on its own terms for its own merits, with a minimum of assumption derived from other approaches, and to see then what degree of correspondence may or may not appear, in what way the results of one approach may or may not illuminate the results of another.

Experiences with the eastern forests and other natural communities since the time of Clements suggest a change of attitude from unquestioning faith in ecological concepts as part of nature and unquestioning assurance in the sufficiency of one's own system of interpretation toward greater modesty before the complexities of natural communities and the limitations of ecologists' understanding. They suggest an attitude of tolerance and open-mindedness, and eclecticism in practice, with regard to the varied possible concepts and approaches to natural communities, no one of which is uniquely determined by nature, each of which may contribute to understanding in a complementary relation to others. They suggest a greater self-consciousness in the use of ecological concepts, a continuing awareness of the role of the man in the interaction of ecologists and natural communities by which ecological understanding grows, of the extent to which the function of the scientist is not simple discovery, but the creation of means of understanding.

SUMMARY

1. Study of the eastern forests of North America has been the source of many ecological concepts, some of which became part of the widely influential system of Clements. Such concepts as formation and association, succession and climax, dominance, vegetational phylogeny, and the complex organism were synthesized by Clements into an orderly, coherent, deductive system of vegetation interpretation.

2. Further experiences in the eastern forests and elsewhere have led to changing views of these concepts:

a. The formation and association seem no longer distinct, clearly bounded entities comparable to organisms or species. With recognition of the significance of vegetational continuity and the principle of species individuality, these have come to be regarded as man-made classes of natural communities.

b. Succession seems a less orderly process than in Clements' view; only a part of the incessant flux of populations in natural communities can be understood in terms of succession. Relative stability of vegetation is not determined by climate alone, and varied approaches to the definition of "climax" are possible.

c. Dominant species do not control the distribution of other species and characterize communities and their environments in the way assumed by Clements.

d. Since plant species are free to change their distributional relations to one another through evolutionary time, evolutionary relations of communities are reticulate. Natural communities do not evolve by phylogenetic descent from past communities in the same sense as organisms.

e. The concept of the community as a complex organism, central to Clements' system, has been largely abandoned as inappropriate or unproductive. Current interpretations emphasize the functional system formed by community and environment, the ecosystem.

3. These changes in individual concepts, taken together, amount to a fundamental re-orientation of the field. The deductive system of Clements has broken down into the more detailed, more complex, and less coherent understanding of an inductive science. Because of multiplicity of ecological factors, effects of chance, and individuality of species distributions, natural communities are not an area of orderly, clear-cut, exactly predictable phenomena to which the system of Clements might be appropriate. A fundamental characteristic of natural communities affecting all ecological concepts is the condition of loosely ordered complexity. Ecological concepts cannot be thought inherent in, or uniquely determined by, vegetation; they are the means of human abstraction by which some of the diverse information about natural communities can be brought into comprehensible forms.

LITERATURE CITED

ALECHIN, W. W. 1925. Ist die Pflanzenassoziation eine Abstraktion oder eine Realität? Bot. Jahrb. 60 (Beibl. 135):17–25.

ALLEE, W. C., A. E. EMERSON, O. PARK, T. PARK, AND K. P. SCHMIDT. 1949. Principles of animal ecology. 837 pp. Saunders. Philadelphia.

BEADLE, N. C. W., AND A. B. COSTIN. 1952. Ecological classification and nomenclature. With a note on pasture classification by C. W. E. Moore. Proc. Linn. Soc. N.S. Wales 77:61–82.

BEARD, J. S. 1953. The savanna vegetation of northern tropical America. Ecol. Monog. 23:149–215.

BEARD, J. S. 1955. The classification of tropical American vegetation-types. Ecology 36:89–100.

BILLINGS, W. D. 1949. The shadscale vegetation zone of Nevada and eastern California in relation to climate and soils. Amer. Midland Nat. 42:87–109.

BÖCHER, T. W. 1938. Biological distributional types in the flora of Greenland. A study on the flora and plant-geography of South Greenland and East Greenland between Cape Farewell and Scoresby Sound. (Danish summ.) Meddel. om Grønland 106(2):1–339.

BOURNE, R. 1934. Some ecological conceptions. Empire Forestry Jour. 13:15–30.

BRAUN, E. LUCY. 1935. The undifferentiated deciduous forest climax and the association-segregate. Ecology 16:514–519.

―――. 1938. Deciduous forest climaxes. Ecology 19:515–522.

―――. 1947. Development of the deciduous forests of eastern North America. Ecol. Monog. 17:211–219.

―――. 1950. Deciduous forests of eastern North America. 596 pp. Blakiston–McGraw-Hill. New York.

―――. 1956. The development of association and climax concepts; their use in interpretation of the deciduous forest. Paper given at meetings of Amer. Inst. Biol. Sci., Storrs, Conn., Aug. 28, 1956.

BRAUN-BLANQUET, J. 1921. Prinzipien einer Systematik der Pflanzengesellschaften auf floristischer Grundlage. Jahrb. St. Gall. Naturw. Gesell. 57(2):305–351.

―――. 1932. Plant sociology, the study of plant communities (Transl. by G. D. FULLER and H. S. CONARD). 439 pp. McGraw-Hill. New York.

―――. 1951. Pflanzensoziologie. Grundzüge der Vegetationskunde. 2 Aufl. 631 pp. Springer. Vienna.

BRAY, J. R. 1956a. A study of mutual occurrence of plant species. Ecology 37:21–28.

―――. 1956b. The use of ordination techniques in interpreting the eastern forest. Paper given at meetings of Amer. Inst. Biol. Sci. Storrs, Conn., Aug. 28, 1956.

BROWN, R. T., AND J. T. CURTIS. 1952. The upland conifer-hardwood forests of northern Wisconsin. Ecol. Monog. 22:217–234.

CAIN, S. A. 1947. Characteristics of natural areas and factors in their development. Ecol. Monog. 17:185–200.

CLEMENTS, F. E. 1905. Research methods in ecology. 334 pp. Univ. Publ. Co. Lincoln, Nebr.

―――. 1916. Plant succession, an analysis of the development of vegetation. Carnegie Inst. Wash. (D.C.) Publ. 242:1–512.

―――. 1928. Plant succession and indicators: A definitive edition of plant succession and plant indicators. 453 pp. H. W. Wilson. New York.

―――. 1936. Nature and structure of the climax. Jour. Ecol. 24:252–284.

―――. 1949. Dynamics of vegetation. Selections from the writings of F. E. Clements, compiled and edited by B. W. ALLRED and E. S. CLEMENTS. 296 pp. H. W. Wilson. New York.

―――― AND V. E. SHELFORD. 1939. Bio-ecology. 425 pp. Wiley. New York.

CONARD, H. S. 1939. Plant associations on land. Amer. Midland Nat. 21:1–27.

COOPER, W. S. 1926. The fundamentals of vegetational change. Ecology 7:391–413.

CULBERSON, W. L. 1955. The corticolous communities of lichens and bryophytes in the upland forests of northern Wisconsin. Ecol. Monog. 25:215–231.

CURTIS, J. T., AND R. P. MCINTOSH. 1951. An upland forest continuum in the prairie-forest border region of Wisconsin. Ecology 32:476–496.

DANSEREAU, P. 1954. Climax vegetation and the regional shift of controls. Ecology 35:575–579.

DU RIETZ, G. E. 1921. Zur methodologischen Grundlage der modernen Pflanzenso-ziologie. 267 pp. Holzhausen. Vienna.

———. 1929. The fundamental units of vegetation. Proc. Internatl. Congr. Plant Sci., Ithaca, 1926, 1:623–627.

———. 1936. Classification and nomenclature of vegetation units 1930–1935. Svensk Bot. Tidskr. 30:580–589.

EGLER, F. E. 1942. Vegetation as an object of study. Philos. of Sci. 9:245–260.

———. 1951. A commentary on American plant ecology, based on the textbooks of 1947–1949. Ecology 32:673–695.

ELLENBERG, H. 1950. Landwirtschaftliche Pflanzensoziologie. I. Unkrautgemein-schaften als Zeiger für Klima und Boden. 141 pp. Eugen Ulmer. Stuttgart.

———. 1954. Zur Entwicklung der Vegetationssystematik in Mitteleuropa. Angew. Pflanzensoz. [Wien], Festschr. Aichinger 1:134–143.

GAMS, H. 1918. Prinzipienfragen der Vegetationsforschung. Ein Beitrag zur Be-griffsklärung und Methodik der Biocoenologie. Vrtljschr. Naturf. Gesell. in Zürich 63:293–493.

GLEASON, H. A. 1917. The structure and development of the plant association. Bull. Torrey Bot. Club 44:463–481.

———. 1926. The individualistic concept of the plant association. Bull. Torrey Bot. Club 53:7–26.

———. 1939. The individualistic concept of the plant association. Amer. Midland Nat. 21:92–110.

GOODALL, D. W. 1954. Vegetational classification and vegetational continua. (Germ. summ.) Angew. Pflanzensoz. [Wien], Festschr. Aichinger 1:168–182.

HALE, M. E., JR. 1955. Phytosociology of corticolous cryptogams in the upland forests of southern Wisconsin. Ecology 36:45–63.

KLAPP, E. 1949. Landwirtschaftliche Anwendungen der Pflanzensoziologie. 56 pp. Eugen Ulmer. Stuttgart.

——— ET AL. 1954. Die Grünlandvegetation des Eifelkreises Daun und ihre Bezie-hung zu den Bodengesellschaften. Angew. Pflanzensoz. [Wien], Festschr. Aichinger 2:1106–1144.

KNAPP, R. 1948. Einführung in die Pflanzensoziologie. I. Arbeitsmethoden der Pflan-zensoziologie und Eigenschaften der Pflanzengesellschaften. 100 pp. Eugen Ulmer. Stuttgart.

LENOBLE, F. 1926. À propos des associations végétales. Bull. Soc. Bot. France 73: 873–893.

———. 1928. Associations végétales et espèces. Arch. Bot. [Caen] 2(Bull. Mens. 1):1–14.

LIPPMAA, T. 1931. Pflanzensoziologische Betrachtungen. Acta Inst. et Horti Bot. Univ. Tartu 2(3/4):1–32.

LIPPMAA, T. 1933. Aperçu général sur la végétation autochtone du Lautaret (Hautes-Alpes) avec des remarques critiques sur quelques notions phytosociologiques. (Estonian summ.) Acta Inst. et Horti Bot. Univ. Tartu 3(3):1–108.

MALIN, J. C. 1956. The grassland of North America: Its occupance and the challenge of continuous reappraisals. *In* Man's role in changing the face of the Earth, ed. by W. L. THOMAS, pp. 350–366. Univ. Chicago Press. Chicago.

MASON, H. L. 1947. Evolution of certain floristic associations in western North America. Ecol. Monog. 17:201–210.

MEUSEL, H. 1939. Die Vegetationsverhältnisse der Gipsberge im Kyffhäuser und im südlichen Harzvorland. Ein Beitrag zur Steppenheidefrage. Hercynia 2: 1–372.

———. 1940. Die Grasheiden Mitteleuropas. Versuch einer vergleichend-pflanzengeographischen Gliederung. Bot. Arch. [Leipzig] 41:357–418, 419–519.

———. 1943. Vergleichende Arealkunde. Berlin. (Fide Walter 1954b.)

MULLER, H. J. 1952. The uses of the past; profiles of former societies. 394 pp. Oxford Univ. Press. New York. 1954. 384 pp. Mentor. New York.

PALMGREN, A. 1929. Chance as an element in plant geography. Proc. Internatl. Congr. Plant Sci., Ithaca, 1926, 1:591–602.

PHILLIPS, J. 1934–35. Succession, development, the climax, and the complex organism; an analysis of concepts. Parts I–III. Jour. Ecol. 22:554–571; 23:210–246, 488–508.

POORE, M. E. D. 1955. The use of phytosociological methods in ecological investigations. III. Practical application. Jour. Ecol. 43:606–651.

RAMENSKY, L. G. 1924. Die Grundgesetzmässigkeiten im Aufbau der Vegetationsdecke. (Russian) Wjestn. opytn. djela Woronesch. 37 pp. (Bot. Centbl., N.F. 7:453–455, 1926.)

RAUP, H. M. 1956. Vegetational adjustment to the instability of the site. Paper given at meetings of Amer. Inst. Biol. Sci., Storrs, Conn., Aug. 28, 1956.

SCHMID, E. 1942. Über einige Grundbegriffe der Biocoenologie. Ber. Geobot. Forschungsinst. Rübel, Zürich 1941:12–26.

SCHMITHÜSEN, J. 1950. Das Klimaxproblem, vom Standpunkt der Landschaftsforschung aus betrachtet. Mitt. der Florist.-Soziol. Arbeitsgemeinsch. [Stolzenau/Weser] N.F. 2:176–182.

TANSLEY, A. G. 1920. The classification of vegetation and the concept of development. Jour. Ecol. 8:118–149.

———. 1935. The use and abuse of vegetational concepts and terms. Ecology 16:284–307.

WALTER, H. 1954a. Klimax und zonale Vegetation. Angew. Pflanzensoz. [Wien], Festschr. Aichinger 1:144–150.

———. 1954b. Einführung in die Phytologie. III. Grundlagen der Pflanzenverbreitung. II. Teil: Arealkunde. 246 pp. Eugen Ulmer. Stuttgart.

——— AND E. WALTER. 1953. Einige allgemeine Ergebnisse unserer Forschungsreise nach Südwestafrika 1952/53: Das Gesetz der relativen Standortskonstanz; das Wesen der Pflanzengemeinschaften. Ber. Deutsch. Bot. Gesell. 66:228–236.

WANG CHI-WU. 1956. A paleoecological interpretation of the eastern forests of North America. Paper given at meetings of Amer. Inst. Biol. Sci., Storrs, Conn., Aug. 28, 1956.

WEAVER, J. E., AND F. E. CLEMENTS. Plant ecology. (1st ed., 1929) 2d ed., 520 pp. McGraw-Hill. New York. 1938.

WHITTAKER, R. H. 1951. A criticism of the plant association and climatic climax concepts. Northwest Sci. 25:17–31.

———. 1952. A study of summer foliage insect communities in the Great Smoky Mountains. Ecol. Monog. 22:1–44.

———. 1953. A consideration of climax theory: The climax as a population and pattern. Ecol. Monog. 23:41–78.

———. 1954. Plant populations and the basis of plant indication. (Germ. summ.) Angew. Pflanzensoz. [Wien], Festschr. Aichinger 1:183–206.

———. 1956. Vegetation of the Great Smoky Mountains. Ecol. Monog. 26:1–80.

18

BOTANISTS AND THE CONSERVATION OF NATURAL RESOURCES

Paul B. Sears

North America has no monopoly on the need for conservation practices or on their exercise. In parts of the Old World the capacity of environment has been lowered almost beyond restoring. Elsewhere excellent patterns have been developed under the spur of necessity, either by authority or by common consent as in Switzerland. In South America Brazil affords an example of an immensely rich environment now being exploited with little or no regard for consequences. But in the United States we see a vast and varied modern nation built up through rapid levies on its resources, yet showing increasing concern to rationalize matters before it is too late.

In some respects, then, the conservation movement, like the Botanical Society of America, is a household affair. The term conservation itself was brought into popular usage largely by Gifford Pinchot and his associates, who defined it as "the greatest good for the greatest number for the longest time." True, he looked for his model to Europe, where sound practice, sanctioned by custom, had come to be based on science. But the problem here was to challenge and modify, with the aid of science, an economy in which science was being applied very largely to the depletion of resources and the disruption of natural processes. It was Pinchot's achievement to be politically effective, a privilege largely denied to his precursors.

Plant life is such an essential resource, and so intimately a part of most resource problems, that it is rather surprising to find few botanists conspicuous in the early phases of the conservation movement. This sounds worse than it was, for there were not many American botanists during the 19th century and the naturalists such as Powell, Muir, and Thoreau who gave good account of themselves usually had a creditable knowledge of botany. William Bartram noted the decline of fish along the Eastern seaboard and expressed concern over the rapid destruction of nature, even in Revolutionary days.

359

But if we add up the score, including Powell and Muir with van Hise, the geologists come off with the pioneer honors.

Two botanists, Hough and Gray, were on the committee of nine appointed by the American Association for the Advancement of Science at its Hartford Meeting in 1873 to memorialize Congress and the several state legislatures upon the importance of promoting the cultivation of timber and the preservation of forests and to recommend proper legislation for securing these objectives.

This committee made some sound recommendations, but the rape of the Lake States forests was getting under way, and only a few prairie state Congressmen seem to have supported the proposal. Had even the most rudimentary measures been adopted to protect seedlings of that year, vast areas of what is now wasteland would be yielding merchantable 83-year-old trees.

Botany was represented by Charles E. Bessey on a second committee of four, appointed at the Toronto meeting in 1891 to report at Indianapolis the following year. This report not only dealt with forestry, but recommended the adoption of careful scientific procedure in managing resources to sustain the growing economy of the United States. The chairman of this committee was the physicist T. C. Mendenhall, an able negotiator. At a meeting which Bessey could not attend, it was decided to junk the general resource measure and concentrate on forestry. The efforts of this committee, collaborating with the American Society of Foresters, resulted in action by President Harrison. The first reserve set aside was Yellowstone Park, and in 1899 Aven Nelson of Wyoming secured free transportation from the Union Pacific Railroad for his party, team, and wagon, to make a botanical survey of that area.

Meanwhile Bessey at Nebraska began directing the attention of his students toward the two great natural plant resources—forest and grassland. Under his auspices a small and short-lived but excellent school of forestry was organized. From it came distinguished leadership in forest research, thanks to the high standard of academic and scientific training its graduates had received. This fact deserves to be underscored at a time when technical schools of various kinds are so insistent upon "practical" and specialized curricula.

So far as grassland is concerned, the record is even more impressive when we consider the work of Shantz, Clements, Pool, Weaver, Arthur Sampson, and Hanson, all of them students of Bessey. If the fundamental studies of this group were being applied to the economy of our great interior grasslands with a measure of the thoroughness that industry exhibits in applying the physical sciences, we might have a healthy and balanced condition instead of the present chaotic waste (Hewes and Schmiedling, 1956).

On a smaller but significant scale other botanists have contributed to the solution of resource problems within their local areas. In Iowa, Pammel and later Dr. Ada Hayden did much to encourage the protection of natural areas. Cowles likewise took a leading part in setting aside the Cook County preserves in the Chicago region and in encouraging a measure of protection of the celebrated dune region. Deam, an amateur botanist to whom we owe what Fernald called the best of our state floras, was instrumental in establishing the excellent system of state forests and parks in Indiana.

But one may search the early membership of the Botanical Society and scan its proceedings without much evidence of great concern over natural resources. This reflects no discredit upon the distinguished scholars who composed it. They had enough on their minds as it was, being but a handful operating on a vast continent, while across the Atlantic a profound revolution was taking place in their discipline.

In his presidential address in 1900 Underwood cites the changes of twenty-five years, beginning with the time when there was, practically speaking, only one botanist in the United States (Underwood, 1900). Previous to 1895 it was almost necessary for botanists to receive their training in Europe. Within a decade this situation was changed, in large measure through the leadership of Harper, Coulter, and Bessey and the lively atmosphere generated by a group of individualists at Harvard.

Economic opportunities for botanists were increasing rapidly at the same time, because of the expansion of state universities and agricultural colleges and of the research and regulatory work of the Department of Agriculture. Botany ceased to be merely an ornament in the female curriculum and a perfunctory part of the training of such physicians and druggists as attended college.

Not only were botanists being produced to supply the need for teachers and government workers, but their training was of greater breadth and higher quality than it had been. In the research laboratories respectable, often distinguished, additions were being made to the new morphology and physiology imported from the Old World. There was notable activity in genetics, cytology, and pathology. And while the almost exclusive interest in taxonomy declined, Americans carried on their full share of exploration and monographic work while making substantial contributions toward basic taxonomic theory (Bessey, 1897).

These advances and the brilliant developments which came in the succeeding half century must all be reckoned as essential to conservation, since they have given us a clearer understanding of an essential natural resource, plant life. At least one study made during the first decade of the 20th century had vital implications for conservation. This was the work of the British plant physiologist Blackman (1905) on limiting factors. His basic idea was not new, having been expressed long before in Liebig's Law of the Minimum and, still earlier, applied empirically to mankind by Franklin and Malthus.

No inference could be clearer from our present biological knowledge than the fact that organisms must come to terms with the limitations of a finite environment. Yet we find little evidence in the prevailing mores, so amazingly responsive to other findings of science, that this inference is valid, let alone understood or appreciated.

For the most direct and explicit contribution of botany to conservation we must turn to the science of ecology, with its vigorous developments beginning around the turn of the century. Conservation is an application of ecology in the same sense that engineering represents applied physical and mathematical science. And while the ecology in question is general, embracing man, other animals, and plants, there are both historical and practical reasons for emphasizing the importance of plant ecology in this connection.

The pioneer work of Warming and Schimper was caught up and carried on by two institutions little hampered by set patterns of botanical interest— Chicago and Nebraska (Sears, 1956). Pound and Clements' *Phytogeography of Nebraska* with its strong floristic accent appeared in 1898, Cowles' *Physiographic Ecology of Chicago and Vicinity* in 1901. In 1901 also at the Denver meeting of the Botanical Society of America, a youthful Clements presented 5 (out of a total of 12 papers on the program) reports to that austere and select body, then numbering 31 members and 17 associates, including Clements. One dealt with the Plant Formations of the Rocky Mountains, others with the Fundamental Phenomena of Vegetation, the Physical Bases of Ecology, a System of Nomenclature for Ecology, and the Application of Ecology in Taxonomy.[1]

If one may indulge in a bit of psychological reconstruction, based upon many small clues and reasonable probabilities, the net effect of this pioneering exercise was less than it should have been. At any rate, during the next six years there were a few papers, mostly by Clements and Cowles, but little sign of general interest until the Chicago meeting of 1907, when Ecology was well represented. At the Baltimore meeting in 1908 when the Society numbered 96 members and 48 associates, there was a symposium on Ecology. Its intellectual quality should have been enough to bring Ecology out of the doghouse, but this was not to be. As a consequence of continuing rebuffs during the next seven years, the ecologists felt obliged to organize their own Ecological Society of America at the Columbus meeting in 1915. This I have been assured (for I find no written record) they did reluctantly, after their efforts to establish a section within the society had proved fruitless.

The move was probably inevitable, however. At the time it permitted the plant ecologists to join forces with the nascent group of animal ecologists. The combination later viewed the rising interest in human ecology with some of the same coolness that it had itself experienced. It also encountered some

[1] I am indebted to Professor Transeau for the reminder that E. W. Hilgard deserves an early and honored place in American ecology. Certainly his magnificent work on the relation of soils to native vegetation justifies this opinion, regardless of labels. Hilgard was a product of the great European universities. Both his teaching and research displayed broad mastery of the sciences.

of the problems of fission which its formation had exemplified. Groups such as foresters, agronomists, and limnologists, whose interests are fundamentally ecological, have found it expedient to withdraw more and more into their especial spheres.

From 1916 on, the parent Botanical Society began holding joint sessions with the Ecological Society. The first evidence of interest in Conservation was an endorsement in 1919 of the Save-the-Redwoods League. Then at the Chicago meeting in 1920 resolutions were passed reflecting an attitude which has persisted and intensified since. The work of the Ecological Society in preserving natural conditions was endorsed, and support of the National Research Council requested. A study of the effect on native species of the clear-cutting of roadsides (now, thanks to weed sprays, an even more serious problem) was urged, and an inquiry into the relation of drainage of upland marshes to floods was recommended, along with an examination of the biological importance of those marshes.

Certainly it is safe today to assume that the vast majority of botanists, officially and individually, are concerned about the conservation of natural resources. But concern is one thing, effective action another. It seems advisable, therefore, to consider the problem of conservation itself.

The meaning of conservation is not a simple matter. If we define it as "wise use," we are dealing in subjective and qualitative terms. Neither wisdom nor utility can be measured impersonally or absolutely. There is a concept of wise use quite prevalent that practically eliminates the usual doctrine of conservation. This is the belief that an expanding and accelerating economy must be served at whatever cost in resources, since science will find ways and means to keep the process going. In sharp contrast to this is the idea that we have an ethical obligation to remote generations, so that resources, like river water under British law, will reach those downstream in amount undiminished and quality unimpaired.

And finally resources are not limited to the physical entities, renewable and nonrenewable, that supply us with needed materials and energy. As resources we should include many processes and relationships in nature, for conservation is in fact concerned not only with problems of *depletion*, but those of *disruption* as well. There is also concern in many quarters to conserve facilities and conditions whose values are intangible—historical, scientific, ethical, and aesthetic.

A somewhat more than cautious, considerably less than middle, ground is that of the economic forecasters, who feel that they have trouble enough in trying to look ahead twenty-five or fifty years at most. Population estimates made in 1935 have been upset. The consumption of nonrenewable resources has been accelerated, with the United States now absorbing more than half the world production of minerals. The rest of the world is eager to follow our pattern of industrialization, a high proportion of the world's people are on low rations, and we continue to produce surplus food and fiber at the cost of depleted soils. Small wonder that the professional economist wants no more trouble than he has.

One thing, however, seems clear. Unless we accept without reservation the ideal of an economy that expands continuously and without limit, some degree of conservation is necessary. Given this premise, the aims of applied science must shift accordingly. Instead of being directed mainly toward speeding up the conversion of raw materials, they must take into account problems of perspective and equilibrium. Such problems are not unfamiliar to the biologist, plant and animal, and are peculiarly ecological.

In a program of this kind it is up to the sciences, physical and biological, to furnish a sound background of facts and principles to be used in the formulation and execution of policy (Sears, 1955). Policy is made by political and social processes. Social science has now developed to the point where it can be of tremendous value in this connection, but empiricism, art, and philosophy shape the decisions, and authority executes them. In our society authority is assumed to rest upon consensus. For this reason the duty of the scientist does not end when he has obtained the facts and derived principles. He must see that they are translated and widely known.

Such, then, are the broad general conditions under which the specific science, botany, seems to me to relate to conservation. If now we follow Sarton and others in agreeing that the roots of science are very ancient, what does the record show?

It certainly shows that as a primitive hunter and gatherer, the human being tested the qualities of the plant kingdom with remarkable thoroughness. This is reflected in the familiar statement that no important food, fiber, or drug plant was unknown to man before the beginnings of recorded history, to say nothing of modern science. One need search no further than the lists of useful plants of the Plains Indians compiled by Gilmore, or Castetter's studies in the Southwest, to be impressed, while adventuring with traditional cuisine in Mexico is an experience for both mind and palate.

Although the gatherers did lay a foundation for the ultimate domestication of plants, it is known that cultures vary widely in their skill at observing and working with plant life. Some have a surprisingly complete system of plant nomenclature, along with a knowledge of field characters and habitats. Others have no more discrimination than implied by our terms "tree," "bush," "weed," or "grass." Correspondingly, there is a wide range of difference in the attention and care given new plant material brought in philanthropically to strengthen the economic base. Some cultures will eat it out of hand, others plant it casually and consume the results without much thought of succeeding years. Still others will accord it the grave respect and efficient handling it should have.

The pile of tiny corncobs in Bat Cave, above the San Augustin Plains in western New Mexico, represents a span of about five thousand years. Yet to the ordinary observer there is less evidence of selective improvement from bottom to top than might have been possible in less than fifty growing seasons. Incidentally, the great lake which once lay below Bat Cave has now dried up, and the alluvial fans which were once maize fields now have a cover of short and mid-grasses. Other cultures in the area, many of whose sites have been studied by the Field Museum, postdate the Bat Cave people and are at higher altitude where springs were available. A similar phenomenon occurred within the Basin of Mexico, circa 500 B.C., when the lakes dried down and human activity shifted to higher altitude at Teotihuacan. Whether modern man can override the limitations of environment or not, their effects upon simpler cultures whose demands were much more modest are clear.

The course and consequences of domestication are too involved for more than brief mention. Domestication of plants made possible leisure and urbanization and placed in man's hands for the first time sufficient potential to disrupt natural processes to a serious degree. The domestication of plants and animals gave rise to competitive types of land use which are still with us in aggravated form. The recent chapters by Weaver and Albertson (1956) on *The Mixed Prairie* contains a mass of data pertinent to this problem. The evidence indicates clearly that moderate grazing represents the most effective economic use of our semi-arid grasslands, and indeed was a normal factor in natural grasslands. It further shows that the varied composition of these grasslands gives them a resilience to the vicissitudes of an extreme climate, to fire, and to biotic episodes that is quite lacking in any kind of monoculture. Only the plow is truly lethal.

But the data also reveal the extent and degree of damage caused by over-grazing of areas that have not been plowed. From this one may infer the loss in moral and economic advantage that handicaps the grazing industry in its efforts to arrest the spread of its destructive rival, agriculture. Granting all the difficulties and hazards of the livestock industry—many of which are familiar to the writer through firsthand experience—it is an interesting fact that this phase of private enterprise often resents the suggestions of competent scientists regarding proper treatment of its basic resource, the range. This attitude at a time when industry is bidding against government and itself for the services of scientists and engineers suggests that in conservation the botanist has a considerable job of education to do.

Conservation rests on a tripod—scientific knowledge, ethical commitment, and action to produce social change. Any botanist who adds competently to our understanding of plant life makes his contribution. To the degree that he becomes aware of the context of his work in the broad perspective of nature he is likely, in my observation, to become sensitive to the ethical obligations of man toward environment. Beyond this, he is often a teacher, and always a citizen. In both roles he encounters moral as well as technical obligations, for he is involved in a human relationship with opportunity to influence the culture of which he is a part.

So far as teaching is concerned, the situation improves steadily. Every shift of emphasis, from the original taxonomy through evolutionary morphology, genetics, physiology, and ecology, tends to leave its residue although creating problems for skillful synthesis. Perhaps least adequately handled at present is ecology, often introduced as an appendage rather than as a vivifying and unifying means of perspective. Perhaps the very disadvantage which botany suffers in competition with other sciences whose relation to our present economy *seems* more obvious may in the end be a help rather than a handicap. Arts (of which teaching is one of the greatest) thrive best when struggling against limitations.

And as a citizen, the botanist can serve well without engaging in the uncongenial and distracting role of evangelism. Most communities drift into resource problems simply because no one really knows what is going on. This applies to the flood problem in New England, pasture and woodlot deterioration in the Midwest, erosion, siltation, and salinity increase in New Mexico, and countless other situations, including land misuse due to the current spread of urbanization.

It is here that the botanist, in his traditional role as naturalist and student of process, can make himself indispensable. Trained to observe the landscape, he need not shout his findings from the housetop. Ordinary conversation with his fellow citizens, and demonstration when it seems necessary, are remarkably effective. All that is necessary is to respect an old rule, "Never underestimate the other man's intelligence, nor overestimate his information."

LITERATURE CITED

A.A.A.S. Summarized Proceedings, 21st and 39th meetings. Bot. Soc. Am. Publ. Nos. 6, 15, 17, 32, 38, 76, 79.

BESSEY, C. E. 1897. Phylogeny and taxonomy of angiosperms. Bot. Gaz. 24:145–178.

BLACKMAN, F. F. 1905. Optima and limiting factors. Ann. Bot. 19:281–295.

HEWES, L., AND A. C. SCHMIEDLING. 1956. Risk in the central Great Plains. Geogr. Rev. 46:375–387.

SEARS, P. B. 1955. Science and policy. Science 121, No. 3148 (editorial).

––––––. 1956. Some notes on the ecology of ecologists. Sci. Monthly 83:22–27.

UNDERWOOD, L. M. 1900. The last quarter: A reminiscence and an outlook. Science II, 12:161–170.

WEAVER, J. E., AND F. W. ALBERTSON. 1956. Grasslands of the Great Plains. IX + 394. Johnsen Publ. Co. Lincoln, Nebr.

19

SOIL-PLANT RELATIONSHIPS
AND PLANT NUTRITION

A. G. Norman

THE SOIL ENVIRONMENT. Although it has been established beyond all doubt that higher plants can be successfully grown to maturity in the entire absence of soil if the root system is immersed in a nutrient solution composed of certain inorganic salts, the fact remains that soil is the normal root environment. Furthermore, the direction of evolutionary adaptation of plant roots must have been toward accommodation to the nutritional and physical environment provided by soils. It would be unwise to assume that in water-culture or nutrient-culture solutions higher plants necessarily find optimum conditions for growth. However, the use of such solution cultures has been of great value in determining which inorganic ions are essential for the welfare of the plant, and in particular in ascertaining those needed only in minute amounts. Solution-culture systems have been particularly helpful in establishing and recognizing symptoms of deficiency or unbalance of particular nutrients, because such symptoms can then be employed diagnostically on soils in which these nutrients may be in poor supply or unavailable. Public interest was aroused a decade or so ago in the practical use of soilless-culture systems for the growth of flowers and vegetables. These went under a variety of names, such as "nutriculture," "hydroponics," etc. Although there are circumstances in which these may offer advantages over culture in soil, this usually arises from some factor not directly related to the growth or fruitfulness of the plant.

In addition to providing proof of the essentiality of particular nutrient ions, solution-culture methods have made it certain that higher plants have no requirement for organic substances for optimum growth, that they are not directly dependent on the mineral particles that constitute much of the solid phase of soils, and that micro-organisms, though ordinarily present in great numbers on root surfaces, are not essential for growth. There is a danger, however, in generalizing too broadly from such conclusions. One cannot safely assume from such experiments that under natural conditions in soil soluble organic substances present in the root zone may not enter the plant, or that there may not be interactions of nutritional importance between the surface of roots and mineral particles, or that micro-organisms in the close vicinity of roots are not involved in activities that affect plant growth. It has to be concluded, therefore, that plant physiological studies in nutrient solutions have certain limitations and that conclusions as to uptake mechanisms, etc., drawn therefrom, though wholly applicable to such circumstances, may not be completely valid or exclusively operate in the case of roots in soil.

PLANT REQUIREMENTS. Plants have the capacity of synthesizing a bewildering array of organic compounds, many of great complexity. Some of the pathways of synthesis and interconversion are now becoming known. The effectiveness of the total operation, the total dry matter synthesized, or the size and fruitfulness of the plant, all are as dependent in ordinary circumstances on the quality of the soil and the nutritional and physical environment which it provides for the root system, as on factors such as light, carbon dioxide supply, and equable temperatures that bear directly on the photosynthetic areas of the plant.

What does the soil provide that is essential to optimum plant growth? First, inorganic nutrient ions; second, water; and third, oxygen. For optimum growth an adequacy of each is necessary at all times; periods of inadequacy cannot usually be compensated for later and are likely therefore to be reflected in a reduction of total seasonal growth.

It is difficult to express plant requirements for nutrients on a meaningful basis except in terms of soil area. In table 1 are given the quantities of the

Table 1. Quantities of some nutrient elements in an acre planting of certain crops [a]

Crop	Yield	N lb.	P lb.	K lb.	Ca lb.	Mg lb.	S lb.
Corn	60 bu.	93	17	55	17	7	11
Oats	50 bu.	44	7	33	10	4	7
Wheat	25 bu.	38	7	19	5	3	6
Soybean	20 bu.	100	12	37	31	20	5
Alfalfa	4 ton	180	19	148	148	30	19
Sweet potatoes	300 bu.	40	7	70	6	10	7
Cotton	1,500 lb.	75	11	45	64	14	12
Sugar beets	15 ton	76	10	50	22	7	5

[a] These figures are the amounts absorbed at different locations by these crops in producing the yields indicated.

major nutrients present in an acre planting of certain crops. As will be discussed later, these amounts may be greater than the minimum requirements, because the content of nutrient elements in plants is related to the supply perhaps more than to the minimum needed. However, these figures are sufficient to indicate that types of land use which involve annual removal of much of the vegetation involve also depletion of the nutrient resources at a substantial rate.

Plant requirements for water can be expressed either on an area basis or in terms of the amount necessary to produce a unit of dry weight. That the growth of plants in great areas of the world is limited by the inadequacy of the rainfall is well known, but the amount required by plants in humid areas is far greater than usually realized. Moreover, relatively short periods of inadequate supply are now recognized to bring about substantial depression in the total seasonal growth if they occur at a critical stage in the growth cycle of the plant. As with nutrients, the quantity of water used to maturity by plants is not necessarily the minimum requirement and is influenced by such factors as air temperatures and humidities. On an area basis the amounts are large. Not infrequently the demand in a summer month may exceed the total rainfall less evaporation for that month, which means that, unless the storage capacity of the soil for water is considerable, there may be a period of inadequate supply. Expressed as weight of water required to produce a unit of dry plant tissue, the figures are also substantial. Some species are more efficient than others in water use, but in general 150–600 pounds of water must be taken up and transpired for each pound of dry matter synthesized. Water is by far the most important plant nutrient quantitatively, and the ability of different soils to supply water greatly influences the array of native vegetation and the selection of crops and crop varieties that can be profitably grown when the land is farmed.

The requirements of plant roots for oxygen cannot be expressed in the same way as the requirements for nutrients or water, though for most species there is no question as to essentiality. Oxygen is needed to maintain aerobic cellular processes in root tissues, and although small amounts of oxygen can reach the roots of some species from the tops through internal air spaces, the major source is from the soil atmosphere. Many attempts have been made to determine the composition of the soil atmosphere, and some objections have been raised to most of the procedures used, but even so it appears probable that ordinarily the soil atmosphere does not differ greatly from the air above in amounts of the major components. The salient difference is that the oxygen content may be a little lower, and the carbon dioxide content appreciably higher, than in normal air. That the differences are not greater is due to the rapidity of gaseous diffusion and the continuous process of equilibration between the soil atmosphere and the infinitely large reserve in the air above. This means that the porosity of a soil really determines the oxygen supply to the roots and that oxygen deficiencies are only likely in soils of low porosity or where the pores are filled with water to such an extent that gaseous diffusion is greatly hindered. Whereas air contains about 21 per cent oxygen, no adverse effects due to oxygen deficiency seem to develop in most species until the oxygen content of the root atmosphere is reduced to 5 per cent or less, if the carbon dioxide content is not excessive. Soil physicists have given much thought to the problem of expressing the capacity of a soil to supply oxygen to plant roots. The total pore space alone is not a satisfactory measure because the size and distribution of the pores determine the degree of "aeration" of a soil at different moisture levels. A fine-textured soil will have a greater pore space than a coarse sandy soil, but would not necessarily provide a better root environment in so far as oxygen supply is concerned. In the field aeration is largely determined more by the degree of aggregation of the individual soil particles into larger structural units than by the size distribution of the component soil particles. Much of the interest in soil conditioners arises from the improved aeration that can result if the extent of aggregation of fine-textured soils is increased.

MICRO-ORGANISMS IN SOIL. If, then, the soil environment is one from which the plant derives nutrient ions, water, and oxygen, how does it differ from an aerated water culture in which are present soluble salts supplying all the essential nutrient ions that ideally should meet plant requirements? The answer to this question could lead into a discussion of soil chemistry and the forms in which the essential nutrient ions are presented to plant roots. However, it is pertinent at this stage to point out that any definition of soil should include the statement that it is characteristically the habitat for organisms other than higher plants and that soils ordinarily contain extensive and diverse populations of micro-organisms. The soil organisms are indeed potent as soil-forming agents, and higher plants are interlopers in an intensely active and competitive microbiological world. The living component of soils, its microflora and microfauna, constitutes a metabolic pool of nutrients. To a degree higher plants may be said to be dependent on some of the by-products and end products of the activities of micro-organisms in the soil. Plant and animal residues, in or on the soil, are decomposed by micro-organisms. The nutrients which they contain are released for re-use. In nitrogen transformations the soil population plays a vital part, inasmuch as the only reserve of this element in the soil is in the organic form, unavailable to plants until mineralized.

Much more attention has been given to bacteria, fungi, and actinomycetes in soils than to protozoa and the other components of the soil fauna. Quantitative studies of the distribution of bacteria show that millions of organisms are present per gram of top soil. Such figures are often baffling unless it is recognized that a million bacterial cells, 1μ by 0.5μ in size, would have a volume of only 0.0002 mm^3 and that a gram of soil may have a volume of 0.8 cc. and a surface greater than 1 m^2. More important, however, is the fact that the microbial cells are concentrated where there is food. In the vicinity of plant residues, or fragments of organic material, dense colonial growth may occur. Moreover, microbial cells, as they die, themselves form food for other organisms.

It has long been recognized that in the immediate vicinity of plant roots micro-organisms are particularly abundant. Indeed it would be correct to say that plant roots are virtually encompassed by a microbial mantle. The zone immediately adjacent to plant roots, which has been called the rhizosphere, is therefore a zone of intense microbial activity. The organisms present seem often to be qualitatively as well as quantitatively different from those present at a distance from the roots. Furthermore, there is reason to believe that different plant species growing in the same soil do not have identical rhizosphere populations. These organisms presumably develop because soluble organic substances are liberated from plant roots and different species may not liberate the same compounds. In a sense, plants may be said to determine their microbiological associates. In sterile systems a number of amino acids have been identified as coming from plant roots, but the physiology of this phenomenon has not been fully studied. Only from the ubiquity of rhizosphere populations can it be deduced that organic excretions, emanations, or exudations from plant roots are general.

There is no evidence that the rhizosphere population is in any way essential to plant growth. Growth in sterile soil or sterile nutrient solutions is at least as good as in non-sterile environments. However, this does not mean that the presence and activity of the rhizosphere population can be ignored when considering the nutrition of the plant. The microbiology, and presumably therefore the biochemistry, of a cropped soil is quite different from that of a soil free of vegetation.

Some special relationships between soil micro-organisms and plants ought to be mentioned here. The rhizosphere population at times contains pathogenic organisms that can directly injure root tissues. Most organisms of this type are relatively unspecific and cause injury to diverse plant species. The damping-off of seedlings is frequently due to the presence of pathogenic fungi. Root rots may be caused by bacterial invasion.

There are, however, beneficial relationships between soil organisms and plant roots that involve the transfer of nutrients. The best-known and in a sense the least understood of these is the case of the nitrogen-fixing bacteria (rhizobia) which invade and cause nodules to develop on the root system of some leguminous plants and which, by synthesizing an organic nitrogen compound utilizable by the plants, release them from complete dependence on the supply of nitrate in the soil. The mycorrhizal relationship between certain fungi and many forest trees also is believed to affect the supply of one or more nutrients to the plant, the roots of which are invaded or enveloped by mycelial strands. The mycorrhizal association and the symbiotic system in leguminous plants, though beneficial, are not essential. Ecologically they can be of great importance because they may give the respective host plants nutritional advantages over other plants on the same site which lack the capability of entering into these associations. But leguminous plants or normally mycorrhizal tree species, if provided with an ample and complete nutrient supply, will flourish and make optimum growth in the absence of the microbial partner.

NUTRIENT SUPPLIES AND RESERVES. Returning to the question as to how a soil may differ from an aerated solution culture in supplying nutrient ions, water, and oxygen to plant roots, one has to ask in what form the essential nutrients are found in soils. If they are all present in solution in the soil water, then in considering the soil as an environment for plant growth it would only be necessary to study a water extract of soil, or the liquid phase, which is called the soil solution. For many years, indeed, the view prevailed that components on the mineral fraction of soils are slightly water-soluble and that the supply of nutrients is maintained by solubility replenishment. Difficulties, however, arise in this viewpoint. Analyses of soil extracts or of the liquid phase of soils displaced by pressure or other means revealed very low concentrations of even those nutrients taken up in largest amounts. Although it may take 120 pounds of nitrogen per acre to make a 100-bushel corn crop, it is usually the case that on analysis there can only be found present at any one time 1–2 pounds of nitrate per acre. The nitrate level in the soil solution must therefore be renewed many times over in the course of a single season. Similar and even more striking is the situation encountered with phosphate, which is almost always very low in concentration in the soil solution. To account for the total quantity present in a crop a rapid rate of renewal has to be presumed.

The composition of the soil solutions from soils differing greatly in fertility does not fall in line with the growth behavior of plants grown in these soils. Moreover, the quantities of soluble salts found seem to change greatly with the moisture content of the soil, often in an inconsistent manner. In determining the available supply of a particular nutrient in the soil, therefore, the amount present in the soil solution at any one time is not informative. The crux of the situation is the rate of its renewal or replenishment in the soil solution.

Truog has spoken of the soil as a "frugal custodian" of nutrients, and indeed, on reflection, it will be realized that it is well that this is so. If there was a substantial supply of the necessary nutrients in soil in a soluble form, it would be very susceptible to loss by leaching in humid climates. Drainage waters would rapidly carry away nutrient elements as salts in areas where 20–50 or more inches of water annually passes through the soil mass. It is true that there is some loss of plant nutrients from soil by leaching and that soils in warm climates subjected to heavy rainfall become depleted, but even so the composition of the mineral and organic components of soils in general are such that the reserves of essential nutrients are protected against loss by their relative insolubility.

It has been one of the salient objectives of soil chemists to clarify the mechanisms by which unavailable nutrients become available to the plant. This has been a substantial task because the chemistry of each of the essential elements is different, and although there are certain similarities within groups of these elements, each one has had to be tackled as a separate problem. With some understanding of the transformations involved, the soil chemist has attempted to develop relatively simple procedures that provide some measure of the availability, and therefore the probable release rate, of the major essential nutrients and has had some success in devising "quick" tests that can be used to predict whether or not supplementing the supply by use of a fertilizer would be economically advantageous. Wide use is now made of such tests by farm advisers, fertilizer companies, etc.

If the theory of dependence on the soil solution is inadequate to explain nutrient uptake in the soil, what alternative is there? It is believed by soil scientists that cations, or bases, such as calcium, magnesium, or potassium, can be directly exchanged from the surface of soil particles to the surface of a root in contact with it, without the necessity of being present as a salt in the intervening soil solution. Essentially the difference is that in contact exchange the base may be exchanged for hydrogen, whereas in the soil solution an accompanying anion must be present. The experimental proof of the validity of the contact-exchange theory has presented many difficulties. It is not a matter of proving one correct and the other incorrect. Both mechanisms may be operative simultaneously; both may be in equilibrium. The system may be complicated by the presence of micro-organisms, the surface of which similarly may enter into exchange reactions, and the activities of which may add products to the soil solution.

THE CLAY COLLOIDS. Soils are formed by the weathering of the parent rocks, and the process of weathering involves extensive chemical changes. The mineralogical composition of a soil may not be easy to determine, and the proportion of recognizable minerals present, other than quartz, is often not high. The clay component, arbitrarily taken as that fraction less than 2μ in size, is colloidal in character, with a high ratio of surface to mass, and is largely synthesized during the process of weathering. The type of clay depends on the chemistry of the parent rock and the intensity of the weathering processes. Clays are complex insoluble alumino-silicates, the structure of which is built around tetrahedra of aluminum or silicon linked through oxygen or to hydroxyls. They are micro-crystalline in the sense that there is regularity of arrangement in planes, which regularity is not destroyed by isomorphic substitution, consisting of partial replacement in the crystal lattice by other elements. Clays are in effect insoluble acids bearing a negative charge which can be neutralized by hydrogen ions or other cations. In a neutral soil the clay colloids are fully saturated with bases, whereas in an acid soil there is partial hydrogen replacement. It is these cations which are available for exchange with plant roots, and it is the clay complex that constitutes the reserve of these cations.

Several different types of clay colloid have been recognized, and even within a single type there is some range in properties. However, the different types behave as though they were different kinds of insoluble acids. They have different total exchange capacities, and the ease of replacement of various cations retained by them may be different. In equilibrium with an extracting solution, or with plant roots, the partition of exchangeable bases would not be the same. Some of the major differences between soils in physical properties and nutritional properties are explicable only on the basis of the different types of clay which they contain.

The total exchange capacity of a soil depends primarily on the amount and nature of the clay component. The organic fraction of soils also possesses the property of retaining cations by attachment to carboxyl and hydroxyl groups, and in soils of high organic content the fraction of the total exchange capacity due to the organic matter may exceed that due to the clay. Examples of the exchange capacity of some representative soils are given in table 2.

Table 2. Cation-exchange capacities of some representative surface soils

	Exchange capacity, m.e./100 g.
Cass Sandy Loam, Nebraska	5.7 [a]
Wabash Silty Clay Loam, Nebraska	16.8 [a]
Marshall Silty Clay Loam, Nebraska	17.1 [a]
Sharpsburg Silty Clay Loam, Nebraska	21.5 [a]
Crete Silty Clay Loam, Nebraska	22.6 [a]
Pima Clay Loam, Arizona	40.5 [b]
Mohave Sandy Clay Loam, Arizona	18.5 [b]
Tucson Sandy Loam, Arizona	9.7 [b]
Laveen Sandy Loam, Arizona	6.4 [b]
Davidson Loam, North Carolina	22.9 [c]
Hiwassee Clay Loam, North Carolina	22.3 [c]
Utuado Sandy Loam, Puerto Rico	10.7 [d]
Mucara Sandy Loam, Puerto Rico	30.9 [d]

[a] LIPPS, R. C., AND L. CHESNIN. 1950. *Soil Sci. Soc. Amer. Proc.* 15:329–333.
[b] FLOCKER, W. J., AND W. H. FULLER. 1956. *Soil Sci. Soc. Amer. Proc.* 20:387–391.
[c] NYUN, M. A., AND S. B. McCALEB. 1955. *Soil Sci.* 80:27–41.
[d] ABRUNA, F., AND R. M. SMITH. 1953. *Soil Sci.* 75:411–420.

The array of bases present in substantial amounts includes calcium, magnesium, potassium, and sodium, usually in descending order quantitatively.

Calcium usually far outweighs the other bases, and calcium and magnesium together may account for 90–95 per cent of the total exchangeable bases. In a soil with a total exchange capacity of 15 milliequivalents per 100 g., with calcium accounting for 60 per cent of the exchangeable bases, there would be 3600 pounds exchangeable calcium per acre to the depth of 6 inches. If potassium accounted for 3 per cent of the exchangeable bases, there would be approximately 350 pounds of exchangeable potassium in the same volume of soil. These amounts are far more substantial in relation to the amounts taken up by an acre planting than are the quantities found in the soil solution at any one time. However, a total analysis of the soil would show much larger amounts of such elements as magnesium and potassium, and although the nonexchangeable form is not directly available to plants, these nutrients are slowly released to replenish the supply of the exchangeable form as this is depleted by continual removal of vegetation. This is particularly important in the case of potassium, which often forms the major inorganic component of plant tissue and yet which is not ordinarily a major exchangeable base. The chemistry of soil potassium indeed presents some unusual features, which have been much studied, because even drying and subsequent wetting of clays has been found to change the partition of potassium between exchangeable and non-exchangeable forms.

Much more could be said about the properties of the clay and organic colloids of soils, but it is sufficient here to indicate that the salient and outstanding difference between soils and nutrient solutions as environments for the growth of plants lies in the form of presentation of cations, the major ones, such as potassium and calcium, and minor ones, such as iron, manganese, zinc, and copper.

However, not all the major nutrient ions are cations. There is yet to be accounted for such ions as nitrate, phosphate, sulfate, and borate. Nitrogen availability in soils ordinarily depends on a sequence of microbiological transformations. The soil nitrogen reserves are wholly organic, and the rate of release therefrom is controlled by the activity of an array of organisms, mostly unspecialized. The primary end product is the ammonium ion, which is retained by clay and organic colloids, as are the other bases, and which can be exchanged with root surfaces and utilized directly by some plants.

However, microbial conversion to nitrate ordinarily takes place; it is usually not possible to find more than a trace of ammonia in soils. The rate-limiting step is the liberation of ammonium from the organic reserve, not the oxidation of ammonium to nitrate. The nitrate ion, accompanied by a cation from the exchangeable bases, is found in the soil solution. It does not appear to be retained in any way by the clay colloids. Soil clays do exhibit anion-exchange reactions, somewhat similar to cation-exchange reactions, but at a lower level quantitatively, and probably of significance only with such anions as phosphate and molybdate. The sulfate and chloride ions, like nitrate, do not enter into exchange with clays, because they are unable to replace lattice hydroxyls.

UPTAKE MECHANISMS IN PLANTS. Up to this point the discussion has dealt primarily with the forms in which the major plant nutrients are present in soils, and hardly at all with the mechanism by which these nutrient ions are taken up by plants. The assumption has been made that, if an essential nutrient ion is present in the root zone, it can readily enter the plant. The mechanism of nutrient uptake has turned out to be a much more difficult problem than was thought earlier to be the case, and although much progress has been made recently, especially through the use of radioisotopic tracers, explanations wholly acceptable to all investigators still remain to be developed. For reasons of simplicity uptake experiments are almost invariably carried out in simple salt solutions, and frequently at ionic concentrations considerably greater than encountered in the soil solution. Such experiments, though informative up to a point, are likely to be incomplete. Furthermore, experiments on uptake carried out with whole plants inevitably also became transport experiments in which it is difficult to separate those processes involved in primary entry from those involved in subsequent movement of the ions that have been taken up.

There are certain generalizations about the uptake of ions by plants that should be made.

1. Ion uptake is selective, but very imperfectly so. Ions are not taken up strictly in proportion to the relative concentrations present in the root environment, nor is uptake limited to those ions that are essential for plant growth. Non-essential ions can be taken up in substantial amounts and may compete with the uptake of essential ions.

2. Essential ion uptake is not related to the immediate or total quantitative requirement of the plant. The amount which enters is greatly influenced by the supply in the environment, not by the needs of the plant. There may be uptake greatly in excess of the requirement for optimum growth. This phenomenon is known as "luxury consumption." Luxury consumption is, however, a relative matter. In practice the supply of one or more critical elements may limit growth; the remainder then may be in the zone of luxury consumption. If the supply of the limiting nutrient is later increased, the circumstance with respect to those formerly in excess may be quickly changed.

3. Ion uptake by different species of plants given the same nutrient environment is often very different quantitatively. This fact has to be accommodated in any theory of the mechanism of uptake.

4. Continued ion uptake and accumulation is a property only of living and respiring roots. If added to a nutrient solution, certain metabolic inhibitors, which halt cellular respiratory processes, will prevent ion uptake, as will withdrawal of oxygen or depression of temperature.

5. The mechanisms of uptake of cations and anions are not identical, nor

are they interdependent. Whereas anion uptake is certainly "active" in the sense that it is an energy-consuming process, there is some controversy as to whether cation accumulation involves the expenditure of energy, though an actively metabolizing cellular system is required.

It has been found recently that some revision of the classical concept of a root is necessary. Instead of picturing the external cells of roots as forming a continuous semi-permeable membrane through which must pass the nutrients, water, and oxygen necessary for plant growth, there is now considerable evidence for the view that an external solution can freely penetrate some parts of the root tissue. This region, accessible by simple diffusion, has been described as the "apparent free space," the "free space," or, somewhat ambiguously, the "outer space." The cells of some micro-organisms have similarly been shown to contain certain areas or space, the liquid in which comes quickly into equilibrium with the external solution. Reversible diffusion studies give information as to the volume of this space in roots. In some roots as much as one-third of the root volume has been shown to be accessible. The most carefully determined value is 23 per cent for the roots of young barley seedlings. This free space has not been defined histologically. The obvious suggestion would be that the free space consists of connecting intercellular spaces forming a ramifying system through the root. There is, however, reason for thinking that the accessible regions may involve some part of the cell cytoplasm.

The importance of this concept of an accessible free space in plant roots is that the liquid in the free space may be that from which all active ion accumulation takes place. However, this liquid may contain soluble substances of cytoplasmic origin, which then would be capable of "leaking" from roots. Those root exudations, or emanations, that provide the substrate for the rhizosphere population may have this origin.

If the liquid in the free space is in equilibrium with that outside the roots, then it might appear that the soil-solution theory would be adequate to account for the nutrition of the plant and that interest in the exchangeable base system of the soil colloids would be limited only to its effect on the concentration of cations in the soil solution with which it would be in equilibrium. This has to be modified, however, because root surfaces are capable of retaining cations and have a measurable and rather high cation-exchange capacity comparable to, but not identical with, that exhibited by the clay and organic colloids of the soil. This cation-exchange capacity can be determined by methods similar to those used for soil or by titrating electrodialyzed plant roots. The basis of expression leaves something to be desired, but the figures in table 3 attest to the activity of root surfaces and to the important fact that the roots of different plant species may vary widely in ability to retain cations. Perhaps it is not coincidence that leguminous plants, which are high accumulators of cations, have roots of high cation-retaining capacity. It is important

Table 3. Cation-retention capacity of plant roots

Species	m.e. per 100 g. dry roots	Species	m.e. per 100 g. dry roots
Soybean	58.9 [a]	Rye	15.1 [a]
Red clover	47.9 [a]	Barley	12.3 [a]
Ragweed	58.9 [a]	Alfalfa	41.4 [b]
Potato	38.1 [a]	Soybean	41.1 [b]
Tomato	34.6 [a]	Redtop	14.1 [b]
Corn	26.0 [a]	Reed canary grass	11.8 [b]
Orchard grass	25.6 [a]	Buckwheat	38.7 [c]
Timothy	22.6 [a]	Oats	18.8 [c]

[a] By electrodialysis and titration. DRAKE, M., J. VENGRIS, AND W. G. COLBY. *Soil Sci.* 72:139–147. 1951.

[b] By electrodialysis and titration. MCLEAN, E. O., AND F. E. BAKER. *Soil Sci. Soc. Amer. Proc.* 17:100–102. 1953.

[c] By electrodialysis and titration. MCLEAN, E. O., AND D. ADAMS. *Soil Sci. Soc. Amer. Proc.* 18:273–275. 1954.

to point out here, however, that the methods used for determining the exchange capacity of roots will include sites throughout the free space, in addition to those on the external surfaces of the roots. Direct-contact exchange of bases on the soil colloids would presumably only be possible with the external surfaces. Root surfaces and clay colloids in contact would come to an equilibrium which would depend on the relative ease of replacement of cations on the two insoluble exchange systems.

The processes of diffusion and cation exchanges are essentially physical and involve no expenditure of energy by the cell. Both will proceed at low temperature or in an inert gas. No ion specificities characteristic of the special requirements of the plant are evident in these steps.

The key process of ion accumulation, which is partially selective and which does involve a metabolic mechanism, has been a recalcitrant problem for the plant physiologist. Its full solution yet awaits further clarification of the biochemical events within plant cells. However, the view which is gaining wide acceptance is that the essential feature in uptake is a binding of the ion with a carrier, the carrier being a compound, perhaps analogous to an enzyme, produced by the cell. Carriers are presumed to exist for both anions and cations and to possess specificity or selectivity for particular ions, but this specificity is not absolute, and ions of other elements chemically related in the periodic table may also be bound. The carrier-ion complex is then presumed to be able to pass through some form of barrier or membrane not permeable to the ion alone. Once in this "inner" space, the ion is again released in an irreversible step. The barrier is considered to be quite impermeable to the free ions because, if an ion is once absorbed, it does not then exchange with an isotopically enriched solution containing the same ion. Such "accumulated" nutrients are not subsequently free to move as long as the cells are active.

The evidence for the existence of ion carriers is wholly indirect. It finds support in kinetic studies and in the parallelism shown with enzyme-substrate mechanisms. The synthesis of the carriers is assumed to be dependent on the respiratory process in the cell, but interactions are suspected, thus complicating the picture; that is, one ion may be essential in the synthesis of a carrier for another ion, or even may constitute a part of the carrier complex for another ion.

This theory calls for the uptake of all ions to be dependent upon metabolically synthesized ion carriers. A more restricted theory links anion uptake with the operation of the cytochrome system and regards cation uptake as incidental by exchange for the hydrogen ions liberated in the cell. Inhibitors of cytochrome oxidase activity quench active uptake, but cellular metabolic processes are so interrelated and interdependent that caution has to be exerted in ascribing specific roles to particular mechanisms.

There still remains much to be clarified in the basic process of nutrient uptake and in accounting for root behavior in the nutritional environment provided by soil. There seems to be some doubt among some plant physiologists as to whether the cation-exchange capacity of roots is of any consequence and whether exchange to such sites constitutes any essential part of the ion-absorption process. Because they lack specificity, the cation-retaining sites of plant roots are not believed to be those involved in active uptake; moreover, some are external and some are internal. Most experimentation on nutrient uptake is carried out using very young seedlings immersed in simple salt solutions containing a large excess of the ion under study. By diffusion the free space rapidly comes into equilibrium, and by exchange the cation-retention sites become extensively filled with the cations supplied. The situation in soil may be very different because there the external sites at least will directly reflect the cation array on the soil colloids; through equilibration this will result in a modification of the composition of the soil solution in immediate contact with the external surface of the roots, and therefore by diffusion that of the solution in the free space.

Ultimately it should be found possible to reconcile and incorporate in a unified scheme the soil-solution theory of plant nutrition in soils and the contact-exchange theory. As with the soil population where that in the immediate vicinity of the roots is recognizably different from that at a distance, so it is likely that the soil solution in the immediate vicinity of roots may be substantially modified by the presence of ions on the surfaces of the root and the micro-organisms thereon. The equilibrium reached is likely to be a complex one between the surfaces of clay and organic colloids, on the one hand, and actively metabolizing root tissues and micro-organisms, on the other.

20

PHYSIOLOGICAL ASPECTS OF AGING IN PLANTS

William J. Robbins

I intend to limit my discussion to seed plants and to consider the aging of seeds, individual plants, cells, and meristems. Well-authenticated information on the physiology of aging in plants is scanty. We can safely say that cells, organs, and individual plants age, but the physiological changes which occur and the causes are ill defined and poorly understood.

Even the definition of age differs. It may be measured from the last gametic reproduction or from the establishment of an individual plant by any means, either gametic or agametic. By the first method of measuring age, a cultivated banana plant would be hundreds, if not thousands, of years old because there is no record of the production of viable seed by the cultivated banana; it is propagated entirely by vegetative means. By the second method its age would be measured in days or months.

Although age is usually expressed in units of time the concept of physiological age, which depends on the condition of the plant rather than on the time it has existed, has proved to be of some value. While I am prepared to admit that a plant is as old as it feels, the difficulty is to determine how it feels. Change in leaf shape has been used in some instances to estimate physiological age. However, since for some plants leaf shape is markedly affected by the external environment and is not determined primarily by the internal condition of the plant, this means of measuring physiological age is of limited application.

SEEDS. The aging of seeds is a special problem within the province of this topic because in this instance we have an embryo plant which lies dormant for various periods of time but eventually loses its vitality if germination fails to occur.

The life span varies with the kind of seed and with the conditions of storage. For example, the viability of embryos in the seeds of some kinds of willow disappears within a week after the seeds have matured. On the other hand, seeds of lotus, *Nelumbo nucifera,* which were estimated to be a thousand years old, on the basis of radio-carbon dating, have been found capable of germinating. The length of life of the seeds of other kinds of plants lies between these extremes. Some, like those of *Hevea,* are short-lived; some are intermediate, retaining their viability for years; others have life spans of a century or more.

From the standpoint of the aim of this discussion, we may ask several questions: Does the embryo in a seed age? Is there a gradual deterioration in the potential vigor of a dormant embryo with time, and does the age of seed affect yield? What are the causes for the loss of viability of seeds? Why does an embryo of one kind of seed live for a period measured in days and that of others for centuries?

Various hypotheses have been explored from time to time on the causes for the loss in the viability of seeds. These include the exhaustion of food reserves, the gradual and spontaneous denaturing of protoplasmic proteins, the deterioration of enzyme systems, and the accumulation of injurious products formed in the metabolism which continues slowly, even in a dormant seed.

One of the notable advances in this area is the demonstration that the frequency of mutations in plants grown from old seeds is, in some instances, greater than can be accounted for by the effects of natural radiation to which the seeds were subjected during the period of storage. These spontaneous mutations apparently occur before seed germination and are associated with structural changes in the chromosomes. Such age-induced mutations have some importance if old seeds are used for propagation and may be of significance in evolution. While they may result through the spontaneous deterioration of chromosomal material, there is some evidence that the chromosomal changes are actually caused by the accumulation of mutagenic substances in the seeds, and it has been suggested that these substances and perhaps others eventually reach a level which destroys the vitality of the embryo, perhaps through their action on the chromosomes. The automutagenic substances and the autotoxins assumed to be responsible for the mutations in old seeds and for the eventual loss of viability have not been identified.

We might expect also a gradual deterioration in the vigor of seed embryos with time. However, the evidence on the correlation of the vigor of plants from seeds of various ages is conflicting. Certainly there is no strict relationship. For many seeds rather wide age limits appear to have little, if any, effect on their performance. The few plants grown from thousand-year-old *Nelumbo* seeds showed no marked reduction in vigor and appeared to be normal.

When we consider the differences between species in the morphology and physiology of their seeds, in their length of life under normal conditions, and in the effects of various storage conditions on survival, it seems probable that no single explanation for the effects of age can be applied to all kinds of seeds. The physiological changes which occur in the aging of seeds offer a profitable area for further research.

INDIVIDUAL PLANTS. Just as seeds vary greatly in length of life, so do individual plants. Annuals live for a few months and die; perennials may live for years, some of them for thousands of years, though parts of them—for example, leaves, flowers, and fruits—age, die, and are discarded.

The aging of annuals and their senescence and death is associated in part with the production of flowers, fruits, and seeds, a condition which exists also for some perennials like the so-called century plant, *Agave americana*. For these plants the prevention of flowering may extend their length of life considerably. The *Agave* in its native habitat blooms and dies within a period of eight or ten years. In less favorable areas, parts of southern Europe for example, it may grow for as much as 100 years before its life span is terminated by flowering.

Loss of magnesium by the chlorophyll, a decrease in ability to retain water with consequent wilting and withering, and other causes for the death of annuals have been suggested, all of which are more probably results of senility than causes. The transfer of food reserves, especially nitrogenous substances to the flowers, fruits, and seeds, with a resulting starvation of the vegetative parts, seems a more likely explanation, though the possibility has not been eliminated that the movement of hormonal-like accessory foods to the floral parts is also involved. There is no adequate explanation which tells us why food reserves move from the vegetative to the floral parts.

Physiological changes of various kinds associated with aging may perhaps occur in an annual plant even before flowering. The root system of some annuals has been reported to be less effective in absorption in the latter part of the growth period, and Frank found a loss of nitrogen in older plants of *Oenothera* and *Arabinopsis* amounting to as much as 30 per cent of the maximum. I am not sure how closely these changes are correlated with the formation of flowers.

Various explanations have been offered for the differences in the length of life of various kinds of trees. These include resistance to decay, decrease in the absorption and conduction of water, changes in photosynthetic power, deterioration of protoplasmic proteins, accumulation of ash, etc.

Last summer, as Mrs. Robbins and I visited Windsor Great Park with Sir Eric Savill, the Estate Manager, I asked him why an English oak lives so much longer than the European beech. He said if I would tell him why a birch lives for 100 years he would tell me why the beech lives for 300 years and an oak may survive for 1000 years or more. This expresses more or less faithfully our inability to assign specific causes for the great differences in the normal length of life of various kinds of trees.

Not only do plants become senescent and die, some of them go through more or less well-defined juvenile and adult stages as a part of their normal ontogeny. This aspect of the aging process may be illustrated by the English ivy, *Hedera helix*.

From seed the ivy grows as a vine with five-lobed leaves in a 2/2 ranking. It is plagiotropic and crawls along the ground, rooting at intervals. If it reaches a wall or tree trunk, it grows up the support, clinging to it with aerial roots. Sooner or later the upper portion of the vine changes in growth habit. Oval leaves with entire margins are produced in a 2/5, 2/6, or 2/7 ranking, the growth is orthotropic, aerial roots are no longer produced, and this portion of the plant blooms and fruits.

Cuttings of the juvenile form of *Hedera* root readily and grow as vines, eventually producing under suitable conditions the adult stage, usually at the top of the plant. Cuttings of the fruiting portion of the plant root less readily, but if rooted, grow as shrubs or small trees and retain the leaf characters and habit of growth of the adult form. The arborescent form flowers and fruits; its seeds yield the juvenile type of growth. All species of *Hedera* have juvenile and adult stages and yield arborescent forms from the fruiting adult shoots by vegetative propagation. The juvenile, or vine, stage of *Hedera* differs so much in appearance from the arborescent form that the two forms might easily be mistaken for different species instead of stages of the same plant.

The arborescent *Hedera* has a considerable degree of stability. I have seen at the Huntington Botanical Garden two arborescent specimens of a variegated form of *Hedera* which are nearly 50 years old; these have never shown any reversion to the juvenile or vine type of growth.

There are five specimens of *Hedera helix* v. *arborescens* at Vilmorin-Andrieux, Verrières, France, three of which are now more than fifty years old. They were started as cuttings of fertile branches and are growing on their own roots. One which I have seen is 8 or 9 feet in height and 15 feet in diameter, a large and vigorous shrub. These arborescent forms are very fruitful, and I am told have never shown any tendency to produce the juvenile form, even from the base. I have also examined a number of old arborescent forms of ivy at the Royal Botanic Gardens at Kew and at Edinburgh, as well as elsewhere.

Instances of spontaneous reversion of the arborescent form to the juvenile condition have been reported, and I have examined a few examples which suggest that reversion may occur, but such reversion is the exception and not the rule.

The creeping fig, *Ficus repens,* also has a juvenile and adult type of growth, and cuttings from the fruiting-stage grow as small shrubs. Some of the aroids respond in a similar manner; the juvenile form has small, short-petioled leaves and grows as a vine clinging closely to its support; with age large pinnatifid leaves are formed; rooted cuttings of the latter develop a more or less erect plant bearing little resemblance to the juvenile state.

Juvenile and adult stages have been distinguished for a number of trees including apples, apricots, pecans, beech, oaks, *Hevea*, and citrus, as well as others. Generally speaking, a seed-grown tree—if it has a distinguishable juvenile stage—is juvenile for some years, but eventually the new peripheral growth is adult, with the result that the tree is then made up of a cone in the juvenile condition enclosed by a zone in the adult condition. The juvenile portion of some trees retains its dead leaves in winter, but the adult parts drop theirs. For such trees, beech and oak, for example, one can frequently see specimens grown in the open which in late autumn or early winter have held their leaves in the interior juvenile portion of the tree but have lost them from the peripheral twigs.

Although seedlings of most types of citrus are thorny, this tendency gradually declines in the peripheral portion of the plant with continued extension of growth. Plants grown from buds taken from the base and inner portion of such a seed-grown tree are thorny, while plants which develop from buds taken from the peripheral portion are likely to be nearly thornless. In other words, the budwood transmits the characters of the portion of the plant from which it is taken and the tree growing from such buds continues to completion the succession of changes which characterize the normal ontogeny of the plant. Budwood from commercial varieties which have been propagated vegetatively for considerable periods yields trees which are virtually thornless.

The situation in citrus, so far as juvenile and adult stages are concerned, appears to be essentially similar to that of a number of other kinds of woody plants. There are juvenile and adult stages which are transmitted through vegetative propagation. Trees grown from seed are thornier, more upright, and symmetrical in habit; are of greater vigor and fruit later and less profusely than trees which have been propagated as clones.

Citrus differs, however, in one notable respect from a number of other woody plants. Citrus seeds frequently contain, in addition to the zygotic embryo, others which are derived from the nucellus. Strasburger (1878) found that the supernumerary embryos arose from the nucellus and traced the chain of events in which nucellar buds penetrated the embryo sac and developed into embryos. The nucellus might be considered to be "adult" tissue since it is located in a part of the plant where budwood would normally yield plants with adult characters. The nucellar embryo could be regarded as a type of vegetative reproduction analogous to a bud, cutting, or scion. We might expect, therefore, that plants from nucellar embryos would skip the juvenile stage and show merely adult characters. However, they have the same juvenile characters as those which develop from zygotic embryos.

Hodgson and Cameron (1938) compared two pairs of paper rind (St. Michael) orange trees, one (young clone) obtained by budding from a nucellar seedling, the other (old clone) by budwood from the tree which had produced the nucellar seedling. After nine years the young clone was more upright and much thornier, especially in the lower part of the tree. The old clone bore two years earlier; the young clone had twice the top volume but less fruit. Frost (1938) reported similar results in a comparison of trees grown from budwood from young nucellar seedlings of old varieties with those developed from buds obtained from ordinary orchard trees.

Frost concluded that the regularly occurring developmental changes were not genetic, were not caused by infectious diseases or by the accumulation of inert material in the cells. He considered that they were temporary but persistent modifications of the meristematic cells; these modifications were transmitted through vegetative propagation and perpetuated for indefinite periods even in rapidly dividing cells. They were erased in the formation of zygotic or nucellar embryos. He suggested that with repeated cell divisions changes might have occurred in important cell proteins. These modified proteins were to some degree self-propagated and were perhaps located in the plastids.

Swingle (1932, 1933) referred to the juvenility of nucellar embryos as an "extraordinary recapitulation of a stage in ontogeny already passed by the generation which furnishes the nucellar buds," considered that the nucellar bud developing in the embryo sac underwent rejuvenation, called the phenomenon "neophysis," and suggested that the cause might be hormone-like substances located in the embryo-sac apparatus.

Various criteria have been used to distinguish between the juvenile and the adult stages. Among these are leaf shape, production of pigment (usually anthocyanin), phyllotaxy, shedding of leaves, ease of rooting of cuttings, thorniness, growth habit, and flowering. The juvenile condition is marked by the production of more anthocyanin, retention of leaves during the winter, greater ease of rooting of cuttings, more thorniness, and lack of flowering. No single kind of plant shows all these distinctions between the juvenile and the adult condition, and no one character is a sure and certain indication that a change from juvenile to adult has occurred. Most authorities consider that the greater ability of cuttings to root is most closely associated with juvenility.

The most striking feature of this phenomenon is that both the juvenile state and the adult are transmitted by vegetative propagation. While vegetatively propagated offspring from the juvenile stage proceed to complete the normal ontogeny, vegetative propagations from adult shoots continue to grow as adult for indefinite periods of time, rarely showing for some kinds of plants spontaneous reversion to the juvenile condition. By gametic reproduction the plant is returned to the juvenile stage.

Of particular interest to the problem of the juvenile and adult stages are the recent results obtained with ivy by Doorenbos and those reported by Frank and Renner. Doorenbos grafted 5-cm. scions of mature branches on rooted cuttings of the juvenile form. The new growth of the adult scions in many instances was juvenile; the effect was more marked if leaves were left on the juvenile stock. No effect was noted for the reverse grafts, namely, juvenile scions on adult stock; the new growth of the juvenile scions was not adult. This suggests that something is transmitted from the juvenile to the adult which induces the meristem of the adult to develop juvenile parts. Pursuing this idea Frank and Renner have reported that when rooted cuttings of the juvenile and adult stages of ivy were grown together in the same bottle containing a mineral nutrient solution, the adult produced juvenile growth. If this is correct, it suggests that the juvenile form of ivy produces substances which are excreted, are absorbed by the adult, and induce it to return to a juvenile condition. Frank and Renner found also that treatment of the adult cuttings with cold or X rays caused rejuvenation.

Beissner and others believed that juvenile meristems could be stabilized. They reported that cuttings of *Thuja, Chamaecyparis,* and *Juniperus* taken from juvenile shoots, especially from those in the axes of the cotyledons, grew into plants with juvenile foliage which, by continued vegetative propagation, became "fixed" juvenile forms. However, Woycicki has recently reported a failure to "fix" juvenile forms of *Thuja* by Beissner's procedure. It is probable that the juvenile forms of *Thuja, Chamaecyparis,* and *Juniperus* are mutants rather than stabilized or fixed forms in Beissner's sense.

I believe that mutations and chimeras can be eliminated as explanations for the adult condition since it occurs regularly in the normal ontogeny of the plant and is not transmitted through the seed. I think we can agree that the origin of the juvenile and adult stages must be looked for in the activity of the apical meristem which changes or is changed, at least functionally, with the age of the plant as measured from the seed in such a way as to produce the adult physiology and morphology.

What causes the changes in the meristem? The explanations which have been offered fall into two more or less clearly marked categories. One assumes that the differentiation of a meristem is determined by the materials which come to it from the balance of the plant. The meristem itself does not change during the life of the plant—it does not age. The morphology and physiology characteristic of the juvenile stage as contrasted with those of the adult result from differences in the quantity and quality of the materials which reach the meristem as the plant ages. Mineral salts, carbohydrates, nitrogenous substances, or growth substances and the balance between them have been suggested at one time or another as the factors which detemine whether a meristem produces juvenile or adult characters.

Another hypothesis assumes that meristems themselves age, that they change during the life of the plant. There are young meristems and adult or old meristems. While the activity of each is affected by the materials which come to it from the balance of the plant, the response to any given substances differs because the juvenile meristem is basically different in character from the adult meristem. Evidence to support each of these viewpoints can be presented. I am not prepared to accept the extreme view of Molisch, which is also held by many practical gardeners, to the effect that meristems not only age but become senile, with the result that the length of life of vegetatively propagated clones is the same as that of the seed-grown parent from which the clones are derived.

Without attempting to deal with ultimate causes or to settle the question of juvenile vs. adult meristems, I suggest as a working hypothesis that juvenility is an unstable metabolic state which exists in the meristem and which proceeds through a series of steps to a relatively stable metabolic-state characteristic of the adult meristem. The change from unstable to stable may be associated with the loss in ability to synthesize physiologically important chemical substances and/or the development of the ability to synthesize others. This means that the meristem of the juvenile stage may be characterized by the presence of particular substances of physiological importance which are not present, or present to an appreciably lesser degree, in the meristem of the adult. The steady state of the adult may be upset in the direction of the unstable metabolism of the juvenile by cold, X rays, products from the juvenile, the formation of adventitious meristems, and by the formation of zygotes or of asexual embryos. If these assumptions are correct, it might be possible to isolate and identify substances from the juvenile stage which, introduced into the adult, would cause it to become juvenile, a possibility which is supported by the results on *Hedera*, by Doorenbos and by Frank and Renner, which I mentioned earlier.

CELLS. For the purpose of our discussion, I am considering cells of the apical meristem to be young cells and those of the mature tissues to be cells which have aged; differentiation is considered to be a part of an aging process. On this basis a number of facts may be pointed out and questions raised on the physiological changes associated with the aging of the cells of a seed plant.

Young cells in the apical meristem divide, and for the sake of simplicity I shall not distinguish between chromosomal division, nuclear division, and cell division, though such distinctions are without question important in a full consideration of aging of cells. The ability to divide is lost as the newly formed cells are left behind the meristematic zone in the process of growth, except for such tissues as the pericycle, cambiums, and buds. We may conclude, therefore, that loss of ability to divide is one of the physiological changes which occurs in the aging of cells, though this loss may not be permanent, as is pointed out below. But why do cells lose their ability to divide? In fact, why are they able to divide in the first place? I do not intend to answer these questions, but there are some facts to which I wish to call attention.

One of the curious characteristics of the young cells of apical meristems is their stability. Apical meristems, the cells of which continue to divide, at least periodically, persist through the life of the plant. Those of the oldest-known trees, for example, have existed for more than four thousand years. Not only does the apical meristem persist for long periods of time, it resists change even though subjected to wide variation in environmental conditions; that is, it does not age in the sense that its cells become adult and the meristem as such disappears even when subjected to considerable ranges of temperature, oxygen supply, and other factors. The only instance I can recall where an apical meristem differentiates into mature cells and disappears as such is the transformation of some stem meristems into flowers.

To avoid confusion I should point out that although apical meristems persist as such for the life of the plant and therefore have an inherent stability, the juvenile meristem is functionally unstable since it is transformed to an adult meristem as the plant ages. A distinction is made, therefore, between the stability of meristems as regions of cell division and their functional instability as they pass from a juvenile to an adult condition.

Although division may be regarded as a distinguishing characteristic of young cells, they may exist for long periods of time without division and still retain the capacity for renewed division. I have referred to embryos of some kinds of seeds which may be dormant for centuries. A similar situation exists for dormant buds and also characterizes the periodicity of cell division in the apical meristems of perennial plants. This is another evidence of the inherent stability of young cells.

While the young cells of the meristem are so stable, they are at the same time extremely sensitive. The displacement of cells in the process of growth for a fraction of a millimeter from the meristematic zone initiates the aging changes which result in their becoming mature or adult cells. The stability of young cells under some conditions and their instability under others is a paradox which I present for your consideration.

Some cells, once they have become adult, also have reached a relatively steady state; they may remain alive and unchanged for long periods of time. Cells in the pith of birch trees have been reported to remain alive for 40 years, and parenchyma cells of the pith of some of the giant cacti for 100 years or more. Other mature cells are short-lived. Those of the petals of *Tradescantia virginica,* for example, degenerate and die a few hours after the flower has opened. It appears, therefore, that in their aging some cells may pass from a relatively steady state characteristic of young cells to another steady state in their maturity.

This process, however, is reversible. Some mature cells under some conditions rejuvenate. Kraus and his associates found indole acetic acid and other auxins to induce mature cells of decapitated bean plants to return to a meristematic condition. Mature and fully differentiated epidermal cells of flax, begonia, and *Crassula* under some conditions become meristematic. Severely defoliated apple trees develop meristematic structures, the sphaeroblasts, by the dedifferentiation of cells of the cortex.

To account for the facts I have presented briefly and inadequately is, of course, to account for one of the most fundamental problems in biology. We may talk of metabolic gradients, polarity, electrical potentials, macromolecular structure, and similar generalities, but their contribution to clarifying the questions in which we are interested is limited unless we can define their relationship in more than general terms.

We know that the metabolism of young cells differs from that of older cells. For example, the apical meristem of the stem produces auxins; the older and distal cells produce little or none. Gibbs and Beevers found immature tissues to respire glucose exclusively, or to a large extent by the Embden-Meyerhof-Parnas glycolitic sequence. As tissues aged and differentiated, a direct oxidation pathway assumed more importance, accounting for at least 50 per cent of the respiration in many adult tissues. While we might suspect the relative amounts of critical enzymes to determine the extent to which one pathway or another occurs, it is not known whether this or some other cause is responsible for the difference in the type of respiration in young and old tissues. But even if we distinguish specific metabolic differences between young and older cells, we cannot be sure whether they are the causes or the results of aging.

The observations of Riker and his colleagues on the growth of single isolated plant cells may be significant for our understanding of the persistence of meristems. You will remember that they found that single cells from tissue cultures of marigold and of tobacco grew if cultivated on filter paper which rested on young and actively growing cultures of tissue. However, as the "host" culture became old and senescent, the young culture it supported lost its vigor and it was necessary to transfer the filter paper and the culture on it to a fresh and active mass of tissue. These observations suggest that young cells in an active growing condition excrete substances which induce other cells to divide and that the continued existence of a meristem is the result in part of a kind of autocatalysis; dividing cells induce neighboring cells to divide by the products produced in division. We might even assume that these products diffuse slowly or are evanescent, with the result that they are only effective near the cells which produce them and that their absence or deficiency initiates the aging changes. This is probably far too simple an explanation for the complications of differential aging shown in the cells of a root tip or stem tip, but it is a hypothesis which might well be pursued further.

I am sure that my discussion has given you very little firm information on the physiological aspects of aging in plants. I have raised more questions than I have answered. I hope I have said enough to demonstrate that there are problems in the aging of plants which can be fruitfully investigated. The rapidly developing field of macromolecules and the relation of their structure to biological activity, the greater information on the modifications of development by minute amounts of specific substances, our increasing knowledge of the structure of the cell and the changes which the nucleus and the cell undergo in division and maturation, as well as new techniques such as chromatography, electron microscopy, tagged atoms, tissue culture, and the like, suggest that future progress in some of these fundamental areas may be more rapid than we could have reasonably anticipated 20 or even 10 years ago.

21

GROWTH AND GROWTH HORMONES IN PLANTS

Kenneth V. Thimann [1]

In the fifty years since the Botanical Society of America was founded, plant science has undergone some striking developments, but none of these has been more revolutionary than the discovery of auxin and of the hormonal control of the growth of higher plants. At every stage, from the fertilization of the ovule through all the phenomena of vegetative and reproductive development, the auxins play an important and often a controlling role. At the cellular level, the division of many types of cells, the enlargement of all types capable of enlargement, and the differentiation of xylem constitute the main effects of the auxins. At the tissue level, the formation of roots on shoots, the response of shoots to light and gravity, the growth of fruits, the interrelations between buds and other organs which are included in the term "apical dominance," all appear to be directly and quantitatively controlled by the same hormone. Even the growth of algae (though insufficiently studied to allow of certainty) appears to be subject to the same control. Other phenomena such as the formation of leaves and the initiation of flowering are at least strongly influenced by auxin, although other factors may be the prime causes. Because this fundamental knowledge has led to many successful applications in horticulture and in agricultural practices, the term "revolutionary" used above can almost be transferred as well to these developments in the applied plant sciences and arts. The following is a general summary of present knowledge of the auxins and their physiology, omitting only those topics which are to be treated elsewhere in this volume.

As so often happens, the first developments took place in Europe, while the later stages, though world-wide in distribution, have been pursued most

[1] Support of the author's researches, over a period of years, by the Committee on Growth, acting for the American Cancer Society, and by the National Science Foundation is gratefully acknowledged.

actively in America. The beginning of the story goes back to Darwin, who with his son Francis showed that the extreme tip of a grass seedling controls its ability to curve toward light. Covering the tip with an opaque cap made it insensitive (fig. 1). The coleoptile, a cylindrical sheath surrounding the first leaves of the grasses and cereals, has been used in all these early experiments. Many years after Darwin, Boysen Jensen, in Denmark (1910), cut off the tip of the coleoptile and stuck it back on again with gelatin; the

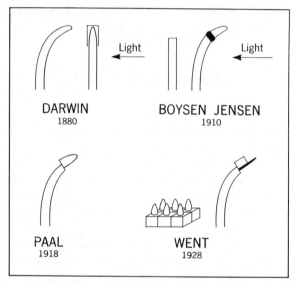

FIG. 1. First developments in study of growth hormones.

rest of the plant could still curve toward light, although if the tip had been completely removed it could not. It was this experiment, falling just within the period of our fifty-year celebration, that gave the first evidence that a material substance, rather than some ill-defined "stimulus," was in control of growth. The explanation was given by Paál (1915) in Hungary, who did not use curvature toward light but stuck the tip on a little to one side; then the plant curved even in darkness (fig. 1). This shows, concluded Paál, that the tip secretes a substance which promotes the growth of the part below it. When the tip is *in situ*, of course, growth is promoted symmetrically. It follows that the curvature toward light must be due to an unsymmetrical distribution of this growth substance, a disproportionately large amount becoming present on the side of the seedling away from the light, causing that side to grow more and thus the plant to curve. It was Cholodny, in Russia (1926), who formulated this clearly and proposed that all *tropisms*, that is, curvatures caused by an external stimulus, are due to the displacement of growth substance to one side. The proof was given almost at once by Went (1928) and Dolk (1930) in Holland. Went first found out how to determine the growth substance quantitatively, by placing the tips of numerous coleoptiles on a block of agar, then putting small cubes of the agar on one side of other coleoptiles whose tips had been removed (fig. 1). If the times and conditions are carefully adhered to, the curvature is proportional to the number of tips used and to the length of time they stayed on the agar. It is evident that we have to do with a substance which is continuously produced by the coleoptile tip; apparently it is readily diffusible and active in small quantities. Using this test, Went compared the amount of the substance diffusing out of the two sides of a coleoptile illuminated unilaterally and showed that the shaded side yielded about twice as much as the illuminated side. Similarly, in a very extensive series of experiments Dolk showed that the lower side of a coleoptile tip which had been laid horizontally yielded about twice as much as the upper side. Thus in each case the redistribution of growth substance was enough to account for the redistribution of growth, that is, the curvature. In the case of geotropism, Dolk showed that the *total* growth did not change, so that the redistribution must be accomplished without loss, but in phototropism the situation is complex.

With Went's quantitative test an attack on the chemistry of the growth substance became possible. It was soon found that coleoptiles, or indeed higher plants in general, are relatively poor sources, and the *auxin* (as it came to be called) occurred much more richly in cultures of certain microorganisms, in malt extract, and in human urine. At this point there occurred an odd contretemps which has never yet been fully explained. Kögl and Haagen Smit in Holland decided to purify the active substance from urine, and after extensive fractionation they came out with two pure compounds, termed auxin *a* and *b*, which have never been encountered again, either in other urine samples or in plant products. The status of these two substances as natural plant auxins is in doubt. However, shortly afterward, the same authors isolated from urine a quite different substance, which was also obtained from yeast, and independently and simultaneously in this country from cultures of the fungus *Rhizopus suinus*. This compound, which has since been isolated from one or two higher plants and identified as present in many others, turns out to be indoleacetic acid:

This substance had been known since 1880, although it was not, of course, recognized that it had the properties of an auxin for plants. Its simple structure has subsequently led not only to its synthesis in quantity, but to the synthesis of many compounds of related chemical structure, which often have turned out to possess valuable growth-promoting activity (see below).

Even before these pure auxins became available, it was discovered that the action of auxins in plants is by no means limited to the simple promotion of growth, whether straight or one-sided. On the contrary, a variety of functions are either controlled or modified by auxin, and it is this fact which has done so much to open our understanding of how the different parts of a plant react on one another to produce that *integration* which is characteristic of the plant as a whole.

In a dicotyledonous seedling the main center of auxin production appears to be the terminal bud, especially the young leaves in it. From here the auxin moves down the shoot by an "active" transport process which is neither diffusion nor mass flow but depends on metabolism. The cells immediately below the bud are caused to elongate. If the auxin is in a certain range of concentration, it may cause some of them to divide. However, the action of auxin in causing cell division seems to be exerted mainly on the cambium and the pericycle or phloem parenchyma. Cambium is certainly stimulated to divide by auxin in low (i.e., physiological) concentrations, and it is to this that the downward-spreading wave of cambial activation in trees in the spring is due. This was elegantly shown by Söding, in Germany, by applying synthetic auxin to young poplar and willow twigs and then counting the number of layers of wood cells laid down. When the auxin is in slight excess, the wood cells formed under its stimulus are of the redwood, or "rot-holz," type, with rounded cross section and thick walls; this is characteristic of the underside of lateral branches or leaning tree trunks. Its formation in these organs is thus connected with the geotropic accumulation of excess auxin on the lower side, described above. Xylem can also be formed from parenchyma cells under the influence of auxin; when a vascular bundle of a young stem is broken or dissected out, new xylem is formed on the inside of the bundle or between the bundles; for this, auxin is essential and its concentration determines the number of layers of xylem elements produced.

Continuing down the main axis of the shoot, the auxin reaches the lateral buds, each in the axil of a leaf. Typically, these buds remain almost inactive as long as the terminal bud is actively growing, a phenomenon known as "apical dominance." Paradoxically enough, this inactivity of the buds is due to the auxin which reaches them. For although the internode below the terminal bud is *caused* to elongate by auxin, the rudimentary internode in the axillary bud is *inhibited* from elongation by the same auxin. The reason for this inhibiting action has been under discussion ever since the facts were brought to light by Thimann and Skoog in 1934. Many theories have been proposed, of which space does not allow a discussion here. The phenomenon is, of course, the basis of the art of pruning, which consists essentially of removing auxin-producing centers so as to allow the growth of buds that had previously been inhibited.

Like all general phenomena, bud inhibition or apical dominance is subject to numerous variations. Some of these shed valuable light on the process, others are merely puzzling. For example, there is a bud in the axil of each of the cotyledons of a seedling. In spite of the wealth of nutrient available in these cotyledons, the bud does not develop, a fact which was observed by Goebel and other early students of growth but could not be explained by them in terms of the nutritional concepts which at that time were universally used. We now know, of course, that the growth of these buds is primarily controlled by the inhibiting action of auxin rather than the promoting effect of the nearby nutrient supply and that the auxin comes both from the terminal bud and from the cotyledon itself. Hence removal of either of these sources usually promotes growth of the lateral bud. Recently, however, there have been described a few cases where removal of the cotyledons actually slows down the growth of the buds in their axils, suggesting that supply of materials can easily become a limiting factor too.

At the other extreme there are, in some bushes, lateral buds close to the apex which, instead of being inhibited by the apex, develop strongly. The extent to which this occurs is greater the more vigorous the growth of the main shoot. Evidently these "anticipatory shoots," as Champagnat has called them, are in some way released from the auxin inhibition.

An interesting variant on the theme is the formation of short shoots, common to many fruit trees and notable in the woody gymnosperms. In apple and other fruits the short shoot is the flowering shoot, or "fruit-spur," but in *Larix* or *Ginkgo*, for instance, it may be purely vegetative and, indeed, always is in young trees, since these do not fruit. If the terminal bud and part of the stem of a young *Ginkgo* tree is removed, two or three of the short shoots become long (though sometimes this only happens in the next season), while if auxin is applied to the decapitated stem they remain short. It seems, therefore, that the lateral short shoot is a bud that is inhibited by auxin only so far as elongation is concerned, but that, unlike an ordinary lateral bud, it can open and allow its leaves to grow to full size.

Somewhat similar to the inhibition of lateral-bud development is the inhibition by auxin of another important trait in plant behavior, namely the dropping ("abscission") of leaves or fruits in the autumn or when sufficiently aged. In many plants, if the blade of any full-grown leaf is removed, the petiole will drop off a few days later, and this makes it convenient to study the process. Abscission results from growth of some cells of special properties at the base of the petiole. If auxin is applied, growth of these cells is inhibited, and hence the petiole stays on more or less indefinitely. Similarly by spraying fruits, especially apples, when nearly ripe they can be made to stay on the trees through autumn winds, or until it is convenient to pick them.

Curiously enough, fruit growers now also spray their trees with auxin very early in the season to *promote* the fall of fruit, a practice widely used as a standard method for thinning apples. The reason for this opposite effect is believed to be as follows: when the ovule is fertilized there is an immediate growth of the ovary, due partly to auxin brought in by the pollen and partly to production of auxin by the ovary tissue itself. Shortly afterward the endosperm begins to produce auxin, and shortly after that the growing embryo itself takes over the task of auxin production. As a result a stream of auxin flows from the young fruit into its pedicel, and this is considered to prevent abscission in the same way as above. The stream is interrupted temporarily, when one tissue which forms auxin takes over from another, and to such interruptions the natural drop of the fruit (e.g., "June drop") is ascribed. But the auxin is applied as spray in a concentration high enough to kill many of the young embryos, and perhaps the ovaries too; their death means the cessation of their secretion of auxin, and therefore the falling of the young fruit. The full explanation may be still more complicated, but the working out of these events has in any case brought out one rather general principle, namely, that the production of auxin is usually a transient activity which is soon given up and taken over by other tissues.

The inhibition of growth processes, such as bud development or abscission, by a substance which primarily causes growth promotion, is hard to understand. A great many theories have been proposed, most of which are open to serious objection, and some workers, finding the phenomenon puzzling, have even attempted to deny the facts. It seems probable that some kind of balance is involved between auxin and other factors and that buds or fruits continue to develop only when this balance is maintained, while excess of either one inhibits. Some of these factors are beginning to be known, but the working out of the process in detail will have to be described in the report of the *next* fifty years.

The above are not the only inhibiting actions exerted by auxin. For the elongation of roots, in opposition to that of shoots, is strongly inhibited by applied auxin. Only at excessively low concentrations, far below those promoting growth of shoots, does auxin promote root elongation, and then the effect is of small magnitude; isolated roots grown in culture and detached short segments of roots usually show a small promotion, but some plants show none at all, only inhibition. The root tip has been shown, by standard test methods, to produce small amounts of auxin, and this is probably in the inhibiting range, since, at least in some cases, careful decapitation without removal of the elongating zone may slightly promote the growth of the root. One characteristic difference between roots and shoots is their opposite tropisms, for roots react positively to gravity and negatively (in many cases) to light. Cholodny in 1927 proposed that these tropisms of roots were due to growth inhibition by auxin—gravity would cause accumulation on the lower side as in shoots, but here the extra auxin supply would inhibit and the root would therefore curve downward. The auxin would come principally from the root tip. While this has in general been shown to occur, no one has really satisfactorily restored geotropic sensitivity in a decapitated root by applying auxin, and all the attempts leave something to be desired. Some synthetic chemicals apparently prevent geotropic curvature without affecting the rate of elongation, while some compounds chemically related to auxins can reverse the tropism, causing roots to grow upward.

Less physiological are the striking inhibitions of growth, often culminating in death of tissue or of the whole plant, caused by large overdoses of auxin. Concentrations from 10 to 1000 times that optimal for growth promotion are needed to cause these effects. They can, of course, only be studied with synthetic auxins, and, indeed, they have actually been very little studied in a fundamental way because attention has been so focused on their application. Many tons of synthetic auxins, especially 2,4-D (2,4-dichlorophenoxyacetic acid) and its relative 2,4,5-trichlorophenoxyacetic acid (2,4,5-T):

$$CH_2 COOH \qquad CH_2 COOH$$

are sprayed annually on weeds to kill them. Sensitivity varies widely from plant to plant. Curiously enough, monocotyledons are in general highly resistant, though their seedlings are of course very sensitive, as we have seen above. In general the synthetic auxins are much more effective and safe weed killers than the strong acids or arsenic formerly used, and the different sensitivities often make it possible to kill weeds without affecting the crop plant growing among them. Mustard growing in wheat is a classical example, and the principle has been used in forestry, where hardwoods can be killed without affecting stands of pine or spruce. It is a paradoxical thought that so far the biggest application of these *growth* substances to practical agriculture is their use to kill plants.

In the preceding pages mention has been made of synthetic auxins without further explanation, and some chemical details should now be given. The commonest auxin of higher plants and also of many fungi was stated above to be indoleacetic acid, and it is on this model that so many compounds have been synthesized and tested. These are mainly the acetic, propionic, and butyric acid derivatives of many aromatic nuclei. Besides 2,4-D, perhaps the most widely used is naphthalene-1-acetic acid:

$$CH_2\,COOH$$

Practically all the active compounds consist of a ring which is more or less unsaturated and a side chain bearing an acid group or a group closely related to it (an ester or an amide, for instance, which can be readily converted to the carboxylic acid, though it is not excluded that they could act without such conversion).

The acid side chains may be linked to the ring nucleus directly or via an atom of oxygen or sulfur as in 2,4-D or in:

$$CH_2\,COOH$$
$$S$$
$$-CH_3$$
$$Cl$$

In 1953 Jones and his coworkers discovered indoleacetonitrile in cabbage:

$$CH_2\,CN$$
$$N$$
$$H$$

There is much evidence that this compound, which is highly active as an auxin in a few plants, but of low activity or none at all in many others, is first converted to the acid (indoleacetic acid) in order to act. Using chromatographic methods and bioassay, a few amides of indoleacetic acid and the related compounds indoleacetaldehyde and indolepyruvic acid have been identified in various plants. The aldehyde, first found by Larsen, in Denmark, appears to be not uncommon in etiolated seedlings. These compounds, too, seem to act primarily by being converted in situ to indoleacetic acid.

A characteristic of indoleacetic acid is the fact that the carboxyl (acid) group is separated from the ring by a carbon atom. There may be more than one, as in indolebutyric acid, which is highly active (though perhaps also after conversion to indoleacetic acid *in situ*), but there cannot be less than one; in other words, the compound in which the acid group is attached directly to the nucleus, indolecarboxylic acid, is inactive:

Until recently no compounds of this pattern, no matter what the ring structure, had been found active, but now we have a few, including some halogenated benzoic acids, showing real auxin activity; so far 2,3,6-trichlorobenzoic acid is the most active. Evidently, then, it is not a particular group nor even a simple spatial pattern which confers activity; it is rather some property of the whole molecule, some arrangement of atoms and charges which enables it to fit on to a receptive surface and thus "activate" it. There has been too much discussion of the exact nature of this spatial arrangement to summarize here. Compounds exist whose auxin activity provides an exception to most or all of the theories, and just recently an active compound which does not even contain a ring was described:

Its activity was not very strong, but seems to be real. The matter is made harder, too, by the wide range of active compounds, which is in striking contrast to the very limited variation in formula which has been found possible with the animal hormones. It is also made difficult by the absence of any *in vitro* or cell-free system on which auxins show satisfactory activity. Many isolated enzymes have been tested at different times, under the influence of one or another plausible theory, but none is activated by auxin. Curiously enough, *tissues* treated with auxin may afterward show marked changes in these same enzymes, but that is another matter. It begins to look as though the whole cell were necessary to auxin activity.

The discovery that auxin promotes not only cell elongation but also cell division in some tissues, which was first made for cambium by Snow, has had far-reaching implications both theoretical and practical. The initiation and downward spread of cambial activity in trees in the spring is due mainly to the production of auxin by buds and young leaves and its polar transport down the stem. It is not excluded that the cambium itself may produce auxin within the stem also. Another example is the cell proliferation that occurs in galls, tumors, and nodules, which can sometimes be ascribed to the overproduction of auxin by the parasite, though the elaborate structural patterns of many insect galls suggest that probably numerous factors are concerned. Galls and nodules certainly contain an excess of auxin, and in some cases galls can be produced by applying auxin, or better, by the combination of auxin and kinetin. Furthermore, the parasites causing galls have in several instances been shown to produce auxin in culture, but because this property is shared by other non-parasitic microorganisms, it seems that it is not the auxin-forming (or kinetin-forming) property alone, but the combination of this with the ability to enter and survive in plant tissues, that is the critical factor in parasitism. In the case of crown gall, the galls continue to grow and will give rise to new galls when pieces are transplanted, even though the bacteria which started the gall have all disappeared. This is interpreted to mean that the role of the bacteria was primarily to stimulate the plant cells to produce, and go on producing, the auxin and/or kinetin. Such an induced change in the host cells has been ascribed to a special "tumor-inducing principle," but this matter is still under investigation.

The practical result just mentioned is the development of the whole new field of plant tissue cultures. Gautheret and Nobécourt, both in France, discovered almost simultaneously in 1937 that isolated tissue fragments would grow indefinitely if traces of an auxin were added to the medium. Recently a number of additional growth-promoting or -controlling factors have been isolated from various sources, including especially coconut milk. These findings have led to a marked revival of experimental morphology and anatomy, which is beginning to make comprehensible many of the details of tissue formation and differentiation. The discovery that when tissues have been cultured for a time with auxin they sometimes develop the ability to grow without it, and now prove to *contain* some auxin, may throw light on problems of tumor development and perhaps be of interest to workers with animal diseases.

Promotion of cell division undoubtedly plays a part in another dramatic effect of auxin—the initiation of roots on stems. It was long known that buds or young leaves on the stem promote the formation of roots at the base of cuttings, and this action was at first ascribed to a root-forming hormone; later on there was some surprise when the postulated hormone turned out to be identical with auxin. The discovery was at once applied by nurserymen for the large-scale rooting of cuttings, and indeed this was, in order of time (1935), the first of the horticultural uses of auxins. The first sign of root initiation is normally given by divisions in the pericyclic layer or close to it, or in multiseriate ray tissue, though on various occasions with cuttings of different plants roots have been reported to arise in phloem, in numerous cortical layers, and even in pith. The cell divisions, in any event, continue and involve adjacent cell layers till a meristem of good size is formed; it is only then, one to many weeks after the treatment, that appreciable elongation becomes noticeable. Indeed, as we have seen above, the actual elongation of formed roots is inhibited by auxin in all but the most minute concentrations. A number of plants, especially forest gymnosperms and the rosaceous fruit trees, show little or no capacity to form roots in response to auxin or do it only under highly restricted conditions, and there is some reason to believe that here other factors than auxin are limiting. These include carbohydrates, general nitrogen supply, biotin, thiamine, purines (especially adenine and guanine), a factor liberated by wounding, and something else (which has not been proven to be a chemical material) which is often present when the tree is very young but decreases rapidly after the third or fourth year. Not all these are involved in any one plant, and there may be others yet undiscovered. But it is certainly not surprising that a process so complex as the new formation of an entire root should require the interaction of a multiplicity of factors, and perhaps it is all the more remarkable that auxin should so often be the principal initiator.

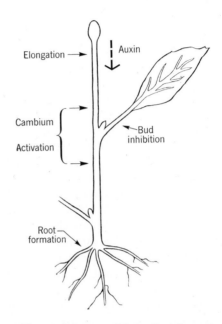

FIG. 2. Diagram of some functions of auxin in the dicotyledonous plant. (*From K. V. Thimann, Amer. Scientist, pp. 589–606, 1954.*)

Some of the functions of auxin are summarized in fig. 2.

Space does not permit detailed description of all the other phenomena on which auxin has been found to act. Clear growth-promoting effects have been reported on certain algae, but not on fungi. The first visible action of auxin is an acceleration of the rate of protoplasmic streaming, a process which requires sugar and depends on oxidative metabolism. Perhaps the most unexpected finding is the action of auxin on flowering. This is exerted most decisively on plants which are close to the border line of the transition from the vegetative to the flowering state. Plants requiring a 16-hour day in order to flower, for instance, were put on a regime of 12- to 14-hour days with a 2- to 4-hour supplementary period at very low light intensity; application of auxin now greatly increased the number of flowers. An effect in the opposite direction is provided by plants requiring short days, which were reduced to two leaves, of which one was exposed to short day and the other to darkness. Under these conditions the plants flowered, but if the leaf in darkness was treated with auxin, flowering could be entirely inhibited. The most striking case, however, is the pineapple, in which flowering is directly elicited by auxin treatment under field conditions; it is enough to pour a few cubic centimeters of naphthalene–acetic acid solution into the crown to bring about flowering in 100 per cent of the plants! The mechanism of this action is not at all understood, but it seems clear that in most plants auxin is not the principal controlling factor for flowering, but rather that it modifies—accelerating or retarding—a process whose main determinants are light and temperature. Gibberellic acid, a growth factor produced by certain fungi, seems to affect flowering more strongly, and perhaps more directly, than auxin.

The greatest puzzle of all, of course, is the mechanism whereby traces of auxin, a relatively simple organic acid, can so dramatically bring about growth or cell enlargement. Growth requires oxygen and a supply of carbohydrate and is further increased (in presence of auxin) by potassium, cobalt, and some organic acids. Abundant evidence shows that it is strictly dependent on the oxidative metabolism of the growing part. So far, however, all attempts to implicate a specific oxidizing enzyme system have failed, not only because no isolated enzyme has been found to be activated by auxin in physiological concentrations, but also because the careful study of tissue responses has not yet focused attention on any one process which could be the initial site of auxin action.

Many comparative studies of different tissues have been made. It has been shown that the continued uptake of water by "storage tissue" as in potato and artichoke is just as much a growth process as the elongation of seedlings and just as much under the control of auxin. This has led to the study of water uptake and its comparison with growth. Of course, the reversible type of water uptake exemplified by swelling and plasmolysis is not involved here, but only the continued phenomenon leading to permanent cell enlargement. From the fact that the process can be inhibited by a number of characteristic enzyme poisons it has been deduced that water uptake, like growth or cell elongation, requires one or more sulfhydryl enzymes, depends upon a supply of carbohydrate as well as auxin, and involves a phosphorylation, the metabolism of certain organic acids, and the oxidation of cell substrates by the specific route of the cytochrome oxidase system. This at first sight would seem to mean merely that growth, or water uptake, depends on the normal oxidative metabolism of the plant, but the relationship is not so simple as this, for growth is much more sensitive to enzyme poisons than is the consumption of oxygen in respiration, and in the case of potato tissue the respiration may gradually become insensitive to carbon monoxide while the water uptake remains strongly inhibited by this poisonous gas. The appearance is rather of a *specific fraction* of the respiratory process being in control of water uptake or cell enlargement. The possibility that this respiratory fragment is specifically using energy to draw water molecules into the cell has been examined, but the evidence is against it; apparently the energy is used instead to modify the properties of the cell wall (or perhaps of the cytoplasmic membrane), and the water then enters as a result of the lessened wall resistance. This too may explain why animal cells are not caused to grow by auxin, although some evidence has been offered that carbohydrate metabolism and glycogen deposition may be modified in liver tissues by auxin treatment. The recent discovery of the presence of excessive quantities of 5-hydroxy-indoleacetic acid in certain human pathological conditions may prove to be of interest in this connection, for the substance has definite, though low, auxin activity.

It is a far cry from the phototropism of etiolated *Avena* coleoptiles to these last-mentioned considerations, and the path traveled has been a long and sometimes a winding one. It certainly could not have been foreseen, or even wildly guessed at, in 1906, although Julius Sachs had even earlier had some glimpse of it in his prophetic idea of "organ-forming substances." Perhaps what would have surprised the botanists of 1906 the most would be the large practical applications of the auxins and of our knowledge of their physiological actions, in horticulture and plant industry. The auxins have provided also a powerful experimental tool for the attack on many long-standing botanical problems, especially the nature of growth itself. And they have greatly illuminated our general understanding of the life and behavior of plants.

LITERATURE CITED

BOOKS

AUDUS, L. J. 1953. Plant growth substances. Leonard Hill. London.

LEOPOLD, A. C. 1955. Auxins and plant growth. Univ. California Press. Berkeley, Calif.

SKOOG, F. (Ed.). 1951. Plant growth substances. (Symposium.) Univ. Wisconsin Press. Madison.

SÖDING, H. 1952. Die Wuchsstofflehre. Georg Thieme. Stuttgart.

THIMANN, K. V. 1956. L'origine et les fonctions des auxines. Centre de Documentation Universitaire. Paris.

WENT, F. W., AND K. V. THIMANN. 1937. Phytohormones. Macmillan. New York.

RECENT REVIEWS

ÅBERG, B. 1957. Auxin relations in roots. Ann. Rev. Plant Physiol. 8:153–180.

ADDICOTT, F. T., AND R. S. LYNCH. 1955. Physiology of abscission. Ann. Rev. Plant Physiol. 6:211–238.

GORDON, S. A. 1954. Occurrence, formation and inactivation of auxins. Ann. Rev. Plant Physiol. 5:341–378.

LIVERMAN, J. L. 1955. The physiology of flowering. Ann. Rev. Plant Physiol. 6:177–210.

MUIR, R. M., AND C. HANSCH. 1955. Chemical constitution as related to growth regulator action. Ann. Rev. Plant Physiol. 6:157–176.

REINERT, J. 1955. Wachstum. Fortsch. d. Bot. 17:697–711.

THIMANN, K. V. 1954. The physiology of growth in plant tissues. Amer. Scientist 1954:589–606. (Reprinted *in* Science in Progress, pp. 111–132. 1955.)

———— AND A. C. LEOPOLD. 1955. Plant growth hormones. Chapter I (56 pp.) *in* vol. III, The hormones, ed. by G. PINCUS AND K. V. THIMANN. Academic Press. New York.

TORREY, J. G. 1956. Physiology of root elongation. Ann. Rev. Plant Physiol. 7:237–266.

22

WEED CONTROL: APPLIED BOTANY

A. S. Crafts

Among the agricultural practices that have benefited by mechanization and chemicalization, weed control has been one of the last to undergo extensive development. Although much fundamental work had been done prior to 1944, introduction of 2,4-D during that year brought about an abrupt increase in activity, and within the last twelve years, weed control has become a multimillion-dollar business. Compared with plant breeding, use of fertilizers, development of insecticides, and mechanization of culture and harvest of crops, however, chemical weed control is still in its infancy.

When we look into the future, attempting to chart the course of agricultural progress, we realize that the bringing in of new arable land, the altering of climate, the improvement of fertilizers, and even the continued breeding of superior crop varieties are all laborious and costly procedures. One of the most promising means for increasing production would seem to be to eliminate competition and plant depredation by the use of modern pesticides. Among these, the herbicides seem most promising.

The growing of plants has always been a struggle. Anyone who has grown up on a farm can remember the perennial job of hoeing weeds in the corn or pulling them from the beets or garden crops. And many a boy has wondered, why grow some plants and destroy others? Why not use the weeds? But agricultural experience has proved the usefulness of crops and the detrimental effects of weed competition. Insects and plant diseases likewise prey on the farmer's crops. Only within relatively recent years have means become available for handling some of these enemies.

Out of the some quarter of a million plants in the world, only a few are useful as crops, and likewise only a few are weeds. But during the development of agriculture, by various means of sifting and screening as superior plants have been found and improved, superior weeds seem to have been carried along to compete with them. Furthermore, insects and diseases have sought out the farmer's choice crops and, until recent times, seem to have placed a definite ceiling on production. It seemed for ages that the evolution of pests was only one step behind the improvement of crops; and man's destiny seemed to hang in the balance between them. The story of this struggle, as exemplified by the activities of the U.S. Department of Agriculture, has been aptly described by Quisenberry (1948). The story of the strides recently made in insect and disease control I will leave for others to tell. I would like to recall a few of the interesting episodes in the introduction and spread of weeds and in the battle now being waged to bring them under control.

SOME SERIOUS WEEDS. As examples of weeds that have seriously affected American agriculture, I have selected Canada thistle (*Cirsium arvense*), Russian thistle (*Salsola kali* var. *tenuifolia*), St. Johnswort (*Hypericum perforatum*), and Halogeton (*Halogeton glomeratus*).

Canada thistle is a perennial weed prevalent throughout Central Europe, including the British Isles. It was brought into the American colonies with seeds and foodstuffs and was reported in Canada early in the seventeenth century, and in New York by 1777 (Dewey, 1901). It spread rapidly during the western migration and was found in California by 1879 (Robbins, 1940).

A noxious weed that spreads both vegetatively and by seed, Canada thistle early proved itself a serious menace to agriculture. It has been named as a noxious weed in the seed laws of 37 states, and it is still spreading. Not only has it invaded cultivated fields, but in the Northeast it is also penetrating the more open areas in forest, park, and range lands where control is impossible. Its wind-borne seeds are carried into every possible site for germination; its dioecious habit is apparently no deterrent to its rapid spread; its vigorous, competitive character enables it to dominate the flora in many open areas that otherwise would produce good forage. The only factors limiting its range seem to be climatic, and it apparently stays in the northernmost tier of states. One hundred years of agronomic research have failed to discover a practical method for eliminating Canada thistle; ten years after the discovery of 2,4-D we are still seeking a satisfactory chemical method for its control.

Russian thistle is an annual of the tumbleweed habit; that is, at maturity it breaks off at the ground line and is blown by winds so that its myriads of seeds are effectively spread. It grows best under semi-arid conditions and tolerates saline soils; it is a weed found in small grains, as well as on fallow lands, abandoned fields, and nontilled areas. It makes its major growth during summer and remains succulent well into autumn on most soils.

Russian thistle was introduced into the United States from Russia around 1874 and was first reported from South Dakota (Robbins et al., 1952). By 1895 it had been reported in 16 states, including California. During World War I many acres of marginal land were plowed and planted to wheat; after the war these lands were abandoned and Russian thistle took over literally thousands of acres. During this war sugar-beet growing developed rapidly in California and the industry held great promise. Then suddenly, about 1925, the curly top virus carried by the beet leafhopper *Eutettix tenellus* broke forth in unprecedented violence and threatened to destroy the industry. Why did this occur?

Before the war, curly top had been a disease of little consequence, injuring relatively few beets because natural circumstances provided an effective control. After beet harvest the leafhoppers were subject to severe decimation by hot dry weather and a lack of succulent feed. There was an obvious gap in their food cycle. But after the war, with Russian thistle widely disseminated throughout the major beet-growing areas, the hoppers migrated from beets to thistle to green winter forage to beets. The cycle was completed, and leaf-hopper populations increased by leaps and bounds; within a period of about five years the beet-growing industry was almost eliminated.

By a three-pronged attack of plant breeding for resistance, insect control, and thistle control, the sugar-beet industry was able to make a recovery; however, the same virus from the same sources has seriously affected tomato growing in California. And direct crop damage from plant competition by Russian thistle has caused no small loss to western agriculture.

St. Johnswort is a rather insignificant member of the plant population of Western European countries, including the British Isles. Early introduced into the United States, it created no problem along the eastern seaboard. Its introduction on the west coast is obscure, but in the early years of the present century it began to take over large areas of excellent range land in the north-coast counties of California. It also spread in the foothill ranges of Oregon, Washington, and Idaho. Introduced free of its natural predators, it thrived prodigiously and became dominant on many hundred thousand acres of productive range land.

Meanwhile, St. Johnswort had claimed similar large areas of range in Australia, and, having successfully controlled prickly pear with insect preda-tors, around 1940 the biological-control people introduced from France a number of beetles known to have a taste for this weed. By 1943 these preda-tors had become established in Australia (Wilson, 1943), and in the following years importations were made into California. Tests were completed, and the beetles were first released in this state late in 1945. Additional releases were made in 1946 and 1947. Within ten years, the major St. Johnswort–infested areas of Humboldt County, California, have been released, infestations along the Sierras are being suppressed, and excellent control is reported from the other states in the Northwest. Meanwhile, work has been started toward biological control of gorse, and insect predators are being sought for yellow star and Italian thistles.

Halogeton glomeratus is an annual of the family Chenopodiaceae and resembles Russian thistle in appearance. It was first found in this country at Wells, Nevada, in 1935, and for several years its harmful effects were not known. However, it spread rapidly over the desert ranges of Nevada, Utah, Idaho, and neighboring states, and as soon as it became dominant over large areas, trouble started. *Halogeton* has the property of accumulating large concentrations of oxalates, attaining values as high as 22 per cent of the dry weight in extreme cases.

Oxalates precipitate calcium from the blood, causing tetany. Sheep may die from eating 5 ounces of the dry plant; cows succumb from 3 to 5 pounds. Poisoning was first recognized in 1942, and new cases have been reported each succeeding year. In one instance *Halogeton* is known to have killed 1,620 sheep in three days, and many smaller losses occur annually. *Life* magazine featured *Halogeton* poisoning in Volume 30, January 15, 1951, and the U.S. Department of Agriculture started investigating means of control late in 1952.

Although considerable progress has been made in finding ways for controlling *Halogeton,* none found so far, and probably none to be found in the future, will take care of the entire problem, for in the two decades since its first discovery this weed has spread over some three million acres of desert range that is not productive enough to pay for any type of control. Biological control by insects is the only method that can possibly handle the situation, and the chances of finding a suitable predator for a plant so closely related to the sugar beet seems unlikely.

WEED LOSSES. One principle of plant control is to allow a disturbed flora to return to its original status so that competition may re-establish a favorable balance or condition. Another is to eliminate the pest plant by frequent and effective tillage. A third is to introduce selective predators that will suppress the pest without harming crops. And a fourth is to treat the pest chemically whenever necessary to keep it at a low competitive level. Of the four examples of weeds cited, St. Johnswort seems to be submitting to biological control. The other three by their very nature cannot be controlled by competition, for each represents a new element in the vegetative complex that has superior competitive ability. The flora cannot return to a previous favorable status because a new factor of great competitive vigor has been introduced, and once established any new balance attained will be less favorable.

Tillage cannot be effective because these weeds have literally "taken to the hills," and gradually they have occupied millions of acres that cannot be treated economically. Biological control is always a possibility, but the chances of finding insects or diseases selective enough are pretty small. And chemicals offer little hope, for they too are costly to produce and apply. Although a few weeds like common mustard, pigweeds, lamb's quarters, annual bindweed, sagebrush, and some of the ragweeds are being economically controlled on millions of acres by chemical means, there is still a host of these pests that resist all control methods.

A good many people, and even some botanists, regard weeds as a personal affliction, thinking of them in terms of the dandelions in their lawns, the purslane in their petunia bed, or the ragweed that makes them sniffle and sneeze in the fall. The cases cited above reveal the fact that weeds are responsible for losses—huge, real losses that affect your income and mine. If I were to add the case for Johnson grass in cotton and vineyards, for bindweed in corn, for wild oats in peas and flax, for "lilies" in rice, for nutgrass in vegetable crops, for commelina and goosegrass in sugar cane, medusa head in ranges, etc., the estimates that place weeds first in the list of agricultural pests would surely be accepted. In the 1920's the Agricultural Committee of the United States Chamber of Commerce estimated losses due to weeds in this country at 3 billion dollars annually. Since that time all attempts to prove this to be an overestimate have failed.

There are several texts devoted to weeds and weed control (Ahlgren, Kling-man, and Wolf, 1951; Muenscher, 1949; Robbins et al., 1952) that ade-quately describe the older work in this field.

WEED-CONTROL METHODS. Recent developments in chemical weed control have far-reaching significance and application. Not only are these of interest to agriculturists, they are also fascinating to plant physiologists and bio-chemists, for they present new evidence on many aspects of plant metabolism.

Chemical methods can be classified as follows:

Selective	*Nonselective*
1. Foliage applications	1. Foliage applications
a. Contact	*a.* Contact
b. Translocated	*b.* Translocated
2. Soil applications	2. Soil applications

Three methods falling outside this scheme are the jar method for treating perennials by soaking their tops in a solution of a herbicide, the cut-surface method wherein the concentrated formulation of 2,4-D or 2,4,5-T is applied to cuts through the bark of trees, and the use of substituted benzenes in irri-gation water to kill submerged aquatic weeds in ditches.

Functionally speaking, all effective herbicides are absorbed into the plant body, and at some site they bring about a biochemical reaction resulting in the death of the plant. Some are translocated; others act close to the site of absorption. Some are selective; others kill all plants they touch. And finally, with some the final killing effect may be complex, involving several mecha-nisms.

Absorption. The older materials—sodium arsenite, sulfuric acid, and sodium chlorate—were applied in massive doses, and they brought about rapid destruction of foliage by their drastic and corrosive action. With the introduction of the dinitro herbicides, when dosage was scaled down to a few ounces per acre (Crafts, 1945), absorption was a different problem. With the discovery of the activating function of acids, it became apparent that penetration of plant cuticle demanded the proper chemical environment. A satisfactory theory of absorption has been elaborated that explains the role of acid in the activation of dinitrophenols and the means by which the phenoxy compounds may be formulated to foster absorption (Crafts, 1945). More recently Orgell (1954) has drawn attention to the role of adsorption in the uptake of foliar sprays and has shown that there is a peak of uptake on the alkaline side of neutrality as well as the plateau on the acid side of the pK value.

In essence, these workers suggest that for ready absorption through the cuticle a molecule must be uncharged or positively charged and it must be soluble in the cuticle. The uncharged molecule can approach the cuticle, dissolve in it, diffuse through, and, if sufficiently water-soluble, part from it into the epidermal cells and so migrate into the mesophyll. The positively charged particle is attracted to the negatively charged cuticle and is adsorbed to it; if soluble in the cuticle it may readily pass into and through it. However, in order to part from the cuticle its positive charge must be removed or neutralized; this could be accomplished by exchange with the contents of the epidermal cells or by enzymatic splitting of the molecule. Accumulating evidence indicates, in the case of urea, that the molecule is split to CO_2 and some nitrogen compound (Tukey, 1954).

The theory of the ready absorption of the associated parent molecules of dinitro and phenoxy herbicides seems well established from over ten years' experience. Apparently Dalapon follows the same rule (Wilkinson, 1956).

Maleic hydrazide and amino triazole seem not to follow this rule. From research in progress, these molecules seem to enter the leaf through an aqueous pathway. This is extremely interesting in view of Lambertz' (1954) evidence for the presence of protoplasmic strands in the cuticle. Also pertinent are the observations of Scott (1955) and Loomis (1956) that the cuticle under the electron microscope has a sponge-like appearance. If it can be conclusively shown that the cuticle combines lipoid and aqueous phases, making possible the entry into the leaf of either fat- or water-soluble compounds, a much wider array of compounds may find use as herbicides. Much research is still needed here.

An important point in the absorption of herbicides is that if they are to be translocated they must be able to migrate into the vascular strands without seriously impairing the photosynthetic mechanism of the leaf, for their ultimate transport into the roots depends upon food movement. This demands a sort of selectivity within the treated plant, for the leaf tissues must be spared whereas the root and bud tissues must be killed. For the chlorophenoxy compounds, differences in maturity may account for this selectivity.

Surfactants are used in most spray formulations, and much research supports the claims that they aid in penetration. Undoubtedly they aid in wetting, and they dry down to a film that holds the chemical in intimate liquid contact with the leaf surface. Do they do more than this? Conceivably some surfactants may alter the cuticle, rendering it more permeable. Here again research is needed to clarify this important point.

Translocation. To kill roots following application to the foliage a herbicide must pass down through the vascular system. Much research substantiates the view that the phenoxy compounds are carried from leaves to roots along with food materials via the phloem (for a review see Crafts, 1951). This mechanism makes certain demands on the physiology of the plant, and many field observations indicate a close correlation between the satisfying of these demands and the success of translocated herbicides. Use of labeled 2,4-D has greatly strengthened the evidence for the mechanism of transport (Crafts, 1956a, b; Leonard and Crafts, 1956).

Evidently two problems confront the user of translocated herbicides. First, he must find the proper time and condition for treatment; second, he must use a formulation that will penetrate the cuticle, migrate to the vascular tissue, and move to the proper site of action without killing the intervening tissues. The first requires that the plant has attained a degree of maturity so that the leaves are hardy enough to take in the chemical; foods must be moving to the roots; the roots in turn must be actively vegetative, having adequate soil moisture for growth. Apparently, given the proper conditions, translocation seldom fails. Problems in this area involve penetration of the chemical, partition from the cuticle, and freedom from adsorption by specific compounds in the plant that hold the chemical away from its site of action.

These problems are tied up with species susceptibility and can only be met by careful studies in the greenhouse and in the field. Those who have worked with modern herbicides realize that there remains at present a tremendous job of fitting compounds into the hundreds of niches that exist in the field. And this involves not only search for new compounds but also careful studies on many of the old ones to make sure that the possibilities of formulation and field practice have been exhausted. A very unfortunate aspect of the whole program of synthesis and screening being carried on by industry today is the fact that not enough weed and crop plants are being used, and the conditions of screening are not varied enough to preclude the possibility of missing valuable chemicals.

Root applications. The application of herbicides to the soil for absorption by roots presents a whole new set of problems. These involve such soil properties as chemical composition, particle-size distribution, colloid content, reaction, organic matter, microflora, depth, etc. Also involved are precipitation, temperature, vegetative cover, crop history, and the like.

All soil treatments by herbicidal chemicals have been conveniently termed soil sterilization, and they are arbitrarily classified as temporary and relatively permanent (Robbins et al., 1952). When crops are involved, the treatments applied before the crop is up are termed pre-emergence, those applied afterward post-emergence. Those not involving crops are usually confined to nontilled areas and are commonly somewhat permanent in their effects.

Turning first to the soil treatments made in crops, that is, the pre- and post-emergence applications, it should be apparent that these must be in some way selective so that the weeds are killed while the crop survives. The matter of selectivity is discussed in the next section; it should be mentioned here, however, that selectivity of herbicides is only relative (Crafts, 1946); a chemical to which a crop is sensitive must be so positioned that it will not come into contact with the crop roots if they are to remain uninjured. Because most weed seeds germinate in the top half inch of soil, excessive leaching is detrimental. And the position of the chemical is a function of soil type and precipitation.

As was pointed out after early pre-emergence trials with 2,4-D (Crafts, 1948), there are four possible conditions that will determine the effects of a given treatment:

1. No rainfall following treatment
2. Very light rainfall
3. Moderate rainfall
4. Excessive rainfall or flooding

It should be apparent that of these four conditions only condition 3 will give success; conditions 1 and 2 will fail because the chemical will not be moved to the proper depth; condition 4 will fail because the chemical will be leached below the rooting zone of the weeds. In regions where crops are dependent upon summer rainfall, soil-applied pre-emergence herbicides have been used with eminent success and only low or excessive rainfall has affected the treatment adversely. Soil type, however, must also be considered; treatments on sandy soils often fail because of excessive downward movement of the chemical. In the semi-arid west where irrigation is more prevalent, these soil treatments are not widely used because many crops come up and grow to considerable size, or even to maturity, without a drop of rain; subsequent irrigation has not proved effective in bringing such herbicides into action.

In spite of the above difficulties, pre-emergence herbicides are finding great favor in the midwest and along the eastern seaboard, and many new, promising chemicals are being tested. These include the phenoxyacetic, propionic, and butyric acids in their 2,4-D, 2,4,5-T, and MCP forms, as acids, salts, esters, and amides. Also included are the carbamates, chloroacetamides, di-thiocarbamates, and a number of coded materials the compositions of which have not been revealed. With chemicals of varying solubility and adsorption, it may be possible to find materials for many widely varying weed situations.

Permanent soil sterilants. Relatively permanent soil sterilization that will completely inhibit vegetation on nonagricultural areas has been achieved for many years. The chemicals used include sodium arsenite, white arsenic, sodium chlorate, boron compounds, and such waste materials as bittern, waste oils, acid sludge, etc. More recently the borate-chlorate mixtures have been extensively employed, and today the substituted ureas of du Pont, urea-borate mixtures, 2,4-D-borate mixtures, and other combinations involving TCA, Dalapon, trichlorobenzoic acid with chlorates and borates are being extensively used. Erbon (Swezey, 1955) of the Dow Company has been announced recently, and undoubtedly other new materials are under test. Studies on the substituted ureas have shown that clay content and organic matter are two soil constituents that determine toxicity. More recent studies indicate that not only clay content but the nature of the clay and the base exchange capacity of a soil may be involved in both toxicity and breakdown.

For example, Hill (1955), reporting on CMU fixation in soils, found that on a bentonite clay of a high exchange capacity, around 150 p.p.m. was required on the clay particles to give 1 p.p.m. in the soil solution, whereas on a kaolinitic clay with a low exchange capacity, less than 1 p.p.m. was required on the clay particles to give 1 p.p.m. in the soil solution. And when organic matter was removed from a sandy soil, adsorption was reduced by approximately 85 per cent. These few figures give an idea of the magnitude of the soil factors that may be involved when one attempts to evaluate a given chemical compound as a soil sterilant.

Precipitation (rainfall) has been mentioned as the predominant factor in the movement of soil-borne herbicides. Probably more important than total precipitation is the rainfall pattern. As early as the summer of 1933, observation of plots treated at Davis with sodium chlorate in 1930 indicated that the chemical was still present at toxic concentrations, in spite of the fact that three winters had elapsed, with a total precipitation of over 40 inches. When the area was diked and leached with 36 surface inches of water, all trace of the chlorate disappeared. Apparently the intermittent nature of rainfall has much to do with the leaching that it accomplishes. A recent report from Tunisia, where a 2 pound per acre application of MCP to morning glory on fallow land in the fall of 1952 resulted in crop injury to wheat in 1955, emphasizes this fact. In this case around 50 inches of rain had fallen during the three winters involved, but this had not leached the chemical below the root zone of the 1955 crop. In fact, the evidence indicated that the injury occurred to the wheat in the young seedling stages possibly from chemical plowed to the surface during preparation of the seedbed.

Selectivity of herbicides. One of the most interesting aspects of the use of herbicides is the selectivity they show. History tells us that selectivity of copper solutions on plants was first noticed by a French vineyardist who was spraying his vines for control of fungus. Noticing that the broad-leafed mustards were killed whereas cereals were unhurt, he tried the material in his grain field and found that he could control the mustard selectively (Robbins et al., 1952). Similar results were soon obtained in Germany and in the United

States, and by the turn of the century iron sulfate, copper sulfate, and sulfuric acid were being used in considerable quantities for this purpose. Selectivity of this type depends upon differential wetting of the leaves and upon the growth habit of the cereal plants. In the latter the meristems responsible for new shoots and roots are protected by the bases of the older leaves and also by their location at or below the soil line; buds of the mustard plant are exposed.

Sodium chlorate received some attention as a selective spray on grains during the 1930's, but it remained for the dinitro-substituted phenols to usher in the new era in chemical weed control. Sinox (sodium dinitro-*o*-cresylate) was discovered in France in 1933. Tested in California in 1938 and 1939, it proved by far the most toxic herbicide available—so toxic in fact that it could be applied by airplane (Westgate and Raynor, 1940). In the early tests it was used at 4 to 6 pounds of active chemical per acre; when its activation by acid salts was discovered, this dosage was cut in half. And the chemical proved useful not only on cereal crops but on flax, peas, onions, and alfalfa as well. During the early 1940's use of this material approached 100,000 acres per year in California.

Use of the airplane placed herbicides into a class with insecticides as capable of application to large areas, making large-scale operations feasible for the first time. Operators were no longer hindered by fence lines and wet or uneven soils. In the case of 2,4-D, use of aliphatic esters in oil relieved the operator of the water requirement and enabled him to cover many hundred acres in a day. For the first time chemical weed control could actually meet the farmer's needs.

The next advance in the use of selective sprays resulted from the discovery that carrots tolerate light fuel oils, whereas grasses and many common broadleafed weeds succumb. Stove oil was first used; then Stoddard solvent was found less persistent on the crops. At present most carrot crops are sprayed one or more times with a light-oil fraction to kill weeds. The method has also been extended to celery in the seedbeds, to parsnips and certain herb crops, and to onions, flax, and forest-tree nurseries.

Oil selectivity is not a matter of wetting, since all plants are thoroughly wetted by the spray. Currier and Peoples (1954) found that the toxicity of an oil is related to the degree to which it saturates the lipoid phase of the plant cells; a highly toxic oil saturates this phase at a lower oil content than does an oil of low toxicity. And selectivity apparently relates to the inherent saturability of the lipoid phase of the cells of different plants; susceptibility results from a low saturation requirement. Apparently all plants of the carrot family require relatively high oil contents for saturation; hence they tolerate oil sprays.

The announcement of 2,4-D in 1944 initiated a new era in the use of herbicides. This chemical is unique in being highly toxic, readily absorbed, rapidly translocated, highly selective, and effective through the soil as well as through the foliage. Production skyrocketed to 20 million pounds in 1948 and has continued to rise since then. Meanwhile, production of 2,4,5-T has reached 5 million pounds per year, the use of MCP to control weeds in certain crops is increasing, 2,4-D and 2,4,5-T propionic acids in various formulations are coming into use for woody-plant control, and a whole series of chlorinated phenoxy butyric acids is being tested.

These compounds have brought a new principle to the field of weed control; in contrast to the older, highly toxic chemicals, they are all growth regulators: they act slowly; in many cases they bring about severe formative effects; apparently they kill by disturbing plant metabolism. Physiologically they present a dilemma, for their effective use depends upon translocation through living tissues, and at the same time they must be toxic enough to destroy roots.

Selectivity of the phenoxy compounds has been studied from many angles, but it still is not clearly understood. In general, plants of the grass family tolerate the chemical, whereas broad-leafed plants are susceptible. Selectivity must relate to the specific properties of the protoplasm. Tests have shown that the grasses do not absorb and translocate these compounds as readily as do the broad-leafed plants, and yet the differences are not great enough to account for the observed selectivity. It has been suggested that 2,4-D acts on or through some specific enzyme system in the plant, and yet many studies have failed to discover which enzyme is involved. And overshadowing the whole subject of selectivity is the fact that it is only relative; grasses may be killed in their seedling stages; cereal crops affected in their seedling stages show injury to their inflorescences; and a number of broad-leafed plants, including strawberries, flax, coffee, Russian knapweed, Aruba, and others, are tolerant. Furthermore, MCP is more selective than 2,4-D, particularly on certain legumes. And many woody species respond to 2,4,5-T that are resistant to 2,4-D. Recently it has been shown that 2,4,5-trichlorophenoxypropionic acid will kill a number of oak species that are not affected by the acetic acid compounds.

A number of new growth regulators, the gamma chlorophenoxy butyric acids, are currently being tested. Working with a series of gamma phenoxy alkylcarboxylic acids, Synerholm and Zimmerman (1947) found that alternate compounds in a homologous series caused leaf epinasty in tomato. The compounds having activity were the acetic, butyric, caproic, and heptanoic derivatives, and these workers proposed that these were being degraded to the acetic acid by β-oxidation, the mechanism responsible for the breakdown of fats in the animal body. In careful studies Wain and his coworkers at Wye College (1955) have shown that this behavior is consistent in wheat cylinder growth tests for a number of homologous series of gamma phenoxy acids. However, in the pea curvature test and the tomato epinasty test the

2,4,5-T, the 2,4-dichloro-5-methyl, and the 2-methyl-5-chloro series failed to produce the response, whereas the 4-chloro, the 2,4-D, the 2-methyl-4-chloro, the 3,4-D, and the 3-methyl-4-chloro series produced the normal alternation in activity. This suggested to Wain that possibly some plants lack the necessary oxidation enzyme system to degrade the higher homologues down to the acetic acid compound where the above three ring substituents are present. Testing proved this to be true, and Wain reasoned from this situation that it might be possible to use certain of the butyric, caproic, and octanoic derivatives as selective toxicants against weeds in crops. Selectivity in this case would depend upon the enzyme make-up of the weed and crop plants, the weeds being able to degrade the herbicide to the acetic compound whereas the crop would be unable to do so.

Trials have proved that the above mechanism of selectivity is effective. Some weeds that respond are annual nettle (*Urtica urens*), Canada thistle (*Cirsium arvense*), fumitory (*Fumaria officinalis*), knotgrass (*Polygonum aviculare*), and mustard (*Sinapis arvensis*). Some crops that tolerate these compounds are celery, carrot, parsnip, flax, red clover, white clover, and alfalfa. Undoubtedly more crops that are tolerant and weeds that are susceptible will be discovered as testing proceeds.

The above work opens a whole new field for weed-control research. Not only do plants differ in size, structure, and appearance, they also vary in chemical composition and in their enzyme systems. This variation provides the basis for many new selectivities dependent upon the presence or absence of specific enzymes. One can scarcely visualize the limits of the application of this principle. Obviously, specific herbicides for specific weeds are to be desired, and from our knowledge of the biochemistry of plants, it seems hopeful that a great number can be found. I know of no area in the fields of biochemistry and plant physiology that offers greater promise to the researcher.

Mechanisms of action. Auxin physiologists for years have sought the biochemical mechanism by which IAA affects growth in plants. Because the formative (auxin) effects of weed killers seem related to the toxic effects (Weintraub, 1952), physiologists interested in the mode of herbicidal action of the 2,4-D class of herbicides have tried to draw a parallel with that of auxin.

In 1938, Koepfli et al. set forth the following structural requirements for auxin activity: (*a*) a ring system as the nucleus, (*b*) a double bond in this ring, (*c*) a side chain, (*d*) a carboxyl group, or a group readily converted into a carboxyl, on the side chain, with at least one carbon atom removed from the ring, and (*e*) a particular space relation between the ring and the carboxyl group.

During the years since 1938 exceptions to most of these requirements have been found and many modifications have been proposed. Theories suggested fall into a wide array, ranging from purely physical mechanisms, wherein the regulator, by affecting surface relations, changes interfacial activity at the plasma membrane to chemical mechanisms involving salt or amide linkages with a protein. Leopold (1955) lists five possible mechanisms of toxic action of auxin-like herbicides: (1) respiratory depletion, (2) cellular proliferation, (3) formation of toxic materials, (4) an activation of phosphate metabolism, and (5) hydrolysis of proteins. In view of the specificities that have been demonstrated and the known relations of structure to function for growth regulators, it seems probable that definite molecular configurations are involved in herbicidal action and that chemical and physical binding of the toxicant with a substrate are involved. Between this reaction at the molecular level and the final herbicidal response by whole plants, many secondary effects may be interposed: cell proliferation, phloem plugging, mitotic aberrations, metabolic disturbances of many types, and even invasion of tissues by fungi and bacteria. In seeking answers to the many questions that arise in the interpretation of field results with herbicides, one cannot afford to overlook any of these effects. Undoubtedly singly or in combination they are responsible for weed killing. One thing seems certain. For compounds having the profound effects on plants that the hormone-like herbicides do, the primary action must take place early in the over-all process of metabolism. Such a process is the one involving oxidation of acetaldehyde to acetic acid and concurrent reduction of acetaldehyde to ethanol mentioned by Freed and Remmert (1956). These reactions are shown to be sensitive to 2,4-D in vitro.

Since 1944 the bulk of the research on mode of action of herbicides has revolved around the chlorophenoxy acetates. Other work has been done, however, that is worthy of mention.

Ivens and Blackman (1949) report that the carbamates disrupt mitosis in roots of barley and peas. Concentrations that inhibited root extension upset cell division and produced nuclear abnormalities. Trichloroacetic acid and its salts have profound formative effects on plants, and they seem to affect top growth more than root tissue. The same can be said of the newer material Dalapon (sodium dichloropropionate). N-1-naphthylphthalamic acid, in addition to being extremely toxic to many plants, destroys the mechanism of geotropism of roots so that they grow upward and may protrude above the soil level.

The substituted ureas, such as 3-(p-chlorophenyl)-1,1-dimethyl urea, are absorbed principally from the soil by roots. After considerable top growth has been made, the shoots start dying back from the tips. Leaves of trees show a mottled chlorosis. Freed (1952) has suggested that nitrogen metabolism is disturbed.

Maleic hydrazide applied as a spray throws plants into a dormancy which, if dosage is heavy, may be prolonged and may even result in death. Potato tubers and onion bulbs are prevented from sprouting normally when the tops are sprayed with MH before harvesttime.

Amino triazole may kill some plants by a slow contact action; others respond by producing chlorotic shoots, and death may eventually result from starvation. At lower dosages a temporary chlorosis may be produced. Evidently the enzymes responsible for chlorophyll formation are affected, but the exact role of this response in plant death is not known.

This is not the place to give a detailed review of herbicidal action. Such reviews have been written by Norman et al. (1950), Blackman et al. (1951), Crafts (1953), and Leopold (1955). The examples that have been given illustrate the great diversity of the mechanisms involved in plant killing with herbicides. They indicate the scope of the field presented for physiological and biochemical studies. And they round out the picture of the impact that chemical plant control has had on agriculture. Use of herbicides undoubtedly represents the greatest advance in agricultural technology since the introduction of artificial fertilizers.

DISCUSSION. Those familiar with weeds and weed control recognize the great contribution the science of botany has made to this field of knowledge. Growth and development of weeds is typical of higher plants in general; the great competitive vigor of weeds is an example of "survival of the fittest" under disturbed conditions; chemical weed control involves and exemplifies many aspects of plant physiology; the methodology of weed control makes many direct applications of the physiology and biochemistry of plants.

It might be interesting, before closing, to examine the other side of the coin: what has weed control contributed to botany? To illustrate this, one might picture what happens in using a systemic herbicide. Following application of a systemic herbicide to a plant, the chemical, if successful, penetrates the cuticle, migrates across the mesophyll, enters the phloem where it mixes with the newly synthesized foods in their movement to points of utilization, and finally enters active cells, usually meristematic, where it brings about a lethal reaction. In this same order I would like to point out some recently acquired knowledge gained through research on herbicides.

Absorption. Many chemicals can move through the cuticle of plants; this so-called impervious coating is apparently more pervious than commonly pictured. Some chemicals, applied in large amounts, alter the cuticle and enter readily; others, used in smaller quantities, may move in as undissociated molecules, soluble in the lipoid cuticle layers; others apparently penetrate through an aqueous phase. Thus the cuticle seems subject to alteration by strong or corrosive chemicals; surfactants in smaller amounts may increase its permeability; and some organic herbicides enter in fat- or water-soluble forms. It seems reasonable to assume that the cuticle is labile and composed of at least two separate phases.

Translocation. In the transport of certain systemic herbicides we have a curious anomaly, namely, the ability of the phloem to carry toxic chemicals through living tissues at concentrations that will kill meristematic cells. Thus there must be a sort of selectivity between tissue systems within the plant. And we are able to utilize this selectivity for killing root systems of perennial weeds, providing we keep the concentration within limits and move the chemical rapidly. This demands proper formulation of the chemicals to facilitate absorption and active synthesis of foods to aid in moving them into and through the plant. Some chemicals that are so moved in plants are phenyl acetic acid, benzoic acid, and the herbicides amino triazole, maleic hydrazide, and the phenoxy compounds.

In plant physiology there is a long-standing controversy concerning the nature of the sieve tubes of the phloem; some picture them as highly active cells that move solutes by means of energy derived from respiration; others view them as passive conduits through which a stream of food materials in solution moves along a hydrostatic gradient developed osmotically as a result of the separation of regions of synthesis from those of utilization. The observations on herbicide transport seem to substantiate the latter mechanism. It is difficult to reconcile the translocation of toxic chemicals with the high metabolic state postulated for the sieve tubes by advocates of the first mechanism. The lack of specificity and the prolonged functioning of this transport system do not fit the concept of high activity required; rather, a simple physical system of a more passive nature would seem better to fit the facts.

Mode of action. Search for the mechanisms of action of the various newer herbicides is occupying the interest of many researchers. Considering first the auxin-like materials, there is a large literature stemming from work on growth regulators. Taking 2,4-D as an example, many enzyme systems have been found to be unaffected by this toxicant. Definition of the requirements for activity have been liberalized. The strict two-point and three-point concepts seem not to hold; for stimulatory effects plus toxicity it seems that a ring nucleus plus a side chain with an acid group and certain structural relations are all that are required. Possibly chemicals lacking the stimulatory action may involve simply the chain structure with the acid group, for example, Dalapon.

When we view the number of chemicals that are active, the variety of plants that respond, and the drastic modifications that are found, it seems obvious that processes of a basic nature, essential to the very life of the plant, are being altered. Study of these processes should start early in the series of reactions that make up the total metabolic machinery of the plant. Selectivity of herbicides has been shown to depend on many differences between species and their many modes of life. Some, at least, relate back to specific enzyme systems and their roles in plant metabolism. It seems logical that most of these should be initial, or at least intermediate, in the chain of metabolism. It seems unlikely from the processes affected that many terminal systems are involved.

Considering tissue differentiation, certain herbicides are able to alter the processes involved to the extent of greatly modifying structure. Typical chemicals exerting such formative effects are the phenoxy compounds, tri-chloro-benzoic acid, maleic hydrazide, T.C.A., Dalapon, amino triazole, and the chloroacetamides. Typical plants are cotton, Tokay grapes, black-eyed peas, certain cereals, and a wide array of weeds.

Finally, with the increasing interest in experimental morphology, it seems possible that these and other yet undiscovered chemicals may be used comparatively to analyze differentiation processes and eventually to characterize and explain them. Such chemical tools have the advantage over surgical procedures of being absorbed, translocated, and eventually metabolized by intact plants.

LITERATURE CITED

AHLGREN, G. H., G. C. KLINGMAN, AND D. E. WOLF. 1951. Principles of weed control. Wiley. New York.

ANONYMOUS. 1951. Sheep killing weed. Life [magazine] 30:55–56. Jan. 15.

BLACKMAN, G. E., W. G. TEMPLEMAN, AND D. J. HALLIDAY. 1951. Herbicides and selective toxicity. Ann. Rev. Plant Physiol. 2:199–230.

CRAFTS, A. S. 1945. A new herbicide, 2,4-dinitro 6 secondary butyl phenol. Science 101(2625):417–418.

———. 1946. Selectivity of herbicides. Plant Physiol. 21(3):345–361.

———. 1948a. A theory of herbicidal action. Science 108(2795):85–86.

———. 1948b. Results of soil treatment vs. contact sprays in corn and cane weed control. Agric. Chem. 3(5):25–27, 81–85.

———. 1951. Movement of assimilates, viruses, growth regulators, and chemical indicators in plants. Bot. Rev. 17:203–284.

———. 1953. Herbicides. Ann. Rev. Plant Physiol. 4:253–282.

———. 1956a. Translocation of herbicides. I. The mechanism of translocation: Methods of study with C^{14} labeled 2,4-D. Hilgardia 26:287–334.

———. 1956b. Translocation of herbicides. II. Absorption and translocation of 2,4-D by wild morning-glory. Hilgardia 26:335–365.

CURRIER, H. B., AND S. A. PEOPLES. 1954. Phytotoxicity of hydrocarbons. Hilgardia 23:155–173.

DEWEY, L. H. 1901. Canada thistle. U.S. Dept. Agric. Div. Bot. Cir. 27.

FREED, V. H. 1952. Mode of action of herbicides other than aryloxyalkyl acids. Symp. Rept. Amer. Chem. Soc. 122nd Meeting. (Atlantic City, N.J., Sept. 14–19, 1952.)

——— AND L. F. REMMERT. 1956. Inhibition of an enzyme by 2,4-D under *in vitro* conditions. Annual Progress Report to W-11 Technical Committee. Feb. 4, 1956. Sacramento, Calif.

HILL, G. D. 1955. Soil factors as related to herbicide action. Paper presented before Section IV of the Charter Meeting of the Weed Society of America. (Hotel New Yorker, New York, Jan. 5, 1956.)

IVENS, G. W., AND G. E. BLACKMAN. 1949. The effects of phenyl-carbamates on the growth of higher plants. Symp. Soc. for Exptl. Biol. 3:266–282.

KOEPFLI, J. B., K. V. THIMANN, AND F. W. WENT. 1938. Phytohormones: structure and physiological activity. Jour. Biol. Chem. 122:763–780.

LAMBERTZ, PETER. 1954. Untersuchungen über das Vorkommen von Plasmodesmen in den Epidermisaussenwänder. Planta 44:147–190.

LEONARD, O. A., AND A. S. CRAFTS. 1956. Translocation of herbicides. III. Uptake and distribution of radioactive 2,4-D by brush species. Hilgardia 26:366–415.

LEOPOLD, A. C. 1955. Auxins and plant growth. Univ. California Press. Berkeley, Calif.

LOOMIS, W. E. 1956. Mechanism of herbicidal action. Paper presented before the Charter Meeting of the Weed Society of America. (Hotel New Yorker, New York, Jan. 4, 1956.)

MUENSCHER, W. C. 1949. Weeds. Macmillan. New York.

NORMAN, A. G., C. E. MINARIK, AND R. L. WEINTRAUB. 1950. Herbicides. Ann. Rev. Plant Physiol. 1:141–168.

ORGELL, W. H. 1954. The isolation and permeability of plant cuticle. Ph.D. dissertation. Univ. of California. Davis.

QUISENBERRY, R. S. 1948. Crop production potentials in relation to freedom from want. Chronica Botanica 11:(4)237–245.

ROBBINS, W. W. 1940. Alien plants growing without cultivation in California. California Agric. Expt. Sta. Bull. 637:1–128.

———, A. S. CRAFTS, AND R. N. RAYNOR. 1952. Weed control. McGraw-Hill. New York.

SCOTT, FLORA M. 1955. Electron microscope study of cell wall growth. 25th Ann. Winter Meeting Western Soc. Nat. (Davis, Calif., Dec. 28–30.)

SWEZEY, A. W. 1955. Baron presents low drift hazard. Down-to-earth 11(3):10–11.

SYNERHOLM, M. E., AND P. W. ZIMMERMAN. 1947. Preparation of a series of γ-(2,4-dichlorophenoxy)-aliphatic acids and some relative compounds with a consideration of their biochemical role as plant growth regulators. Contrib. Boyce Thompson Inst. 14:369–382.

TUKEY, H. B. 1954. The contribution of atomic energy to agriculture. Statement in the Hearings before the Subcommittee on research and development of the Joint Committee on Atomic Energy, Congress of the United States. 37–39. U.S. Govt. Printing Office.

WAIN, R. L. 1955. Herbicidal selectivity through specific action of plants on compounds applied. Agr. and Food Chem. 3(2):128–129.

WEINTRAUB, R. L. 1952. Mechanisms of action of 2,4-D. Symposium Rept. Am. Chem. Soc. 122nd Meeting. (Atlantic City, N.J., Sept. 14–19, 1952.)

WESTGATE, W. A., AND R. N. RAYNOR. 1940. A new selective spray for the control of certain weeds. California Agric. Expt. Sta. Bull. 634.

WILKINSON, R. E. 1956. The physiological activity of 2,2-dichloropropionic acid. Ph.D. dissertation. Univ. of California. Davis.

WILSON, FRANK. 1943. The entomological control of St. Johnswort (*Hypericum perforatum* L.) with particular reference to the insect enemies of the weed in southern France. Austral. Council Sci. Indus. Res. Bull. 169.

23

HORTICULTURE IS A GREAT GREEN CARPET THAT COVERS THE EARTH

H. B. Tukey

From the air the earth looks green—a great green mantle stretched out protectingly and warmly over the good earth. This is a proper concept, because without the chlorophyll that gives this green color, the good earth would not be so good. There would be no life, no coal or wood or oil for fuel, no food-stuffs or fiber, and remarkably little shelter. The green mantle has that wonderful property of being able to capture the energy of the sun and tie it up in what we call the products of photosynthesis—the sugars and the starches and other organic compounds made from the carbon dioxide of the air. No, there would be no plant life and there would be no animal life. The *good* earth might perhaps more properly be called the *green* earth. This is the sort of thing with which Horticulture deals—a great green mantle or carpet covering the earth.

Originally, Horticulture meant the cultivation of a garden. Those plants which were cultivated in gardens or in more intensive types of plant growing acquired the name of "horticultural plants" in contrast to field crops. This has meant flowers, fruits, vegetables, ornamentals, and sometimes herbs and medicinal plants. It represents a certain refinement of agriculture, some of which comes with leisure and which is associated with home.

On this green carpet of Horticulture are gathered all kinds and conditions of men. There are (1) those interested in the science, or biological, side of Horticulture—botanists, chemists, physicists, geneticists, plant breeders, soil experts, and the like; (2) those interested in the business, or affairs, side of Horticulture—seedsmen, nurserymen, florists, fruit growers, vegetable growers, produce merchants, canners, freezers, and the like; and (3) those interested in the home and art side of Horticulture—the amateur gardener, the housewife, and all those who enjoy plants for the satisfaction they derive from them.

Horticulture is not restricted to professional horticulturists. There were stars before there was astronomy, and there were plants before there were professional horticulturists.

THE SCIENCE, OR BIOLOGICAL, SIDE OF HORTICULTURE

Over a period of generations many individuals have developed an understanding of plants and how they grow, which is as though they had become a part of the plant and were able to thread their way in and about it as easily and with as much understanding as they would their own homes. Some people have dubbed this "experience," "common sense," or the "green thumb."

And while all this is fine, there are not enough craftsmen with the green thumb to satisfy all needs. Further, while the green thumb may have its virtues, it may also have its faults. My father-in-law tells a story that illustrates the point. One of the good neighbors a mile or so down the road had an intelligent young daughter, Sarah, who came to the house now and then to help with the cooking. And when Sarah cooked a ham, she invariably cut off the shank portion. Asked why she did this, she replied, "Because mother always cooks a ham that way." The next time my father-in-law visited the neighbors he thought to ask why Sarah had been taught to cut the shank from the ham when she cooked it. At which the mother went straight to the kitchen, returning smilingly with a small pan in her hands, to say, "You see, we always cut off the shank because we did not have a pan large enough to hold a *whole* ham!"

And so, sooner or later, we invariably turn to some system whereby the art and the folklore of a subject may become tested, rationalized, and catalogued, so that it can be handed to a great number of men for use. This is particularly so in America, where the exactitudes of conquering and subduing a continent have left little opportunity for some of the qualities which only time provides. The tendency in America has been to work as much as possible, therefore, by rules and handbooks and charts and tables as the engineer would do when he builds a bridge, so as to remove the guesswork and the gamble.

From this has come a sort of "biological engineering," or in our case "horticultural engineering." It is all based on research and the research method, which is essentially a careful or critical search for knowledge, participated in and enjoyed by many—trained scientists, professional horticulturists, fruit growers, and amateurs alike. It has come alive all over the world. Science knows no geographical or political boundaries.

SCIENTIFIC PLANT BREEDING. Happily, there is already a good start toward "horticultural engineering." The creation of improved varieties of horticultural plants by scientific breeding methods is an example. In the past left largely to chance, new varieties are now made to order for particular needs. The hardy chrysanthemums from Chicago, the hybrid onions from the U.S. Department of Agriculture, the Great Lakes lettuce from Michigan, the improved Pascal types of celery from Cornell, the disease-resistant cabbage from Wisconsin, the V-peaches from Canada, the Cortland apple, the Stanley plum, and the Catskill strawberry from New York, the series of Haven peaches from Michigan, the Shasta and Lassen strawberries from California, the Latham red raspberry from Minnesota, the Blakemore strawberry from Louisiana—these are all products of scientific plant breeding. In the United States, 55 per cent of strawberry production, 75 per cent of red raspberry production, and 90 per cent of blueberry production are now represented by varieties created by scientific effort.

CHIMAERAS, POLYPLOIDY, AND PLANT BREEDING. The scientist has learned that many fruits are truly monstrosities, or chimaeras as they are properly called. The chimaera of mythology possessed the head of a lion vomiting flame, the body of a goat, and the tail of a serpent! Some bud sports, many variegations, and such odd fruits as the Sweet-and-Sour variety of apple, with one portion sweet and an adjacent portion sour, are now explained as chimaeral and composed of a mixture of tissues of varying genetic make-up—not the uniform, solid, simple creation we have often surmised.

Basically, most plants are diploids; that is, they have two identical sets of chromosomes in each cell. The raspberry, for example, has two sets of seven chromosomes—a total of fourteen. Plants with more than two sets of chromosomes are called polyploids. Specifically, if they have two sets, they are diploids; if three sets, triploids; if four sets, tetraploids—and so on.

Many polyploids have arisen in nature during thousands and thousands of years by chance doubling of chromosomes. From these, man has selected many desirable forms for cultivation, which are now the varieties of commerce. The cultivated strawberry is an octoploid, with eight sets of chromosomes; and the blackberry ranges from diploid to twelve-ploid.

The thornless blackberry is found to consist of a layer of thornless tissue covering an interior tissue of thorniness. When a "thornless" blackberry is propagated from stem cuttings, the resulting plants are thornless because the thornless tissue still continues as the other layer. But when propagation is by root cuttings, the resulting plants are frequently thorny, for the reason that roots arise from the internal "thorny" tissue.

Further, a plant chimaera may consist of a mixture of diploid and polyploid tissues, in which the typical number of chromosomes (diploid) may be covered or mixed with a higher (polyploid) or lower (haploid) number of chromosomes. Since polyploid tissues are frequently coarser than tissues which contain a smaller number of chromosomes, the result may be apple fruits with uneven polyploid sectors or ribs, flowers with large and small petals in the same flower, and anthers which contain pollen with varying chromosome number. When such anomalous flowers are used as parents in breeding, the resulting progenies are in consequence confusing and unpredictable.

The red bud sports of apple and pear are frequently only "skin-deep." The red pigment change may occur only in the outer layer or layers of the fruit, yet completely cover the internal layers of non-red characteristics. Likewise, plants with pubescent or hairy leaves and fruits may give rise to smooth or glabrous forms through a mutation in the outer layer of the plant so that hairs do not develop from epidermal cells. The typically smooth-skinned nectarine is but a bud sport of the typically fuzzy peach. It is not surprising that peach trees give rise to nectarines and that nectarines give rise to peach trees.

The variegated leaf patterns of the garden and the conservatory are the products of various combinations of layers of cells containing different pigments. Thus a section of the outer layer may appear colorless because it contains no pigment. Another section contains light green pigment. Beneath may be a layer of dark green pigment or red pigment. The whitish, reddish, green, and shaded segments, blotches, and patches are the result of these overlapping and variously arranged chimaeral tissues. Small wonder we have had difficulties in the past in understanding the vagaries of some of our cultivated plants.

But the plant breeder is no longer ignorant of these situations and he need no longer wait ages for an accident of nature to produce a desired change in chromosome number. By means of a drug (colchicine) derived from a species of *Colchicum,* he is able to induce an artifical change in one season so so as to provide him with just the plant material he needs for breeding purposes.

Thus, the southern muscadine grape is a diploid with 40 chromosomes. It does not cross readily with the northern bunch grape which has 38 chromosomes. By treating both species with colchicine, the chromosome number of each has been doubled (tetraploid). These new forms will now combine to blend the characters from both species. Again, a variety of apple may have three sets of chromosomes (triploid) and may not be useful as a parent in breeding because of the abnormalities which arise during reduction division. Happily, the plant breeder can induce a doubling up of the chromosome number to form a fertile hexaploid which can now be successfully used in breeding.

The plant breeder has been given additional new tools by the geneticist, cytologist, chemist, and plant physiologists. By performing a Caesarian section on immature fruits, removing the partially developed embryos, and culturing them like incubator babies as with certain species of Prunus, he has succeeded in making heretofore impossible crosses. By the use of certain growth-regulating chemicals he can prevent abscission of the flower as with the lily, until fertilization has been effected.

The contributions of hybrid vigor have been put to valuable use. In the case of those plants which carry the male flowers and the female flowers in separate parts, as in corn, it has been possible to remove the male parts (tassels) easily and so effect the cross-fertilization from selected inbred lines to produce seed stocks with hybrid vigor and other desired characters. But with many other plants which carry both male and female parts in the same flowers, as the onion, snapdragon, tomato, petunia, and carrot, the tedious separation of male and female parts has made hybrid seed expensive and difficult. Here again, however, the plant breeder has used his scientific skills effectively. He has located individual plants which are by nature male-sterile, as with male-sterile onions. He has found ways of producing lines of male-sterile onions, which when planted with selected male-fertile lines produce an abundant supply of hybrid onion seed. Other vegetable and flower plants are responding to this approach, promising to revolutionize the seed trade.

The plant breeder has learned, also, that certain varieties when used as parents tend to stamp their offspring with desirable characters, while others are inferior sires. He knows that the Deacon Jones apple transmits size, that the Mills grape transmits high quality, and that the Lloyd George red raspberry and the Premier strawberry are superior as parents. On the other hand, the Baldwin and Rhode Island Greening apples and the Seckel pear, though desirable in themselves, are most inferior parents.

It may not be out of place to comment on the importance of the variety and of those who serve by the creation of improved sorts. The variety is the keystone of the industry. It is to the fruit industry what the new model is to the automobile industry. Until the Concord grape, there was no grape culture in America worthy of the name. The Bartlett (Williams) pear is the basis of pear production, and the Montmorency cherry is virtually the entire sour cherry industry.

In Michigan prior to 1920 there were hundreds of acres of unproductive land on which lived families of low income. The creation of new varieties of blueberries by scientific plant breeding has developed an industry now approaching 4 million dollars in annual crop sales. A breeding program in apricots promises to establish an apricot industry, and a red-centered strawberry suited to southwestern Michigan will ensure the maintenance of canning and freezing outlets. It is apparent that plant breeding must become increasingly more local. The general-purpose variety is useful, and that is what is aimed at, but the future implies a variety not necessarily for a continent, nor for a large region, but rather for a given purpose in a restricted locality. It implies breeding, not alone for specific details of improvement, but with great imagination for entirely new industries.

POLLINATION AND FRUIT SET. As recently as the 1890's, pollination and fruit set were little understood by commercial fruit growers and their importance was poorly appreciated. Compatibilities and incompatibilities are now better known. No one today would plant a solid block of Delicious apples, Bartlett pears, Windsor sweet cherries, or J. H. Hale peaches. These varieties have been found to be self-unfruitful for one reason or another. The modern orchardist must select varieties to interplant for effective cross-pollination and fertilization. And he would not use as pollenizers such triploid varieties as the Gravenstein and Baldwin apples, nor the J. H. Hale peach, all of which have defective pollen. This has been the product of research.

In commercial practice, the bee may be used as the agent for pollinating with some regard to temperature, bee flight, and number of bees required for a given area. Traps have been devised so that pollen is scraped from the creatures as they enter the hive loaded with pollen. In turn this pollen has been placed in trays at the hive egress, so that bees emerge coated with proper pollen ready for business. Hand pollination has been found practical in some areas, and shot-gun shells loaded with pollen have been fired with some success at trees in the unfortunate modern tempo of treating everybody and everything as an adversary!

Some plants, as the tomato and cucumber, will respond to applications of certain chemicals, such as *para*-chlorophenoxyacetic acid for fruit setting, and will produce seedless fruits without pollination and fertilization. Further, it has been found that the tomato does not set fruit when night temperatures are below 59°F. Under such conditions, hand spraying with plant-regulating chemicals and raising the night temperature by artifical covering have both proved effective. As an additional practical sidelight, the knowledge that tomatoes do not set fruit in early spring until night temperatures are above 59°F. has made it possible to forecast several weeks in advance when the main crop of tomato fruits will reach the local market.

BLOSSOM THINNING AND FRUIT DEVELOPMENT. In recent years, securing a set of fruit has become less of a problem generally in orchard circles than thinning off excess fruits. Here it has been found that early thinning is most effective, beginning with blossom thinning. It is interesting to note in this connection that as long ago as 1835, Robert Manning of Salem, Massachusetts, one of America's early pomologists, found that by removing all the blossoms from some biennially bearing apple trees and not from others, he caused some trees to fruit one year and others the next, thus ensuring fruit each year. However, thinning of fruit by hand is now largely a thing of the past. In its place are chemical thinning and pole thinning of various types, in which blossoms and young fruits are literally beaten or brushed crudely from the trees.

Thinning of apples by means of blossom-thinning sprays has become standard practice in large areas, and there is some success with peaches from applications several weeks after bloom. Dinitrocresols have been used in some regions, but growth regulators, such as naphthaleneacetic acid and naphthaleneacetamide, have been found more effective in others. It has been learned that such sprays tend to "knock off" the weak blossoms and leave the strong, so that the quality of the remaining fruit is improved both by reduction of competition and by "the survival of the fittest." The concentration of the chemical is adjusted to the variety, the season, and the vigor of fruit buds; that is, stronger concentrations are used with varieties which characteristically set heavily, with trees with vigorous fruit buds, and in seasons where weather at blossom time is highly favorable to fruit set. Weaker concentrations are used under the opposite conditions. Blossom thinning has proved one of the most effective agents in maintaining annual production in American apple orchards. Yet there is a feeling in some quarters that the fruit industry will be better served by the use of solid blocks of a single variety of small controlled trees upon which the blossoms are caused to set where desired, rather than removed by somewhat uncertain means after they have set.

To this end, studies with growth-regulating chemicals have shown some possibilities. For example, the Kadota and Mission varieties of fig commonly set fruit parthenocarpically, whereas the Calimyrna variety requires pollination and fertilization. Yet this last-named variety can be caused to set fruit parthenocarpically by the use of certain growth regulators and without the aid of the caprifying wasp. It now appears that the varieties which set fruit without resort to pollination have a higher content of native hormone than does the Calimyrna. Research shows that fruit set and fruit development are related to liberation of specific hormones by pollen, by endosperm, by embryo, and probably by other parts. Extracts of corn pollen and of corn embryo will set tomato fruits. It is not too much to expect that the research worker will in time appear with methods of controlling fruit set more exactly.

Research in the field of plant regulators has made, and is still making, contributions to the horticultural industry equal to, if not greater than, any other field of endeavor at the moment. Not only are blossoms and fruits both set and thinned, but the time of blossoming may be delayed. Maleic hydrazide has proved suited to the raspberry and related brambles. No practicable method of delaying fruit blossoming of tree fruits has yet been devised, but the possibilities are there. Fall applications of such materials as 2,4-dichlorophenoxyacetic acid and naphthaleneacetic acid to cherry trees, for example, have resulted in a 7- to 10-day delay in blossoming, but winter injury to the tree is not uncommon and the developing fruit is often misshapen and unmarketable.

Sprays of certain plant regulators, as indolebutyric acid, applied to developing figs at the proper time, cause them to ripen 14 days after treatment as compared with 75 days for typical development of non-treated fruit. The strawberry fruit develops because of the diffusion of plant-regulating materials from the achenes which dot its surface. About the sixteenth day after bloom, the supply of regulator is low. Additional amounts of synthetic regulators, as beta phenoxyacetic acid, applied at about this time, apparently induce continued growth and increased size. Improved size of blackberries has similarly been secured by similar treatments.

The application of plant regulators to prevent pre-harvest drop of fruit has become standard practice with both apples and pears. The action is apparently to delay the development of the abscission zone in the pedicel of the fruit. Naphthaleneacetic acid and naphthaleneacetamide are the materials most frequently employed. Proper timing with relation to temperature, rainfall, and fruit development is critical. 2,4-Dichlorophenoxyacetic acid has been found to be effective and specific in the prevention of pre-harvest drop of the Stayman and the Winesap varieties of apple. Curiously, this material is ineffective with a number of other apple varieties. 2,4,5-Trichlorophenoxypropionic acid causes apples not only to ripen early but also to color early. But success has been uncertain. Fortunately, this material is also effective for reducing pre-harvest drop.

BLOSSOM INDUCTION AND PHOTOPERIOD. One of the features of Horticulture is that it frequently removes plants from their natural habitat and places them in an environment where one or more climatic variables is markedly altered. Thus, a glasshouse may reproduce the temperature at which a plant grows in its native habitat, but the characteristic long day length of summer may be replaced by a short day length of winter with resultant alteration of flowering habit. Further, the horticultural industry variously demands flowers, fruits, seeds, and special vegetative parts from different kinds of plants. Accordingly, there is great concern about the factors which both induce and reduce blossom formation, reduce and induce seed development, and promote and retard various vegetative structures. This is a major field for horticultural research which offers additional great promise.

Light, day length, temperature, nutrition, and various chemical treatments have been shown to induce blossom formation. Thus, in the case of the tomato, a cool temperature early in the life of the plant induces the formation of flower clusters, a fact which explains why Northern tomato plants grown in the field directly from seed may in a cool season produce fruit earlier than Southern-grown transplanted plants.

An undesirable effect of early cool temperatures is found with early celery. When exposed to cool temperatures, blossom formation is induced and seedstalks are produced (bolting) which makes such celery unsalable. Lettuce tends to form blossoms and seedstalks with high summer temperatures and long days. Breeding programs for these crops are aimed at selecting plants with "non-bolting" characters.

Some plants, as the chrysanthemum, respond to short day length. By extending the day length with artificial light, plants may be prevented from forming flowers. By reducing day length, they may be induced to flower. By proper attention, chrysanthemums can be brought into flower at any month of the year.

Other plants, as the cineraria, respond to long day length and may be similarly controlled in flower formation by adjusting the day length.

Plant regulators may likewise exert a profound effect upon blossom formation. For example, N-m-tolylphthalamic acid will increase blossom number in the tomato and naphthaleneacetic acid is used commercially in Hawaii to control flowering in the pineapple.

More recently, the gibberellins have been shown to affect flowering in several plants. Applications of gibberellic acid to some biennial plants, as the carrot and the collard, have resulted in these plants developing as annuals.

ENVIRONMENTAL ADAPTATION OF HORTICULTURAL PLANTS. Matters of soil, location, and site are perhaps now as well understood as any aspect of Horticulture. It is known that certain areas are suited to peaches, others to pears, potatoes, celery, and so on. Yet too much of this has been learned by bitter experience. The new technique is to study adaptation by controlled experiments and to be able to predict. Thus, branches of trees are enclosed in cooled and in heated chambers as desired to simulate different climatic conditions. It is found by this means that sour cherry fruits grow rapidly at high night temperatures for a period immediately following full bloom, but that they develop slowly, with low quality and with poor color, if the night temperatures are high late in the season as the fruit is maturing. Accordingly, it would seem that the sour cherry would be best suited to an environment where early summer temperatures were relatively high, followed by cool night temperatures prior to harvest. That the sour cherry industry is confined largely to Michigan, Wisconsin, and New York is thus seen to be more than chance.

Delayed dormancy of fruit trees is another problem in adaptation which has been met by research. Considerable distress has been experienced in Southern sections in some seasons with delayed and scattered foliation and blossoming and attendant financial reverses. The answer has been found in varying hours of chilling required by different varieties of peaches, so that varieties which are adapted to the long chilling provided by Northern winters do not break dormancy in Southern regions. Varieties of tree fruits for the South are now catalogued as to the amount of chilling required to break dormancy. Further, breeding programs recognize these facts and have successfully developed varieties of peaches adapted to southern California and to other Southern regions. The shift of peach production southward even into Florida is a direct outcome of this type of research.

The bulbing of onions, the tubering of potatoes, the bolting of celery and lettuce, and the adaptation of certain floricultural crops and woody ornamentals to various geographical locations are now better understood and predictable. Recently it has been shown, for example, that the Northern distribution of certain azaleas and rhododendrons is limited in nature by the fact that in the relatively longer summer day lengths of Northern latitudes, these plants do not mature properly and are subject to killing by winter cold. Also, some varieties of strawberries tend to form flower buds in long days and are therefore successful in Northern regions, whereas other varieties form fruit buds in shorter days and so are adapted to other regions.

Further, plants are grown in large constant-temperature tanks where the root temperature can be properly maintained. With a root temperature of 45°F., strawberry plants require less fertilizer for the production of the same amount of dry weight than they do at 75°F. Further, there is a difference in soil-temperature requirements between varieties. When it is realized that there may be as much as 30 degrees difference between the temperature of soil under mulch and under clean cultivation, such information has real significance.

Another recent contribution to orcharding has come from studies involving the growing of fruit-tree rootstocks at controlled root temperatures. Until recently, there has been great difficulty in determining the natural adaptation of several of the clonal Malling apple rootstocks. Now it is found that certain of these rootstocks, such as Malling IX, produce new roots even at root temperatures of 44°F., whereas they disintegrate in soil temperatures of 77°F. and higher. On the other hand, French Crab seedling rootstocks produce no new roots at 44°F., but grow luxuriously at 77°F. or higher; and Malling VII seems adapted to a wide range of soil temperature, producing roots at 55°F. as well as at 77°F. The results explain the growing popularity of Malling IX in the North and of Malling VII as a widely adapted apple rootstock in the United States and the abandonment of Malling IX in Southern regions in place of French Crab rootstocks which will tolerate high soil temperatures.

Temperature studies of this kind may also reveal much regarding adaptation of varieties, responses to plant regulators for blossom thinning and pre-harvest drop, coloring of fruit, and development of good finish in association with various spray materials.

NUTRITION AND FERTILIZERS. As regards fertilizers and fruit-tree nutrition, the case no longer rests with chemical analysis of the soil alone. Analyses of the tissues of the plant have been found valuable to supply additional information. The use of nitrogen has become fairly well standardized with either fall applications or early spring applications. But, as dependence has been placed largely upon nitrogen, other materials have been found of increasing importance, such as phosphorus and potassium. Various other deficiency troubles also have been identified and have been corrected by the application of specific materials, as the little-leaf disease of citrus with zinc and the internal corking of apples with boron. The trend now is to use leaf analysis by the spectrographic method for large-scale surveys of nutritional status and as the basis for rapid determination of plant needs. Balance between various elements is receiving considerable attention, as, for example, the relation between calcium and boron, in which boron aids in the efficient use of calcium.

Perhaps the outstanding contribution to general orchard-management practices has been the use of mulches. While first found beneficial in apple orchards, they have since proved of value for pears and to a limited degree for peaches and cherries. Minor element deficiencies have tended to disappear under mulch, potash and phosphorus have become more readily available, and moisture supply has been increased. Associated with mulching are improved soil structure, better aeration, and increased penetration of rain. The mulching materials used are usually spoiled hay from a nearby farm, bearing out the axiom that "it is an ill wind that blows nobody good." Mulching has proved "better than we know" and has been one of the major shifts in orchard management in America.

As the appraisal of nutrition becomes more refined and more exact, there is considerable interest in foliar sprays. Such deficiencies as manganese, magnesium, zinc, and boron have been corrected by foliage applications. Further, it has been shown that bark applications may be effective under certain conditions. Sprays of nitrogen, mostly in the form of urea, have proved valuable supplements to soil applications. Urea is easily applied in the regular spray program and may be absorbed in a few hours. It may be applied to apple trees early in the spring in delayed dormant and pre-blossom sprays when this element is needed to assist in fruit set. Additional sprays may be made if the season so requires. Such a wait-and-see program tends to the production of fruit of high color, since no excess of nitrogen is permitted as maturity approaches.

Not all plants respond equally well to sprays of urea. Apparently there is a relation between toxicity to urea and response from it; that is, the peach, potato, and cherry respond very little and will withstand concentrations of 10 to 20 pounds of urea to 100 gallons of water. The plum responds next in order and will tolerate 8 to 10 pounds. The pear responds slightly less than the apple and will withstand 6 to 10 pounds. For the apple, about 5 pounds is correct. The grape and the cucumber respond readily and will tolerate only 3 to 4 pounds.

An old bit of research, which still lays a heavy and controlling hand (some might even say a dead hand) upon much horticultural thinking and practice, is the so-called carbohydrate-nitrogen relationship. It is worth repeating here because, though it may represent an oversimplification or only a partial statement of the truth, it nevertheless is a good example of the synthesis of research into a working hypothesis—more of which we today so badly need. In American terminology we say "it works" and let it go at that. However, this does give the opportunity at this point to stress that in our quest for something new we in research have failed, too often, to put the pieces together into some framework of usefulness. The job is not done when the experiment is completed. It is done when it is made intelligible to others and can be used by them. This, then, is the excuse for introducing so elementary a topic as the carbohydrate-nitrogen relationship and one which, from the standpoint of the scientist, may properly be called naive.

Simply stated, nitrogen is secured by the plant principally from the soil and is influenced in amount and availability by temperature, soil moisture, root penetration, and other soil environmental factors. On the other hand, the carbohydrates are manufactured in the green portion of the plant from the carbon dioxide of the atmosphere in the presence of light. The general idea is that the ability of a plant to fruit is indicated by the relationship between carbohydrates and nitrogen in the plant.

On this basis, fruit trees may be placed in one of four classes as regards C-N relationship and fruiting:

Class I is the plant which has an abundance of nitrogen but a deficiency of accumulated carbohydrates. It is the thin-wooded, spindly, weak tree that grows in the shade. It is like an undernourished child. It does not develop and does not fruit.

Class II is the adolescent, which, supplied with an abundance of both nitrogen and carbohydrates, keeps on growing exuberantly, with large dark green foliage, but does not get down to the business of fruiting.

Class III is the highly productive individual, in which sufficient reserve carbohydrates have accumulated to provide for fruit-bud formation and fruiting. This is the age of maximum production and the joy of the successful fruit grower.

Class IV is the age of senescence and decline, where carbohydrates have accumulated to such a degree that the foliage is yellowish in color, the tree biennial in bearing, and the characteristics of age appearing—not unlike the man who accumulated sufficient avoirdupois to be termed "a bit heavy" or even "corpulent," and who is content to sit by the fire in his slippers, except for sporadic outbursts of enthusiasm from time to time which slowly diminish.

With these four classes clearly in mind, it has been shown that much can be done in the fruit plantation to control the behavior of a tree. The weak tree of *Class I* needs to be brought into the sunshine, where it may manufacture more carbohydrates, pass into the adolescent stage of *Class II,* and there accumulate a sufficiency of carbohydrates to settle down into the productive period of middle life (*Class III*). Conversely, the aging tree of *Class IV* can be rejuvenated and brought back into the productivity of *Class III* both by severe pruning, which removes excess carbohydrates, and by application of nitrogenous fertilizers, which increase the nitrogen balance.

Further, ringing and girdling are helpful in bringing a tree from *Class II* of adolescence over into the productive *Class III* by virtue of the fact that carbohydrates are induced to accumulate above the ring or girdle. Root pruning is similarly helpful, but for the reason that it reduces the intake of nitrogen. High summer temperatures may delay fruiting in young trees because the tree respires carbohydrates too rapidly to accumulate a sufficient amount for fruitfulness. Pruning a young tree excessively removes the carbohydrates, prevents accumulation, and tends to keep the tree in the weak, non-fruiting *Class II*.

Insect and disease attack and caustic sprays which injure the foliage all likewise tend to reduce the carbohydrate supply and delay fruiting.

Many mortals have recognized the similarity of all of this to the behavior of animals and have dreamed wistfully, but forlornly, upon some method of rejuvenation, such as Ponce de León sought in the Fountain of Youth several centuries ago.

PROPAGATION AND WEED CONTROL. The propagation of horticultural plants by vegetative means has been greatly improved by research. Studies have shown the differences which exist in plant parts used as cuttings which are taken from plants of varying age and composition. Plants in the so-called "juvenile condition" root more readily than do so-called "adult plants." In the apple, cuttings taken from plants no older than two years from seed may be rooted easily, but with difficulty thereafter.

Etiolation favors rooting of hard-to-root material; and leaching with water has sometimes favored rooting, as though some inhibiting substance had been removed in the leaching.

A number of plant regulators, such as indolebutyric acid, have been found helpful in the rooting of cuttings. However, the general effect has been more to speed up the process of rooting than to induce new roots to form.

Since many horticultural crops require intensive culture with much hand labor for the control of weeds, research on chemical control of weeds has received much attention and with considerable success. Certain oil sprays have proved effective with some crops, and sulfuric acid has proved of value with others. The most spectacular results have followed the use of plant regulators, such as 2,4-dichlorophenoxyacetic acid and 2,4,5-trichlorophenoxyacetic acid. These materials have proved selective in action. 2,4-Dichlorophenoxyacetic acid has proved valuable in controlling broad-leafed weeds in strawberry beds, the strawberry being resistant to the chemical. Isopropylphenylcarbamate is helpful for control of chickweed, and EH-1 for pre-emergence treatments. Another interesting possibility is the destruction of strawberry runners by chemical means, thus permitting retention of the old bed for longer periods of high productivity.

THE NATURE OF HORTICULTURAL RESEARCH. And finally, a word about the pattern of research. Research is the critical search for knowledge. The word is often used to imply only professional or high-level scientific activity. One sometimes hears the expression "pure research," as though there were a form of research which is impure. The terms "fundamental" and "basic" are employed often with the connotation of superiority. Yet, fundamental research is simply research which is fundamental to something else, as trees are fundamental to lumber and lumber is fundamental to carpentry. What is fundamental research of today is the applied research of tomorrow, only to be replaced in turn by something else fundamental.

It would seem that the real test of research is its *quality*. A fruit grower, vegetable grower, seedman, or florist who is diligently and self-critically seeking information is a useful research worker. There is no reason to exclude anyone from the field; in fact, the more inclusive the term can be made, the better. Some of the most worthwhile leads and suggestions have come from the careful study and observations of amateurs. In the final test there are but two kinds of research—good research and bad research—the product of the long hard road requiring much time, or the easier and shorter road of mere superficial and often misleading observation.

Of course the emphasis in the program of research may vary. There may be the emphasis on solving the little problem that arises day by day—what we call "trouble-shooting"—and there may be the more carefully considered development type of research. Also there may be the closely directed research, and there may be disinterested research, of which patience and free time are the essence.

Ordinarily, the support of research begins with the closely directed form. But the disinterested form, which may be at the moment less spectacular and often viewed with impatience, is the one which is being accepted more and more as the real "payoff" in significant achievement. As someone has said, it is more profitable just to dig than to dig specifically for a gold nugget. Urged on by love of digging, one may dig deeper and in a new vein. Practicality often is synonymous with shortsightedness. Horace Walpole coined the word "serendipity" for the gift of finding valuable or agreeable things not sought for. Dr. Irving Langmuir speaks of "the art of profiting from unexpected occurrences."

This does not mean, of course, that some degree of common sense should not prevail. If one is hunting elephants, he might more properly select Africa than London for his hunting grounds, yet an elephant escaping from the zoo might perhaps reward a hunter of big game, even in the streets of London. Or, to put it as someone else has done, "Even a blind hog occasionally gets a chestnut."

It would seem obvious, however, that research workers in Horticulture should properly stay in the field of Horticulture. In fact, it is doubtful if the research worker in Horticulture should ever take his eye off the commodity, the individual, and the industry he serves. This limitation is hardly to be looked upon as confining. There is plenty of latitude.

Generally speaking, the horticultural industry is well aware of the value of research. But it is becoming increasingly aware of the dividends of the long-range, not closely directed type of research. More and more a publicly supported research laboratory may be asked to spend less of its time and energy on so-called "practical" problems and be left to spend the larger percentage on the "cast-your-bread-upon-the-waters" type. No reflection is meant upon the abilities of highly trained research workers, but much of the developmental research can be carried on even better by advisers and practical men in industry.

It goes without saying that this type of research does not mean laziness, disorder, and lack of imagination. Columbus may have discovered the New World by accident, but at least he was on the high seas looking for something. This should be the privilege or reward offered only to the best-trained, the most industrious, the most imaginative, the most well-intentioned research worker and research institution. The returns of research are fabulous, even fantastic, as any will recognize who will look about for a moment and perhaps glance only at the contributions to Horticulture from chemistry in 2,4-D and DDT, or of Kidd and West upon storage, or in virus-free stone-fruit stocks. Research is the great opportunity for the modern investor.

THE AFFAIRS, OR BUSINESS SIDE, OF HORTICULTURE

The discussion so far has been aimed primarily at problems of production. But the greatest change that has come to research in American Horticulture during the past decade has not been along the lines of production; it has been along the lines of outlets, markets, and consumer acceptance.

This has been brought about by the tremendous competition between food-stuffs on the American market. In 1951 there were 125 different fruits and vegetables offered for sale in competition, 98 of these in larger-than-carload lots. Some of these products are relatively newcomers in quantity, such as escarole, dasheens, cranshaws, papayas, mangoes, kumquats, avocados, and prickly pears. The housewife is no longer required by necessity to take what is set before her, but may select what she wishes; and she is a very shrewd and efficient buyer.

Studies of the purchasing activities of Mrs. Housewife and the retail store have revealed interesting facts. As an example, it has been found that in the Detroit market between November and February the sale of oranges averaged $32.00 and of apples $29.00, both together constituting two-thirds of the fresh-fruit sales. Retailers set aside an average of 97 square feet of floor for display of fruits, of which 25 per cent was for apples. Apple sales averaged $1.19 for each square foot of display space. When the display space was increased 10 per cent, sales increased 4 per cent. A 2-pound unit of sale moved less fruit than larger units up to 6 pounds. Bulk displays placed alongside packaged displays increased sales as much as 35 per cent.

This is the kind of research and information which is being explained to growers. The result is that they are concerned as never before with matters of outlet and consumer acceptance. It is being realized that the channels of marketing are like a chain—a very poor instrument with which to push, but a very good one with which to pull. The movement of the chain begins when Mrs. Housewife buys something in the retail store. The pull is then felt clear back to the producer.

It has been found that the American diet has shifted remarkably in 40 years. The per capita caloric intake has declined from 3,500 to 3,200, expressed largely in reduction in consumption of potatoes by nearly a half, and cereals by nearly a third. On the other hand, there has been an improvement in the use of the so-called protective foods. Yellow, green, and leafy vegetables have increased about one-third. Fruits have increased about 14 per cent. Milk and dairy products have increased a third, and eggs have increased nearly as much.

Further, within the family of horticultural products there has been some shifting. The per capita consumption of apples was approximately 60 pounds 40 years ago, and it is now about 26 pounds. On the other hand, citrus has increased from 16 pounds to 50 pounds. Interestingly enough and to the surprise of American fruit growers, the per capita consumption of watermelons is the same as for apples—26 pounds. The consumption of lettuce is 21 pounds, of celery 12 pounds, of tomatoes 30 pounds.

Another change has been the increase in processing of horticultural products. More than half of all the vegetables and more than half of all the fruits produced in America are now processed in one way or another. Frozen foods, fruit juices, and prepared baby foods have increased tremendously in amount. In fact, the quantity of so-called "baby foods" is equivalent to 36 pounds per year for all children under three years of age! Over 60 per cent of the retail stores in the major cities are now equipped with frozen-food cabinets.

Still another study reveals that on the average for the nation, only 25 to 30 cents of the consumer's dollar ever reaches the fruit grower, the other 70 to 75 cents being spent for handling, packaging, transportation, and selling. And finally, it has been shown that families of high income purchase substantially more fruits and vegetables per capita than families of low income.

It is small wonder that when these facts have been brought to the attention of the fruit grower, some radical changes have been made in his thinking. It means that the fruit grower has interested himself in carrying on some of the marketing operations, which have been so remunerative, such as prepackaging, cold-storage operations, and merchandising, and that he is interested in producing a product which will compete successfully with other lines which have high market acceptability.

Obviously, many marketing problems originate in the field. The first consideration in this respect is an orderly supply of quality fruit. Many of the orchard practices that have been discussed are a result of this competitive pressure, particularly efficient insect and disease control, supplemental irrigation, blossom thinning, and foliar application of nutrients.

The second consideration is the delivery of a quality product to the consumer. Studies have shown that removal of field heat close to the place of production is imperative. The farm cold storage and large cooperative cold storages are the result. Hydro-cooling is receiving new attention, in which packed fruit is flooded with ice water as it comes in packages from the packing plant. Sour cherries are being placed in tanks of cold water at the farm and transported experimentally by tank truck to the processing plant, thus reducing both handling costs and fruit temperature at one swoop. Revolutionary thinking involves mechanical harvesters—even going so far as to think of tree defoliants which will leave the fruit for some sort of mechanical harvester.

Since the shortage of labor is the major problem on American farms, every conceivable gadget has been introduced to effect efficiency. Pneumatic pruners and hydraulic pruning and harvesting platforms have shown their worth. A strawberry-planting machine will set 25 acres of strawberries in a day. In the pruning of black raspberries a vertical and a horizontal power mower has been devised which hacks the plants into control most brutally, but most efficiently. It will be interesting to see what progress the fruit grower, the agricultural engineer, and the manufacturer will make in these directions in the next few years.

THE ART AND HOME SIDE OF HORTICULTURE

It is the art and home side of Horticulture that at the moment is crying for attention. We become so involved in the biological and the affairs side that we overlook the one that is likely to be the most important in the years immediately ahead. As Dr. Crow of Canada once said: ". . . horticultural science could make no greater mistake than to underestimate the importance of Horticulture at large to the amateur and his special interests."

Abraham Cowley in his essay on "The Garden" explained the esteem in which gardening should be held by reminding us that: "The three first men in the world were a gardener, a ploughman, and a grazier; and if any man object, that the second of these was a Murtherer, I desire he would consider, that as soon as he was so, he quitted our Profession, and turn'd Builder."

Or the remarks of Francis Bacon: "God Almighty planted a garden; and indeed it is the purest of human pleasures. It is the greatest refinement of the spirits of man, without which buildings and palaces are but gross handiworks; and a man shall ever see that when ages grow to civility and elegancy, men come to build stately, sooner than to garden finely, as if gardening were the greater perfection."

L. H. Bailey has written: "Every generation sees some great addition to the depth and meaning of the home. . . . Every perfect home has its library; so in turn it must have its garden—a room, perhaps out-of-doors, in which plants grow. . . . One third of our city and village improvement is Horticulture. Another third is architecture; and the other third is common cleanliness and decency."

Dr. W. H. Camp tells us that gardening began twenty thousand years ago when man first used cultivated plants for food. Many of these plants remained as a matter of sentiment or because they had become associated with religious ceremonies. Tulips, hyacinths, narcissus, Star-of-Bethlehem were first used as bulbous crops, like onions and garlic. Others had medicinal properties, as foxglove (*Digitalis purpurea*) from which is derived digitalis; and sweet scabious (*Scabiosa atropurpurea*) which was used as a cure for the itch. Rosemary, sage, lavender, and many mints were valued as herb plants. The root of elecampane was used as a tonic. Its age is indicated by its name, which is a corruption of the Roman *inula campana*. The garden pyrethrum (*Chrysanthemum commineum*) is closely related to the source of the insecticide, pyrethrum, derived from the dried heads of *C. cinerariaefolium*, used to rub on the body against lice and fleas.

Perfume, too, had its value, as a substitute for soap and water in times when baths were less frequent. The sweet-scented orris root was used as a dusting powder. Rose petals, lilac, lily-of-the-valley—how many of the fragrances we value have come from flowers. The dye saffron is from *Crocus sativus*. The drug colchicine is from the autumn crocus (*Colchicium autumnale*).

According to Dr. Camp, the garden began its entry into the home when the early Egyptians painted scenes on walls and floors. The cooler winters of Persia brought these scenes indoors woven into rugs and wall tapestries. The Romans put them on wallpaper. And so, many of our wallpaper, rug, and tapestry designs trace directly back to the garden, through the Romans, the Persians, and the Egyptians. It is worth noting that of 25,000 species of plants which are cultivated about 10,000 are cherished for their ornamental value as flowers.

The Japanese and Chinese dwarf trees and potted plants are but attempts at copying extensive royal gardens in miniature. Or, as Dr. Camp puts it, the garden in a fish bowl is a direct lineal descendant of Chinese gardens which Marco Polo saw; of Indian gardens in which Gautama (the founder of Buddhism) preached; of the royal game preserve and hunting park which already were common in Mesopotamia when Abraham left Ur of the Chaldees to go over into the land of Canaan. The fish-bowl garden is therefore a miniature Garden of Eden. *The World Was My Garden*, writes David Fairchild. "The World in Your Garden," writes W. H. Camp.

Someone needs to chronicle more completely the importance of Horticulture to modern society. The fleur-de-lis appears in heraldry. The Chinese willow pattern, involving peach tree, willows, and garden, is only one of many familiar horticultural designs on dinnerware and dinner service. Rugs, tapestries, wallpaper, mural paintings, furniture, Corinthian columns, ironwork, pottery, jewelry—all have some touch of Horticulture. Bailey says, "Rob the race of the art suggestions that it has had from plants and you rob it of its architecture and its decorations."

In music we find the "Last Rose of Summer," MacDowell's "To a Wild Rose," Tschaikowsky's "Waltz of the Flowers." Most of such music is soft, warm, tender, or sweet. In poetry there are Wordsworth's daffodils in "I Wandered Lonely as a Cloud," Tennyson's "Flower in the Crannied Wall," the Mother Goose rhymes of childhood, Stevenson's *A Child's Garden of Verses*, and the sentiments of James Whitcomb Riley. One of the most beautiful passages in literature is "Consider the lilies of the field, how they toil not, neither do they spin; yet I say unto you that even Solomon in all his glory was not arrayed like one of these."

In triumph we give the laurel wreath, or in modern usage, "Orchids to you"—a combination of the highest phylogenetic form and the ultimate in modernity! In sorrow, we give the funeral wreath and the floral tribute. In affection we offer flowers—". . . a rose by any other name would smell as sweet."

And if you will analyze, you will see that Horticulture is associated mostly with the senses of sight, smell, taste, and touch—seldom with sound. It is entwined with the tender, with affection, with pleasure, with harmony, with refinement, with lovely form, pleasing flavors, colors, and aromas, and with beauty. It is touched by ease, luxury, home, and children. Conflict, bustle, clash of personalities, noise, and confusion have no place in horticultural terminology.

It is because of some of these values, associated with healing, that medicine turns to Horticulture. The nervous tensions of modern living are eased by the creative and muscular outlets of gardening. The cures that have been effected and the maladies that have been prevented are uncounted. "Horticultural therapy" is a branch of occupational therapy that is developing rapidly.

On the social side, gardening is the safety valve of society. Better than standing armies and regimented recreation is the outlet of the garden. One may garden as little and as inexpensively as he likes, or as much and as extravagantly as he likes. With the drift to the cities, the country is found in the backyard garden and is carried indoors in house plants and window boxes. When grandmother can no longer tend her garden, she is found seated lovingly and shawl-covered in a rocking chair next to the window in which are growing the plants that she loved best. Plants and gardens anchor society. A geranium growing in the yard signals a home of warmth, permanence, and hospitality.

Gardening means health, stability, and happiness. The 20 million Victory Gardens did more for America than produce food. The support which industry has given to the garden movement indicates the value it has found in gardening. The appointment of committees and commissions to promote better use of leisure time on the part of both rural and village people is recognition of the trend. There must be more emphasis on living and less on making a living. This is the field in which horticulturists could well afford to spend more of their time, energy, and resources.

IN CONCLUSION

Horticulture is a field involving plants—fruits, flowers, vegetables, ornamentals, nursery crops, and the like. It has its science side, its affairs side, and its artistic, esthetic, and social sides.

As scientists working in this field, horticulturists are biologists and must tie to biology, but as they are also horticulturists, they provide a bridge, a connecting link, the liaison between biology and the business and the art sides. As L. H. Bailey has well stated, "The horticulturist is the man who joins hands with the plant biologist on the one side and with the affairs of men on the other, and whose energies are expended in every way in which plants appeal to men." The horticulturist could do no better than to chart his course with this as his compass.

LITERATURE CITED

Camp, W. H. 1947. The world in your garden. Nat. Geographic Mag. 29:1–65.

Cullinan, F. P. 1954. Looking ahead in horticultural research. Proc. Amer. Soc. Hort. Sci. 64:526–534.

Dermen, Haig. 1954. Colchiploidy in grapes. Jour. Heredity 45:159–172.

Kraus, E. J., and H. R. Kraybill. 1918. Vegetation and reproduction with special reference to the tomato. Oregon Agric. Exp. Sta. Bull. 149.

Tukey, H. B. 1948. Horticulture in science and society. Proc. Amer. Soc. Hort. Sci. 51:685–694.

———. 1953. Research developments in fruit culture in America. Ann. Rept. East Malling Res. Sta. 1952:47–54.

24

BOTANY AND MEDICINE

H. W. Youngken, Jr.

Obviously, man's first interest in plant life dates back to earliest time when, in order to survive, he soon recognized a need to become familiar with the plants of his environment and to engage in food-crop development. This was long before botany took form as a science. Concomitantly with the earliest need of plants for food there was a keen awareness of the values of many forms of plant life as sources for medicines. Admittedly, the use of plants in early medicine was often cloaked in mystery, and physician-botanists, of which there were many, were frequently better psychologists, philosophers, or in many cases tribal witch doctors, than medical scientists. Nevertheless, the influence of a botanical interest in medicine, or medicine in botany as one might also look at it, was stimulated early and long before both sciences became formalized as we know them today.

Before dealing with some of the modern concepts of botano-medico relationships it is perhaps pertinent that several of the highlights of early materia medica which played an important part in the development of botany as a science be reviewed. Indeed, it was this aspect of medicine, and later pharmacy, in which many of the closest bonds between botany and medicine were first made. In the pages that follow it will be seen that even today much of the influence of botany on modern medicine comes from an interest in certain plants which yield therapeutically useful constituents. The fact is that many of these plants were described as useful crude drugs in the materia medicas of ancient time.

Undoubtedly the early descriptive materia medica and botany texts of Greek and Roman physician-botanists such as Theophrastus (often called the Father of Botany), Dioscorides, Pliny the Elder and Pliny the Younger, Galen, and others had much to do with the beginnings of scientific botany. On the other hand, the botany of the first centuries A.D. could hardly be called a science.

Students of medical and pharmacy history are well aware of the great influence played on medical practice since 77 A.D. by the famous *De Materia Medica* of Dioscorides, the Greek physician-botanist, as this compendium of plant, animal, and mineral drugs became the "bible" of drug knowledge for more than fourteen centuries. In fact, the descriptions of Dioscorides were often extensively copied in the herbals and medical botanies which followed soon after the advent of printing in the early 16th century. As the years of the renaissance passed, writers of herbals began to show more originality and imagination. From this trend, which was sorely needed, emerged the beginnings of descriptive plant morphology, and still later plant taxonomy.

Although at first drawing heavily upon much of the style of Dioscorides, during which the medical virtues of various plants were extolled, more descriptive imagination characterized the early German, Italian, and British herbals. Writings were frequently supplemented by various grades of artistic drawings and woodcuts. Folklore and empiricism were, indeed, the only bases upon which these early botano-medico compendia were written. Nevertheless, beginning with the herbals of the German "Fathers of Botany," for example, in the works of Otto Brunfels, *Herbarium Vivae Icones* and *Simplicium Pharmacorum* (1542) and Hieronymus Bock, *De Stirpium* (1552), a greater botanical interest was aroused in medicinal plants. Undoubtedly the German herbals had much influence on others which soon followed in the 16th, 17th, and 18th centuries. William Turner's *Herbal,* corrected and enlarged to include three parts, was published in 1568. John Gerarde published his famous *The Herbal, or General History of Plants* in 1597, and a parade of famous descriptive histories, plantarum, flora, and/or catalogues of various kinds of plants became available from then on. Among other authors of early renown were Caspar and Johann Bauhin, Petrus Borellus, Andreas Caesalpinus, Valerius Cordus, Nehemiah Grew, Adam Lonicerus, Petrus Matthiolus, John Parkinson, and John Ray. There were many more. All in some measure copied the general format of the herbals which preceded them.

In modern times we commonly refer to several of the botanical remedies so extensively described in these more ancient printed herbals as the crude drugs of domestic medicine. Many are still employed much as they were centuries ago as the agents of the homeopathic physician; whereas the isolated and purified active principles or refined extracts of others still serve the medical doctor in the present age of chemo-therapeutic drugs.

Fortunately plant taxonomy as a science did not remain long bound by the methods of classification so artifically employed in the botanical works of the 16th and 17th centuries. A keener awareness of plant morphology was obviously stimulated to some degree by the use of plants for medical purposes, as it was also stimulated by the knowledge of the plants of the time. The result of a greater interest in plant morphology, which was generated to some extent by the early herbals and the direct influence of comparative natural history and phylogeny which soon became dominant, pointed to an urgent need for systematic plant classification according to more scientific relationships. These relationships were at first largely structural ones, based upon comparative plant anatomy. Later, in the early 18th century during the Darwinian period, they became intensified to include more phylogenetic relationships. Indeed, the beginning of this new interest in comparative structural and phylogenetic relationships was reflected early in the writings of Nehemiah Grew, *An Idea of a Phytological History* (1673) and *Anatomy of Plants, with an Idea of a Philosophical History of Plants* (1682). Soon after, in the 18th century, came also the great works of Linnaeus and Jussieu, which established many of the fundamentals of plant taxonomy as this phase of botany is known today.

It was probably at this period that botany as a science shook off much of the medical influence which had dominated many of the 16th- and 17th-century writings. On the other hand, botany continued to be a major subject of medical-school teaching until well into the 20th century. Apart from the general biological or natural-science value of botany in medical education, which was soon relegated by medical schools to fundamental science departments of universities, the applied aspects of medical botany such as medicinal plant exploration, identification, and crude drug studies gradually were taken over by faculties of pharmacy. It may be said that even today the closest bonds between medicine and botany lie in the applied pharmaceutical aspects of botany.

Great advances were made during the late 19th and early 20th centuries in standardizing the descriptive nomenclature of botanical drugs. Pharmacognosy, that area of pharmacy which deals with natural products as pharmaceuticals, had been established as a science by a German medical student at Halle in 1815. For more than one hundred years this pharmaceutical science in which plant drugs are extensively studied has been responsible for carrying on medical aspects of botany, particularly those aspects that are important in drug standardization, drug plant exploration, and medicinal plant chemistry. Much of the changeover of medical botany to pharmacy was, in fact, due to the importance of drug standardization, the need to set standards in order to combat a vicious practice of adulteration and/or drug substitution which became rampant during the 19th century. Using the conventional methods of the anatomist, pharmacognosists soon began amassing extensive histological descriptions of almost every medicinal plant used by mankind. Many of these became reference descriptions for standard materia medica and pharmacopeia compendia. So intensive was this type of research in pharmacognosy between 1900 and 1940 that much less effort was devoted by the pharmacognosist to plant chemistry and physiology. The science unfortunately soon became a predominantly descriptive science of crude botanical drugs. It has only been during the past decade that this trend has been somewhat changed whereby greater interest has been shown by several experimental pharmacognosists in plant chemistry, biochemistry, and physiology. As a result pharmacognosy has now begun to deal more extensively than before with these aspects of experimental botany as they can be related to medicinal plants. This change has also been greatly reflected in the teaching of pharmacognosy in pharmacy schools, and it can be observed in the publications and textbooks of more modern pharmacognosists. This has brought experimental botany somewhat closer to experimental medical pharmacology. Botanical drugs reached a peak in the numbers that were employed in medicine and pharmacy at the turn of the 20th century. At that time the major contents of pharmacopeias and formularies of many nations, including the *United States Pharmacopoeia*, the *British Pharmacopoeia*, *British Codex*, and *National Formulary* of the American Pharmaceutical Association were the descriptive standards of crude plant drugs and some of their medicinally valuable constituents.

Beginning with the time of Wohler, the distinguished German chemist, early in the 19th century, and with the advance in medical pharmacology, which began almost one hundred years later under the stimulus of John Jacob Abel, much of the empiricism that had been formerly applied to the drug action of plants as medicines had given way to rationalism. Today drugs from plants which are to be used in the treatment of disease must have had tried and trusted chemical, pharmacological, and clinical scrutiny. Many of the older botanicals, galenicals, and crude biological and mineral mixtures have, in general, failed to survive the exacting tests of modern methods for evaluating drugs. The very nature of their composite make-up—ballast plus biologically active components when the latter can be found—has placed them beyond the realm of critical evaluation. How much more exacting it is for a chemist and pharmacologist to demonstrate the properties of a pure and single crystalline compound, regardless of its source. Therefore the use of a great number of plant drugs per se in medicine has significantly decreased. On the other hand, the "pharmacotherapeutics" of several purified plant constituents (digitoxin, cocaine, quinine, caffeine, morphine, codeine, reserpine, ergotamine, etc.) has remained important to medical science.

The age of "pharmacotherapeutics," which means the study of the uses of drugs in the treatment of disease, has followed the "pure compound line." It is based, wherever possible, upon a correlation of pharmacological action with pathological physiology or the microbiological aspects of disease. To a great extent it has been based also upon relationships between chemical structure and pharmacological action, the so-called "molecular structure-activity" relationship. Out of this development has come the age of chemotherapy, the latter stimulated in the late 19th century by the contributions of the German biologist Paul Ehrlich, his "magic bullet" and antisyphilitic arsenicals. Botanists will recall that this period was about the same time as the great contributions to that science of Charles Darwin, Engler and Prantl, and Edward Strasburger. The chemotherapeutic age in medicine was given great exploitation in 1935, when the Nobel Prize winner Domagk discovered the chemotherapy of prontosil, the forerunner of the synthetic sulfa drugs. Modern therapeutics such as the sulfa drugs, barbiturates, synthetic quartenary ammonium salts, local anesthetics, and several antihistaminics all originated as the result of the development in chemical structure-activity relationships.

This does not mean, of course, that specific chemical configuration can be entirely reliable in predicting drug action. Indeed, much evidence to the contrary is available. For example, there are many instances among compounds which affect the central nervous system (nitrous oxide and ethyl ether) and others (the antibiotics) where such relationships do not hold true. But certainly investigations of plant, animal, and synthetic medicinals and their structural-pharmacological relationships have led the modern advance in new pharmacotherapeutics, and most likely this approach will continue to lead the way.

REINVESTIGATION OF PLANTS FOR MEDICINE. With a modern advance in synthetic medicinal organic chemistry there has developed recently a very keen interest in the re-investigation of the constituents biosynthesized by plants and animals. Again botany has become a tool of medicine through the need to properly select plants for new drugs. Research in this phase has increased more during the last decade, because of success with the antibiotics and plant drugs such as rauwolfia, than at any time during the previous period of the 20th century. It has also brought medical scientists into closer contact with botanical experts in taxonomy, anatomy, and plant biochemistry. Such investigations have been prompted by three general interests: (1) the search for plant constituents responsible for a biological activity, the latter implied by the use of a crude drug in folklore, foreign or domestic empirical medicine; (2) the search for newer therapeutically active chemical derivatives of natural compounds, especially those compounds which have already been well established; and (3) the investigation of the biochemical and physiological role played by plant and animal constituents in the organisms producing them. Indeed, investigations in each of these interests are sometimes interrelated, and a discovery in one pursuit might very well open the way for fruitful discoveries in other closely related interests. Modern research observes no boundaries either in its pure or applied aspects. The discussion that follows will deal largely with the first two of these interests.

1. THE SEARCH FOR PLANT CONSTITUENTS. *Antibiotics.* It has been stated that the most recent stimulus leading to the investigation of plants for biologically active compounds began about two decades ago in the early 1930s. It may be recalled that this was the period when Fleming, Florey, and Chain described the antibiotic properties of extracts from the blue-green mold *Penicillium.* From these observations came the antibiotic crystalline penicillin. But lest we become too smug in our beliefs that the use of antibiotics from

molds and soil bacteria began in our generation, it must be noted that molds were employed for similar purposes by the Chinese thousands of years ago. And several hundred years ago North American Indians are known to have employed both soil and rotting wood for the prevention of wound infections and for healing festered cuts. Nevertheless, the penicillin discovery was the forerunner of the modern antibiotic age, and it undoubtedly set the stage for a tremendous interest in the *re*-investigation of lower and higher plants for new biologically active constituents. More than a thousand plant species have now been screened for newer antibiotics, and at least two hundred antibiotics have been discovered in living organisms since 1929. Yet, thus far only about a dozen therapeutically useful antibiotic compounds have been successfully isolated from molds, bacteria, and soil actinomycetes, all lower plants. Most of these have been procured since 1939 when Dubos isolated tyrothricin from the filtrates of cultures of *Bacillus brevis;* streptomycin was discovered from cultures of an actinomycete in 1944, bacitracin in 1945, polymyxin and chloromycetin in 1947, aureomycin in 1948, terramycin in 1950, and erythromycin in 1952.

More than one hundred higher plants have also been studied for therapeutically effective antibiotics, and although antibacterial compounds have been procured, their usefulness in therapy has not been significant either because of toxicity or their ineffectiveness when employed clinically. These sources have included such plants as garlic (*Allium* spp.), the wild ginger (*Asarum* spp.), senna leaves (*Cassia* spp.), honeysuckle, blessed thistle, and lichens such as Spanish moss (*Ramalina* spp.), and *Rocella*. Several other higher plants might be included with the list.

The well-established and the less well known antibacterial compounds which we possess do not thoroughly meet the requisites for the most ideal antibiotic, and the search must therefore continue. Since some bacteria possess abilities to become antibiotic-resistant and since there are large numbers of pathogens which remain outside the sphere of antibiotic influence, man is far from secure in his reliance upon the chemotherapeutic agents of this type. Furthermore, although total penicillin and chloramphenicol synthesis have been accomplished, unfortunately the production of them via the test tube is beset with numerous problems which have delayed the economic application of such synthesis methods. Tetracycline (Achromycin) is, of course, obtained by a semi-synthetic process from the naturally occurring antibiotic chlortetracycline. It is thus reasonable to expect that the parade of new agents in this field from living organisms will continue and perhaps increase at as rapid a rate as it has since 1944.

Vasodilators and antihypertensive agents. Since glyceryl trinitrate was discovered by Sobrero in 1847 and amyl nitrite was introduced to medical practice by Guthrie about ten years later for the treatment of angina pectoris, nitrites and organic nitrates have been, with few exceptions, the outstanding agents in the treatment of angina and arterial hypertension. However, an intensive re-investigation of one well-known plant drug, *Veratrum viride,* or green hellebore, and a similar study of two lesser-known plant drugs, *Ammi visnaga* (Khella) and *Rauwolfia* species, have resulted in several new and useful pharmaceuticals of the hypotensive class. Certainly the supremacy of the nitrites and/or nitrates in this field has now been challenged. *Veratrum* and *Rauwolfia* represent botanical crude drugs which have been employed in folklore domestic and foreign medicine for centuries and for a variety of purposes. Among these, for example, the roots and rhizomes of *Veratrum viride,* a plant indigenous to parts of North America and Europe, have had application in galenical forms as a bird poison, insecticide, emetic, cardiac tonic, and use in eclampsia; Khella, the dried fruit of *Ammi visnaga,* a plant which grows wild in the eastern Mediterranean basin, has been used for renal colic and as a diuretic. One of its crystalline components, khellin, was reported in 1930 to have direct relaxing action on visceral and coronary artery smooth musculature. The dried roots of *Rauwolfia serpentina,* a small shrub of India, have been used empirically by people of India for a large variety of conditions, such as in the treatment of snake bites, insanity, high blood pressure, and cardiac disease. Some of its alkaloid principles were first isolated by the Indian chemist, Siddiqui, in 1931. These older botanicals have been most extensively re-investigated chemically and pharmacologically since about 1947. As a result we now have numerous modern pharmaceutical preparations of these once obsolete drugs, preparations containing crude drug materials and their isolated constituents. Among the latter constituents are the alkaloids jervine, cevine, and protoveratrine from *Veratrum,* reserpine and recanescine from *Rauwolfia,* and the dimethoxy-furanochromones khellin and visnagin from Khella. In pharmacy many of these constituents are dispensed under trade names, for example, Veriloid and Veralba for *Veratrum,* Raudixin for *Rauwolfia* root, Serpasil, Sandril, and Reserpoid for *Rauwolfia* alkaloids, Eskel, Visnico, and Ammiven representing Khella components; and there are several others. The large number of such products reflect the extensive commercial development of these once "obsolete" drugs.

The question naturally raised is what differences do *Veratrum, Rauwolfia,* and khellin possess with each other and over other well-established vasodilators in the treatment of essential hypertension? *Veratrum* and its alkaloids cause widespread reflex vasodilatation, including that of cerebral and renal arteries, and its effects are more rapid than the other two botanical agents. However, much evidence can be shown that *Veratrum* alkaloids or crude drugs are not significantly effective by the oral route in the majority of ambulatory hypertensive patients, and rather high incidences of toxicity have been reported following their use, i.e., vomiting and hiccoughing. Much better results have been reported from the use of the alkaloids via the parenteral route. When combined with rauwolfia and hexamethonium compounds these become even more useful. There is evidence that single purified *Veratrum* alkaloids do not possess the efficiency of alkaloid mixtures of the crude drugs. Furthermore, some patients develop a decrease in sensitivity to all forms of *Veratrum* after a few weeks of medication.

Rauwolfia and its alkaloids are much slower in their onset of activity than *Veratrum* and khellin. On the other hand, as a hypotensive agent *Rauwolfia* reduces arterial blood pressure and slows the heart rate somewhat in the same manner as *Veratrum* by inhibiting centrally mediated cardiovascular reflexes. *Rauwolfia* is efficiently absorbed by the oral route, but it possesses a significantly long latent period before activity can be observed. This phenomenon has not been clearly explained. Incidences of toxic effects have been much less than those from *Veratrum* medication, but nevertheless some side effects such as nausea, headache, dizziness, and diarrhea have been reported following *Rauwolfia* alkaloid medication. Sensitivity to the actions of this drug has not yet been significant.

One of the outstanding attributes of *Rauwolfia* and its alkaloids has been its tranquillizing action on the higher centers of the central nervous system. This sedation effect is unlike that of the barbiturates and other hypnotics. It has widespread application in the treatment of schizophrenia and other forms of mental disease, particularly such as cause deep mental depression. In fact, the use of this drug in neural psychopathic conditions has almost superseded its use as an antihypertensive agent. *Rauwolfia* medication has practically replaced frontal-lobotomy operations in many mental hospitals in the United States. Its effect in this respect has indeed created significant social problems as far as long-term mental patients are concerned. One must realize, however, that it still is early to predict the true lasting virtues of the drug when so employed in our mental hospitals.

A sidelight on the development of both *Rauwolfia* and *Veratrum* drugs has been a need for the proper identification of these plant and crude drug materials. More than ten species of *Rauwolfia* yield known alkaloids, but only two or three possess alkaloids of medicinal value. It was soon found that difficulties in isolating active constituents and in obtaining consistent results with extracts of both drugs were due to the prevalence in commerce of several different species, many of which later were found to be lacking in the desired principles. This situation led to the need for establishing careful means for identifying raw materials and resulted in many useful discoveries, as far as the cellular elements of both drugs are concerned, by which different species can be detected in every form before being processed chemically.

Khellin, the component of *Ammi visnaga,* has not proven to be the efficient hypotensive agent that was originally attributed to it. It does, however, possess a more direct antispasmodic effect on the smooth musculature, including the blood vessels, than does *Veratrum* or *Rauwolfia.* It enhances coronary blood flow and in this aspect has a persistent effect; but rather insignificant effects have been noted as far as decreasing blood pressure and heart rate. The action of khellin as a smooth muscle relaxant has led to its use in bronchial asthma with some success. It is rapidly and efficiently absorbed and found to be widely distributed in the body. Side effects from khellin medication have been chiefly those of nausea, mental depression, and some insomnia. But its margin of safety has been considered to be rather wide.

All these hypotensive agents have more persistent activity than the nitrites and nitrates, but in general their onset of action is not as prompt. The locus for *Veratrum* and *Rauwolfia* activity appears to be in the cerebrum and hypothalamus, that is, much higher up in the central nervous system than other hypotensive agents such as the tetraethyl ammonium and hexamethonium drugs. The nitrites, on the other hand, act essentially on the musculature of the end organs without nerve innervation. When combined with the latter drugs the virtues of *Veratrum* and *Rauwolfia* as hypotensive agents are often more useful. It is for this reason that a large variety of mixtures which include several types of each botanical constituent and organic nitrate or hydralazine compound (Apresoline) are employed. The search for hypotensive agents among other plants has continued at a rapid rate in many laboratories, and it is likely that newer hypotensive compounds from still other "old" botanicals will turn up.

Muscle relaxants and antispasmodics. A number of botanicals have in the past been employed for sedative effects in intestinal and stomach cramps and essential or functional dysmenorrhea. Research in the pharmaceutical industry has frequently pursued the search and synthesis of new and better antispasmodics. Atropine and atropine-like synthetics certainly lead the field of antispasmodics today. But side effects from most of these still limit their applications. It is largely for this reason that the search continues. Plant drugs such as *Viburnum, Aletris, Helonia,* blessed thistle, Jamaica dogwood (*Piscidia* spp.), and *Potentilla* (silverweed) are examples of a few botanicals that have entered into pharmaceutical formulations for antispasmodic purposes. These are plants which are indigenous to areas of the United States, and Jamaica dogwood particularly to the West Indies. The activity of some of the crude extract materials of the above plants has been supported in a rather haphazard way by clinical data, but because of the composite nature of their mixtures and since significant active chemical components have not yet been isolated from them, it has been difficult to properly evaluate them. Many factors are involved in the formation of plant constituents, for example, the influence of growing seasons, soil conditions, and methods of harvest and drying. These factors are often reflected in the decrease or increase of activity that can be shown when extracts of such plants are tested pharmacologically. Until more knowledge is achieved relative to the effects of such factors on the formation of active principles of the above plants, it is very difficult to know when to collect materials which will have the most potent activity.

Laboratory investigations which employ tissue tests both in vitro and in living animals do show rather positive muscle sedative effects when highly purified extracts of all these plants are biologically tested. For example, *Viburnum* and *Potentilla* extracts show about equal activity to that of papaverine in isolated uterine and intestinal muscle strips. Several components of *Potentilla* (silvery cinquefoil) have been found to have approximately the same results. Petroleum ether extracts of the bark from Jamaica dogwood show even better relaxant activity and give indication of possessing a depressant effect on the nervous system.

One of the very interesting plant substances that has recently invited considerable interest along these lines is licorice root, *Glycyrrhiza glabra*. A number of investigators in Holland, Belgium, Scotland, and in the United States during the past three or four years have reported clinical evidence for a desoxycorticosterone-like (Doca) activity in licorice root. Although the degree of effect did not match that of the pure adrenal-gland hormone, nevertheless it has prompted further investigation of the true activity of the "old" botanical drug licorice in the treatment of adrenal hypo function, particularly Addison's disease. An estrogenic activity and an extract which gave chemical tests for estriol have been reported for licorice root by Costello and Lynn in the United States.

Along with these investigations some attention has recently been given to antispasmodic and anti-ulcer activities which Nelemans and Molhuysen in Europe have shown by in vitro tests to exist in licorice root extracts. Many extract fractions of the root have been tested in our laboratories, and several of these have shown very consistent antispasmodic effects that can be observed in rat and guinea pig intestinal and uterine muscle strips. This is greater than papaverine and about one-fiftieth that of atropine. The anti-ulcer activity of the drug is currently being investigated by at least two major pharmaceutical companies. It will be most interesting to follow progress in this approach, for to date no significant toxic effect has been attributed to the drug. The major problem is one of chemical isolation, for often when pure crystalline compounds are obtained from plant drugs of this type, they fail to show significantly the desired activity. As is often the case, botanical investigations of new species of drug plants and their sources proceed rapidly when the slightest evidence of therapeutic activity is shown, only to await the skills of a chemist for their more practical application.

Miscellaneous. A number of other drug plants have recently turned up with rather extraordinary new uses apart from those previously mentioned. For example, the irritating resin of the May apple, *Podophyllum peltatum*, which has long been employed as a cathartic and which years ago was used to destroy venereal warts, has now yielded three very active compounds, called peltatins. These have been found to destroy cancerous tumors in mice, and the application of such activity is being investigated in humans.

The juice from the "old" drug *Aloë,* again the source of a well-established cathartic, has now been applied in the treatment of atomic-radiation burns. Collins and Collins reported similar effects in the treatment of X-ray burns as early as 1935, and Rowe in 1941 showed the curative principles to be present in the rind and pulp of the plant leaves. It is interesting to note that this extractive has now proven to be the only effective agent in the healing of the peculiar burns inflicted on the natives of the South Pacific during the fallout of radiation particles from atomic-bomb explosions in that area a few years ago.

Mescaline, a narcotic-like alkaloid from a cactus, *Lophophora williamsii* (mescal buttons, or peyote), growing in southwestern U.S.A., is being currently investigated in humans for its effects on the cerebral centers, an activity which produces initial stimulation accompanied by hallucinations and later intense cerebral depression. Such activity under carefully controlled conditions can serve as a kind of chemical and biological tool for inducing effects against which to measure the psychiatric activity of the tranquillizing drugs rauwolfia and Chlorpromazine. Indeed, the psychic effects of any drug are difficult to assess without some critical evaluation that can be measured and controlled. It is, of course, too early to evaluate completely so specialized a technique as would be involved by the use of a drug such as mescaline to produce a schizophrenic state.

2. THE RE-INVESTIGATION OF WELL-ESTABLISHED PLANT COMPOUNDS. *Steroid sapogenins.* Two very widely distributed classes of chemical compounds known to exist in plants are the steroids and alkaloids. Many of these lend themselves to chemical modification by various means. Among the steroids many have recently been extracted from several species of *Yucca, Agave, Dioscorea,* and *Strophanthus,* and these have been employed for chemical and biosynthetic purposes. They are chemically called sapogenins. A great many sapogenins hemolyze red blood cells and therefore are toxic to humans. However, several are now found to possess a useful "precursor" value in the chemical synthesis of medicinal agents as the adrenal hormones, cortisone, and hydrocortisone. This was first shown about 1948 by the chemists at Merck Chemical Laboratories and in other pharmaceutical laboratories. As a result since that time more than two thousand species of plants have been screened for sapogenin-cortisone precursors under the leadership of the Eastern Regional Research Laboratory group of the U.S.D.A. Others have also investigated plants for such compounds which would serve as chemical starting materials in corticosterone synthesis. At the present time progesterone is the principal intermediate in cortisone synthesis, but there are four sapogenins which are used for progesterone synthesis. One of these, diosgenin from the "old" botanical drug *Dioscorea,* Mexican yam, is most useful in this respect. From this finding one is set to speculating whether the natives of Mexico, Central America, and Africa, where most of these plants grow, weren't cor-

rect, after all, centuries ago, in attributing considerable benefits to certain yam roots and *Strophanthus* fruits in the treatment of adrenal hormone and corpus luteum–deficiency diseases.

Alkaloids. In the realm of alkaloids that can be separated from plants there are many examples of new drugs prepared by chemical modification of existing molecules. This has been especially true among certain tropane types, for example, the cocaine and atropine alkaloids. Since Einhorn prepared the local anesthetic procaine (Novocaine) from cocaine of coca leaves in 1905, a series of other similar local anesthetics (butacaine, Tutocaine, etc.) have been prepared. Homatropine and other atropine synthetic derivatives have likewise resulted from chemical studies of the tropane alkaloids of plants.

One of the most interesting results from similar investigations of plant alkaloid molecules has taken place in the last five years in the case of the indole alkaloids of the fungus drug ergot, a parasitic fungus infecting rye and other grass in inflorescences. Ergot contains a wealth of pharmacologically active constituents, and about seven physiologically active alkaloids have been isolated from the crude drug. The effects of ergotamine, ergonovine, and ergotoxine as uterine stimulants and oxytocics have, of course, been well established for quite some time. Re-investigations of two ergot alkaloids during recent years have resulted in additional therapeutic uses, such as the relief of migrainous headaches and the treatment of hypertension. Ergotamine was first proposed for migraine by Maier in 1926, but it has only been since about 1948 that some rationale has been suggested for this. The cause of migraine is still not clearly explained, but the recent theory by Wolf relates the intensity of migraine pain to the degrees of pulsation of brain arteries, mainly branches of the external carotid. Ergotamine is known to decrease the amplitude of arterial pulsation. Hence the favorable effects of this fungus alkaloid in migraine relief might be explained on the basis of this action.

In about 1943 a group of investigators, led by Arthur Stoll in Basel, Switzerland, were able to hydrogenate chemically the natural alkaloids of ergot, particularly ergotoxine. In the meantime, it had been noted that the ergotoxine alkaloid was, in fact, a complex of about three other alkaloids named ergocornine, ergocristine, and ergocryptine. By chemical reduction of ergotamine and the ergotoxine complex their respective dihydro derivatives have been prepared. The interesting result of this from a physiological point of view is the fact that this chemical modification significantly alters several of the effects ascribed to the natural alkaloids (vasoconstriction, oxytocic activity, etc.), especially that of ergotoxine. Ergotoxine dihydrogenated derivatives produce very little vasoconstriction, and they decrease arterial pressure. Heart output is slightly decreased. The interest in these plant derivatives for treatment of hypertension comes largely from the fact that hydrogenated compounds depress the vasomotor center in the medulla and possibly stimulate a "vasodepressor" center. At any rate, this direct depression action on the central nervous system and the reduced action on peripheral vasoconstriction form the basis for the medical use of these compounds in hypertension.

Ergot alkaloids, for example, ergonovine, have been the chief chemical sources for the synthesis (and probably biosynthesis) of an indole acid known as lysergic acid. This acid is found in the crude drug, but it has had only academic interest up until a few years ago. An amide derivative, known as lysergic acid diethylamide, has been prepared from lysergic acid, and this derivative has been shown to have marked stimulating and, later, depressant effects on the higher brain centers. Effects are produced by extremely small doses, for example, 0.25-mg. doses, in humans. Visual perception is greatly altered, and marked hallucinations occur. More important, however, is the depressant effect of this drug on the mind. Humans are reported to respond as though in a hypnotized state and to reveal events which might otherwise be retained as guarded secrets. Human subjects are reduced mentally to placid followers of the slightest persuasion. A very startling account of the actions of this new drug have been vividly described in the Canadian magazine *McLeans,* in October, 1953. The article is entitled "My Twelve Hours as a Madman" by Sidney Katz. The military applications of such a compound are far-reaching. There are strong indications that lysergic acid diethylamide (LSD-25) has already been put to military and political use by some foreign nations.

3. INVESTIGATIONS OF CERTAIN BIOCHEMICAL AND PHYSIOLOGICAL ROLES PLAYED BY DRUG-PLANT CONSTITUENTS WITHIN ORGANISMS PRODUCING THEM. This area of research has been of recent interest in medicine. It involves an application of principles of plant and animal biochemistry and physiology in a special kind of way. Researches in pharmaceutical and medical sciences, such as pharmacognosy and pharmacology, have recently become more intensive in this direction. Although details of this field of research will not be discussed here, it might be mentioned that considerable practical application can arise in medicine from the knowledge of cellular biochemistry. The explanation of the chemical effects of drugs on cellular function and, in turn, the tissues is often made clear when one can understand how and under what conditions an animal-gland constituent is formed biosynthetically. This is somewhat applicable to plant cells, for the knowledge of the chemical pathways and reactions by which constituents are formed in plants has potential value in: (1) Contributing to the complete chemical synthesis of a natural product. (2) Understanding the relationships of certain chemical structures to the physiology of the cell. For, indeed, the essential metabolites of plant cells are generally the same as for animal cells. It is often easier to demonstrate a biochemical response to a drug in certain lower plants (yeast, bacteria, etc.) on the cellular level than in laboratory animals. (3) Improving natural-product production by adding selective chemical precursors to plant-growth

substrates and to fertilizers, precursors which are known to be either starting points or intermediates in the biosynthesis of the desired compound. Increased production of certain antibiotics such as penicillin was brought about as a result of numerous studies in this area.

The literature is now expanding with the reports of both academic and applied aspects of this phase of research. Although much of the knowledge of the how and why of natural-product formation is lacking and truly hypothetical, nevertheless fragments of the biochemical puzzle are gradually being put together and it is very likely that the several ramifications of these pursuits will soon influence greatly the search for new and better drug products from plants. Thus concepts of plant physiology and biochemistry enter phases of medicine both from an academic and practical standpoint.

CONCLUSION. Plant cells fundamentally are chemical factories, and many possess a rich supply of therapeutically useful constituents. As long as man is driven to seek better medicines, particularly those which have selective actions, he will explore the laboratories of nature. With the improved techniques at his command today (and these undoubtedly will be expanded in the future), it is likely that new drugs will continuously emerge from plants. Many of these will be the result of the re-investigations of older botanicals, and the clues for pursuing such investigations will frequently come from a more careful attention to the history of botany in medicine and to the customs and folklore remedies of bygone generations. Other new drugs will come from the great efforts of the chemist who seeks by the application of the simple and most complex rules of organic chemistry to modify the products of nature in order to suit his objectives in medicinal chemistry.

Obviously, drug plant chemistry in botany has loomed largest of all since the age of the herbals in the relationships of this science with medicine. On the other hand, from the beginning of medicine a knowledge of plant distribution, morphology, and taxonomy has played a supportive role in the procurement of plants for medical purposes. As long as plant drugs are tools in medical diagnosis and treatment of disease, specializations in botany must be consulted. Indeed, newer knowledge in plant physiology, genetics, and plant biochemistry contribute well to the fundamental studies of medical biochemistry and pharmacology.

25

ON THE POPULARIZATION OF BOTANY

Donald Culross Peattie

> . . . art thou officer?
> Or art thou base, common and popular?
> —SHAKESPEARE, *King Henry V.*

How to attract more young students to the study of botany was the announced subject of one session of botanists who met in December of 1924 in Washington, D.C. I attended because I was just then quitting the ranks of professional botanists for free-lance writing as a popularizer. But no one in that gathering of intellects there in a classroom of the Central High School (empty of students over the Christmas holidays) proffered any ideas on the subject. They appeared, rather, to be reading into the record (as Congressmen say) miscellaneous matters which they wished to impress on other botanists or merely to get off their chests. Others, looking very wise, said nothing. But they were all, I felt, boring each other exquisitely, and when the gavel fell to signal the end of a futile session, there was an almost undignified rush for the door. As the youngest person in the room, I allowed my betters to precede me. Then I looked back at the high-school classroom. Give botany a wide miss, kids, I thought, until botanists can do better by you than they did by each other here today.

When I was invited by the *American Journal of Botany* to submit this paper, with the suggestion that it was hoped that some intelligent high-school student (among others), coming on the *Golden Jubilee* number, might be induced by it to turn to botany for a life work, I remembered that long-ago non-meeting of great minds in Washington.

It is not my intent or business to tell botany teachers how to run their courses, still less to suggest that they could make them more popular. Obviously teachers know better than I do how that could be done, or whether it should be done. My purpose here is to speak of the popularization of botany outside of classrooms and to tell a little of my firsthand experiences in popularization, which go back now thirty years during which I have earned most of my living in that way. Sometimes, indeed, I was not making much of a living, especially at the beginning when I ran a "Nature column" in the *Washington Evening Star* and wrote articles for *Nature Magazine*. At the same time I was finishing and trying to find a publisher for my first book, *Cargoes and Harvests*, a popularization of economic botany. And I can still recall how much I had had to learn about the skills of popularization and how little I had been prepared for it, even in the correct point of view, by my formal botanical training.

Base, common, and popular I must then have seemed to my botanical friends like a lieutenant broken to the rank of sergeant or corporal. At Harvard, in most of the classes I had attended, economic botany had been despised as something tainted with commercialism, and as for popularization, it was considered no part of botany at all but to belong, rather, to the discipline (if any) of journalism. As for the interest I had always had in linking botany with other things in life—philosophy, for instance, human history, folklore—the breadth of my interests had often been taken as proof of my shallowness, and sometimes roused outspoken criticism. Thus in the big midwestern university where I first began my botanical studies, I was told by a laboratory assistant (now a well-known professor), "The way I size you up, you're one of these smatter-artists we get around here sometimes."

After digesting this, I decided to accept the judgment, not in the spirit in which it had been intended, but in my own way. I reflected that Darwin, for instance, whose interests ranged from volcanoes to orchids, from earthworms to tropical island birds, had been a smatter-artist. And it was the very power of his pen to popularize that (with the even more popular pens of those smatter-artists Thomas Huxley and Alfred Russel Wallace) had raised the storm over evolution. And but for the storm, the world might still be largely in ignorance of evolution, and even in scientific circles it might now be a dustcatcher on the academic shelves. For evolution as a concept had a long pre-Darwinian history, but each time it had come up it had been allowed to die unnoticed by the scientists themselves—perhaps for the lack of a public storm over it.

For that matter, who was ever more of a smatter-artist than Linnaeus, "father of botany" (so-called)? His interests and writings ranged from the migration of birds to the ethnology of the Lapps, from forest management to the life history of the reindeer and its tormentor, the botfly, and the reindeer's chief sustenance, the lichens. True that Linnaeus was not the first to demonstrate the sexuality of plants, but he was the first to popularize it, with the result that even botanists, however reluctantly, came to accept it. He was not the first to employ binomial nomenclature with its implied concepts of genus and species (he had indeed a less keen sense of genera than Tournefort and of species than Ray), but Linnaeus it was who made binomial nomenclature "stick." Linnaeus was not the first naturalist who ever went to Lapland to see living subarctic and arctic plants instead of journeying to museums and libraries to study dead or merely described organisms. But he was the first to breathe life and glory into the subject. He taught the world the importance and the beauty of arctic Nature. He overtook and outstripped all his predecessors on the great north road, because he knew how to write popularly. And because he was a smatter-artist he pulled everything together into an ecological whole. If he had been as good and pure a botanist as my midwestern laboratory assistant he would never have written the *Lachesis Lapponica* and the *Flora Lapponica*.

So few botanists have ever read much Linnaeus except for a hasty reference now and again to the *Species Plantarum* that I am going to suggest, if you want to know what good popularizing is, that you read the *Lachesis* in its entirety, and in the *Flora* peruse at least certain pages. His account of *Polytrichum commune,* for instance, deals with a moss so base, common, and and popular that I cannot remember any other botanist who has one interesting thing to say about it. The importance of *Sphagnum* is better developed by Linnaeus than by any subsequent botanist whose work has fallen under my eye. His accounts of the mismanagement of the Norway spruce and the Scots fir show how his mind could stray to the principles of forestry before any forestry existed. The exposé of water hemlock (*Cicuta virosa*) as a stock-poisoning plant is a piece of original research that put an end to age-old superstitions. Linnaeus even manages to popularize a *Carex,* for which he is surely entitled to some kind of honorable mention, since nobody seems to have done so since.

"Some of the early botanists like Gerard," wrote Thoreau, back in 1860, "were prompted and compelled to describe their plants, but more of them nowadays only measure them, as it were. The former is affected by what he sees, and so inspired to portray it; the latter merely fills out a schedule prepared for him, makes a description *pour servir*. . . . I rarely read a sentence in a botany which reminds me of flowers or living plants. Very few, indeed, write as if they had seen the thing which they pretend to describe."

Is Thoreau justified in these rankling charges—that botanists seldom write "as if they had seen the thing they pretend to describe"? And does he overestimate Gerard and the other herbalists, whom most of us were taught to look upon as old wind-bags of an age of (comparative) botanical ignorance? Let us see for ourselves. Here (without revealing its identity as yet) is a description of a well-known species by a preeminent modern botanist:

"Aments lateral, terminating in short spurs or branches of a year's growth or more, short or globular, developed in early spring; the staminate from leafless buds; the pistillate mostly with leaves below. Anther locules opening transversely. Pollen grains simple, globular. Leaves linear, 2.5–3 mm. long, soft, deciduous, very many in a circular cluster on the short spurs, developed in early spring from lateral scaly and globular buds, or scattered and spirally arranged along the shoots of the season. Pistillate aments crimson or red, rarely greenish, in flower. Cones 2–3.5 cm. long."

There, in all its precision of modern terminology and measurement, in all its admirable brevity, is the description of a well-known tree as given by my deeply respected teacher, the late M. L. Fernald, in Gray's *Manual,* eighth edition (1949). True, I have mingled the full generic description with the very impoverished specific one, but I have suppressed nothing except the names, Latin and vernacular. And I now ask you, without rereading it, what species it describes?

Doubtless many botanists could name it from the above analysis, and just as undoubtedly others could not. And nobody, surely, could make these plant parts and organs, as given above by Professor Fernald, assemble and stand themselves up into a living tree.

Now turn to Gerard and discover if Thoreau has exaggerated the old herbalist's powers of delineation and his ability to make us see this same species, recognizable to those who know it, and vivid, at least, even to those who have never beheld it. Space does not permit a complete reproduction of Gerard's words, but here are excerpts:

"The Larch tree is of no small height, with a body [trunk] growing straight up. The bark whereof in the nether part beneath the boughs is thicke, rugged, and full of chinks; which being cut in sunder is red within and in the other part above smooth, slipperie, something white without: it bringeth forth many boughs divided into other lesser branches, which be tough and pliable. The leaves are small and cut into many jags, growing in clusters thicke together like tassels, which fall away at the approach of Winter: the flowers or rather the first shewes of the cone or fruit be round, and grow out of the tenderest boughes, being at length of a grave red purple colour: the cones be small, and like almost in bigness to those of the Cypress tree but longer and made up of a multitude of thin scale like leaves under which the small seeds having a thin velme [velum] growing on them very like to the wings of Bees and wasps: the substance of the wood is very hard, of colour, especially that in the midst [heartwood] somewhat red, and very profitable for workes of long continuance.

"It is not true that the wood of the larch cannot be set on fire, as Vitruvius reporteth of the castle made of Larch wood, which Caesar besieged, for it burneth in chimmies and is turned into coles, which are very profitable for Smithes.

"There is also gathered of the Larch tree a liquid rosin, very like in colour and substance to the whiter hony of Athens or of Spaine, which notwithstanding issueth not forth of itself, but runneth out of the stock of the tree, when it hath been bored even to the heart with a great and long auger and wimble.

"There groweth also upon the Larch tree a sort of Mushrum or excresence, not such as is upon other trees, but whiter, softer, more loose and spongie than any other of the Mushrums, and good for medicines, which beareth the name of *Agaricus* or Agaricke. Among all the trees that beare *Agaricus,* the Larch is the chiefe, and bringeth most plenty of Agarick.

"The Larch tree groweth not on the mountains of Greece or Macedon, but chiefly upon the Alpes of Italy, hard by the rivers Benacus and Padus and also in other places in the same mountains; it is also found in the hills of Moravia . . . also in Silesia . . . and the border of Poland. . . . It groweth plentifully in the woods of Gallia Cesalpina. . . . In Lumbardy and Pied-mont, in Italy, there be whole woods of Larch trees.

"Of all the Cone trees only the Larch tree is found to be without leaves in the Winter: in the Spring grow fresh leaves out of the same knobs from which the former did fall.

"This tree is called in Greek λαριξ: in Latine also *Larix:* in Italian and Spanish *Larice:* in High Dutch *Lerchenbaum:* in Low Dutch *Lorkenboom:* in French *Meleze. . . ."

This is enough to show that Thoreau was right; the old herbalist does indeed describe a plant so that we can *see* it, while Fernald, who could talk fascinatingly about all the North Woods trees, from a rich field knowledge of them, did not permit himself to be fascinating when writing of them. He even passes over an outstanding feature of the Larch, one by which you can tell it almost as far as you can see it—the mast-like and unbranched trunk that goes straight up through the tree, giving out horizontal branches. But Gerard, you will note, presents this fact in the very first sentence, as if he were looking, as he wrote, not at an herbarium specimen but at a living tree.

One may say of course that Fernald was a busy botanist engaged in the production of a long and serious-minded work, and, life being so short, he had not the time to go into all the details which a leisurely and gossipy old sixteenth-century herbalist indulged in. The facts are, however, that Fernald (1873–1950) lived longer than Gerard (1545–1611), and Gerard's herbal is an even more compendious work than Gray's *Manual,* eighth edition. So who had more time at his disposal?

The essential difference between the two botanists must lie in their approach. Gerard's is that of the popularizer.

A definition of popularization is probably overdue in this article. My definition would be that popularization of a science is the communication of the enthusiasm one feels for a subject to a reader who has essentially no previous knowledge of it, certainly no technical knowledge, and cares about it only in so far as the writer makes him care. The popularizer is one who "makes old things sound new and new things sound familiar."

There is a sharp distinction between popularization, which is in general addressed to a mature-minded if hard-to-get public and the writing of a simplified school textbook. For the reader of an elementary textbook is usually of an adolescent or just post-adolescent mentality and is not only compelled to read the assignment but even to buy the book—a condition of affairs that the free-lance popularizer may well envy! The writer of a textbook which succeeds in getting several big state "adoptions" may sometimes look forward, I am told by a prominent publisher, to an income from his book, alone, of something in the neighborhood of $10,000 a year, for some years at least. And he is under no compulsion to make his book interesting, or to make students feel that they would like to go on with the subject here expounded.

But in popularizing any subject, the author has to remember on every page, in every sentence, that the reader is not obliged to buy the book at all. He can buy any other book on the market, in whatever field he may choose, or he may spend his money in some quite different way. So that the popularizer of an unsensational subject like botany finds himself in competition not only with other books of the same sort, but with all the books in the world, while the reader of it admits no obligation to "get certain things," as my old Virgil teacher used to say while killing the poetry with prosody and parsing. The reader expects you to bring him the points that seem important to you. You cannot say to him "you *ought* to be understanding this even if I do not make myself easily clear; you ought to be liking this." The reader, at the first suggestion of this sort, will start skipping pages, and there is nothing to prevent him from skipping off to the motion pictures or some other occupation, and never reading your book again. I respectfully submit that popularization has very stern disciplines of its own, and if any one thinks they are easy to master, let him try to make a living within their exacting limits.

Yet despite all one may urge in favor of popularization, many a scientist harbors strong mental reservations about it. Of these reservations the most serious and the only one I shall have time to deal with here is the matter of inaccuracy. There are two classes of inaccuracies in any sort of writing. The first is unintentional and includes the mere "slip," such as a typographical error. Thus an excellent flora written by one of the high officers of systematic botany contains the statement that the stems of a certain plant are "covered with stout pickles." This is merely ludicrous, yet it has caused its author, he tells me, poignant shame. Or the mistakes may be due to sheer ignorance; nobody knows better than I how deeply one may blush for this sort. Or the facts and statistics may go out of date, leaving a book high and dry. My first work, *Cargoes and Harvests*, suffered this fate; it is now so out of date in spots as to be untrustworthy. And Kerner von Marilaun's incomparable *Natural History of Plants* has similarly suffered. Its physiology, in particular, is woefully antiquated, and all of it has a leisurely mid-Victorian approach that gives it a frumpish look, which is a pity because many portions, especially those dealing with the flora of the Alps, may still be read with delight.

The second great class of error is not, like the first, understandable, for it is to deceive by exaggerations or by stating as observed fact that which in fact no one has ever observed and which could not in the nature of things possibly happen. Snake stories, fish stories, and sea monster stories are sources of this unforgivable sort of error; in recent times, however, wolf stories were the favorite of one very popular writer.

Plants, being immobile, have not, in our times, lent themselves to much nature-faking except for a few hoaxes such as the one in *The Atlantic Monthly* about a quarter century ago about "blue dandelions," and the man-eating plants of Florida—a myth which has now been removed for its own safety to Madagascar. True, there were some whoppers told about plants in the Middle Ages, but it may be questioned that the medieval herbalists always had the intention to deceive the public with things they knew to be untrue. They were but repeating the vulgar superstitions of the age, just as Johannnes Kepler mingled his brilliant astronomy with astrological rubbish which he believed along with everyone else.

But if there are few nature-fakers in the botanical field today, neither are too many writers practicing the popularization of our science. We would be hard put to it to find the equal of entomology's Fabre, of ornithology's Hudson, or marine biology's William Beebe.

There is a considerable body of competent paraphrasing and simplification of botanical information, but very little truly inspired popularizing. Let me make the difference clear by example. Before me lies a little book on ferns and their allies, written by a good scientist and illustrated with accurate but unattractive outline drawings. It gives the habitats and ranges as well as brief descriptions of about 100 species and will quickly lead a student to their names, Latin and vernacular. As this is the chief aim of the little book, one must judge it by its aims only and say that it is an adequate, competent job—one more book among scores almost exactly like it on the same subject, fern identification. It is, however, only a *simplification* of its science, not a piece of creative popularization. It simply is not interesting except in so far as the Pteridophytes are interesting—if you are already deeply versed in them. The author makes no pretense at telling what he undoubtedly knows about this fascinating phylum of plants. A far finer job of popularization in this same line was done by Willard Clute in *Our Ferns, Their Haunts, Habits and Folklore* (1938) illustrated by Ida Clute and William Stilson with a beauty and freedom that is far more true to nature than the tight little "correct" pictures in the book to which I have referred above.

But for greater contrast, read *Plants, Life and Man* by Edgar Anderson (1952). Anderson is as high an officer of the botanical fraternity as one could ask—a geneticist who sees plant life in terms of inheritance, evolution, hybridity, and all the social implications that follow from plant breeding and plant introduction. He is yeasty with ideas, highly important ones, and sometimes highly disturbing to the conventionally minded botanist. He is even interested in the weeds of city alleys—indeed I should have said especially interested. He is more fascinated still by the flora of the farmyard manure pile. And (hold your hats, we're going around a curve) he states that most botanists cannot even name some of our commonest garden flowers correctly, for the reason that the commoner the plant the less botanists know about it: "Bring back a collection of rare little alpines from the Continental Divide. There will be a score of experts who can name them for you . . . pick one of the modern bearded irises from your own flower garden and . . . two out of three botanists will probably tell you that your plant belongs to *Iris germanica,* which it certainly does not. . . ." If by this time the systematic botanist is nettled by Anderson, that is because he is interested in nettles both botanical and figurative.

I am not disturbed by the fact that Anderson's organization is free-wheeling, or his presentation, like champagne, sends bubbles up the nose. My only complaint is that Anderson doesn't write more books. In fact I find this quite infuriating in him. On the other hand, my friend the author of the fern guide often produces a little book; his organization is always impeccable; he never misses his target because he is shooting at point-blank range. Anderson, with his sights elevated very high, might conceivably miss his target some day, but he would be bound to hit something beyond the horizon, even if it were nothing but the complacency of my own ignorance.

One of the greatest challenges to a popularizer of botany is to see how well his job can be performed by somebody who is not a botanist. I am thinking in particular of the description, in W. H. Hudson's *Far Away and Long Ago,* of the great "thistle years" on the Argentine pampas. Here is a common weed, of European origin, the cardoon thistle *Cynara cardunculus.* And see what Hudson, an ornithologist, does with the mounting horror of the thistle, when you could hear the harsh leaves crackling as in their growth they freed themselves from their cramped position with a jerk; when a gaucho on horseback could barely see over the tops of the thistle; when the thistles crowded to the windows of the houses like a sleeping-beauty wood and women feared to be left alone; when fire raged through the dead stalks completing the apocalyptic curse.

In America, surely, we have vegetation quite as interesting as the cardoon. Yet where is the botanist who writes the full story of sagebrush, bluegrass, sawgrass, buffalo-grass, gramagrass, greasewood, creosote-bush, longleaf pine, with all their historic and social as well as ecological and botanical implications? One of my friends, a deeply respected prairie-states ecologist, studied the ecological and social aspects of some of these, writing with great earnest-

ness and a desire to be helpful, but he never quite mastered true popularization. Perhaps his difficulties may be summed up in the remark he once made
to me when I took him an article I had written and asked him to read it
over for errors. In due course he returned it to me and (he was the most
ceremoniously courteous of botanists) was so good as to say "No, no errors,
Peattie. But I see you couldn't resist the temptation to be interesting."

If you can bring yourself to yield to this temptation, then practically the
whole field of botany lies open to you. It has only been superficially touched
here and there. I suggest as a challenge to those teaching botanists who regard
a knowledge of plant physiology as the backbone of every introductory course
and the indispensable prerequisite to any further knowledge that they try
popularizing their subject. By that I mean writing a book for out-of-college
adults, that a publisher will publish, or an article that so fascinates the editor
of a magazine as to make him reach for his voucher pad. In fact I can think
of only two occasions when this has been done with even partial success—an
article by Charles D. Stewart in *The Atlantic Monthly,* April, 1929, entitled
"The Tree as an Invention" and a book, *This Green World* (1942), by Ruther-
ford Platt who is a businessman who never took a botanical course in all the
years he was at Yale.

Perhaps (this is a dreadful thing to say and I am going to regret it as
soon as I've said it) this was almost an advantage, for Mr. Platt didn't and
perhaps still doesn't know too much about his subject. Many editors have
found that if you invite the great Professor Whatzisname to write on his
life-long specialty, he is apt to choke up, cannot get out what he knows,
despises his audience, and above all cannot submit himself to the discipline
of brevity. Possibly, too, he is very weary of his subject, with which he has
lived and slept for thirty years. He may not know that, but the editor and
reader hear the sound of weariness, the a-hemming of the strained voice. It
might do him good to be a smatter-artist for a few years. He might write
more freshly if you could sidetrack him with a sudden new hobby in another
aspect of botany.

Again, I'd like to suggest to the morphologists, some of whom consider
themselves the salt of the botanical earth, that they try popularizing their
subject. I recall asking one of them what it is that makes wood beautiful. He
frowned before saying "Why, the grain, I suppose," but then, reflecting that
the word "grain" has no precise meaning, he corrected himself, and dismissed
me by suggesting that I ask them over in the Esthetics Department. Plainly
it was not, he considered, a subject that a sound plant morphologist should
even be caught thinking upon. Ah, but it is, my late and much revered friend,
it is! If you were alive today I would recommend to you an article entitled
"Why Wood Is Beautiful," by George N. Lamb, in *American Forests* for
May, 1938. For there are very good morphological reasons to explain the
burning-bush type of crotch figure, the crotch and swirl figure, the plum-

pudding figure of Cuban mahogany, the fiddleback, the bird's-eye, the roll, the pigmenting of quarter-sawed rosewood and zebrawood, the clash of oak, the leaf and oystershell figures, the peanut figure of Japanese ash, the rope and mottle and broken-stripe figures.

If I were asked the best methods that a popularizer should adopt I fear I might be obliged to say that I am not sure. I mean that my own rules for myself are not necessarily applicable to anyone else. And further, there are three chief media of popularization, allowing for a few overlaps. That means three different techniques.

To begin with the book-reading public—the purchaser of a book is *not* "the man in the street" (whoever *he* is) but a most exceptional sort of person, one who goes into a bookstore, pays from $2.50 to $12.95 for a book, takes it quite off the street and into his home, to read it. That being the case, you should set your sights, if you are writing a book, for a very unusual intellect, one quite as keen as your own, without, however, any preconceived interest (of which you can be sure) in your subject. You have to write *up* to him, not down. He is a doctor, lawyer, or other professional who is paying you the honor of giving you his attention for as long as you can hold it. The best you have to offer is none too good.

The reader of a magazine may include the above people, but it is also likely to include a large number of intelligent women. (If you despise women's intellects, you'd be well advised not to write for magazines.)

The reader of the newspaper is, in one sense, everybody, but nobody reads all parts of a paper. Those who read "Nature columns," for instance, are not usually Long Island R.R. straphangers, but men and women, especially women, who are looking for the wonder and beauty in the things about them. If wonder and beauty are words that make you feel embarrassed, there is no danger of your becoming base, common, and popular.

Finally, there is the choice one must make between impersonality and being personal. Most scientists are very modest, or at least I suppose it is modesty that causes them to state their facts with no reference to themselves. There are times and places where this is decidedly the most appropriate method. But I have noticed that the great scientists who have also been great popularizers, Alfred Russel Wallace, William Beebe, W. H. Hudson, Auguste Forel, and Henri Fabre, and (some of the time) Darwin, have taken the reader's hand and led him up to the subject. Ask yourself what you would rather read, an account of the conquest of Mt. Everest told personally, with all the trials and errors, the sufferings, and emotions of triumph, by those who adventured on that terrible peak, or an impersonal statement of the topography of this mountain and an evaluation of the methods and equipment used in conquering it.

I particularly recommend that every popularizer should read the works of Henri Fabre. I read him not in the hope that I could equal him, but as an inspiration, and for an analytical study of his methods. Fabre, remember, was a man who never wrote anything except popularly. His most profound studies were written in popular style, and this threw the formal entomologists of France so badly off that it took them about forty years to realize that he was worthy of the privilege of associating his name with theirs. Even Pasteur thought Fabre was just a peasant-schoolmaster-scribbler, and it was Darwin who was the first to realize his greatness. The important point about Fabre as a model is that he regards the reader as neither above him nor beneath him; he looks him squarely in the eye. He doesn't hoard his pearls, either, but immediately turns out his pockets in front of us. He is, above all, never omniscient. He tells us frankly of his bewilderment, his ignorance, his mistakes (which he sometimes did not know were mistakes). He tells us of his children and of his neighbors, two-legged, six-legged, eight-legged, and myriapod, and of how he was dismissed from his position as schoolmaster because what he taught was denounced as corrupting the innocence and piety of youth—the same charge that was brought against Socrates, you'll recall. What Fabre was forced to drink was not poison hemlock but the bitter lees of ostracism and poverty.

But what Fabre is communicating to his readers, young and old, is a sense of the wonder and beauty in all things. When he was teaching algebra and geometry to a room full of bored teen-agers, ready to make trouble for him the moment he lost their interest, and was armed only with a piece of chalk, he told them of the "desperate curve of the hyperbola." If this sounds to you like purple prose, then you are entitled to say so, but I am willing to gamble that the phrase, once heard, will never be forgotten. I could not, today, define a hyperbolic curve without cheating by looking in the dictionary, but I shall forever be able to remember its course, because of Fabre's description of it.

I began this paper with a quotation from Shakespeare, who was never afraid of purple prose and indeed slung reams of it through all his plays. I am going to close with a quotation from a botanist who will express far better than I could do, and in quite un-purple but also unequivocal words, what he believed to be the relationship of popularization to the discipline of botany as a whole.

I quote from pages 3 and 4 of *The Living Plant,* by William F. Ganong. "An important phase of *Botanical Education* . . . will be the production of works, on the *Natural History of Plants,* which will set forth, with a combination of scientific accuracy and literary charm, not only the technical and economic aspects of plant life, but also those historical, legendary, and imaginative aspects which give to a study its widest human interest. Indeed, the production of such works may be viewed as the logical aim of all botanical study."

26

BOTANICAL HISTORY

Andrew Denny Rodgers III

The study of the history of science is the study of the evolution of a branch of scientific learning and the cultural influences surrounding its development. Its basis must be factual, particularly with reference to events occurring within a given period or periods; and its foundation includes elaborations of principles, concepts, and ideas promulgated as of that time, more especially those sustaining survival value and on which subsequent scientific history has been predicated. A student of the history of science does not argue the validity or invalidity of points of view though their origins, enlargements or refinements, modifications, and modern contributive worth should be recognized and in instances considered fully. Foremost the historian's function is that of the exposition of facts and their interpretation in the light of later knowledge. The historian, in this author's opinion, should remain primarily a historian, however much the duty devolves of understanding and comprehending the full significance of the scientific subject matter organized and described. But he should refrain from exscinding, discussing, affirming, or denying any or all current scientific truth embodied. That is the scientist's function, and although the historian must adhere to rules of scientific objectivity and impartiality withal, he should first differentiate with as much clarity of thought as possible that subject matter which has become history and that which still belongs to the domain of current science still under investigation.

In other words, the scientific historian is a fact finder and expositor of facts of and from the past, those data reasonably settled and part of the science's fairly well-established structure. As in other realms of human activity, the historian takes up where men and women have completed an era of activity and accomplishment or where one scientist or a group of scientists has brought to consummation an outstanding investigation or event worthy of permanent recognition. The historian builds an edifice with materials supplied by the scientist. He must not be greedy and overstep his bounds, and for his work he should await such time as scientists are in reasonably definite agreement as to established truth. The historian is not the final arbiter. Scientists themselves should be.

In even historical presentations the frailty of the human equation will be present to greater or less degree; and for that reason, more often than not, contributions to learning are first indicated. As in other areas of workmanship, principles of analysis and synthesis apply; and the full-stature history may have to emerge from numerous earlier contributions. Years ago Dr. George Sarton of Harvard University sanctioned the biographical method as a valid organizing technique. Around central biographical figures, and with thumbnail or more elaborate sketches of other scientific coworkers or subordinates of the periods concerned, the histories or stories of developmental science may be organized and written in first instance.

Research materials, depending upon the subject and period, may be found in many quarters: from botanical and plant-science journals of the period, including those since discontinued in publication; from interviews with, and letters from, workers in the science; and from collected desiderata (letters, manuscripts, memoirs, diaries, articles, etc.)—all gathered together, organized chronologically or otherwise, and coordinated for purposes of writing constructive, restrained, impersonal, and truthful narratives. This author's experience has taught him that perseverance and a refusal to become discouraged yield eventually the necessary source materials and documentation. He has discovered that collections of utmost value may be found in unexpected places ranging from attics to basements in homes and in, of course, offices, laboratories, old file cabinets, etc., of botanical departments and institutions. Letter correspondence always has a sender and sendee; and, though the property right remains in the sender, the whereabouts of permissibly usable materials should be checked at both ends. Libraries and institutions maintaining manuscript divisions are often the most effective starting points both for their own collections and for leads to other collections.

Plant-science research of the Americas, Europe (including the British Isles), and other continents has many such institutions: to list a few in the United States, Harvard University (Gray Herbarium, Farlow Herbarium, Arnold Arboretum, etc.), the Boston Society of Natural History, Yale University (library, Botany department, Sheffield Scientific, and Yale Forest, schools), the New York Botanical Garden, the Academy of Natural Sciences of Philadelphia, the American Philosophical Society (library), the National Archives of Washington, D.C., Smithsonian Institution, Library of Congress (manuscript division), and the United States Department of Agriculture (library and research centers), Cornell University (main library, departments, and colleges), the Missouri Botanical Garden, and libraries and departments of many universities and colleges from the Mississippi basin to the Pacific coast. Frequently, furthermore, valuable collected materials may be found in libraries or appropriate repositories of nearly all the various experiment stations throughout the United States and the Dominion of Canada. Ingenuity of the researcher will determine how effectively and extensively use can be made of such institutional facilities irrespective of direct or indirect affiliation; and, as subordinate and supplementary aids, facilities of state and regional Historical Society libraries and work may nearly always be located. Bibliographies of older and more recent books relevant to the subject should also be consulted; and often to locate each and all of such the card index files of the Library of Congress, and of the New York, Boston, and Chicago public libraries, should be checked.

In preparing a manuscript, the author, if he plans publishing and if fortunate to know in advance his or her company or press, should follow format rules of the prospective publisher. That has become of salient practical importance since manuscript requirements vary and much time can be saved by advance knowledge of such requirements.

Dominant is the persuasion that only by books or articles written will materials be perpetuated in proper historical perspective for posterity. This author knows that had his work been begun a quarter century earlier his studies would have been advantaged by other collections which in the interim had been either destroyed, lost, or divided among many beneficiaries. Nothing displaces assiduousness of workmanship, as well in gathering research matter as in their organizing and writing. Books are never prepared by research alone, and often an author can become bogged down by letting his research stray into details comparatively unimportant (that is, not germane to the main subject) or by accumulating more research than he can effectively handle. It is well to put reasonably complete subject matter into first writing as soon as possible. In course of such first writing, the author will learn weak points and where and what further study and research is required; and the final manuscript will represent several exercises of this discipline. With further work of necessary condensations, the final accomplishment will culminate.

In all humility the foregoing is submitted as representing a fair summary of one writer's practical experience in this field. His hope is that, where collections are not already started, institutions and scientists themselves will assemble materials in historical botany—manuscript or collection centers thereby being established or built, to which others may add, and of which yet others may make use. The need of such in the more recently created branches of botanical investigation and scientific learning is urgent. Instead of periodic destruction of materials as in some quarters of the past, there should now be substituted carefully selected and durably preserved collections. How much of early American botany's background history would be known today had not Torrey, Gray, Farlow, Engelmann, and yet other pioneers possessed a historical as well as scientific sense? And, further, how much of their and later periods' history would be available had not men of the leadership at Harvard University and at the New York and Missouri botanical gardens preserved their collections? Fortunate this author was in early acquaintance with Mr. C. A. Weatherby of Harvard and Dr. J. H. Barnhart of the New York Botanical Garden. Other men of the leadership stature of Torrey and Gray in taxonomic botany and of L. H. Bailey in American horticulture are and will be known as fundamental investigation extends and deepens the total science's orbits. May adequate biographies of more recent as well as older historical leaders in all phases of plant-science investigation not fail for want of adequate collections of materials and data concerning their lives and work and the lives and work of coworkers of their periods who helped make their generations' work great!

At the Sesqui-Centennial Exposition held in 1926 at Philadelphia commemorating 150 years since signing of the American Declaration of Independence, John Merle Coulter characterized "the progress of science [as] one of the most outstanding features of the sesquicentennial period." Thirty more years of active work has since been added; and botanical science's advancement has been extended in pure and applied fields beyond even the prophecies of those times. History's claims to full recognition in that and other branches of science are patent. The subject matter and needs are abundant. Some of us, unable for diverse reasons to become "professionally trained historians of science," have contributed our studies more as what I. B. Cohen (*Science* 114:3 Dec. 21, 1951) has properly called "devoted amateurs." Large and important segments of professional botany, horticulture, forestry, and other branches of investigation in the plant sciences in their broadest sense were begun similarly on the American scene: by nonprofessionals or amateurs who devotedly and generously gave of their individual substance and portions of their work lives to the founding or promotion of a beloved science. Records prepared by them have provided bases for subsequent study and investigation; and, with the help or collaboration of professionally trained men, portions of their pioneering work have survived the test of time admirably. In a sense they each and all were cornerstone layers.

Now in study of the history of science, however, with more and more colleges and technical schools introducing the subject into their curricula in full or specialized forms, the subject is gaining in recognition and doctorates are being offered in at least four universities in the United States. The time will arrive, to quote Professor Cohen further, when studies will fully "provide a mature understanding of the nature of science, as well as its growth, its place in our society, and its role in the development of our culture." The need still exists for full-scale "summaries and syntheses," predicated in science and in history, and in major instances more than biographies in presentation. A summons to young scholars is more than ever abroad in the land today to build anew where as yet none or a dearth of historical works has thus far been presented, or more completely on bases of "accuracy of fact and reasonableness of interpretation" where thus far contributions to knowledge have been submitted as offerings of fundamental structure.

27

THE ROLE OF STUDY OF ALGAE
IN THE DEVELOPMENT OF BOTANY

Gilbert M. Smith

Long before the founding of the Botanical Society of America fifty years ago, contributions to the various phases of botany had become so numerous that nobody could be familiar with the literature of the entire field. The end of the time when this was no longer possible cannot be stated with certainty, but broadly speaking, it may be said to have ended with the death of Sachs, a man who has been called "the last of the great epitomists." In this age of specialization we have reached a point where it is becoming more and more difficult for a man to cover the literature past and present even in his own specialty. Thus outside of their own special field of interest many botanists have only a scanty knowledge of contributions from other fields of botany that have advanced botanical science as a whole. In this review of progress in study of algae emphasis will be placed on those contributions that are general botanical significance instead of on those that are of interest only to phycologists.

Until early in the nineteenth century practically all contributions to botany were in the field of taxonomy. Linnaeus' *Species Plantarum* (1753), the official starting point for the nomenclature of plants, places 14 of the recognized genera among the "order" algae. Today, only 4 of these genera (*Conferva, Ulva, Fucus,* and *Chara*) are considered algal in nature. Within a few decades after publication of the *Species Plantarum* botanists who were specialists on algae appeared on the scene. In their floristic studies of algae of various regions they soon realized that there were species additional to those described by Linnaeus. They described the new species that they discovered but placed them in one of the four algal genera recognized by Linnaeus. This practice was continued even when hundreds of species had been added to the Linnaean genera. Examples of this are to be seen in Dillwyn's (1802–1809) *British Confervae* and in Turner's (1808–1819) four-volume treatise entitled *Fuci*.

Early in the nineteenth century phycologists began to have the temerity to describe genera additional to the sacred four recognized by Linnaeus. New genera appeared in the literature at a rapid rate, and many of the earlier established genera were divided into two or more genera. With the establishment of a number of genera there came the grouping of them into taxa of higher categories. Lamoroux (1813) was the first to do this. He placed marine algae in a "family" he called the Thalassiophytes and divided this family into six "orders," the three most important being the Fucacées, Floridées, and the Ulvacées. Distinctions between these taxa were made in part, but not exclusively, upon color. The next significant grouping into major taxa was proposed by Harvey (1836, 1841) when he divided algae into four "series" (Melanospermeae, Rhodospermeae, Chlorospermeae, Diatomaceae), each with a number of families. Distinction between the first three was made on the basis of their brown, red, or green color. This distinction on the basis of color has stood the test of time and has been found to be correlated with distinctive types of reproductive structure. The names Harvey applied to his major taxa were soon supplanted by other names, the Melanospermeae being called the Phaeophyceae, the Rhodospermeae called the Rhodophyceae, and the Chlorospermeae called the Chlorophyceae. Harvey's Diatomaceae included both desmids and diatoms, but it was soon realized that desmids belonged among the Chlorophyceae.

The major taxon variously called Chlorospermeae or Chlorophyceae also included blue-green algae. These were first segregated by Stizenberger (1860) in a separate taxon that he called the Myxophyceae. Somewhat later Luther (1899), primarily on the basis of flagellation of motile reproductive cells, segregated certain of the supposedly grass-green algae into a class that he called the Heterokonteae (Xanthophyceae).

Until the beginning of the present century the flagellates with chromatophores of various colors were considered protozoa, and almost all our knowledge concerning them was due to the efforts of protozoologists. An exception must be made in the case of the *Chlamydomonas-Volvox* series. For nearly a century botanists have placed this series among the Chlorophyceae. Beginning more than three quarters of a century ago botanists were in general agreement that the Chlorophyceae have arisen from a unicellular flagellated organism of the chlamydomonad type. Many also thought that the flagellated reproductive cells of the Phaeophyceae indicate that they have arisen from a unicellular flagellated ancestor. Correlated with this was the gradual appearance of the view that flagellates related to unquestionable algae should be placed among the algae instead of being placed among the protozoa. Although not the pioneer in this idea, Pascher was the chief advocate of it and the discoverer of many new algae obviously related to pigmented flagellates.

For some time certain botanists had held that the dinoflagellates should be considered algae. Their argument was based on the discovery of certain unicellular, free-floating, and sessile forms whose life cycle involves a formation of motile cells of a gymnodinoid nature. These botanists held that the immobile phase is comparable to that of unicellular coccoid Chlorophyceae and that the motile phase is zoosporic in nature. Many protozoologists held that the swarmers are dinoflagellates and that the coccoid phase in the life cycle is cyst-like in nature and comparable to the cysts known to be formed by many dinoflagellates. In 1927 Pascher gave further evidence supporting the view of botanists. This was the discovery of multicellular branched and unbranched filamentous algae whose zoospores have a structure typical of dinoflagellates. The argument for including the chrysomonad flagellates among the algae rests on a greater number of cases. There are a considerable number of multicellular algae with swarmers typical of chrysomonads, a fact which seems to warrant inclusion of chrysomonad flagellates among the algae.

Taxonomists have long been interested in a natural classification of the plant kingdom but differ with regard to the primary taxa that should be recognized. Today there are two schools of thought concerning the number of divisions into which the plant kingdom should be segregated. One school follows the idea that the most primitive of the plant kingdom is the Thallophyta, which consists of two subdivisions, the Algae and the Fungi. According to this system the various distinctive series of algae are each given the rank of a class in the subdivision Algae. The second school holds that differences among the algae are of sufficient magnitude to preclude grouping of them in a single subdivision or even division. According to this conception the algae should be segregated into more than one division. All systems adopting this idea follow in general the proposals of Pascher (1914, 1921, 1931a). He holds that certain classes of algae, as the Rhodophyceae and the Phaeophyceae, differ so markedly from other algae that they merit the rank of divisions. Other classes of algae, as the Chrysophyceae, Xanthophyceae, and the Bacillariophyceae (diatoms) are thought to have sufficient in common to warrant inclusion in a single division. European botanists, especially the British, generally adhere to systems which place algae in a subdivision of the division Thallophyta. Many American botanists prefer those systems which abandon the division Thallophyta and which segregate algae into a number of divisions.

The foregoing discussion of progress in taxonomic study of algae may have left the impression that the primary concern of phycologists has been that of floristic studies and arrangement of algae according to a natural system. This is far from the case. The structure of reproductive organs, especially those of Chlorophyceae and Phaeophyceae, is so simple and so easily observed that it attracted the attention of phycologists almost as soon as the compound microscope supplanted the hand lens in the study of algae. Vaucher (1803) was one of the first in this field. He studied reproduction in a number of algae and in *"Ectosperma"* (now known as *Vaucheria*), and he described and figured the sex organs now known as antheridia and oögonia. Among other algae, although not realizing its significance, he described and figured successive steps of conjugation in species of *"Conjugata"* now referred to *Spirogyra* and *Zygnema*. He was more fortunate than many present-day teachers of botany in that he saw germination of the zygote of *Spirogyra.*.

The erroneous ideas of Vaucher and contemporary students of reproductive structure of algae rests in part upon their interpretation of them in terms of floral structure. For example, Vaucher refers to the reproductive structures of *"Ectosperma"* as anther and as seed. Another curious erroneous idea arose shortly after discovery of motile reproductive cells of algae. It was thought that formation of swarmers by algae was really a metamorphosis of certain cells into "infusoria" (protozoa) which eventually metamorphosed back to plant cells. Proponents of this idea held to it as late as 1850.

A start toward proper understanding of the nature of reproductive bodies of algae came with Agardh's (1836) abandonment of the floral terms used for them and when he began calling reproductive cells spores instead of seeds. He was not the first to use the term "spore" since it had been used before in connection with mosses. Agardh distinguished between motile and non-motile spores but did not give them special names. The term zoospore, now so widely used, was coined by Decaisne (1842) but applied indiscriminately to both sexual and asexual swarmers. An important distinction was made by Pringsheim (1855) when he distinguished between sexual and asexual swarmers. He restricted the term zoospore to asexual swarmers.

It was through study of reproduction in algae that botanists' ideas concerning the essential features of sexual reproduction were clarified. Long before the middle of the last century botanists were aware of the necessity of pollination for the formation of embryos of seed plants. By the middle of that century there had been a demonstration that a pollen grain forms a pollen tube which grows to the egg cell in the embryo sac of an ovule. There then arose the following controversy: does the tip of the pollen tube grow into the embryo, or does something passing from the tip of the pollen tube (either a liquid or a discrete body) stimulate the egg cell to develop into the embryo? This controversy was settled by discoveries made in algae. Here it was shown for the first time that the essential feature in sexual reproduction is the fusion of male and female elements. In 1854 Thuret showed that antherozoids are attracted to the "octospores" (eggs) of *Fucus* and that there is no development of an egg into an embryo unless antherozoids and egg come together. Thuret did not see the actual fusion of antherozoid and egg but inferred that this took place. Thuret's inference was confirmed the next year by Pringsheim (1855) when he reported for *Oedogonium* that an antherozoïd first comes in contact with an egg and then fuses with it. Demonstration of the fusion of antherozoid and egg in *Oedogonium* and *Vaucheria* led De Bary (1858) to interpret conjugation in *Spirogyra* and allied genera as essentially the same process, even though the two fusing protoplasts are identical in size and form. Within a few years there was discovery that certain algae have a fusion of two flagellated cells, cells which were given the name gamete by De Bary and Strasburger (1877). Fusion of two motile gametes was first observed by Pringsheim (1870), who found it in *Pandorina*. He recognized that this is a more primitive type of sexual reproduction than a fusion of antherozoid and egg. In *Pandorina* the two of a fusing pair are unequal in size. What is more frequently the case, a fusion of two motile gametes of identical size was first reported in *Ulothrix* (Cramer, 1871).

We now know that the nuclear fusion following a union of gametes is a feature of fundamental significance. This was discovered by Hertwig (1876) when studying fertilization in the sea urchin *Toxopneustes*. The first record of this for the plant kingdom is that by Schmitz (1879) for *Spirogyra*.

The great diversity of types of gametic union recorded for algae has contributed greatly to our ideas concerning what is often called evolution of sex. A more accurate phrase than "evolution of sex" would be progressive differentiation of gametes. Certain species of *Chlamydomonas* and *Dunaliella* show that there may be gametic union without any specific differentiation of gametes. In these species every cell is capable of functioning as a gamete under proper conditions. Gametic union in the great majority of algae is in advance of this in that the protoplasts of all or certain cells of a thallus give rise to one or more gametes. Among them the most primitive type is a union of two gametes of like size and structure, a type known as isogamy. Among isogamous species with both gametes motile, one of a uniting pair is male and the other female, but it is impossible to determine microscopically which is which. This is not the case when one of a uniting pair of motile gametes is regularly larger than the other, a type of gametic union known as anisogamy. Here there is good reason for believing that the larger of the two is the female gamete. An evolutionary loss of flagella by the female gamete of an anisogamous form, coupled with retention of flagella by the small male gamete, leads to those algae in which a small flagellated male gamete (antherozoid) unites with a large non-flagellated female gamete (egg), a type of gametic union known as oögamy. The evolutionary series frequently cited as exemplifying an evolution from isogamy to oögamy is the family Volvocaceae of the Chlorophyceae. Here *Gonium* is isogamous, *Pandorina* is anisogamous, *Eudorina* is transitional between anisogamy and oögamy, and *Volvox* is oögamous. In this series with a progressive differentiation of gametes there is also a progressive increase in number of cells in a colony together with a progressive differentiation into somatic (vegetative) cells and gametic cells. The assumption is frequently made that there is a correlation between progressive differentiation in type of gametic union and progressive specialization in structure of the colony. The incorrectness of this assumption is shown by certain unicellular Volvocales, including *Chlamydomonas, Chlorogonium,* and

Polytoma. Within each of these three unicellular genera the type of gametic union ranges from isogamy to oögamy. Progression from isogamy to oögamy has arisen independently more than once among the algae. In the Chlorophyceae this is found in the Volvocales, the Ulothricales, and the Siphonales, three orders not closely related to one another. The same progressive change from isogamy to oögamy is also found in the Phaeophyceae, algae wholly unrelated to the Chlorophyceae.

Algae have also been of service in development of concepts concerning the difference between maleness and femaleness. Are maleness and femaleness two distinct categories, or are they different degrees of the same category? The latter idea is to be found in Hartmann's theory of relative sexuality, a theory which he first clearly enunciated in 1925. For heterothallic (dioecious) species Hartmann holds that the intensity of sexuality in either female or male gametes may not be the same for all individual plants of a species. Female gametes from one individual of a species may be of a strong intensity of sexuality, whereas those from another individual of the species may be of a weak intensity. The same holds for male gametes. Female gametes of either intensity unite with male gametes of either intensity. On the other hand, when in the presence of female gametes of strong sexual intensity, female gametes of low sexuality behave as male gametes and there is thus a union of two gametes of the same sex. Male gametes of low and high sexual intensity behave in a similar fashion. Thus maleness and femaleness are to be considered different degrees of the same category. Hartmann's theory of relative sexuality was based upon study of sexual reproduction in certain isogamous and anisogamous algae.

Relative sexuality has been found in *Enteromorpha* (Hartmann, 1929) and in *Dasycladus* (Hartmann, 1943), isogamous algae in which it is impossible to differentiate between male and female gametes. It has also been recorded for *Ectocarpus* (Hartmann, 1925, 1934), an isogamous alga but one in which it is possible to differentiate between male and female gametes by behavior of the two during gametic union. Union of male gamete with male gamete, and female gamete with female gamete, has also been found in *Bryopsis* (Hartmann, 1955), an anisogamous species in which gametes of the two sexes are microscopically different. Moewus (1939b) has reported relative sexuality for *Chlamydomonas eugametos*. Hartmann (1955) questions this because Förster and Wiese, working in his laboratory, have been unable to confirm it in cultures supplied by Moewus.

Two sets of substances of a hormone-like nature are involved in gametic union. These are the gamones involved in the coming together of gametes and the termones determining the sexuality of gametes. A secretion of gamones into surrounding water was first observed by Geitler (1931) when working with *Tetraspora*, whose sexual reproduction is isogamous. He filtered off the water in which gametes of one sex were swimming and then added gametes of the opposite sex to the filtrate. This caused an immediate agglutination of the gametes, even though gametes of the opposite sex were not present in the filtrate. This behavior to filtrates or centrifugates is not peculiar to *Tetraspora* but has been found in other isogamous algae with motile gametes, including *Botrydium* (Moewus, 1940c), *Chlamydomonas* (Moewus, 1933), *Dunaliella* (Lerche, 1937), *Ectocarpus* (Hartmann, 1937), and *Protosiphon* (Moewus, 1933). My studies on various species of *Chlamydomonas* indicate that the gamone causing an agglutination of gametes of opposite sex is not a chemotactic gamone.

Beginning with the work of Pfeffer, several investigators have shown a chemotactic response of antherozoids of pteridophytes and bryophytes. These investigators assume that entrance of antherozoids into an archegonium is due to a chemotactic substance (gamone) secreted by the egg, but there has been no actual demonstration of this. A secretion of a chemotactic gamone into the surrounding water has been demonstrated for two oögamous algae, *Fucus* and *Sphaeroplea*. This was shown for *Fucus* by taking water containing many eggs, centrifuging, filling capillary tubes with the centrifugate, and placing the tubes in a dish containing swimming antherozoids (Cook et al., 1948; Cook and Elvidge, 1951). When this was done there was a clustering of many antherozoids around the end of the tube. Pascher (1931b) devised an ingenious method for demonstrating that eggs of *Sphaeroplea* excrete a chemotactic substance. Short lengths of white thread were placed in a dish containing female filaments with ripe eggs. After lying in the dish for a time the threads were transferred to a dish containing motile antherozoids. Soon thereafter there was a marked accumulation of antherozoids in the vicinity of the threads. This persisted for an hour or more but then disappeared. Moewus (1939a) has studied the chemotactic gamones of *Chlamydomonas eugametos* by means of Pfeffer's capillary-tube method. He reports that male and female gametes each secrete a chemotactic gamone and that gamones of the two are not identical. Others have not been able to duplicate his results.

Attempts to show the presence of termones have centered around reactivation of gametes that have become sexually inactive. In *Ectocarpus* Hartmann (1937) took female gametes that had become sexually inactive and placed them in a filtrate from sexually active female gametes. When this was done the female gametes became sexually active and fused with male gametes. In a similar manner male gametes were reactivated. These experiments are inconclusive as demonstrating the presence of termones because it is possible that loss of sexuality by the gametes was due to a loss of gamones rather than to a loss of termones. An activation of sexually inactive cells of *Chlamydomonas eugametos* by means of centrifugates from sexually functional cells has been recorded by Moewus (1940a). He identifies the termones as derivatives of the carotenoid protocrocin. The termone (gynotermone) of female cells is said to be pikrocrocin. The termone (androtermone) of male cells is said to be safranol. Sexual activity in sexually inactive female cells was induced by pikrocrocin, and that of sexually inactive male cells was induced by safranol.

In an investigation of *Monostroma* Moewus (1940b) reports that zoospores may be made to function as gametes by means of extracts obtained from thalli. *Monostroma* is a close relative of *Ulva*, being generically distinguished from it because the sheet-like thallus is but one cell in thickness. *Monostroma* is heterothallic, all cells of a thallus producing gametes of the same sex. When germinated in water the protoplast of the greatly enlarged zygote divides to form 32 quadriflagellate zoospores. When zygotes are germinated in extracts from thalli there is a formation of 64 swarmers that are biflagellate. A biflagellate swarmer formed when germination takes place in a thallus extract is able to function as a gamete and one of the same sex as that of the thallus from which the extract was obtained.

The problem of the course of evolution among algae is of broad interest because there is universal agreement that algae have given rise to all plants standing higher in the evolutionary scale. For the Chlorophyceae and the Xanthophyceae Blackmann (1900) proposed the widely adopted theory that the most primitive members of these groups were of a unicellular flagellated type and that there were divergent evolutionary lines from the primitive type. One of these tendencies, the volvocine, was toward an aggregation of flagellated vegetative cells into progressively larger and more specialized colonies. This is a blind evolutionary end in which none of the colonies evolved a more complex structure than is found in *Volvox*. Another tendency, the tetrasporine, was toward an organization of non-flagellated immobile cells into colonies of increasing complexity of structure. This was the line that gave rise to the higher plants. Still a third tendency, the endosporine, was toward a unicellular condition without cell division but with multinucleate cells of elaborate complexity among advanced forms. Later, Pascher (1914) pointed out that similar evolutionary tendencies are to be found among the Chrysophyceae.

Evolution along the tetrasporine tendency has been accompanied by evolution of a variety of life cycles. The concept of a life cycle involving a rhythmic alternation of sexual and asexual generations was first clearly enunciated by Hofmeister (1851) as a result of his studies on the life cycle in certain bryophytes and pteridophytes. However, it was not until forty years later that the accompanying periodic doubling and halving of the number of chromosomes was first pointed out by Strasburger (1894). The question of an alternation of generations among algae was raised (Pringsheim, 1856) shortly after discovery of alternation of generations in land plants. Even as late as 1903 Davis, with considerable justification, stated that alternation of generations with an accompanying alternation of chromosome numbers had not been definitely established for algae. A year later Williams (1940a, 1940b) showed that the brown alga *Dictyota* has such a life cycle, but one in which the two generations are identical in vegetative structure. For the Rhodo-phyceae, Yamanouchi (1906) showed that sexual thalli of *Polysiphonia* are haploid and that tetrasporic thalli are diploid. Other phycologists soon showed that a similar condition obtains in other Rhodophyceae with thalli producing tetraspores. The alternation thus discovered in *Dictyota* and in the Rhodo-phyceae differs from that found in bryophytes and other land plants in the following two respects: the two generations are vegetatively identical, and each is independent of the other from the beginning. An alternation in which the two generations are identical in size and vegetative structure has been called isomorphic alternation by Fritsch (1935). The contrasting type where the two differ in size and vegetative structure has been called heteromorphic alternation. Among algae this was first found in the Phaeophyceae and is now known to occur in many of them. Discovery of a heteromorphic life cycle among Phaeophyceae was not made until gametophytes were grown in cultures started from zoospores discharged from unilocular sporangia. The gametophytes developing from these zoospores are always filamentous and of microscopic size. Union of gametes produced by gametophytes results in a diploid sporophyte that is often of macroscopic size and of complex structure.

A life cycle in which a multicellular haploid generation alternates with a one-celled diploid phase was first found by Allen (1905) in *Coleochaete,* a member of the Chlorophyceae. With the finding of the same for certain other Chlorophyceae, phycologists tended to make the generalization that this is a characteristic of the entire class. This generalization became invalid when an isomorphic alternation was found in *Enteromorpha* (Hartmann, 1929) and in *Cladophora* (Føyn, 1929). A similar life cycle is also known for certain other Chlorophyceae. The only reported case of a heteromorphic alternation of multicellular generations among Chlorophyceae is that of *Stigeoclonium* (Juller, 1937).

The alternation of generations among algae contributes to an understanding of that among higher plants. Firstly, it shows that evolution of an alternation of generations is not dependent upon migration from an aquatic to a terrestrial environment. Secondly, it shows that an alternation of generations has ap-peared many times instead of but once during the evolution of plants. Thirdly, algae do not show whether the sporophyte arose by modification of the gametophyte, or is to be interpreted as an entirely new generation inter-calated between two successive gametophytic generations. One may have very positive views concerning the relative merits of the modification (homologous) and the intercalation (antithetic) theories of origin of an alternation of gen-erations, but the algae do not furnish conclusive proof for either theory.

Algae have been of service in the advancement of plant physiology because they are the best experimental material in certain fields of this discipline. *Valonia* and *Halicystis* have proven especially suitable for studies on per-meability. These algae have cells that are up to half an inch in diameter and have such large central vacuoles that the cell sap may be sampled without difficulty. Chlorophyceae are the most suitable algae for the study of photosynthesis because their pigments are identical with those of land plants. The Chlorophyceae best adapted for such studies are those in which clones can be maintained in vitro for indefinite periods and which can be grown in pure culture free from all contaminants. For these reasons *Spirogyra* is unsuitable for most studies on photosynthesis, whereas *Chlorella* and *Scenedesmus* are admirably suitable. During recent years many of the fundamental advances in our knowledge of photosynthesis have been obtained through experiments with *Chlorella* and *Scenedesmus*. Additional information on photosynthesis has been obtained through study of Phaeophyceae and Rhodophyceae, algae which contain photosynthetic pigments not found in green plants.

Phycologists are frequently asked the question, of what use to man are algae? This question is usually asked by people familiar with the luxuriant growth of seaweeds along the seashore, who think of them as an untapped source of plant products. One can point out that they are used to a certain extent. Thus they are the source of such gels as alginates and agar. Marine algae are also used as food to a limited extent by Japanese and Chinese. For a number of years the British Government has supported an extensive research program seeking additional products of commercial value that can be obtained from seaweeds. Support of the project was to be terminated in 1957 because no promising leads had been found.

With the population of the world increasing at the present rate there will come a time when the available agricultural land will no longer be able to supply food in adequate amounts, despite improvement in agricultural practices and development of better-yielding crops through the efforts of geneticists. Even today there are regions in the world where the population is much larger than can be supported by the available acreage of arable land. For this reason there has been widespread popular interest in the proposal that fresh-water algae be cultivated as a supplemental source of food for man and domestic animals.

Studies on mass cultivation of algae have been made in several laboratories, notably in the laboratory of the Department of Plant Biology of the Carnegie Institution of Washington. Almost all such studies have been with *Chlorella pyrenoidosa*. Preliminary studies on mass culture of this alga have been *in vitro* in the laboratory. Spoehr and Milner (1949) have shown that it may be cultured in such a manner that there is either a high fat or a high protein content. When cultured so that there is a high protein content it may comprise more than 50 per cent of the dry weight. Computations by Spoehr (1951) based upon culture in vitro in the laboratory estimate that there might be a yield of 40 tons of dry high-protein material per year per acre. This is a much higher yield of protein per acre than is known for any agricultural crop.

Cultivation of *Chlorella* on a large scale out of doors is quite different from cultivation of it in small batches in the laboratory. This introduces many new problems, especially those of an engineering nature. Thus far, outdoor cultivation has been in pilot plants with a capacity of a thousand or more gallons of culture medium. In one such outdoor pilot plant it has been estimated (Burlew, 1953, p. 272) that when operated under optimum conditions the dry-weight yield would be at the rate of 100 pounds per acre per day. This is at the rate of 17.5 tons per acre per year. As yet the costs per pound of *Chlorella* for running such pilot plants are so high that it is economically unprofitable.

LITERATURE CITED

AGARDH, J. G. 1836. Observations sur la propagation des algues. Ann. Sci. Nat. (Bot.) II, 6:193–212.

ALLEN, C. E. 1905. Die Keimung der Zygote bei *Coleochaete*. Ber. Deutsch. Bot. Ges. 23:285–292.

BLACKMAN, F. F. 1900. The primitive Algae and the Flagellata: an account of modern work bearing on the evolution of the Algae. Ann. Bot. 14:647–688.

BURLEW, J. S. 1953. Algal culture from laboratory to pilot plant. Carnegie Inst. Wash. Publ. 600:1–357.

COOK, A. H., J. A. ELVIDGE, AND I. HEILBRON. 1948. Fertilization, including chemotactic phenomena, in the Fucaceae. Proc. Roy. Soc. London B, 135:293–301.

——— AND J. A. ELVIDGE. 1951. Fertilization in the Fucaceae: investigations on the nature of the chemotactic substance produced by the eggs of *Fucus serratus* and *F. vesiculosus*. Proc. Roy. Soc. London B, 138:97–114.

CRAMER, C. 1871. Über Entstehung und Paarung der Schwärmsporen von *Ulothrix*. Bot. Zeitg. 29:76–80, 89–91.

DAVIS, B. M. 1903. The origin of the sporophyte. Amer. Nat. 37:411–429.

DE BARY, A. 1858. Untersuchungen über die Familie der Conjugaten (Zygnemeen und Desmidieen). 91 pp. Leipzig.

——— AND E. STRASBURGER. 1877. *Acetabularia mediterranea*. Bot. Zeitg. 35:713–758.

DECAISNE, J. 1842. Essais sur une classification des algues et des polypiers calcifères de Lamouroux. Ann. Sci. Nat. (Bot.). II, 17:297–380.

DILLWYN, L. W. 1802–1809. British Confervae: or colored figures and descriptions of the British plants referred by botanists to the genus *Conferva*. 231 pp. London.

FØYN, B. 1929. Untersuchungen über die Sexualität und Entwicklung von Algen. IV. Vorläufige Mitteilung über Sexualität und den Generationswechsel von *Cladophora* und *Ulva*. Ber. Deutsch. Bot. Ges. 47:495–506.

FRITSCH, F. E. 1935. The structure and reproduction of the algae. Vol. 1. 791 pp. Cambridge Univ. Press, New York.

GEITLER, L. 1931. Untersuchungen über das sexuelle Verhalten von *Tetraspora lubrica*. Biol. Zentralbl. 51:173–187.

HARTMANN, M. 1925. Untersuchungen über relative Sexualität. I. Versuche an *Ectocarpus siliculosus*. Biol. Zentralbl. 45:449–467.

HARTMANN, M. 1929. Untersuchungen über die Sexualität und Entwicklung von Algen. III. Über die Sexualität und den Generationswechsel von *Chateomorpha* und *Enteromorpha*. Ber. Deutsch. Bot. Ges. 47:485–494.

———. 1934. Untersuchungen über die Sexualität von *Ectocarpus siliculosus*. Arch. Protistenk. 83:110–153.

———. 1937. Ergänzende Untersuchungen über die Sexualität von *Ectocarpus siliculosus*. Arch. Protistenk. 89:382–392.

———. 1943. Die Sexualität. 426 pp. S. Fischer Verlag, Jena.

———. 1955. Sexualitätsprobleme bei Algen, Pilzen und Protozoen. Biol. Zentralbl. 74:311–334.

HARVEY, W. H. 1836. Algae. *In* J. T. MACKAY, Flora Hibernica. Pt. 3, pp. 157–254. Dublin.

———. 1841. A manual of the British algae. 229 pp. London.

HERTWIG, O. 1876. Beiträge zur Kenntniss der Bildung, Befruchtung und Theilung des thierischen Eies. Morphol. Jahrb. 1:347–434.

HOFMEISTER, W. 1851. Vergleichende Untersuchungen der Keimung, Entfaltung und Fruchtbildung bei höherer Kryptogamen. 179 pp. Leipzig.

JULLER, E. 1937. Der Generations- und Phasenwechsel bei *Stigeoclonium subspinosum*. Arch. Protistenk. 89:55–93.

LAMOUROUX, J. V. F. 1813. Essai sur les genres de la famille des Thalassiophytes non articulées. Ann. Mus. d'Hist. Nat. (Paris) 20:21–47, 115–139, 267–293.

LERCHE, W. 1937. Untersuchungen über die Entwicklung und Fortpflanzung in der Gattung *Dunaliella*. Arch. Protistenk. 88:236–268.

LINNAEUS, C. 1753. Species plantarum. Vol. 2, pp. 561–1200. Stockholm.

LUTHER, A. 1899. Ueber *Chlorosaccus* eine neue Gattung der Süsswasseralgen, nebst einigen Bemerkungen zur Systematik verwandter Algen. Bihang K. Svensk Vet.-Ak. Handl. 24 (Afd. 3, No. 13):1–22.

MOEWUS, F. 1933. Untersuchungen über die Sexualität und Entwicklung von Chlorophyceen. Arch. Protistenk. 80:469–526.

———. 1939a. Über die Chemotaxis von Algengameten. Arch. Protistenk. 92:485–526.

———. 1939b. Untersuchungen über die relative Sexualität von Algen. Biol. Zentralbl. 59:40–58.

———. 1940a. Carotinoid-Derivate als geschlechtsbestimmende Stoffe von Algen. Biol. Zentralbl. 60:143–166.

———. 1940b. Über Zoosporen-Kopulation bei *Monostroma*. Biol. Zentralbl. 60:225–238.

———. 1940c. Über die Sexualität von *Botrydium granulatum*. Biol. Zentralbl. 60:484–498.

PASCHER, A. 1914. Über Flagellaten und Algen. Ber. Deutsch. Bot. Ges. 32:136–160.

———. 1921. Über die Übereinstimung zwischen den Diatomeen, Heterokonten und Chysomonaden. Ber. Deutsch. Bot. Ges. 39:236–248.

———. 1927. Die braune Algenreihe aus der Verwandtschaft der Dinoflagellaten (Dinophyceen). Arch. Protistenk. 58:1–54.

———. 1931a. Systematische Übersicht über die mit Flagellaten in Zusammenhang stehenden Algenreihen und Versuch einer Einreihung dieser Algenstämme in die Stämme des Pflanzenreiches. Beih. Bot. Zentralbl. 48:317–332.

PASCHER, A. 1931b. Über Gruppenbildung und "Geschlechtswechsel" bei den Gameten einer Chlamydomonadine (*Chlamydomonas paupera*). Jahrb. Wiss. Bot. 75: 551–580.

PRINGSHEIM, N. 1855. Über die Befruchtung der Algen. Monatsber. K. Akad. Wiss. Berlin 1855:133–165.

————. 1856. Über die Befruchtung und den Generationswechsel der Algen. Monatsber. K. Akad. Wiss. Berlin 1856:225–237.

————. 1858. Beiträge zur Morphologie und Systematik der Algen. I. Morphologie der Oedogonieen. Jahrb. Wiss. Bot. 1:1–81.

————. 1870. Ueber Paarung von Schwärmsporen, die morphologische Grundform der Zeugung im Pflanzenreich. Monatsber. K. Akad. Wiss. Berlin 1869:721–738.

SCHMITZ, C. J. F. 1879. Untersuchungen über die Zellkerne der Thallophyten. Sitzungsber. Niederrhein. Ges. Natur-u. Heilkunde Bonn 1878:345–376.

SPOEHR, H. A. 1951. *Chlorella* as a source of food. Proc. Amer. Phil. Soc. 95:62–67.

———— AND H. W. MILNER. 1949. The chemical composition of *Chlorella*: effect of environmental conditions. Plant Physiol. 24:120–149.

STIZENBERGER, E. 1860. Dr. Ludwig Rabenhorst's Algen Sachsens resp. Mitteleuropa's Decade I-C: systematisch geordnet (mit Zugrundeleggung eines neuen Systems). 41 pp. Dresden.

STRASBURGER, E. 1894. The periodic reduction of the number of chromosomes in the life-history of living organisms. Ann. Bot. 8:281–316.

THURET, G. 1854. Recherches sur la fécondation des Fucacées, suivies d'observations sur les anthéridies des algues. Ann. Sci. Nat. (Bot.) IV, 2:197–214.

TURNER, D. 1808–1819. Fuci. Vol. 1, 164 pp. Vol. 2, 162 pp. Vol. 3, 148 pp. Vol. 4, 153 pp. London.

VAUCHER, J. P. 1803. Histoire des Conferves d'eau douce, contenant leurs différens modes de reproduction, et la description de leurs principales espèces, suivie de l'histoire des Trémelles et des Ulves d'eau douce. 285 pp. Geneva.

WILLIAMS, J. L. 1904a. Studies in the Dictyotaceae. I. The cytology of the tetrasporangium and the germinating tetraspore. Ann. Bot. 18:141–160.

————. 1904b. Studies in the Dictyotaceae. II. The cytology of the gametophyte generation. Ann. Bot. 18:183–204.

YAMANOUCHI, S. 1906. The life history of *Polysiphonia violacea*. Bot. Gaz. 41:425–433.

28

COLLEGE BOTANY COULD COME ALIVE

Hiden T. Cox and John A. Behnke

The mid-century Earth visitor from outer space finds science and technology booming. The Botanical Society of America is thriving. But botanical education is in a sad plight. Botany has been "inadvertently" omitted from biology curricula; many botany departments have suffered attrition or amputation; enrollments have dwindled until we have teachers to burn; even the subject matter is being raided by microbiologists taking over mycology and groups breaking away to form independent fields, e.g., bacteriology and many fields of agriculture.

Who is to blame for these mid-century doldrums? Administrators? Perhaps in part. Zoologists? Only if pride and aggressiveness regarding the importance of their field is blameworthy. Chemists? True, they have made hay by taking on plant tissues and organic compounds and have emphasized bio*chemistry* instead of *bio*chemistry, but—. Botanists? Guilty and charged with the major responsibility. They have been at times meek and aloof, at times bullheaded and uncooperative. They have lacked pride in their profession; they have accepted too readily the "sissy" label for their work. With the world inescapably dependent on their plants and looking ahead to a photosynthesis-energy era, they have sought to hide plants with strange labels and in newly created categories. Their success in making the study of plants virtually unintelligible to the layman would almost seem to be by design prompted by some strange idea that by multiplying baffling terminology, botany would gain intellectual stature.

How did this all come about? Must it be so? What can be done about it? Let's take a quick look at what has happened during these five decades, and then set up a few Mt. Everests for botanists to climb in the years ahead. It would be folly to try to chart the specific trails in detail. That must be done as we go. But at least we should have some idea of where we want to get.

As we look back, we see four major areas of change during the fifty years: (1) development of new scientific disciplines or new emphases in the old ones; (2) growth of interdependence in the sciences; (3) blossoming of controlled experimentation and instrumentation; and (4) major contributions of plant science to human welfare, especially through agriculture. We will attempt some elaboration of only the first two. The last two would be impossible to cover here and are not too pertinent to our topic.

The most important new discipline of the half century is genetics. Its contribution to the enlargement of our botanical knowledge has been incalculable, especially in plant physiology and taxonomy. In a broader biological area, it has been the key to our understanding of cytology and of the mechanisms of evolution. Plant physiology and cytology have in themselves made tremendous strides during the period. Ecology, although rooted in ancient times, became a full-blown field during this period. Hand in hand with it and hard-pressed by an expanding population and economy, conservation became a field both of solid importance and of sentimental and often missionary-like zealotry.

To categorize the interdependence of the sciences, even with a focus on botany only, would fill a fair-sized book, a book that probably should be written. Here we can merely suggest that in addition to the interrelations with zoology, chemistry, and physics—obvious and traditional—it will be very worthwhile to keep an eye on the rising subdisciplines of meteorology, solar energy, and radiology. Specialization has led to subdisciplines rivaling in importance major scientific fields. New "specialties" may be expected to develop and take on importance in the future. Photosynthesis itself may well become one of these nearly autonomous disciplines.

What have the effects of these changes been on botanical education? The need for a broader background and training has led to a greater emphasis on work in chemistry, physics, and mathematics. Such a trend can reach ridiculous extremes. One institution requires biology majors to take—in addition to the usual biology course load—chemistry through physical chemistry and biochemistry, two years of physics, three years of mathematics, one year of geology, and one year of statistics. However, in this institution, as in many others, little of the content of these courses has been incorporated in the biology courses themselves.

We can hardly credit the botanists with leadership in this broadening process. Most of it has come about in spite of them and the bitter opposition of a large and vocal segment of the profession. Botanists have taken a more positive role in the introduction of new biological courses on the more advanced levels—cytology, general physiology, genetics, and general ecology, plant and animal. (We choose to avoid the unfortunate redundant term bioecology.)

At the same time, our educational system has undergone radical changes.

In most respects, the sciences have been slow to adapt themselves to these changes and they still fall far short of meeting the requirements of the present, not to mention the future, situation. With education of the masses, the importance of treating science—through the various sciences—as a method of problem solving, as a way of thinking, and as a part of one's cultural and intellectual heritage has become of the utmost importance. Instead of meeting this challenge and opportunity by the imaginative development of a new conceptual framework for the presentation of the intellectual legacy of the sciences, scientists have reshuffled and "watered down" the classical informational approach, usually reluctantly. All students, often by compulsion, have been forced into some variation in style of a Germanic strait jacket designed for the molding of future Doctors of Philosophy. Vocationalism has blinded us to the fact that the best preparation for any life work—or life itself—is a critical, discriminating mind. Educational ruts are cut deep, and only positive resourcefulness will get us out of this one.

Perhaps it is too much to hope for, but we can dream about botanists as the coonskin-capped pioneers of the next fifty years. It would mean dropping the meekness or the belligerent reactionary approach and turning to a constructive creative one, in step with or a jump ahead of the times—not just current scientific or botanical research, but social, cultural, ideological, and educational trends and needs. Let's point the way in a few directions, recognizing that a blueprint today will undoubtedly need complete redrawing five years from now.

The conceptual scheme of courses should undergo constant rethinking. Outmoded courses must go, and new conceptual arrangements of botanical knowledge must be developed. Sacred cows in the form of traditional content of courses must be under constant critical scrutiny and must be slaughtered when their usefulness has ceased or even when, with our limited pasturage, younger and newer specimens are more deserving of our attention.

Our botanists with the "new look" might well take a new look at their educational aims, as well as the aims and values of all the sciences. The result should be a new framework for the presentation of facts—an emphasis on the applications of the methods of science and on the challenge of the unsolved problems and the undiscovered principles and facts. Only by such an approach can superior talent be attracted to the profession, and at the same time botany will be revitalized for the general student.

The place to begin, the crucial area, is the beginning courses. The basic approach will be the same regardless of whether we are working up botanical material for a general biology course or the content of a year-long first course in botany. Since in many institutions a biology course is here to stay, our enlightened botanist might well start by a surprise visit to the zoologist, who is probably in charge of the course. He would not be carrying the usual substantial log on his shoulder but would be loaded with constructive suggestions and material about *plants* that could be profitably introduced into the general course. His confidence in the value of his contribution would be tempered by a disarming spirit of cooperation that even a hardheaded zoologist could not resist. Since the zoologist, if typical, has been no more imaginative about modernizing the presentation of *his* material to general students, this unexpected meeting might start a peacetime chain reaction leading to the creation of real power.

In the preceding paragraph, we said the material would be plants; we meant plants, not borrowings from chemistry or some other discipline. The student would learn what a plant looks like, how it grows, what keeps it alive, how it reproduces, how it dies, what it's good for, and a good deal on what we *don't know* about it. What plant? Any plant at all, and no harm will be done if only one form is used throughout the course. How about using a horticultural variety familiar and interesting to the student? Botanists have made a grave mistake in thinking they must avoid such forms, the ones students want to know about because they have encountered them at home or will be using them in their gardens or yards. Perhaps this is a form of "practical application" which too many botanists consider beneath their professional pure-science dignity. Why? Is there anything degrading about what is interesting? Are we so resistant to the precepts of the professional educator that we must reject what he advocates even when our common sense and experience indicate that he is right?

Suppose our first-year botany course is gone; biology has replaced it. Why haven't more of us seen the opportunity of developing an interesting and valuable second-year general course? If properly handled, it could serve at least three important functions. It could give those planning on a professional career in botany or any of the related sciences a badly needed broad survey of the field and its many facets and opportunities. This same kind of survey is of the utmost importance to prospective teachers of biology and general science and could be of far greater value than equivalent time spent in specialized courses on the Bryophytes or even plant nutrition. It isn't inconceivable that such a course could be of value in general education as well.

Beyond this first full-year course in botany we admit to being less sure of our own ideas. Not every college or university can staff and maintain a full-blown set of course offerings for advanced botany majors. Perhaps the majority cannot. These institutions should not be discouraged since, obviously, many universities have reached preeminence in a single field of botany. Probably it is better to concentrate on one or a few fields rather than to spread courses over all fields of plant science. This decision must be made by the botany faculty at each individual institution, based upon local conditions. Perhaps the decision is an academic one since, in a manner of speaking, specialization is specialization no matter what the botany field may be. Research methods, laboratory techniques, searching of the literature, diligence of observation, summation of results are learned equally well from specialization in plant morphology as from specialization in plant biochemistry.

We do suggest, however, that there has been, and perhaps still is, a regrettable tendency to splinter-course offerings at this higher level, to compartmentalize arbitrarily the study of botany into too many courses. The departmental chairman is likely to feel that his department is not up to snuff if it offers fewer courses than other universities of similar size and stature. In our knowledge there is one institution that offers twenty-one "catalogue" courses in the botany department. These courses cover the entire field of botany. It is an impressive listing, especially when one considers that this is a two-man department.

Would it not be better to realign advanced undergraduate courses along broader disciplinary lines? Could not a course in Parasitism be offered which certainly would include much of the meat presently offered in courses in virology, plant pathology, bacteriology, and mycology? Why should not the basic underlying principles of plant physiology, nutrition, and biochemistry be presented as a coordinated whole, rather than as three separate courses? A rattling good course in General Vascular Plant Morphology might well replace our university catalogue listings of pteridology, plant morphology, anatomy, cytology, and the necessary accompanying course in microtechnique. Taxonomy and systematics form a disciplinary unit whether applied to Agrostology, Common Weeds, or the Local Flora of Upper Bathurst County.

We are not here condemning graduate courses in these highly restricted fields. They are obviously necessary to the training of a professional botanist seeking an advanced degree. We are suggesting that a rearrangement of course offerings along these or similar lines would be more attractive to students at the advanced undergraduate level, and we make bold to say that they might be more valuable from an educational and cultural standpoint.

Is this the answer to the sad plight in which botanical education finds itself today? Perhaps it is; perhaps it is not. The real answer, we suspect, will come eventually as a result of many articles of this type. It will come from unbiased, unemotional soul searching on the part of all botanists. Articles such as this one should be encouraged to stimulate all of us into thinking along many lines. Short notes, letters to the editor of various botanical publications, longer articles, books—in short, anything that will bring into the botanical public domain the ideas all thoughtful botanists now are having will be valuable. We submit that this soul searching is perhaps the most important single thing that botanists can do today.

29

THE ODOR OF BOTANY

Harry J. Fuller

"Botany is in bad odor in American universities. I am mad about plants and would never wish to be anything else but a botanist. If anything could stop me, however, it would be one of these courses (the average general botany course). These are the kinds of courses by and large which have gotten botany into the bad odor it's in. They are mostly botany taught by plant physiologists or geneticists or something else who are quite rightly ashamed of being botanists, seeing what most of them are like, so each produces courses with as little botany in them as possible. To get botany back where it should be we need to design a course as far away from the norm of these courses as possible."

This provocative and scarcely equivocal paragraph is from a letter which came to my desk a short time ago from one of our country's distinguished botanists, a scientist of unusual imagination and ability, a member of the National Academy of Science, a man of broad and deep education and of wide scientific and humanitarian interests. When a man of his caliber writes thus, he should command our attention and a fair hearing (after we have recovered from our initial irritation, of course). My first reading of that paragraph both annoyed and troubled me; my subsequent readings have almost erased that annoyance in view of the patent sincerity of my correspondent. But I am still troubled, for, although I regard some of his remarks as unjust and extreme (I am convinced that the effluvium of botany is no more noxious than that emanating from history or physics or family living or zoology or English literature or restaurant management or television science or any of the other subjects in which American universities currently grant degrees), I admit to a degree of truth in his contention. And that bit of truth must inevitably trouble us botanists, for if there is one thing which binds us into both a professional organization and a confraternity of the mind, it is our love of plants and of the science of plants.

The Golden Jubilee Volume Committee which invited me to write this paper suggested (in addition to veiled private hints to me by one of its members about laws governing libel) that, since this is the Golden Anniversary Year of our Society, it might be appropriate for authors of these special papers to review the progress of fifty years in the various aspects of American botanical science about which we are writing. This instruction seemed at first easy of fulfillment in view of the usual human assumption that progress and the passage of time are inseparable twins. Then came that letter, and with it doubts. Has the teaching of general botany during this last half century really shown progress, or only an illusion of progress, or a confusion of progress with change? Certainly there have been numerous changes in general botany teaching within the past five decades: remarkable advances in visual aids in the form of better charts and models, Kodachrome slides, and time-lapse motion-picture films; improved student microscopes, for one of which Robert Brown or Wilhelm Hofmeister might have given a left arm; better-looking textbooks with more readable and more attractive typography and enormously advanced reproduction of photographs and drawings; highly "objectified" examinations which can be graded by machines; shifts in classroom techniques—the abandonment of lecturing by some botanists as an outmoded medieval relic (I have the nasty suspicion that some, at least, of those who disparage lecturing as a teaching device do so because they are incapable of giving an eloquent and exciting lecture!), the substitution for lectures of a laboratory-cum-discussion method of teaching; and changing emphases upon subject matter, with diminished stress upon morphological details and correspondingly increased accent upon physiological and behavioral aspects of plants. And with these changes, of course, has come another change, one obviously not of our making, the change in the populations of general botany, the bourgeoning numbers of students (using that loosely and charitably) in our introductory courses.

If we examine carefully into these changes, we find that not all of them are truly signs of progress. I have viewed, for example, some twenty-five sound films on plants and have found only three without at least one serious factual error in the narration. Increasingly mechanical techniques of examination, while they may save botany professors hours of labor and may postpone for a time those academic thromboses, actually give little measure of a student's ability to put two and two together and come up with four, or to demonstrate his critical sense, or to analyze, in his own way, the strengths and weaknesses of experimental setups and results. Similarly, changes in classroom methodology are not necessarily indicative of progress; the effectiveness of teaching is basically a function of a teacher's knowledge and enthusiasm and personality, and such procedural changes are at best only nibblings around the pedagogical fringes. If we place the credits against the debits, we should find, I believe, that we *have* made progress in our teaching of introductory botany; we should find also, if we balance the books honestly,

that the real progress is slight enough to fail to justify an attitude of complacency or self-adulation on our part.

One of the features of that introductory paragraph which annoyed me at
first reading is its implication that the alleged odor is exclusively a product
of botanists and their obtuseness. While we must assume a considerable part
of the responsibility for the odor, we must in all fairness refuse to accept total
responsibility. Certainly, some university administrators and administrative
attitudes must share a portion of the blame, if blame there be. The plain fact
is that the teaching of introductory botany (and of other lower-division
undergraduate courses as well) is quite commonly regarded, at least in many
larger universities, as a second-rate activity, one scarcely worthy of the
full-time devotion of a facultyman. Reflections of this attitude are seen in the
too-prevalent beliefs that a professor has arrived when he has sloughed off
the chore of teaching lower-division students, that a facultyman who wants
to devote his efforts largely to the teaching of such students is not quite
bright, and that the teaching of introductory courses is scarcely to be regarded as an intellectually respectable or scholarly activity. These attitudes
are more tangibly reflected in the commonly higher salary scales of research
professors and of graduate professors as compared with those of facultymen
who are primarily teachers of undergraduates. Thus, an important incentive
to improved teaching is often lacking, particularly in some of our larger
universities. An examination of the academic origins of American botanists
indicates that a disproportionately large number came from small liberal-arts
colleges, which, probably through their greater emphasis upon the value of
inspired undergraduate teaching, succeeded in enkindling in that disproportionately large number of young people a passion for plants and for botany.

This too-prevalent attitude of academic administrators toward the importance of teaching undergraduates is reflected also in the common practice
in many universities of using low-cost semi-slave labor to give instruction to
undergraduates, that is, the employment of part-time graduate assistants for
such teaching. In many large universities, all the teaching of laboratory work
in introductory science courses is performed by such part-time assistants.
And in freshman rhetoric, certainly the single most important undergraduate
college course in these days of life-adjustment frolicking in high schools,
all or most of the teaching in many universities is done by graduate assistants.
I hasten to add that teaching by graduate assistants is not invariably and
per se bad, but it does have two strikes against it: first, it is inexperienced
teaching, done by persons who lack the background and breadth of knowledge requisite to illumined instruction, and, second, it is a subordinate activity
of these assistants, whose major concern naturally is the completion of
graduate courses, graduate research, and graduate theses. When teaching
is an incidental or secondary job, it is almost never really superb teaching.
I am aware, of course, that graduate assistants may obtain valuable experi-

ence as a consequence of their work as teaching assistants, and I do not propose the elimination of such teaching; what I argue for is less frequent use of such teaching in general botany and more supervision of this type of teaching by experienced teachers in the full-time faculty ranks.

The administrative culpability in the matter of the aforementioned botanical odor appears also in the often niggardly budgetary support of general botany teaching. Many of us who have been engaged mainly in the teaching of general botany have traveled steerage class so long that we simply do not think to ask for a cabin-class or even a tourist-class ticket. We use the same slides long past the time when only the ghost of safranin is left, we patch and repatch our charts, and, as for asking for a new greenhouse or additional greenhouse space just for the teaching of general botany—well! In many universities it is a relatively simple matter to acquire funds for the construction of a new research greenhouse or for a self-recording, free-wheeling spectrophotometer, or a series of controlled-temperature rooms, hooked either in series or in parallel, or an air-conditioned ultra-microtome with automatic shift and hot and cold running water—but ask for greenhouse additions so that undergraduate students in introductory botany may grow and experiment upon living plants, and see how far up the administrative ladder your request is likely to ascend! Perhaps we are guilty of what a former president of our Society, Neil Stevens, called the "excessive meekness of botanists."

Not all the odor is of administrative origin, of course. Much of it, the greater part of it, in all probability, is of our making. And, in all fairness, we must admit that the administrative attitudes which I have criticized reflect in considerable degree faculty attitudes, for administrators do not administer *in vacuo* or by reading fresh chicken entrails; they even consult their professors from time to time and seek advice of them. How have we botanists failed to bring the teaching of general botany to the level of excellence which it deserves? I believe that our faults have been chiefly the following:

1. We have too often failed to realize that the majority of our general-botany students will never have the pleasure of a second course in botany, that most of them will not become professional botanists. As a consequence of this unawareness, we frequently teach general botany as though all our students were going to become botany majors. We may carry our research interests too often and too intensively into the general-botany classroom and may feel affronted if someone suggests that some of the things in which we are especially engrossed might be omitted from general botany without educational loss. Morphologists may not regard general botany as botany at all if some of those life histories are omitted, and plant physiologists may consider themselves and general botany short-changed if some of the details of mineral nutrition, ion absorption, and respiration are played down. (I have finally mustered the courage to omit from the third edition of *The Plant World* the

life cycle of that wheat rust fungus, and I still have sneaking feelings of treason.)

2. We have been, like many other academicians, slaves to tradition. We have, most of us, studied general botany courses of remarkably uniform organization. We began our study of botany with cells, we journeyed through the bodies of flowering plants, noting details of their anatomy, metabolism, reproduction, and inheritance as we traveled, and then we took a tour of the plant kingdom, omitting not a single phylum nor a single traditional life cycle. And we commonly go on teaching general botany in accordance with that same pattern. Breaking with tradition is always a psychologically difficult wrench, but perhaps we need to steel ourselves to make such a break. If we are interested in training young people to follow in our steps as professional botanists, we can pour upon and into them all the requisite details of plant structure, physiology, inheritance, taxonomy, and phylogeny in the advanced courses in which they will necessarily register. But in dealing with students who will not become botany majors, we should be willing to admit that other aspects of plant life may be more suitable to their education: how plants grow, why they grow where they do, how they differ in their cultural requirements, their biological relationships with animals, their involvements in human life and in the great nature cycles, etc. I believe that the inclusion of more of these "natural history" features of plants in our general botany courses might constitute the greatest improvement which we could effect in the teaching of general botany, at least in so far as subject matter is concerned. In this connection, emphasis upon the relations of botany with other sciences is clearly indicated, as exemplified by the topic of the origin of cultivated plants, which cuts across the fields of archaeology, anthropology, geography, physics, philology, and botany. Certainly the work and writings of Merrill, of Mangelsdorf, of Weatherwax, of de Candolle, of Vavilov, and of others in this general field would constitute a stimulating, educationally broadening, and scientifically respectable topic for inclusion in general botany, even at the expense of the life cycle of Ulothrix or of the morphology of the reproductive parts of Cycadales.

A concomitant of our cleaving to tradition is our too-frequent belief that, if a topic has direct relation to human life, it is possibly unscientific or at least intellectually too demimondain for inclusion in a university-level botany course. I shall never forget, for example, a taxonomist whom I knew who, upon being asked to identify several cultivated garden ornamentals, responded grandly, "I'm sorry I don't know what these are. As soon as plants are cultivated, I lose interest in them." That this attitude is not rare is indicated, I believe, by the fact that our knowledge of the botany of many important cultivated plants is woefully inadequate. I have observed that some plant physiologists, though they are well versed in the theoretical bases of mineral nutrition of plants, know little of the manufacture, composition, and uses of different types of commercial fertilizers; when such botanists teach general botany, it is clear that fertilizers receive brief mention, if any. One of the legitimate ways of vitalizing general botany is emphasis upon its pragmatic involvements. I do not suggest for a moment that general botany should become horticulture or economic botany, but I affirm my belief that we can make our subject more appealing and more significant to undergraduate minds if we utilize every opportunity to demonstrate the practical importance of botany, emphasizing always, of course, the "pure science" bases of practical applications.

3. We have too often turned out of our graduate schools plant scientists whose educational backgrounds have been extremely specialized (from the semantic viewpoint I prefer "fragmented" to "specialized") and who, really not botanists in the best sense of that label, are poorly equipped to teach general botany. Yet general botany, to its detriment, is sometimes taught by persons so narrowly educated in plant science. We should be more precise and more realistic in planning the graduate work of young people who are likely to teach general botany to ensure that they acquire broad education in *botany* and in related sciences, as well as specialized education in their research fields. If we cannot always do both, then we should take care that the ultra-fragmented product is not assigned the task of teaching general botany. We should not dream of turning a paleobotanist loose upon a research project in enzymology, nor should we assign a plant nutritionist to a problem on phylogenetic implications of wood anatomy, but too often we assume that a graduate degree in plant science, irrespective of the formal education which led to that degree, automatically fits a man to teach general botany *sans odeur*. Sometimes it works, but too often it doesn't.

4. We have perhaps become too much concerned with the insides of plants in our teaching of general botany. Never have so many drawn and quartered sections of so many plants been examined, studied, and sketched by so many students. Important up to a point, such study has often resulted in neglect of a holistic, or synthetic, study of plants, a kind of study possibly more important in general botany than the fragmented, analytic study so often emphasized. The study of whole plants, of course, means the study of living, growing plants in both greenhouse and the out of doors. It involves further the culture, the handling, and the care of living plants by students. Treatment of grafting in a lecture or in a textbook can never approach in interest for students the opportunity for them to make their own grafts of living plants, nor can the study of germinating seeds and of seedlings, brought into a laboratory and carefully rationed cafeteria-style, ever equal in educational value or in interest the actual planting of seeds by students in a greenhouse bench and the subsequent observation of seedlings growing from these seeds. In developing further our study of whole living plants, we need to increase the numbers of field trips in our general botany courses and to plan more

carefully the work of field trips in such fashion as to enable students to make, in so far as they can, their own observations and to draw their own conclusions from them. Too often our field trips are simply conducted tours for which the instructor acts merely as guide lecturer. My thumping the tub for the study of living plants reminds me of a taxonomist, long since gone to wherever taxonomists go, who, so accustomed to studying desiccated herbarium specimens, was always ill at ease when he was asked to identify living plants; if he could postpone the identification to a time convenient for him, he pressed, then mounted, the specimen on a herbarium sheet before proceeding to his identification!

5. Laboratory study in general botany has often become too mechanical, too stereotyped, too restrictive, too dependent upon a laboratory manual which lays it all out on the line and which thus gives students little opportunity for independent work, for the display of initiative, for the exercise of imagination, for the satisfaction of personal curiosity. Instead of functioning as a consultant or adviser, the laboratory instructor too often becomes a *Gruppenführer* whose duty it is to lead his students in standardized fashion through a set of detailed directions and who often talks too much in doing so (one of the essential features of good laboratory work, like an essential feature of good library work and of good music, is abundant silence). We should have smaller laboratory sections, better facilities for growing and studying living plants, more experienced and more adroit teachers in charge of laboratory classes, and more flexibility for the inquiring student to satisfy his curiosity in ways best suited to his own mind and personality. I shall not soon forget a year which I spent as a laboratory teaching assistant under a master teacher of general botany; each laboratory section of general botany had twenty students, and abundant greenhouse space was available for their work with living plants. At the first meeting of the semester, the professor placed on the main table about twenty jars, each containing seeds of a single plant species. The students were shown the seeds and the greenhouse, were given a few brief preliminary instructions, and were then told that they could do anything they wished with the seeds and the greenhouse for two weeks. My function was simply to stand by, to answer occasional questions, to procure for each student any supplies and simple equipment which he wanted to use in his independent study of the seeds and the seedlings into which they grew, and, at the end of the fortnight, to have the students summarize the results of their work. I have not seen again such display of interest, curiosity, inventiveness, and enthusiasm by general-botany students as this type of laboratory operation elicited.

I do not suggest that these faults are deliberately conceived and executed, that they are of universal occurrence in general botany courses, or that they have arisen as a consequence of the nature of botany. Some of these shortcomings may be the result of the very human business of getting into ruts, others are the consequences of regarding general botany not as a fundamentally important intellectual discipline, but rather as a kind of academic sideline subservient to the direction of graduate study or to concentration upon personal research. Many teachers of general botany are aware of these weaknesses but are so circumscribed by practical pressures that, despite their awareness of them and their desire to eliminate them, they are unable to do so. Inadequate laboratory space, lack of greenhouse facilities, and shortage of experienced and stimulating instructors combine to produce an educational environment which often precludes the possibility of making these desired improvements, at least on an extensive scale. It is difficult, nay impossible, to provide for a truly exploratory type of laboratory work with a large degree of individual freedom for students when one must handle 700 students in a semester in three laboratory rooms; under such conditions, the hand-holding laboratory manual and the *Gruppenführer* are inescapable. One of the partial solutions to this problem lies in raising entrance standards, especially in some of our state universities which appear to accept any student who can walk, talk, and remain upright for several hours at a time, to exclude those students who are totally incapable of college work and who will flunk out anyway at the end of their first semester in college. Our specific teaching weaknesses are thus in part directly related to administrative policies and problems. Perhaps the first effective step in achieving certain improvements in the teaching of general botany might be the vigorous and persuasive selling of our practical teaching needs to deans and presidents. Perhaps it is time for us to lay aside that "excessive meekness" and to march up to the ticket window with a demand for at least a cabin-class ticket!

I am certain that most of us would not agree with my correspondent's allegation that botany, at this half-century mark in our Society's history, is redolent of *Symplocarpus foetidus*. I am equally certain that most of us would agree in all honesty that general botany is scarcely fragrant in the manner of *Plumeria acutifolia* or *Canangium odoratum*. To make it so will be one of our most important and fruitful tasks during our next half century.

30

BOTANY FOR LIVING

Clarence J. Hylander

At significant milestones, such as the Golden Jubilee of the Botanical Society of America, it is natural to pause and review the progress made by contributions of American botany. But our appraisal should not be entirely with a backward look into the accomplishments of the past. We should also face in the other direction, with a forward look toward what our science can do in the years to come. The following random thoughts come to mind, after twenty-five years of experience in interpreting botany to the general student and the public and after an illuminating interlude as executive secretary of the American Institute of Biological Sciences during its formative years. These are concerned not with the contributions that will undoubtedly be made by botanical research and its application to human needs nor with making botany a vocation that will attract greater numbers of students into botanical careers, but with botany as a field of knowledge which can increase our enjoyment of life. Let us think, for a moment, of botany for living, as well as a means of earning a living.

In order to evaluate the role of botany in the lives of our citizens in the years to come, we need to appreciate how tomorrow's living habits will differ from those of past decades. If we realize the development of trends in living, we will discover new opportunities for botanists to share their subject with the public. Plants are becoming more and more a vital part of everyone's life.

We are all well aware of the far-reaching technological changes which have taken place in the past few decades and which have had a great influence in our daily lives. A new word has been coined—automation—for what in reality is nothing new. But call it what you will, because of it physical drudgery in earning a living is fast disappearing. Working hours for the average man are being shortened, and leisure hours proportionately increased. Most incomes are rising to unprecedented heights. Many families today have both the time and the money to enjoy avocational and recreational activities undreamed of when most of us were selecting botany as a life work. How has this "new look" in the economic and social picture affected the living habits of the average American, and hence the average student, and what bearing does it have on the educational role of botany?

Three trends are evident. First is the reversal of the former population shift from country to city, from farm to apartment house. We are now witnessing a mass migration in the opposite direction, from cities to suburbs and even to the outlying hinterland. Many industries are moving into the country, and with them move thousands of families whose previous botanical experiences have been limited to tending a window box of geraniums or keeping a pot of philodendron alive. Suburban living has brought millions into closer contact with nature; these emancipated city dwellers are discovering the joy of being surrounded by trees and flowers, of having spacious gardens and ample opportunities for outdoor living. The majority know little of the flora that surrounds them and of how to care for living plants in the outdoors. Suburbanites of my acquaintance have all shown a delightful eagerness in wanting to make up for this ignorance.

A second noticeable trend is the increasingly popular American pastime of trips in the family car to the country, varying from an evening picnic at a roadside park to a month's stay in Yosemite. The ubiquitous car has become a magic carpet transporting millions of Americans to our many county, state, and national parks and recreation areas. There is now more time for such trips and more funds for making them possible than ever before. We all know of the amazing number of visitors to our national parks every summer. Again, as in the move to suburban living, this restless movement has brought Americans into closer contact with nature than has been true in the immediate past. Ours is a botanically unique country, blessed with a variety of fascinating scenery of which vegetation is an important part. The American on wheels sees a wide range of botanical treasures, from saguaro forests in Arizona and redwoods in California to cypress swamps in the Everglades; these arouse his curiosity and interest and powerfully motivate him to acquire more information than otherwise would have been the case.

A third trend is increasing longevity. Greater numbers of men and women, still able-bodied and energetic, are suddenly retired and freed from routine of office or factory, with the prospect of many carefree years doing what they please. Many are at a loss for hobbies and activities to make this golden period of their lives a satisfying and healthy one. A large number seek the sunnier climes of our southern and southwestern states, where outdoor living and gardening can occupy their time from sunrise to sunset. Working with plants, and developing special interests in certain groups of plants, appeals to many of these men and women. Often they find themselves surrounded by a totally strange assemblage of exotic plants and new living conditions in which to grow them. Like the suburbanite and the traveler, this group .

of Americans is eager to feel at home amid new plant neighbors. They can enjoy their newfound freedom more if they have at least a nodding acquaintance with the native flora and the rich variety of introduced species.

These three trends offer a great opportunity for botanists, but with the opportunity is an obligation. Ours is the responsibility for presenting botanical knowledge with such a selection of content as can be of value to individuals affected by these changes in living habits. For those who write as well as teach, there is the added privilege of interpreting their own experiences and of translating the treasures which lie hidden in technical journals and abstruse texts into prose understandable to the layman. In matching botanical education to the new trend in living, we as leaders should introduce such material, where it is relevant, into the traditional content of botany. It is also worthwhile remembering that as botanists we are more fortunate than our fellow scientists in chemistry and physics, whose subject matter does not lend itself to such avocational and recreational application as does ours. This presents a great challenge. However, academic indifference to the future interest of the general student and layman, or an ivory-tower philosophy as to who shall be the chosen few to drink at the fountain of botanical wisdom, could well keep us from meeting the challenge adequately.

Elsewhere in this volume Donald Culross Peattie has contributed a thought-provoking article on the importance of popularization of botany and the trials of a popularizer. Everyone who has tried to depart from the orthodox presentation of botanical information will agree with Peattie. There is no need of reiterating the point that more widespread willingness of botanists to share their enthusiasm and knowledge with the layman would be a fine beginning toward meeting these trends. In this connection, an additional fact is worth noting. Why do so few professional botanists contribute articles of a popular nature? Much that appears in magazines and books is written by self-taught naturalists who may be journalists or businessmen, with botany as a hobby. This is no criticism of their excellent contributions, but to have to rely on those who are technically untutored in our field to take up our case is certainly a reflection on professional botanists. How much easier it should be for the botanist trained in his subject to translate firsthand information into accurate but readable articles acceptable to publishers.

In a recent conversation with the editor of *Natural History*, the magazine published by the American Museum of Natural History, we discussed the relatively small percentage of articles by botanists as compared with that of zoologists. We agreed that botanists seem to find it harder to write so that an editor, and hence the general reader, will be interested. Botanists seem more handicapped by use of traditional nomenclature and an excessive burden of technical vocabulary. If this is so, we have much to learn from our zoological colleagues to make the world of plant life available to the public.

In looking ahead, what goals should we have in view to assist our students and readers in preparing for the changing American way of life? At the risk of seeming critical of colleagues and fellow enthusiasts in botanical fields, I shall have the temerity to put a few of my long-standing beliefs in print.

It is nothing new to suggest that botany be made the study of living plants in their natural environment; however, this obvious statement has to be repeated over and over again, to offset the tendency of the laboratory-trained graduate student to present botany only as a laboratory subject in which the parts of a plant are thoroughly studied but the whole plant ignored. This entails that the botanist who is a teacher or writer should spend much of his time outdoors with plants and should take every opportunity to travel and observe, in order to widen his range of experience with the flora which forms the foundation for his subject. After some years spent in graduate school and teaching, immured by a world of microscopes, herbarium sheets, and test tubes, I took a half a year to roam the United States from coast to coast, to familiarize myself with the plant life in the various parts of the country from which my students came. The experience was at the same time exciting and depressing: exciting in the wealth of information gathered on common members of our vegetation ignored by texts and reference books; depressing because of a realization that my teaching had been conditioned by the provincial content of a traditional curriculum. Upon my return, my missionary zeal prompted me to write a popular survey of the floristic richness of our land, as encountered by the average tourist. *The World of Plant Life* was a major labor of love, but at least it is a satisfaction to both publisher and author that such a ponderous volume is still in demand twenty years later. Thus my first suggestion would be for botanists to leave their classrooms, their summer research laboratories, and local collecting grounds for an adventurous month or two far afield, perhaps to our major national parks. In so doing they will not only enrich their own competency, but also mingle with the average American and discover what his interests are, the questions he wants answered. They will be surprised to find that a botanist is most welcome in any group and is usually surrounded by an impromptu nature class as he pauses to answer a casual question.

As we face our students or visualize our potential readers, we can certainly allow time for digressions from the traditional presentation of the subject in view of the future interests of our suburbanite, traveler, and retired couple. Lucky are these individuals if they have had even a general botany course, planned for the student for whom this will be his only exposure to plant science, with a view to the avocational and enjoyment possibilities which stem from botany. Such a general introductory course can also create an awareness of the salutary effects of a familiarity with plants, its potentialities for relaxation from the tension ever increasing in our modern way of living. As botanists we know the serenity which comes from close association with plants; why be selfish and consider this a monopoly of our profession? Friends of mine who are hunters and fishermen admit the therapeutic aspect of their trips comes from close contact with nature. This becomes a more pleasurable experience when the plants they encounter can be recognized by name and their habits are known.

It is a strange inconsistency that men are generally as interested in gardening and other plant hobbies as women; foresters, horticulturists, nurserymen, and landscape specialists are usually men. Our most talented hobbyists in raising special types of plants, such as cacti, peonies, and orchids, are men. Yet among young people botany is often considered a field of knowledge best suited to old maids and emasculated males. At the high school level botany is often avoided in planning a college course because of the misconception that our subject is not a "he-man" one. My college career in teaching included a real challenge when I and my colleagues in the botany department had to "sell" botany at Colgate University, an all-male college. We soon learned that much must be added to the available material in the older textbooks and great ingenuity used in motivating the subject matter to make botany courses acceptable and valued by the students who voluntarily select them. The more the subject matter revolved about living plants in the outdoors, the more students attended the courses. Plants will always, I hope, be of interest to the ladies; their presence as students and partners in any botanical adventure adds an understandable stimulus to our work. But when our young students become enmeshed in the modern trends of living, they will thank us many times over if we have given them a background in the enjoyment of plant life which they can profit from all their lives.

Apart from general botany, some of the more specialized courses present opportunities which must not be overlooked. Plant taxonomy should not be based on an excessively detailed study of a particular flora, nor limited primarily to specific areas familiar to the teacher; neither should it be preoccupied with rare species which always thrill the professional taxonomist but are rarely a problem in the everyday life of the average American. Some of this may be necessary. But there can be added enough of the representative and significant species to be encountered in all our states to give the future layman some general knowledge to start with. A particular lack in many taxonomy courses, and perhaps also in field botany, is the neglect of cultivated species. Often the introduced varieties are more common than the native ones. Having had a thorough taxonomy course at Yale, I was dismayed at my ignorance on a first trip from New York to Key West, as I discovered pawlonias in blossom, chinaberry trees loaded with fruits of last year, avenues lined with casuarinas, and a host of exotic palms. If one spends a full week or two on the species of *Crataegus* there isn't much time left to brief future visitors to our parks or travelers in the southland on the outstanding genera, native and introduced, which they will encounter.

Plant physiology can be made a most valuable botanical subject to the future suburbanite and gentleman-gardener. The care of plants, indoors and out, requires an intelligent appreciation of all the factors that enter into keeping a plant alive—the water requirements of various plants under different growing conditions, the use of fertilizers, and transplanting techniques are a few that come to mind. Perhaps more emphasis could be placed on ornamentals for laboratory experiments and less on agricultural species. Relatively new aspects of plant physiology, such as hydroponics, use of hormone sprays and growth stimulants, weed killers, and soil conditioners could well be made a part of the course content. Plant physiologists would find a ready market for articles dealing with care of plants, based on research discoveries which often do not become publicized as much as they ought to.

Plant ecology can also be made a subject of interest to others than future botanists. The relation of living plants to their environment is a dynamic and thrilling field of botany; it becomes illustrated so beautifully whenever one drives across the country from east to west or north to south. Long hours of otherwise tiresome driving pass quickly as one looks for the appearance of new plant communities and appreciates the reason for the existence of such outstanding vegetation types as the Pacific evergreen forest, the prairies, the deserts, and the eastern deciduous forests. Plant ecology also becomes helpful to the stay-at-home, in preserving the natural vegetation on the land around his home and in introducing new plants into the proper niches in his bit of nature.

Gardening is a corollary to life in the suburbs and country. Beginning with the first narcissus and *Forsythia*, and ending with the last frosted chrysanthemum, this activity occupies much of the leisure hours of every member of the family. From Florida to California gardening is a twelve-month avocation, and the favorite topic of conversation wherever one goes is some unusual varieties which have just bloomed in someone's garden. The money wasted in acquiring unsuitable plants and the efforts expended in trying to make them grow in impossible locations are appalling. A trip to the nursery becomes more fruitful when the amateur gardener has gained some familiarity with plant names and identification and knows enough about ecological conditions at his home and physiological demands of particular plants to select wisely.

There is no need for teachers to revamp the curricula which have stood the test of time and which are necessary to produce our research botanists and professional plant scientists. However, with the above long-range views in mind for those students who may never use botany as a profession, at logical points in the presentation of the subject, emphasis can be shifted to include material which will be of benefit at some future date to those who some day will become "the average American."

For those who extend their teaching to reach the large invisible audience of the general reader, selecting subjects in the writer's experience which mesh into the pattern of modern living will make more certain the acceptance by editors, who after all do know what the public wants. In such writing, it is wise to lay aside our professional vocabularies and try to convey our enthusiasm and knowledge in words of common usage.

After all, the greatest joy in being a botanist comes from sharing one's love for living plants with those less fortunate individuals who do not have an opportunity to pursue botany as a life work.

31

MORE PLANTS FOR MAN

W. H. Hodge

Someone has said that our modern civilization, at the threshold of the atomic age, is still content to sow and harvest the crop plants of the Stone Age. It does seem remarkable that of the thousands of species of higher plants known to science today, relatively speaking only a handful, mostly of ancient lineage, are the ones still widely cultivated as our major crops. That these particular plants have served mankind well is indicated by their ability to support a rapidly increasing population down through the centuries. Yet the origins of these plants are lost for the most part in prehistoric time. Compared to them a neophyte like the Pará rubber tree (*Hevea brasiliensis*), a mere century old in culture, is but a babe in agriculture's arms.

Since earliest time man has focused his attention on the possible utility of the members of the green world around him. The very antiquity of our major crops is ample proof of aboriginal preoccupation with plants. The first manuscripts and books on botany were also devoted principally to utilitarian species. Man's interest in bringing together information on useful plants has continued to the present, and in our libraries may be found accounts of such plants of regions as widely scattered as Guam and Trinidad, Venezuela and Zanzibar. In this field is a wealth of information largely uncorrelated, based on practically every area of the world.

We have long known that plants exist which produce fibers, proteins, latex and waxes, vitamins, alkaloids and glucosides, pigments, tannins, and oils. Who is to say, though, that we are utilizing the best species available for each purpose? Medicinal aloe is still collected primarily from the two species known to the ancients, who discovered this drug. Is this to admit that among the scores of *Aloë* species described in recent times a better drug source may not exist? Man simply has not investigated this possibility. And so it goes with many of our economic species. The aloe-like century plants (*Agave*) of the New World constitute another good example; sisal and henequen, important fiber-yielding species of commerce, were known and grown by Mayan and Aztec Indians. Yet among the several hundred agaves known today, many of which were unknown to those Indians, there may well be producers of better fiber.

Botanists have classified our plants so that we may recognize one from another and associate whole groups of related kinds, but what potential use the greater proportion of these may have for man is basically still a matter for investigation. Unfortunately, many botanists today too frequently isolate themselves from studies of economic species as though this casts some sort of stigma upon them or upon their profession. On the contrary, the facts of plant life are just as worthy of study when based upon an economic group as otherwise, and have the added advantage of enabling the scientist to relate himself and his work better to the public in general.

Every beginning science student learns that living plants are nature's primary chemical factories in which a multitude of different organic compounds are manufactured. Many of these compounds, like quinine, are highly complex, and their artificial synthesis may be seemingly impossible or economically unsound. Other compounds, like indigo, have proven of easy commercial synthesis so the plants which originally supplied them are no longer grown as crops. Unfortunately for mankind, plants have no advertising agencies to promote a market for the mine of still unknown and hidden compounds which are available as by-products of their daily metabolism. Modern civilization has tapped the more obvious end products, but undoubtedly many unknown chemical substances lie waiting the day they can be recognized and put to use.

Thus a new era of plant investigation appears to be beginning wherein there is not so much concern with the obvious end products of flower, stem, root, or leaf, but rather with the chemical constituents that the plant produces as it grows in nature and how these constituents may be used. We are beginning to be aware of compounds in plants which, though perhaps chemically related, are far more subtle in that their mere presence when taken internally may affect the secretion of hormones or may affect the human nervous system in ways still largely to be determined. It is in this field that more plants for man will be found. Some will become important directly to agriculture as new crops, while others will have an indirect import in the contribution of the knowledge of useful new compounds to chemistry.

Today there is still much to be desired in the line of a *coordinated* and concerted effort to discover new sources of utility in plants. Coordination is emphasized because much, indeed practically all, of what we have learned in this field has come by chance. For example, within but a decade or two we stumbled upon certain plants whose rotenone content has immense insecticidal value, yet these species have been known and used as fish poisons by primitive tropical peoples for hundreds of years. Curare, that South American poison which is now valued by modern medicine for use in shock therapy, was also discovered in a similar fortuitous manner.

All too frequently, only when a specific need arises, are scientists detailed to make an intensive screening of the thousands of plants known to be used by the world's primitive peoples. That much "pay dirt" still remains to be recovered is shown in the results of the recent search for cortisone precursors in plants. A century ago in Central Africa, David Livingstone noted the use of the pounded seeds of one of the species of *Strophanthus* as the source of a deadly arrow poison. Though subsequently used as an official drug (a heart stimulant), it was not until 1929 that the chemical sarmentogenin was found as a compound. It proved to be a potential cortisone precursor. Yet it took a research program coordinated by botanists and chemists, initiated since World War II, to recognize that the chemicals in *Strophanthus* seed originally used for killing could also be used for saving men's lives. Through the same program various species of *Agave* and certain tropical yams (*Dioscorea*) have proven to be even better cortisone sources.

One of the most rewarding areas in this field of more plants for man should lie in a systematic survey of the world's aboriginal plants. A team of ethnologists, botanists, and chemists would play cooperative parts. Such a survey should not be delayed, for with civilization advancing as rapidly as it is, much of the vast stock of plant lore gathered by primitive tribes will soon be lost. Curiously enough, even in the United States where our Indian population is no longer primitive, such lore is still proving of value. An investigation made of the drug plants used by Nevada Indian tribes a decade or so ago brought forth the discovery in the ordinary creosote bush (*Larrea divaricata*) of a complex acid which prevents fats like butter and lard from becoming rancid. Although chemists have recently found that the acid is easily synthesized, had it not been for this ethnobotanical study we would not have this important new compound today.

Still awaiting the chemurgic attention that it deserves is our native jojoba (*Simmondsia chinensis*), a wild shrub of our Southwest whose edible oily seeds have been long known and eaten by Indians. Jojoba seed seems to have great industrial potentiality, yielding an oil identical to sperm oil, a hard wax of high purity similar to carnauba wax, and numerous acids such as pelargonic, hydroxy, and dibasic—of great value in the making of synthetic lubricants, low-temperature plasticizers, tough fibers, plastics of the nylon type, and heat-resistant rubbers.

Support for research in bringing together the tremendous backlog of isolated and scattered reports on new potentially economic plants and for their analysis or re-examination in relation to chemical constituents is a field which offers great promise in the development of more plants for man. Already certain countries, for example Australia and India, recognizing the potential value of the work, have initiated comprehensive surveys of their economic species.

Such surveys as have been made have yielded without exception something of economic importance, even though often in a direction not expected from the objectives of the research. It is always difficult to comprehend why an industrial giant like the United States, so dependent for its well-being on the products of the green world, has until now failed to support adequately scientific research in this field.

Administrators are accustomed to requests for the development of new varieties of economic plants to alleviate emergencies of one kind or another. The need is obvious. The necessities of war in respect to strategic plant material are likewise understandable, but the tremendous benefits that can be obtained from the objectives of basic research on new, potentially useful species seem to be difficult to comprehend. Nowadays few would argue against the tremendous costs of atom-smashing equipment. Not so many years ago requests for such would have received scant public consideration. Research on the potential utility of the great bulk of the world's plant population is where atomic research was twenty-five years ago. It is hoped that botanical scientists in general and economic botanists in particular can be more articulate in describing the needs and benefits of this type of research in relation to its benefits to mankind. If the objectives are comprehensible, financial and administrative support eventually will be found.

32

BOTANICAL ASPECTS OF THE PAPER-PULP AND TANNING INDUSTRIES IN THE UNITED STATES

An Economic and Historical Survey

Edmund H. Fulling [1]

It is always impressive to state that modern man has not found any really important food or fiber plant that was not known and utilized centuries ago, in some cases even by primitive man; that of the approximately quarter-million species of known flowering plants, only some 3,000 have been used; and that of these, there are only two really important food plants—rice and wheat; two fibers—cotton and flax; and two oil plants—coconut and cotton.

A more realistic understanding of plant utilization directs attention to the manifold ingenious ways in which modern man utilizes thousands of kinds of plants, less extensively, to be sure, than the above-mentioned, but, nevertheless, to such a degree that the present high standard of living in many parts of the world is, to a very great extent, the result of such utilization. One may well wonder which is the more worthy of awesome contemplation, the ingenuity of man in discovering and utilizing the utilitarian qualities inherent in plants, or the fact that plants, in their complicated make-up, offer him such a seemingly endless array of raw materials upon which to exercise his ingenuity—oils, fibers, vitamins, waxes, latices, alkaloids, and other drugs, all

[1] The author herewith gratefully acknowledges the valued assistance of the following authorities in furnishing certain data in this article and for critical reading of it in manuscript: PAPER-PULP: Dr. I. H. Isenberg, Research Associate, the Institute of Paper Chemistry, Appleton, Wisconsin; and Professor C. E. Libby, Pulp and Paper Technology, North Carolina State College, Raleigh, N.C. TANNING: Mr. E. L. Drew, Economist, Tanners' Council of America, New York, N.Y.; Mr. B. W. Roberts, Vice President, Barkey Importing Co., New York, N.Y.; and Dr. Fred O'Flaherty, Tanners' Council of America, University of Cincinnati.

apart from the food and construction value, respectively, of comestibles and woody plants.

Though without documentary evidence to support such a contention, it seems safe to state that at least one-half of all processed and manufactured products of modern industry throughout the world are plant products in one way or another, and that one-half of the other half is dependent on some plant product somewhere along the line—witness, for instance, the role of plant tannins in drilling muds; of a palm resin, dragon's blood, in photoengraving; and of diatomaceous earth in countless filtering operations.

Plant explorers have contributed to this development by finding the valuable plants in the wild; taxonomists have contributed by establishing their identity and that of related species which may possess similar desirable qualities; and plant breeders have improved upon the plants originally found in the wild by the explorers. The significant advances have resulted, however, from progress in engineering and applied chemistry, stimulated by favorable economic factors that have made the progress and changes in plant utilization feasible. The areas of enterprise in which industrial plant utilization have thus advanced are numerous, and the history of two of them is briefly surveyed in the following.

PAPER PULP. *Pre-wood-pulp era*. Ancient Egypt of 2000 B.C. is frequently referred to as the birthplace of paper, that is, of the writing material which the Romans called "papyrus," from the earlier Greek name for the material. Papyrus was a compressed laminated sheet of reed stalks (*Cyperus papyrus*) and as such was not paper in the modern sense of the term.

Paper is, as it has been for over 1,850 years, a felted sheet of individual, separated, microscopic plant cells obtained as a pulp by treating vegetable material in a variety of ways. Some 2,000 kinds of plants have been found to furnish cells, referred to as "fibers," suitable for this purpose. Discovery of such utilization has been credited to one Ts'ai Lun of China in 105 A.D. It is not known whether he actually made paper himself, but it is recorded that he presented such material to the Emperor that year. A biography of this man, compiled in the fifth century of our era, states that it was he "who conceived the idea of making paper from the bark of trees, hemp waste, old rags, and fish nets."

In the course of the next thousand years the art of papermaking progressed by way of Mongolia, Persia, and Arabia into North Africa. In the twelfth century it entered Europe with the Saracens by way of Spain and then slowly became established in various centers on the Continent.

In America, in what was later to become the United States, the first paper mill was established near Germantown, Philadelphia, in 1690 by William Rittenhouse who had worked as a papermaker in Amsterdam, Holland. By the time of the American Revolution, British America had other mills in the Colonies of New Jersey (1726), Massachusetts (1728), Maine (1731–1734),

Virginia (1744), Rhode Island (1764), Connecticut (1767), and New York (1769–1773). By 1769 there were 40 paper mills in Pennsylvania, New Jersey, and Delaware, annually producing £100,000 worth of paper. In the year of Independence, Maryland acquired a mill. In 1789, 53 mills operated within the range of the Philadelphia market alone. Massachusetts had 20 mills in 1795; Connecticut, 16 in 1810. The year 1811 saw 76 of them in Delaware and Pennsylvania. By 1814 the total number in the United States was estimated to be 187.

As other states entered the industry, the number rose to 800 by 1855. Florida, in 1900, was the last to join the parade, and at that time papermaking was pursued in 35 states. In the interim since 1690, many mills, very likely failed, and others consolidated. In 1954, 482 companies operated 775 paper mills and 319 pulp mills in the United States.

Until 1817 all paper manufactured in the United States was handmade, and until 1740 all such handmade paper was manufactured on molds imported from England. That year American molds were first made by Isaac Langle, a German immigrant, in Pennsylvania. In 1817 the first paper machine in America was erected by Thomas Gilpin near Philadelphia, and in 1827 the first Fourdrinier machine in the States, imported from England, was set up at Saugerties, New York, in the mill of Henry Barclay. Other machines, at first imported, but before long "Made in America," gradually replaced the hand-operated molds. In 1829, however, 54 of the 60 paper mills in Massachusetts still followed the handicraft. In 1845 that state had 89 mills; Connecticut had 37; and only two handmade-paper mills remained in America. In 1866, the Willcox mill of Pennsylvania, established 137 years earlier, ceased making paper by hand, the last of America's handmade-paper mills except two short-lived revivals, one of which was operated from 1928 until 1931 by Dard Hunter Associates in Lime Rock, Connecticut.

For more than 150 years the early American paper industry depended for raw materials almost entirely on the vegetable fibers in cotton and linen rags, as the mills in Europe had very largely relied for centuries since the Saracens carried the art of papermaking into Spain in the twelfth century. By the middle of the eighteenth century, however, a growing scarcity of rags plagued the expanding American paper industry, so much so that in 1776 the Massachusetts General Court appointed a Committee of Safety in each locality to encourage the saving of rags. So great was the need for paper at that time that legislation was enacted which gave exemption from military service for all skilled papermakers. This exemption prevailed as late as 1812.

At the end of the eighteenth century almost every periodical, in both Europe and America, carried the admonition "Save your rags," and in 1799 quantities of writing paper manufactured in one Massachusetts mill bore the watermark "Save rags." Public notices of various sorts, in verse and prose, implored the people in this respect. The founding of newspapers, one after another, in addition to the increasing publication of books and even of popular magazines, was primarily responsible for this surge. Among the newspapers that called on the people were the *Boston News Letter* in 1769, the *Boston Gazette* in 1798, the *Courier* of Norwich, Connecticut, the *North Carolina Gazette* in 1777, and the *Cheshire Advertiser* of Keene, New Hampshire, in 1792.

In 1800 the 16 mills in Connecticut alone consumed 320 tons of rags. By 1829 the 60 mills in Massachusetts were annually using 1,700 tons of them. In 1855, 405 million pounds of rags was reported as needed by the 800 paper mills in the United States.

The shortage had become so acute, even at the beginning of the century, that by 1812 importation of rags from Europe began. The ultimate in expediency seems to have been achieved in 1856 when the Stanwood and Tower mill in Gardiner, Maine, began importing Egyptian mummies, their woven linen wrapping and papyrus fillings to be converted into wrapping paper for grocers, butchers, and other users of coarse paper. To take advantage of this bizarre source of vegetable fiber, Stanwood had to compete with the Egyptian railroad which for a ten-year period made use of no other fuel than the well-wrapped mummies of the Nile valley—sacred bulls, crocodiles, ibises, cats, and humans. Little wonder that an epidemic of cholera broke out among the rag pickers and cutters in Stanwood's mill. Also in 1856 a manufacturer in Onondaga County, New York, made paper from mummy wrappings. Both he and Stanwood may have gotten the mummy idea from Dr. Isaiah Deck, a New York scientist, who in 1855 compiled a manuscript in which he advocated such utilization, with data on quantities of mummy wrappings available and probable cost.

Many short-lived efforts to alleviate the shortage in a more orthodox manner were made with other plant fibers before a real solution was found. In May, 1789, J. Hector St. John Crèvecœur presented to the American Philosophical Society of Philadelphia a printed book, "the leaves of which," in his words, "are made of the roots and barks of different tress [sic] and plants, being the first essay of this kind of manufacture." In 1799 Chancellor Robert R. Livingston held a patent on papermaking improvement based on utilizing the alga frog spittle. Among other early United States patents on paper manufacture were the following involving vegetable fibers:

1802—Corn husks, Allison and Hawkins, Burlington, N.J.
1809—Seaweed, Samuel Green, New London, Conn.
1814—Corn, John McThorndike
1828—Sea grass, Elisha H. Collier, Plymouth, Mass.
1829—Straw and corn, John W. Cooper, Washington Township, Pa.

1838—Beach grass, Isaac Sanderson, Milton, Mass.
1838—Corn husks, Homer Holland, Westfield, Mass.
1841—Palm leaf, E. Thorp & Sons, Barre, Mass.

In 1828 William Magaw, of Meadville, Pennsylvania, began making paper from straw, an operation that was initiated the same year also in Chambersburg, Pennsylvania. It was said that an edition of the New Testament was printed on the cheap yellow paper made in this fashion. In 1871 American production of straw paper was estimated at 100 tons a day.

In 1834 Dr. Jones, of Mobile, Alabama, made paper from both stalks and husks of corn, as well as various kinds of wood and bark, particularly birch and poplar. That same year Dr. Daniel Stebbins, of Northampton, Massachusetts, imported paper mulberry trees (*Broussonetia papyrifera*) from China with the thought of using the inner bark, as was done in China and Japan, where this species had been among the first plants to be used in papermaking. A few reams of paper were made from it, but growing the trees offered insurmountable difficulties, and the venture was probably even less successful than that of cultivating the same species in Virginia as a basis for an American silk industry. Ancient-looking and gnarled successors to, if not the originals of, those trees still stand along one of the streets in Restored Williamsburg.

In 1855 several parcels of tule (*Scirpus lacustris* and *S. tatora*) were sent from California to eastern manufacturers for testing as possible papermaking material. In 1856 Henry Howe of Baltimore seems to have used bagasse.

In 1860 the *New Orleans Bulletin* reported attempts to use 11 kinds of material growing in Louisiana, including bagasse, cotton stalks, wild indigo, and banana.

In 1862 a mill in Lee, Massachusetts, searching for new and plentiful papermaking fibers that could be harvested in New England, successfully made paper from *Gnaphalium*. About the same time use of cactus as a papermaking material was undertaken in a grain mill in San José, California, modified for the purpose. The experiment was unsuccessful, but the mill was later used for making paper from straw and waste paper.

Esparto grass (*Stipa tenacissima*) from Mediterranean lands had long been used in England for paper pulp, and in 1863 and 1864 one Boston mill imported between 300 and 400 tons of the material. Because of high duty, importation of the fiber was not continued, and efforts by European representatives of the U.S. Department of Agriculture to obtain seed for America were unsuccessful. Some seed was secured from Paris seedsmen in 1868 and was introduced into the South, but nothing practical was accomplished.

In 1869, okra (*Hibiscus esculentus*) was used in a mill at Chickasabogue, Alabama, and in 1870 the *Mobile Register* was printed on it. A book published that year listed nearly 100 substances that had been tried, including such oddities as mummy cloth and ivory shavings. In addition to trees of various kinds, it mentioned:

alga	couch grass	moss
aloe	palm	mulberry
asparagus	esparto	nettle
bamboo	ferns	oakum
banana	flag leaves	peat
beet root	flax	plantain
blue grass	floss silk	reeds
bran	frog spittle	rice straw
Brazilian grass	grape vines	rushes
broom corn	gutta-percha	sawdust
burdock	hay	seaweed
cabbage stumps	hemp	sorghum
coconut husks	hollyhock	straw
cottonseed	hop vines	thistles
cotton stalks	jute	water broom
corn husks	marshmallow	

Sixteen years later another survey, world-wide in coverage, raised the list to nearly 500, with more vegetable and non-vegetable oddities.

Hemp (*Crotalaria* and *Cannabis*), jute (*Corchorus*), and swamp cane (*Arundinaria gigantea*) of the South were also tried, but were either insufficient in available quantities or not wholly satisfactory. In 1860 rags still constituted 88 per cent of all papermaking material, which means that other fibers were contributing at least 10 per cent.

In 1898 an English syndicate unsuccessfully attempted to make paper from sugar-cane bagasse in a mill on the Mississippi some 20 miles below New Orleans. Additional sources of rags or some new fibrous material had to be found.

Wood pulp. The first steps toward a solution were made in Europe—France, England, and Germany in succession. In France in 1719, René Antoine Ferchault de Réaumur, a naturalist and physicist, was intrigued by the American wasp which converts wood into the paper-like material of its nest. He presented his observations to the French Royal Academy and challenged the papermakers of Europe, so dependent on rags, to emulate the wasp. Thirty years later he chided himself and them for not yet having done anything in the matter.

From 1762 to 1771, Dr. Jacob Christian Schäffer of Germany pursued experiments on a great variety of materials, including various kinds of wood (e.g., aspen, beech, mulberry, spruce, willow), as possible sources of papermaking fibers, and published a six-pamphlet treatise on the subject. Several other experimenters followed, and then came Matthias Koops of England who, in 1800, first made use of straw, wood, and various other vegetable fibers on a commercial scale. He thus became the founder of industrial paper manufacture, but went into bankruptcy after three years.

The step from experimentation and abortive industrialization occurred in Germany, where, in 1840, Friedrich Gottlob Keller, a German weaver of Hainichen, Saxony, obtained a German patent on a wood-grinding machine, undoubtedly based on the experiments of Koops in 1800.

Contemporaneous with Keller, but working independently, was Charles Fenerty, a Nova Scotian. Experiments which he began in 1839 resulted two years later in a groundwood sheet of paper made from spruce pulp. Halifax thus was the site of the first groundwood paper in America. Fenerty was of the opinion that both hard- and softwoods, especially spruce, fir, and poplar, would be suitable for pulping, but the apathy on the part of Canadian papermakers precluded further development of his ideas.

In the United States some of the earliest alleged uses of wood pulp have been doubted by later critics. For instance, there is a claim that basswood bark and wood were employed by Matthew Lyon of Vermont as early as 1798. And the *Crawford Messenger*, of Crawford County, Pennsylvania, October 28, 1830, has repeatedly been referred to as the first American newspaper printed on wood-pulp paper (aspen and lime), but later paper analysis has shown that edition to have been printed on stock manufactured from very short linen rag fiber.

In 1854 John Beardsley of Buffalo, New York, submitted to a local newspaper three specimens of paper which he had made from basswood. In 1857 Platner and Smith, at Lee, Massachusetts, also made some experimental paper from wood. And in 1863 Stanwood and Tower, the mummy defilers, allegedly produced groundwood pulp in their mill at Gardiner, Maine. This seems to be substantiated by definite statements at the time that the *Boston Weekly Journal* of January 14, 1863, was printed on "paper made of wood, a new process." This has been accepted as the earliest authenticated use of wood pulp in an American newspaper.

Historically interesting as these earlier short-lived efforts may be, the real beginning of commercial groundwood pulp in the United States was in December, 1866, when two wood-grinding machines, resulting from Keller's pioneer work, were imported from Germany. The following spring they were set up by Albrecht Pagenstecher at Curtisville, now Interlaken, near Stockbridge, Massachusetts.

Chemical pulping of wood began in 1852 with Burgess and Watts' English patent on the soda process, using caustic alkali at a high temperature. The process was not well received in England, and the inventors came to the United States, obtained an American patent in 1854, and set up operations on the Schuylkill River, near Philadelphia. After experimenting with straw, cornstalks, bamboo, and cane, they concentrated on non-resinous woods, particularly poplar, hemlock, and white wood. This chemical process, it is to be noted, antedated Pagenstecher's setup by about thirteen years.

In the year that Pagenstecher began his mechanical groundwood operations, a second chemical technique, the sulfite process, was patented in the United States by B. C. Tilghman, who had begun experiments in France. And in 1884 a German patent was granted to C. F. Dahl in Germany on his development of the sulfate process.

These three chemical processes for pulping wood—soda, sulfite, sulfate— and mechanical grinding to obtain groundwood pulp are still the processes in use today, with modern improvements, to be sure, and their initiation in the mid-nineteenth century paved the way for the tremendous increase that has since transpired in the industrial utilization of wood fibers throughout the world in the manufacture of paper.

Woods other than basswood and aspen undoubtedly were utilized by the pioneer wood-pulp manufacturers, but these two were preferred because of their resin-free nature and other inherent qualities that make them suitable for pulping. It was not long, however, before attention became focused on spruce, two species of which grew in abundant quantities in the northeastern States and eastern Canada, with a close relative on the Pacific Coast. For many years the first two of these, eastern red spruce (*Picea rubens*) and eastern white spruce (*P. canadensis*), particularly the former, were the American woods par excellence for pulping; and as the great stands of timber in the Pacific Northwest later became exploited, Sitka spruce (*P. sitchensis*) joined them.

The preeminence of spruce as pulpwood until the very end of the fourth decade in the twentieth century was a result, primarily, of its long (3 mm.) strong fibers (tracheids in anatomical terminology), comparatively free from resins, gums, tannins, and other components objectionable in other woods; of its light color, general soundness, and fair freedom from knots, rot, and other defects; and of the high cellulose content of the fibers, easily separated from other substances. In addition, it was available in ample and accessible quantities, and pulping techniques to use resinous woods profitably were not developed until the 1920's.

In 1899 spruce attained a high of 76 per cent among all pulpwoods in the United States. It continued long thereafter to be the leader, reaching a quantitative peak of nearly 3½ million cords in 1920. During the intervening two decades, however, its percentagewise preeminence declined to 60 per cent by 1916, and then to 23 per cent in 1939.

In 1916 at least 15 other native woods supplied the pulp mills. Eastern hemlock (*Tsuga canadensis*) was second—14 per cent; poplar, consisting of the two aspens (*Populus grandidentata, P. tremuloides*), was third—8 per cent. The remaining 16 per cent consisted, for the most part and in descending order, of balsam fir, pine (mostly southern yellow, some jack pine, and a little white pine), beech, maple, white fir, and cottonwood. Still smaller quantities of chestnut, cottonwood, Douglas fir, tamarack, elm, basswood, birch, gum, sycamore, and cucumber also entered into the mills.

In the 1920's the great stands of western hemlock (*Tsuga heterophylla*) and mountain hemlock (*T. mertensiana*), large forest trees in western Canada and the Pacific Northwest, were increasingly exploited for pulpwood. From half a million cords in 1906, and 13 per cent of all pulpwood in 1919, that utilization rose to about one million cords in 1925, to 20 per cent in 1939 and close to three million cords in 1948. Today these hemlocks and Sitka spruce are the leading pulpwoods for American and Canadian mills on the Pacific Coast, but Douglas fir is becoming increasingly important there for kraft pulp.

Increases and decreases in the utilization of one kind of wood over or under others in the manufacture of paper pulp have not been occasioned by finding more technically suitable material—spruce fiber is still unexcelled. The changes have come about because of economic factors and technological advances—availability of pulpwood in various regions of the country, prices of standing timber, and development of processes permitting broader utilization. It was these factors that provoked the phenomenal rise in southern pine pulpwood from 69,000 cords in 1906 and less than 5 per cent in 1919 to more than 35 per cent in 1939, when it first surpassed spruce, and to over 10 million cords in 1948.

This great increase in the utilization of woods once regarded as too resinous for pulping had its inception in the discovery of the sulfate process in Germany in 1883. Because of the strength in the pulp and paper produced by this method, they are commonly referred to as "kraft" pulp and paper, from the German word "Kraft," meaning "strength." The first kraft pulp in North America was made at East Angus, Quebec, Canada, in 1907.

The first attempt to make paper from southern pine was at Pensacola, Fla., about 1903. The effort was unsuccessful, but in 1911, after the mill equipment had been bought and moved to Orange, Texas, the process was changed from the soda to the sulfate technique, and manufacture of paper in the South became a reality—the first sulfate pulp from yellow pine in the United States. That same year, it is claimed, witnessed a sulfate pulp mill at Roanoke Rapids, North Carolina. Which of these two mills blew the first digester, as the expression goes in the industry, will probably never be known. Not until a decade later, however, did southern pine appear in paper on a commercial scale—that was in the issuance of the *Birmingham Age-Herald* on June 20, 1921, in which the pulp was referred to as having been made from "Alabama spruce pine." The trees had been cut in Alabama but were shipped to Niagara Falls for pulping and manufacture into paper.

Credit for the pioneer work in utilizing wood for paper pulp goes to Koops of England and to Keller and Dahl of Germany, but for the boom in southern pine pulp which followed that initial trial of 1921, the laurels belong to Dr. Charles Holmes Herty. The indefatigable work of this industrial chemist in the 1930's influenced the economy of the South in a manner reminiscent of cotton-gin days. In 1931 Dr. Herty predicted that within five years, the making of newsprint from southern pine would be entirely feasible and that a new industry of enormous proportions would arise in the South as a result. On January 17, 1940, in fulfillment of his prophecy, a new mill at Lufkin, Texas, with a potential daily output of 150 tons, produced the first newsprint from southern pine for continuous commercial consumption.

In 1954 the United States produced 26.6 million tons of paper and paperboard from 19.8 million tons of wood pulp, 8.1 million tons of waste paper, and about 1.2 million tons of other fibers in agricultural wastes—wheat straw, cotton and linen rags, cotton linters, linseed flax, sugar-cane bagasse, Manila hemp, sunn hemp, common hemp, sisal, jute, wool—and of mineral or synthetic nature. The wood pulp called for 29.2 million cords of pulpwood, 85 per cent of which was softwoods. A year later, 1955, total consumption in the United States, including imports from Canada, increased to a record figure of 33,332,000 cords.

An appreciable portion of these softwoods was imported from Canada, as has long been true, and consisted of the following species:

> *Abies amabilis,* amabilis fir
>   *balsamea,* balsam fir
>   *concolor,* white fir
>   *grandis,* grand fir
>   *lasiocarpa,* alpine fir
>   *magnifica,* red fir
>   *nobilis,* noble fir
> *Larix laricina,* tamarack
>   *occidentalis,* western larch
> *Picea canadensis,* white spruce
>   *engelmannii,* Engelmann spruce
>   *mariana,* black spruce
>   *rubens,* red spruce
>   *sitchensis,* Sitka spruce
> *Pinus banksiana,* jack pine
>   *contorta* var. *latifolia,* lodgepole pine
>   *ponderosa,* ponderosa pine
>   *resinosa,* red pine
>   *strobus,* white pine
> *Pseudotsuga taxifolia,* Douglas fir
> *Thuja plicata,* western white cedar
> *Tsuga canadensis,* eastern hemlock

heterophylla, western hemlock
mertensiana, mountain hemlock

Of these Canadian imports, spruce and balsam fir predominated in the East and Lake States; hemlock, Douglas fir and true firs in the Pacific Northwest.

Of the domestic pulpwood, three-fifths were cut in the South. About 90 per cent of this southern pulpwood was southern yellow pine, principally loblolly (*P. taeda*). The remaining 10 per cent consisted of the following pines:

Pinus caribaea, slash
clausa, sand
echinata, shortleaf
glabra, spruce
palustris, longleaf
rigida, pitch
rigida var. *serotina,* pond
virginiana, Virginia

Hardwoods have always been secondary sources of pulpwood. Among other reasons is the shortness of their fibers as compared with those of conifers (1 mm. vs. 3 mm.). Furthermore, the three standard methods of pulping yield less than 50 per cent of the original wood by weight, which is true also of softwoods by the sulfite and soda methods. Such return is too low to compensate for inferior quality in hardwood pulp. A remedy for this is offered by the so-called semi-chemical process of pulping, which yields about 20 per cent better return than the conventional chemical methods and thus promises possibly greater pulp utilization of low-grade hardwoods.

The hardwoods, which made up 15 per cent of the pulpwood in 1954, consisted principally of aspens and gums. More specifically they were:

Acer rubrum, red maple
saccharum, sugar maple
saccharinum, silver maple
Aesculus octandra, buckeye
Ailanthus glandulosa, ailanthus
Alnus rubra, red alder
Betula lutea, yellow birch
papyrifera, paper birch
Castanea dentata, chestnut
Fagus grandifolia, beech
Fraxinus americana, ash
Liquidambar styraciflua, sweet gum
Liriodendron tulipifera, yellow poplar
Magnolia acuminata, cucumber

grandiflora, evergreen magnolia
virginiana, sweetbay
Nyssa aquatica, water gum
sylvatica, black gum
Populus spp., cottonwood
balsamifera, balsam poplar
grandidentata, large-toothed aspen
tremuloides, trembling aspen
Quercus spp., oak
Tilia americana, basswood
Ulmus americana, elm

Hardwoods today account for nearly 70 per cent of the growing forest volume in the eastern United States, and greater pulping use of them in the future can be expected as softwood supplies are depleted and pulping practices are still further improved.

AGRICULTURAL RESIDUES. America has long been so richly endowed with an abundance of raw material that little thought was given, until recent decades, to the utilization of industrial wastes. These include an annual accumulation of some 250 million tons of agricultural residues—straws, stalks, stems, hulls, cobs, nutshells, fruit pits, and sugar-cane bagasse. Considerable investigation has been devoted, particularly at the four Regional Research Laboratories of the U.S. Department of Agriculture, toward converting each of these categories into useful commodities, and the success achieved in some of them has been noteworthy.

Among such products have been fine bleached papers and boards, made, respectively, from wheat and rye straws and bagasse. Particularly impressive has been the conversion of flax stalks into cigarette paper, a development which strikingly illustrates that political upheaval, international turmoil, and the resulting economic disruption may lead to new plant-utilizing industries and to consequent liberation from foreign sources of raw material.

Up to World War II, American cigarette manufacturers had been annually importing about 10 million dollars' worth of paper in which to wrap their 200 billion yearly output of fumatory rolls. Only flax fiber is suitable for such paper, less than one-thousandth of an inch in thickness, and only Europe could furnish the fiber, not direct from the flax fields which grew it but in the multitudinous bales of long-used and oft-washed linen rags that accumulated in France, Italy, Poland, the Balkan Peninsula, and elsewhere on the Continent. France had a monopoly on the conversion of these rags into fine papers and was the supply source for 90 per cent of the paper in American cigarettes.

One of the French factories, at Troyes in northeastern France and catering exclusively to American markets, was operated by an American citizen, Harry

H. Straus. Alarmed by the impending cataclysm that soon engulfed Europe, he began efforts in the mid-1930's to Americanize his industry by moving it to the New World. But linen rags were not sufficiently abundant in the United States to assure a supply of raw material, and the flax being grown by farmers in 19 States to produce a prewar annual output of 6 to 15 million bushels of flaxseed for the paint industry was of the low, branched type, productive of abundant seed but not suitable for fiber. Only on a relatively few acres in Oregon was the taller, less-branched linen flax being grown.

By 1939, however, and through the coordination of financing facilities, the investigations of engineers, organic chemists, and plant geneticists, American production of cigarette paper first began on a large scale at the Ecusta Paper Co., Pisgah Forest, N.C. The first shipment of paper to cigarette manufacturers was made on the day Hitler's tanks rolled into Poland, and since then the manufacturers have been freed of foreign sources. Equally important has been the very lucrative market for the huge mounds of deseeded flax stalks which annually accumulate on flax farms in Minnesota, Wisconsin, and other States, and which formerly were disposed of, to a large extent, only through fire. In 1937, when almost all needed cigarette paper was still imported from Europe, only some 10,000 tons of such seed-flax straw was sold to industry, but for uses other than paper. By 1950, 40 times that quantity, 400,000 tons, was reported as providing the paper for nearly all the cigarettes produced in this country. Half a million tons of waste flax thus will saturate the market for this outlet, and increased production of airmail, bond, bible, and other high-priced papers will gradually absorb the surplus flax straw which in 1948 amounted to 4½ million tons. The rag pickers of America may not be able to gather so much old linen as their European prototypes, but the demands of the American paint industry for linseed oil and the achievements of cellulose chemists will very likely henceforth assure a domestic supply of flax for fine papers and a remunerative market for flax waste.

TANNING. Tannins are chemically complex, dark, organic compounds, characterized as a group by certain chemical and physical properties and widely distributed throughout the Plant Kingdom. Nearly all plants contain them, to some degree at least, in bark, wood, leaves, and/or fruits; in certain genera they accumulate to a marked degree.

Among their properties are water solubility and that of acting in aqueous solution on the protein of animal skins in such manner as to render pelts strong, flexible, impervious to water, imputrescible, and resistant to decay and wear—in other words, to convert them into leather. Advantage was taken of this quality by primitive man, perhaps as early as 12,000 years ago. Subsequent development in Egypt, 5,000 years ago, then in China, over 3,000 years ago, and later in Greece, Rome, and Medieval Europe brought vegetable tanning to modern times as probably the oldest of plant-utilizing arts along with charcoal production.

Domestic materials. BARK. Craftsmen skilled in the art of tanning were among the early English colonists in the New World. A tabulation of artisans and workers in Virginia in 1620 included tanners and leather dressers, but whether they pursued their professions at that time or depended wholly on imports of leather goods to fill their needs is not known.

They came also to New England, and within a year or two after the arrival of the *Mayflower* in 1620, perhaps the first tannery in British America was set up by Micah Richmond and Deacon Crumby of Plymouth. More reliance has been placed on the record that Experience Mitchell, a tanner who came in the good ship *Ann* in 1623, established a tannery at a settlement called Joppa, where he treated hides for 60 years. Subsequently the firm of Experience Mitchell and Sons maintained a tanning business for 170 years. Other immigrant tanners, too, entered the industry, and by 1650, 51 tanneries were operating in New England.

Sometime prior to 1635, Captain Matthews operated a tannery in Virginia, and 1638 saw the first tannery in New Amsterdam. The first one in New Jersey, at Elizabethtown, began in 1660.

Unlike the early American paper-pulp industry, which developed in particular centers, that of tanning was nearly everywhere an integral part of colonial life almost from the beginning. Rapidly increasing population made the demands for leather constantly greater. Probably 200 tanneries were operating in the Colonies in 1700. Toward the middle of the eighteenth century nearly every town north of the Virginias had its own tannery. By 1750 more than 1,000 of them had been established; the number rose to 2,400 by 1800; and in 1810 over 4,460 were operating in 17 States and 6 Territories. An all-time peak of 8,229 tanneries may have been attained in 1840. Since then, except for slight deviations, there has been a very steady decline in the number of American tanneries. From a few over 600 in 1921, the number fell to about 385 in 1935, then rose to about 450 in 1939, and was back at 350 in 1950.

Oak bark had long been the principal tanning material in Britain and many parts of Continental Europe, and the first American tanners turned to the American species of *Quercus,* especially to chestnut oak (*Q. prinus*), but also to the black (*Q. velutina*) and white (*Q. alba*) species.

Before many years, however, the abundant supply of eastern hemlock (*Tsuga canadensis*), with 8 per cent to 10 per cent tannin in its bark, brought it into early and prominent use, especially in New England and New York, while in the central and southern Colonies oak bark was still the preferred material.

Increased slaughtering of both domesticated and wild animals fed the prospering tanneries with hides, and the great abundance of native tanbark with which to convert them into leather supported a philosophy of inexhaustible natural resources. In 1810, when the value of American tannery products was about 200 million dollars, one writer expressed the prevailing attitude when he wrote that "bark, abundant everywhere in America, is redundant in new settlements where the tanning business facilitates the destruction of the forests which obstruct agriculture."

Toward the close of the nineteenth century, however, gradual depletion of the available oak and hemlock supplies in New England compelled the industry to move westward and southward. Pennsylvania and West Virginia then became centers of bark production. Demand waxed so great that the bark of trees felled for lumber was not sufficient to satisfy the tanneries and many acres of virgin hemlock were cut down for their bark alone. In 1900 hemlock constituted over 70 per cent (more than 1 million cords) of all the tanning bark collected in the country; it was the leader then, and still led in 1909, but by that year it had declined to about 65 per cent and 700,000 cords.

From Pennsylvania and West Virginia the harvesting of hemlock bark followed the course of the lumber industry into the Lake States, especially Michigan and Wisconsin. In one year, from 1915 to 1916, production in Wisconsin rose from 20,000 to 100,000 cords. By 1928, however, the harvest in these two states had fallen to a 25-year high of 63,000 cords. By 1951 it declined to 4,400 cords, primarily as a result of economic factors, not of scarcity of material. Around 1918 there were 36 tanneries in the United States using Michigan and Wisconsin hemlock; in 1952 it was still being used, but in only 10 companies. At the beginning of the 1920's perhaps 10 per cent of all hemlock bark used in the United States came from states other than those previously mentioned and by importation from Canada, for in 1919 it was estimated that over 90 per cent of the total was harvested in Maine, Massachusetts, New York, Pennsylvania, Wisconsin, Michigan, and West Virginia.

With a growing scarcity of hemlock and oak barks in the East near the close of the nineteenth century, tanners turned their attention to the virgin stands of western hemlock (*Tsuga heterophylla* and *T. mertensiana*), with 10 to 12 per cent tannin in the bark, in the Pacific Northwest, and to tanbark oak (*Quercus densiflora = Lithocarpus densiflora*), with 10 to 30 per cent tannin in the bark, along the Coast Range from southwestern Oregon to Santa Barbara, California. Commercial tanning had been carried on, on the Pacific Coast, since the gold rush of 1849, and by 1859 there were 29 tanneries in Sonoma County alone. In the ten-year period 1881–1890, 240,000 cords of tanbark oak was collected in California to support the industry. By 1905 the figure fell to 50,000 cords. By 1920, however, after exploitation of western hemlock had developed, about 2,200 tons of bark, two-thirds of it hemlock, was being used annually in the tanneries of Oregon and Washington.

In 1950 an estimate was cited to the effect that a minimum of 50,000 tons of western hemlock bark was annually available for tanning extraction in

Oregon and Washington, and it was claimed that modification of prevailing logging practice, which prevented peeling of bark in usable form, could increase the supply to 150,000 to 200,000 tons.

For the most part, native American tree barks used in tanning have been employed in the crude form, that is, crushed in some manner and then added to the tanning vats where the tannins were leached from them. Since their tanning content averages 10 per cent, it has always been necessary that tanneries be located as close to tanbark sources as possible in order to eliminate transportation costs on the 90 per cent waste material. Preparing aqueous extracts of the bark near the source of supply as an operation apart from treating hides has been the means of obviating such cost and of permitting tanneries to operate nearer their markets. A leaching patent toward this end was granted as early as 1791, but ninety years later the census of 1880 still recognized only three tanning agents—oak bark, hemlock bark, and sumac leaves which had meanwhile come into use; bark extract had not yet acquired any importance. And by 1890, a century after that first patent, only 5.6 per cent, by value, of all tanning agents used were extracts.

Subsequent development may have been greater, but in 1950 there were only three hemlock and oak bark extract plants in California, Pennsylvania, and Virginia, with a combined annual capacity of 32 million pounds of 25 per cent extract.

Hemlock and oak bark were the backbone of the American tanning industry until importation of foreign materials, discussed later, began at the close of the nineteenth century. Since then they have for many years been the second and third principal domestic sources, surpassed only by chestnut wood extract, discussed next. And in the entire picture of vegetable tanning materials, as shown in table 1, they occupied only eleventh place as a group in 1950.

WOOD. Perhaps the most important technical discovery in the utilization of native tannin sources was that contained in the communication of William Sheldon in 1819 to the *American Journal of Science,* wherein he presented his findings and views on the "Application of Chestnut Wood to the Arts of Tanning and Dyeing." The bark of the European chestnut (*Castanea sativa*) had been used in England as a substitute for oak bark, but now, for the first time, attention was directed to the wood of American chestnut, containing 5 to 15 per cent tannin, as a possible industrial source of the material. Similar pronouncement, regarding the European chestnut, has been credited to a French chemist Michel, the same or the following year; and in 1870 chestnut extract was manufactured in Europe.

Like so many other significant discoveries, Sheldon's was not followed up in America until just before the twentieth century when the abundance of native chestnut (*Castanea dentata*) in the southern Appalachians provoked the establishment of numerous chestnut wood–extracting plants in North

Table 1. *Vegetable tanning materials used in the United States in 1950*

Materials			Quantities, 1,000 lb.ª	Tan units ª		%	Botanical sources
				1,000	b		
Alder	D	b	6	1	32		Alnus sp.
California tanbark	D	b	6,892	689	22		Lithocarpus densiflora
Chestnut	D	lwe	123,281	47,217	2	21	Castanea dentata
Chestnut	F	lwe	1,054	738	20		Castanea sativa
Divi divi	F	f	710	270	25		Caesalpinia coriaria
Eucalyptus	F	b	1,971	1,183	16		Eucalyptus spp.
Gambier	F	lt	2,222	933	19		Uncaria gambir
Gambier	F	lle	2,300	966	17		Uncaria gambir
Hemlock	D	b	10,723	965	18		Tsuga canadensis
Hemlock	D	be	4,790	1,197	15		Tsuga canadensis
Mangrove	F	b	7,370	2,580	11		Rhizophora mangle
Mangrove	F	be	8,634	5,439	8		Rhizophora mangle
Myrobalans	F	f	14,057	4,920	9		Terminalia chebula
Myrobalans	F	lfe	1,030	361	24		and
Myrobalans	F	sfe	300	180	28		Terminalia bellerica
Oak	D	b	22,317	2,008	12		Quercus alba and
Oak	D	be	6,927	1,732	13		Quercus velutina
Oak, chestnut	D	b	18,262	1,644	14		Quercus prinus
Pecan	D	s	1,492	269	26		Carya illinoensis
Pecan	D	se	42	12	30		Carya illinoensis
Quebracho	F	lwe	44,596	15,609	4	43	{ Schinopsis balansae and
Quebracho	F	swe	120,184	78,120	1		{ Schinopsis lorentzii
Spruce	D	swl	32,665	8,166	6		Picea spp.

524

Sumac	F	l	2,300	713	21	*Rhus coriaria*
Sumac	F	lle	559	196	27	*Rhus coriaria*
Tara	F	fp	264	119	29	*Caesalpinia spinosa*
Tropical nuts [c]	DF	s	45	8	31	
Valonia	F	f	9,651	3,378	10	*Quercus aegilops*
Valonia	F	fe	1,042	625	23	*Quercus aegilops*
Wattle	F	b	46,468	13,011	5 }	{ *Acacia* spp.
Wattle	F	be	30,480	18,898	3 } 15	{ *Acacia* spp.
Blended and miscellaneous			31,000	7,500	7	
				219,647		

b = bark
be = bark extract
D = domestic
F = foreign
f = fruits
fe = fruit extract
fp = fruit powder
l = leaves, ground
lfe = liquid fruit extract

lle = liquid leaf extract
lt = leaves and twigs
lwe = liquid wood extract
s = shells
se = liquid shell extract
sfe = solid fruit extract
swe = solid wood extract
swl = sulfite waste liquor

[a] 1 tan unit = 1 pound 100% tannin. The figures, the latest assembled, were provided by the Tanners' Council of America.
[b] Figures in this column indicate relative importance in terms of quantities of tan units.
[c] Myrobalans, pecans, and valonia?

Carolina, Virginia, and Tennessee. The extract has usually been marketed as a 25 per cent liquid, but at times has been evaporated to solid form containing 65 per cent tannin.

In 1900, 64,000 barrels of liquid extract was produced. Consumption figures for 1918 report over 48 million pounds of solid extract, $316\frac{1}{4}$ million pounds of liquid. In 1922, 43 plants in the United States were extracting domestic material and produced 428,500,000 pounds of 25 per cent liquid that year. Chestnut extract made up 90 per cent of this and consumed 496,000 cords of wood; the remaining 10 per cent was hemlock and oak extract. In 1940 there were 21 domestic extraction factories operating in Alabama, California, New York, North Carolina, Pennsylvania, Tennessee, and Virginia, and four idle plants in Carolina and Virginia. Chestnut extract production that year was 360 million pounds of 25 per cent tannin, and the total extract capacity of all 21 plants was 63 per cent of that of the 43 plants functioning twenty years earlier. This decline in the number of extracting units and in their combined production was prophetic of the final demise of the industry in 1956, as noted later.

In the last normal year prior to World War II, about 60 per cent of all domestic tannin was obtained from chestnut wood. The remainder at that time was furnished almost equally by chestnut oak and eastern hemlock barks.

The devastating havoc wrought by the chestnut blight in the former great stands of this tree in the eastern United States is an oft-told tale. Within thirty years from the discovery of the disease in the New York Zoological Park in 1904, it spread from Maine to Michigan to Alabama and annihilated the species as a self-replenishing source of lumber. The extermination was not, however, a total economic loss, for the tannin content of the wood preserved the standing dead trees against decay. Millions of them, their bark gone, have stood as a sun-bleached ghastly gray leafless forest in many parts of the southern Appalachians and have contributed to a flourishing lumber industry which prospered on providing chestnut wood—worm-eaten or not— for interior trim. Mill waste and wood unsuitable for lumber have fed the tannin-extracting plants, and the extracted wood has then found use in the hardwood paper-pulp mills of the region. To a large extent, tannin extract has been a by-product of paper manufacture in areas where pulp mills have been the principal consumers of second-grade hardwood material.

In 1942 the Appalachian Forest Experiment Station estimated that there were 22 million units of standing chestnut trees in the mountains of northern Georgia, Kentucky, North Carolina, Tennessee, Virginia, and West Virginia and that they ensured a 24-year supply of raw material for the 16 extracting plants in the area. A more conservative estimate the previous year gave 15 to 20 years.

The color bestowed upon leather by the various tanning materials is of prime importance in evaluating those agents, and in this respect chestnut extract has lost favor in very recent years. The tannin content in the long-dead trees was manufactured 25 to 40 years ago, and after a quarter century or more, without any replenishment, it has deteriorated in industrial use-fulness. In addition, the paper-pulpmaking quality of the spent wood has been lowered, and the remaining stands of dead trees are less accessible than previously harvested material was. For these reasons chestnut lumber is scarcely obtainable; paper-pulp manufacturers no longer want the wood; and if they could use it, first extracting the tannin, there would no longer be a market for the by-product. The last commercial extraction of chestnut wood tannin was carried out in February, 1956.

These latest developments mean that the tanning industry in the United States, as will be shown, is desperately more dependent upon imported stock than ever before, so far as vegetable agents are concerned. And a conspicuous example of integrated industrial plant utilization, feasible as a result of favor-able economic factors and technological development, has been brought to a close by wholly natural forces.

Foreign materials. At the beginning of the American tanning industry, domestic wages and the consequent price of tannin were sufficiently low so that importation of foreign tanning materials held no attraction. As wages and prices increased, however, and as the requirements of the leather indus-try grew beyond the domestic supply of tannin, a demand for foreign tannins developed. The demand began shortly before the year 1900; by the time of World War II foreign tannins were meeting about 60 per cent of the domestic needs.

wood. The most important of foreign botanical sources has always been the heartwood of quebracho (*Schinopsis balansae* and *S. lorentzii*), forest trees 20 to 40 feet in height, covering some 300,000 square miles along the watercourses and on the plains of central South America, embracing southern Brazil, southeastern Bolivia, Paraguay, and northern Argentina. The name "quebracho," signifying "axe breaker" in Spanish, is applied to several South American trees in allusion to the hardness of their wood. That of *Schinopsis* is one of the hardest and heaviest known, having a specific gravity of 1.35 and a weight of 75 pounds per cubic foot. It has extensive use for railway ties in Argentina, and in this service is said to resist decay for more than half a century.

Excepting chestnut, quebracho is the only wood that has been commercially used as a source of tannin. The heartwood contains 20 per cent to 28 per cent, the bark 5 per cent to 15 per cent, but the sapwood only 3.5 per cent.

The first importation of the wood came to this country in 1897. In 1909 quebracho furnished 38 per cent of all tannin extract used in the United States. In the year ending June 30, 1914, it constituted 87 per cent of the total value ($3,864,000) of all tanning agents brought to this country. In the last normal year prior to World War II and during the prewar depression, quebracho tannin still made up 72 per cent of all tannin imports. In 1936 it constituted 85 per cent of imported material and 40 per cent of all tanning material used.

Exportation of quebracho wood, formerly imported into the United States for extraction here, has been prohibited in recent years,[2] and only the extract, prepared in South America, is now generally available, in liquid and solid forms. According to the data in table 1, these two forms made up 43 per cent of all tannin units utilized in the United States in 1950.

Other foreign materials. Among the other foreign vegetable-tanning materials which have been imported in crude form or as extracts since it became economically feasible, fifty years ago, to do so, are:

DIVI-DIVI. 40 to 45 per cent tannin. Pods of a small tree, *Caesalpinia coriaria,* indigenous to the West Indies, Mexico, Venezuela, and northern Brazil.

GALLS. Insect-induced malformations on various plants in the Old World. Best known are the oak galls on *Quercus infectoria* of Asia Minor and eastern Mediterranean countries.

GAMBIER, OR WHITE CUTCH. 35 to 40 per cent tannin. Extract from the leaves and young branches of *Uncaria gambir,* a shrubby plant, wild and cultivated in the Malayan region.

MANGROVE BARK. 10 to 40 per cent tannin. Mostly red mangrove (*Rhizophora mangle*) but also *Avicennia nitida, A. tomentosa,* and other species and genera. The great abundance of these trees and shrubs as jungles in tidal areas throughout tropical and sub-tropical regions probably constitutes the world's greatest single potential source of tannin, but extensive profitable exploitation has not yet been achieved. Formerly imported principally from Portuguese East Africa, Madagascar, and the East Indies; since the 1930's largely from Colombia and Venezuela.

MYROBALANS (spelled in several ways). 30 to 40 per cent tannin in the husks. Dried fruits of *Terminalia chebula,* a 40- to 60-foot tree native to, and cultivated in, India for timber as well as the tannin-yielding nuts. Secondary sources in India are *T. bellerica, T. pallida, T. travancorensis,* and *T. citrina.*

SICILIAN SUMAC. 20 to 35 per cent tannin. Leaves of *Rhus coriaria,* native to the Mediterranean basin and extensively cultivated in Sicily and southern Italy for tanning. Brought to the United States soon after the Civil War, probably as the first foreign tanning agent to be imported.

TARA. 35 to 55 per cent tannin. Dried pods of *Caesalpinia spinosa.* Bolivia, Chile, Colombia, Ecuador, and Venezuela. Imported from Peru.

VALONIA. Acorns of Turkish oak (*Quercus aegilops*) of Asia Minor and the Grecian Archipelago. The cups contain up to 45 per cent tannin.

---

[2] $16,000 worth of the wood was imported from Paraguay in July, 1955, according to a census report.

WATTLE BARK. 30 to 40 per cent tannin. Second most important material now imported. From several species of Australian acacia, but almost entirely from black wattle (*Acacia mollissima = A. decurrens* var. *mollis*), now extensively cultivated in South Africa, especially Natal. Other Australian species contributing to the cultivated African supply are green wattle (*A. decurrens*), silver or blue wattle (*A. dealbata = A. decurrens* var. *dealbata*), and golden wattle (*A. pycnantha*).

Consumption and uses. In 1950, the latest year for which complete figures have been assembled, the consumption of all categories of vegetable tanning materials in the United States was as indicated by the data in table 1. This consumption took care of only 30 to 35 per cent of all leather, on an area basis, produced that year; the remaining 65 to 70 per cent was processed by non-vegetable agents, principally chromium salts.

While 95 per cent of all industrial tannin is utilized in leather processing, the remaining 5 per cent is important to certain other industries. Principal among them is that of petroleum, where up to 40,000 tons of quebracho and other extracts, along with pecan shells, has been used in one year to reduce the viscosity of oil-well drilling muds. Lesser amounts go into preservative treatment of fishing nets, ink manufacture, boiler-water treatment, plastics, and medicinal preparations for treating burns.

An economic problem and possible botanical solutions. In 1956 the American tanning industry consumed about 120,000 tons of 100 per cent tannin extract. Not more than 40 per cent of this was furnished by domestic sources. The most important of these, namely, reserve supplies of chestnut wood extract—providing only about 10 per cent of the over-all needs—was rapidly nearing exhaustion and would not be replenished, according to present indications, for future demands. Chestnut oak and eastern hemlock barks, the second and third most important domestic sources, are not economically available in sufficiently large quantities to be significant. The most important of the foreign sources, quebracho wood in Argentina and Paraguay—supplying 40 per cent of our needs—is becoming progressively more inaccessible in the South American jungle, is controlled by a cartel, and is always subject to export embargo because of an expanding South American tanning industry. And the second most important foreign source, wattle bark—furnishing 25 per cent of our needs—is largely shunted into Commonwealth tanneries because of Empire preferences. In brief, of the three principal sources of vegetable tanning, furnishing 75 per cent of our needs, one is approaching extinction and the other two can be discontinued at any time by war or embargo or rendered prohibitively costly by economic factors or political machinations.

The American tanning and other tannin-utilizing industries are thus seriously threatened by a shortage in their principal raw material. This shortage can be alleviated in three ways:

a. By discovering new, and increasing the consumption of already used, non-vegetable tanning agents

b. By increasing the use of already utilized native American vegetable sources other than chestnut wood, and by employing other native sources not yet exploited

c. By promoting domestic cultivation and harvesting of exotic tannin-yielding plants

Of the potential native sources, the most exploited so far is tanbark oak bark of California, already referred to. Use of this bark has always been confined to the few tanneries along the Pacific Coast, where it is usually blended with quebracho. In California it is the principal source, but in the entire national picture it constituted only 0.8 per cent of all domestic tannins in 1942. The trees, up to 80 feet in height, cover some three million acres in California and southern Oregon. When cut, they sprout quickly from the stumps, a second cutting is possible at the end of twenty years, and the wood is suitable for conversion into paper pulp. Greater exploitation of this two-product forest species has thus been advocated, envisioning a new 6-million-dollar annual economy for the state of California. Technological advances, suitable economic conditions, and proper silvicultural practice may some day render the tanbark oak an important arborescent replacement of South American quebracho as an industrial source of tannin.

Other unused and waste tanniniferous native barks not fully exploited are those of Florida scrub oak (*Quercus laevis*) with 10 per cent tannin; western hemlock (*Tsuga heterophylla*), 15 per cent; Douglas fir (*Pseudotsuga taxifolia*), 10 per cent; Florida mangrove (*Rhizophora mangle*), 31.5 per cent; and a mixture of 15 Tennessee Valley oaks, averaging about 8 per cent tannin.

Other than the foregoing barks, the only commercially potential native sources of vegetable tannin investigated so far have been canaigre root and sumac leaves.

Canaigre,[3] or tanner's dock (*Rumex hymenosepalus*), is a polygonaceous perennial herb, up to 3 feet in height with leaves up to 20 in. long, native to the southwestern United States and northern Mexico, where the Indians and Mexicans have long used the roots in preparing leather. The roots contain 10 to 35 per cent tannin and first came to the attention of the U.S. Department of Agriculture in 1868. Not until ten years later, however, was an analysis made of them, and the first recorded attempt to market the roots on a commercial scale was in 1882; in 1886 a canaigre tannery was built in Tucson, Arizona; the next year large-scale shipments of roots went to Scot-

---

[3] Corruption of the common Spanish name "caña agria" (sour cane) in Mexico. Known there and in New Mexico also as "yerba colorada," or "red root," and in the United States as "wild rhubarb."

land, England, and Canada; and by 1892 there was production of a semi-solid, 48 per cent tannic acid, extract at Deming, New Mexico, more than two million pounds of which was sold on American markets.

In more recent years extensive investigations have been pursued [4] regarding the agronomy and processing of canaigre, but whether commercial production of tannin from the roots is feasible is still unknown. Problems of production, harvesting, and extraction must still be solved.

Perhaps more promising as a native source of tannin is the abundant growth of wild sumac in the United States, especially the three species, dwarf or winged (*Rhus copallina*), smooth (*R. glabra*) and staghorn (*R. typhina*). Sicilian sumac (*R. coriaria*) of southern Italy, as already mentioned, has long been important in southern Europe and has been imported into the United States except for interruption in wartime. American tanners have preferred it to native species, but proper procedures in harvesting and drying the domestic growth allegedly produce tannin satisfactory in both yield and quality. Up to 1920 considerable quantities of the native leaves were harvested each year in Virginia and manufactured into extract for dyeing as well as tanning. Accurate data on the sources and amounts harvested are not available, but it has been reported that in 1933 sumac dealers purchased more than 640 tons of domestic sumac and that from 1937 to 1944, consumption of the leaves by five leading manufacturers of extract averaged 1,100 short tons annually.

Several investigations of this domestic source have been conducted, the latest of which concluded that:

a. Of the eight species growing wild in the eastern and southern parts of the United States, *Rhus copallina, R. glabra,* and *R. typhina* are the most promising for commercial development and that *R. trilobata* might prove of value under certain circumstances. The remaining four species (*R. aromatica, R. lanceolata, R. microphylla, R. virens*) have certain objectionable features.

b. Tannin from any of the species except *R. aromatica* and *R. virens* seemingly would produce leather of satisfactory color.

c. The average tannin content of moisture-free leaves of all the species varied from 19.32 to 39.14 per cent.

d. Tannin content in some cases varies according to sex, shading, and height of the plants.

e. Over an area of about 12,000 square miles in southern Virginia alone, approximately 43,000 long tons of dry sumac leaves would be available annually.

---

[4] By the Eastern Regional Research Laboratory of the Bureau of Agricultural and Industrial Chemistry of the U.S. Department of Agriculture and by the Division of Drug and Related Plants.

Another survey,[5] begun in July, 1940, was broader in scope and surveyed all the natural tanning materials of the southeastern United States over an area of some 468,000 square miles. Three species of sumac in the area and 199 kinds of trees were studied to give qualitative and quantitative estimates of tannin in their wood and bark. Only Darling plum (*Reynosia septentrionalis*) and buttonwood (*Conocarpus erectus*), both of Florida, and the sumacs of the entire region were regarded as displaying any potential commercial value.

Other native materials that have received some study are the heartwood of redwood (*Sequoia sempervirens*) and the leaves of mountain misery (*Chamaebatia foliolosa*), a low evergreen shrub of the Sierra Nevadas. At one time, at least, an extract was prepared from the roots of cabbage palmetto (*Sabal palmetto*) in Florida.

The third manner in which the tannin shortage facing American industry might be alleviated, that of cultivating exotic sources in America, would seem to apply only to possible wattle growing in California and the southeastern states. Only experiments have been conducted at the University of California.

THE ROLE OF BOTANISTS. It was previously stated that the principal advances in industrial plant utilization lie in the fields of applied chemistry and engineering. Apart from the contributions of foresters and forest pathologists, as biologists in perpetuating and protecting paper-pulp timber, there is, however, a potentially very important role that may be played by the plant breeder and geneticist. A long-range viewpoint is imperative for such work, and economic factors as well as further curtailment of raw materials will largely determine when the findings of such investigations will become industrially remunerative.

A significant experimental beginning in this direction has been made in hybridizing poplars for pulp. A poplar-breeding project, advocated in 1916 by Dr. Ralph H. McKee, then head of the Paper and Pulp School in the University of Maine, was later placed under the supervision of Dr. A. B. Stout, Director of Laboratories at the New York Botanical Garden, and carried out under the guidance of Dr. E. J. Schreiner, subsequently Chief Geneticist of the U.S. Forest Service. The principal result of this project was the production of hybrid poplars which reached 70-foot heights and suitable size for lumbering in five years. In Florida nine paper companies have started a seedling-breeding program in cooperation with geneticists at the University of Florida, and other companies are working with colleges in North Carolina, Texas, and Mississippi on similar programs. Rapidity of growth is but one objective in such breeding work; desirable grain effects

[5] Sponsored by the General Education Board of the Rockefeller Foundation and conducted in the Chemistry Department of the University of North Carolina.

and particular wood properties sought by the pulp industry are others. The day may come when pulp fiber, made to order, will be the heritage of the paper-pulp industry from the plant breeder.

So far as the present writer knows, efforts have not yet been made to increase the tannin-yielding quality of any plant. Investigations toward improving the domestic industrial sources of tannins have so far been concerned with surveying the wild tannin-yielding plants in southeastern United States, with utilization of Douglas fir bark in the Pacific Northwest, with growing wattle in California, and with the agronomic problems associated with growing canaigre as an annual crop in the American Southwest.

LITERATURE CITED

PAPER-PULP AND TANNING

BROWN, N. C. 1919. Forest products—Their manufacture and use. 471 pp. Wiley. New York.

————. 1950. Forest products—The harvesting, processing, and marketing of materials other than lumber, including the principal derivatives, extractives, and incidental products in the United States and Canada. 399 pp. Wiley. New York.

PANSHIN, A. J., E. S. HARRAR, W. J. BAKER, AND P. B. PROCTOR. 1950. Forest products—Their sources, production, and utilization. 549 pp. McGraw-Hill. New York.

STAMM, A. J., AND E. E. HARRIS. 1953. Chemical processing of wood. 595 pp. Chemical Publishing. New York.

PAPER-PULP

ANONYMOUS, 1869. The esparto grass. U.S. Dept. Agric. Rep. Com. Agric. 1868:260–267.

————. 1956. New trends are gaining momentum. Pulp and Paper 30(7):60–61.

ALLEN, J. H. 1938. History of making pulp and paper in the South. Southern Pulp & Paper Jour. 1(1):9–12, 40, 41.

ARONOVSKY, S. I., L. E. SCHNIEPP, AND E. C. LATHROP. 1951. Using residues to conserve resources. U.S. Dept. Agric. Yearbook 1950–51:829–842 [p. 837].

BOOKSHIRE, S. R. 1945. Fine papers from domestic flax—The story of Ecusta. Paper Ind. & Paper World 27:543–546.

DODGE, C. R. 1897. Useful fiber plants of the world. U.S. Dept. Agric. Fiber Invest. Rep. 9.

HUNTER, D. 1930. Papermaking through eighteen centuries. 358 pp. Rudge. New York.

————. 1947. Papermaking—The history and technique of an ancient craft. 2d ed. 611 pp. Knopf. New York.

————. 1952. Papermaking in pioneer America. 178 pp. Univ. of Pa. Press. Philadelphia.

ISENBERG, I. H. 1956. Papermaking fibers. Econ. Bot. 10:176–193.

McMillen, W. 1946. New riches from the soil—The progress of chemurgy. 397 pp. Van Nostrand. Princeton, N.J.

Munsell, J. 1876. Chronology of the origin and progress of paper and papermaking. 263 pp.

Schreiner, E. J. 1949. Poplars can be bred to order. U.S. Dept. Agric. Yearbook 1949:153–157.

Sutermeister, E. 1954. The story of papermaking. 209 pp. S. D. Warren Co. New York.

Weeks, L. H. 1916. A history of paper manufacturing in the United States, 1690–1916. 352 pp. Lockwood Trade Jour. Co. New York.

Tanning

Bailey, L. F., and W. H. Cummings. 1948. Tannin and secondary products from oak slabs. Jour. Amer. Leath. Chem. Assoc. 43:293.

Bandekow, R. J. 1947. Present and potential sources of tannin in the United States. Jour. Forestry 45:729–734.

Beebe, C. W., F. P. Luvisi, and M. H. Happich. 1953. Tennessee Valley oak bark as a source of tannin. Jour. Amer. Leath. Chem. Assoc. 48:32–41.

Calderwood, H. N., and W. D. May. 1947. Scrub oak as a potential replacement for chestnut. Jour. Amer. Leath. Chem. Assoc. 42:62.

Clarke, I. D., J. S. Rogers, A. F. Sievers, and Henry Hopp. 1949. Tannin content and other characteristics of native sumac in relation to its value as a commercial source of tannin. U.S. Dept. Agric. Tech. Bull. 986.

Frey, R. W., and I. D. Clarke. 1941. Tannin content of Sitka spruce bark. Jour. Amer. Leath. Chem. Assoc. 36:576.

Happich, M. L., C. W. Beebe, and J. S. Rogers. 1954. Tannin evaluation of one hundred sixty-three species of plants. Jour. Amer. Leath. Chem. Assoc. 49:760–773.

Howes, F. N. 1953. Vegetable tanning materials. 315 pp. Butterworth's Scientific Publications.

Krochmal, A., and Sherman Paur. 1951. Canaigre—A desert source of tannin. Econ. Bot. 5:367–377.

Onthank, A. H. 1917. The tannin industry. 65 pp. National Shawmut Bank. Detroit, Mich.

Pollak, L. 1923. The tanning extract of the U.S.A. Jour. Amer. Leath. Chem. Assoc. 18:12–21, 61–92.

Roger, N. F., W. H. Koepp, and E. L. Griffin. 1954. Hemlock slabs as a source of pulp and tannin. Jour. Amer. Leath. Chem. Assoc. 49:75.

Rogers, J. S. 1952. Native sources of tanning materials. U.S. Dept. Agric. Yearbook 1950–1951:709–715.

———. 1952. Potential tannin supplies from domestic barks. Tannin from waste bark. Northeast Wood Utilization Council Bull. 39.

———, H. N. Calderwood, and C. W. Beebe. Study of tannin content of barks from the Florida scrub oaks, Quercus laevis and Q. cinera. Jour. Amer. Leath. Chem. Assoc. 45:733.

Russell, A., et al. 1942–1945. Natural tanning materials of the southeastern

United States. Jour. Amer. Leath. Chem. Soc. 37:340–356; 38:30–34, 144–148, 235–238, 355–358; 39:173–178; 40:110–121.

SMOOT, C. L., AND R. W. FREY. 1937. Western hemlock bark, an important potential tanning material. U.S. Dept. Agric. Tech. Bull. 566.

SNOW, E. A. 1952. Oak slabs and cordwood as a source of tannin and pulp. Jour. Amer. Leath. Chem. Assoc. 47:563.

—————— AND L. F. BAILEY. 1949. Tannin from oak slabs. Jour. Amer. Leath. Chem. Assoc. 44:737.

WATSON, M. A. 1950. Economics of cattlehide leather tanning. 248 pp. Rumpf Pub. Co. New York.

33

BOTANIC GARDENS—WHAT ROLE TODAY?

An "Operation Bootstraps" Opportunity for Botanists

George S. Avery, Jr.

Most people have the idea that a botanic garden or an arboretum is a park without a place to play games, a place where plants bear labels with unpronounceable names—something like an old-fashioned museum. In the past thirty years our whole concept of a successful museum has changed, but most botanic gardens still go along in the old way. To be sure, many of them are great outdoor flower shows in the spring and early summer; but this brief display can hardly justify the financial outlay for year-around care. It is important, therefore, that botanic gardens play a twelve-month, active, and useful role in their communities.

The object of this story is to review briefly (1) how botanic gardens got their start, (2) what most of them now offer, and (3) what I think the future holds if we botanists have the imagination to grasp the opportunities that lie before us.

HOW BOTANIC GARDENS GOT THEIR START. One does not have to go back much over a hundred years to reach the time when botanic gardens were still either gardens of medicinal plants ("Physic Gardens") or gardens laid out in the Linnaean manner to show plant relationships. Some were designed to show economic uses of plants. Each of these reflected the culture of its time, and small exhibits in these or similar categories are still common in botanic gardens of today. They have a historical role and are not to be lightly passed over, though we must be frank enough with ourselves to realize that they are of greater interest to botanists than to the public generally.

Of the hundred or so botanic gardens and arboretums in North America, most were started by amateurs—dedicated people interested in nature and

536

possessing the acquisitive instinct of the collector. Such men were Henry Shaw, who in 1859 founded and generously endowed what is now the Missouri Botanical Garden in St. Louis, and James Arnold, a New Bedford merchant who on his death in 1869 left part of his residuary estate to be devoted to the advancement of agriculture or horticulture. This fund helped give birth to the Arnold Arboretum; other later gifts from amateurs made possible its development. While these two are typical of the major gardens or arboretums started many years ago, there are other more recent examples, such as the Morton Arboretum in the Chicago suburb of Lisle, founded and endowed by Joy Morton in 1922; and Longwood, developed by Pierre du Pont as his private estate and on his death left as a richly endowed public garden (at Kennett Square, Pennsylvania, near Wilmington, Delaware). There is also Kingwood Center, in Mansfield, Ohio; this garden was made possible by the late Charles Kelley King, who left most of his considerable estate to found Kingwood.

Many of the botanic gardens in Europe had similar beginnings. In England, the famous Royal Botanic Gardens at Kew started as the private garden of Sir Henry Capel, an enthusiastic horticulturist who died in 1696. The property was eventually purchased by the Crown and opened to the public in 1841, early in the reign of Queen Victoria. The Royal Botanic Garden in Edinburgh, Scotland, had its beginning in a small property owned by two physicians and was operated as a physic garden as long ago as 1670.

Inspired and generous amateurs also have been responsible for founding libraries and museums of art and natural history. It was the generosity and vision of Andrew Carnegie that gave vital impetus to the growth of the free public library system. Such are the cultural fruits of a free society.

Many of the institutions that were started through private initiative are now in part or wholly tax-supported. The two great endowed botanic gardens in New York City were founded by amateurs, and throughout the years since their founding, private enterprise has been coupled with municipal generosity in their support. Other institutions may some day become supported in a similar way if the public is persuaded of their value.

WHAT DO BOTANIC GARDENS AND ARBORETUMS OFFER TODAY? They are primarily outdoor collections of labeled living plants, the whole being more or less effectively landscaped. Most of them play passive roles in their communities. Some are slanted toward the native vegetation of their region, and thus are of greatest interest to amateur naturalists of the area. These are sometimes the "outdoor laboratories" of colleges and universities, generally little used except for a few class field trips each year or for student recreation. Their greatest justification is doubtless in providing a setting of beauty for the institution to which they belong and which they serve in a more or less organized way. While their existence is justified, they could hardly be said to play a dynamic role in our contemporary culture.

A few botanic gardens have been beautifully landscaped, and some are large enough to be pleasing to drive through in motor cars in blossom time. Others are smaller and more intimate and occasionally show the proper landscape use of carefully chosen species and varieties of ornamental plants— the best that decorative horticulture offers. Some have magnificent special exhibits, such as great hedge displays. Still others are made up of many smaller

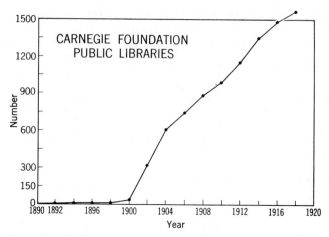

FIG. 1. Carnegie libraries. 1,572 library buildings were erected in the United States by Carnegie grants to municipalities. Mr. Carnegie made available nearly $40 million for this purpose. Libraries were built in 46 states; 22 states got 25 or more libraries each. Canada also received 125 libraries, and some 700 were constructed in other British Commonwealth countries. This was a tremendous stimulus to the growth of the free public library system throughout the world. Compare with graph on total public libraries. (*Data from Carnegie Grants for Library Buildings* 1890–1917. *Compiled by D. R. Miller.* 40 *pp. Carnegie Corporation of New York,* 1943.)

gardens, the kind any of us might like for our own. From the last, in particular, people may learn what plants to use in their gardens, and in what combinations, and what constitutes good garden design. Such displays make a good beginning, but attractive and interesting though they may be, it takes a popular educational program to "put them to work." Too few public gardens and arboretums have really put their plant collections to work for the average citizen.

Perhaps the most effective way to reach the public is through a program of well-organized popular courses in which people can learn by doing. Such courses might meet three to six times at most, for the greater the number of meetings the less the popular interest. The traditional semester-long courses associated with the captive-type education offered by colleges and universities is no criterion here, where there is no degree-seeking incentive, no requirements, and no reward other than personal satisfaction. Purely lecture courses for the general public are likely to fall flat; but lecture demonstrations supplemented with learning-by-doing laboratory, greenhouse, and occasional field experience, are almost sure to win and keep a following. Popular courses for children are a part of the pattern too, as are summer gardens for children.

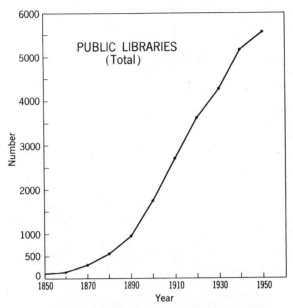

FIG. 2. All public libraries. There were about 100 public libraries in the United States in the year 1850. In the ensuing hundred years the number of libraries increased approximately 60 times while the United States population increased only sixfold. At the end of the Carnegie-grant period in 1917, about half the libraries in the United States had come from Carnegie funds. (*Data from 5,557 of the 6,072 libraries reporting to the U.S. Department of Health, Education and Welfare in 1950.*)

Here at the Brooklyn Botanic Garden we offer 25 to 30 popular courses for adults each year. Some of them attract as few as 15 students, and most of them from 25 to 100 or more. They meet three to five times and are given once or, in some cases, twice each year. The most heavily attended courses are those on House Plants, Home Landscaping, Flower Arrangement, Christmas Decorations, Bonsai (dwarfed plants as the Japanese grow them), and Spring Planting. We have learned that those who teach are as important as the subject matter. People *like* the atmosphere provided by a dynamic instructor—one who knows the subject from experience, not from books. They *enjoy* learning from someone who knows, someone who can make learning interesting and easy. Above all, they like to learn by doing.

The people who are challenged by this hobby are as varied as the plants they choose to grow. Enrolled in Brooklyn Botanic Garden courses, for example, are doctors, lawyers, business people, tradesmen, nurses, secretaries, and many housewives. These amateur gardeners are eager to exchange experi-

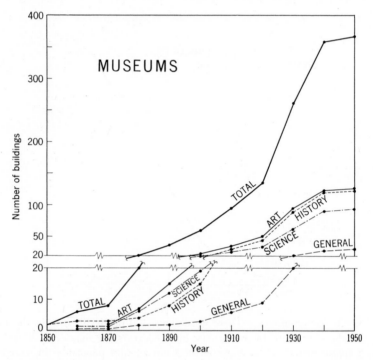

FIG. 3. Museums. 368 museum buildings were constructed in the United States over the period 1850–1950. (*Data from Museum Buildings, Vol. I, by Laurence Vail Coleman. 298 pp. American Association of Museums, Washington, D.C., 1950. All graph data compiled by Charlotte Mentges.*)

ences, learn of new varieties, and try new methods. Whether house-plant culture, flower arrangement, orchid growing, or flower painting, working with plants is, in the civilized world, probably the nearest thing to a universal avocation.

What about traditional botany? A great many people who come to take Botanic Garden courses tell us they wish they had studied botany in college so they would now know plants. They are thinking chiefly of the shrubs and trees used in landscaping today. But had they studied traditional college botany, there is about one chance in a hundred that they would have learned to recognize any of the plants commonly used in ornamental horticulture. For this reason alone, if for no other, I think we might well take a discerning look at the present emphasis in botany courses, textbooks included (particularly if we want to discover reasons for declining enrollment in botany courses).

Broadly, I suppose, the study of botany comes down to "plants in the laboratory," "plants in the wild," and "plants under cultivation." In the first category, to which highest priority is generally given, the greatest em-

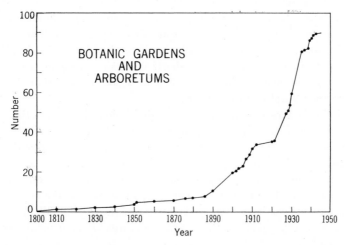

Fig. 4. Botanic gardens. About 100 botanic gardens and arboretums were established in the United States and Canada before 1950. It appears that in this sphere of American culture we are 100 years behind the development of the public library system. Needed: greater imagination on the part of those trained in botany and horticulture plus foundation and municipal support to start new gardens. (*Data from Arboretum and Botanical Gardens of North America, by Donald Wyman. 103 pp. Chronica Botanica, Vol. 10, No. 5/6, 1947.*)

phasis is on theoretical botany, that is, laboratory science planned essentially for pre-professionals. This emphasis, perhaps desirable for the relatively few who are to become professional botanists, offers little to the many students who will be amateurs all their lives. The second category, plants in the wild, does offer something for the amateur. Here the ecological view creeps in, and many more amateurs are sparked with lifetime interest. Yet even this approach has distinct limitations. A friend tells of her experiences studying the ecology of the county where her college was located. The plants were all wild species of that region; almost none of these grew where she was later to make her home, a thousand or more miles away. Had there been courses emphasizing the more or less universal plants of "ornamental horticulture" she would have acquired useful knowledge that could have given pleasure all her life. This explains the importance of the third category—plants under cultivation; yet, curiously, such subject matter is almost universally missing from botany curriculums.

WHAT CHALLENGING OPPORTUNITIES LIE AHEAD FOR BOTANISTS AND BOTANIC GARDENS? Our industrial economy and resultant urban living have freed the greater part of the population from the endless chores that once kept most people from pursuing cultural interests. The forty-hour (Saturday-free) week coupled with laborsaving gadgets and greater average income have produced so much leisure that millions sit by the hour watching television. Granted, some of it is excellent, but God help us as a nation and individually if TV gets more than its share of people's leisure time. TV provides entertainment of a passive sort, but it is debatable whether it can build or maintain a culture or create constructive tradition. In short, increasing freedom from gainful occupation has brought us into the midst of a social revolution that could easily lead to cultural impoverishment.

One of the factors determining what can be done in leisure time is the limitation of available space. This applies particularly to dwellers in cities and towns (which includes most of us). The lover of wilderness or the active sportsman needs open country to indulge his hobby. He must go where he can find it and often spend endless and tiring hours getting there and home again. People who are fortunate enough to have discovered the enjoyment of ornamental plants can have exercise, creative experiences, and all the riches of a continuing hobby right in their own dooryards or apartments, whether large or small.

People are interested in plants in their own particular ways and will seek popular courses that seem to offer opportunities for expanding their grasp of a subject. Let a person collect three or four varieties of African violet, and with the addition of a fifth he becomes a collector. He is a candidate for a popular course in house plants. Similarly, a few years' experience with the use of young forest trees in a "foundation planting" makes the intelligent home owner ready and eager for a course in landscaping.

What if most Americans could recognize 100 or more fine ornamental plants and know most of them really well? What if they knew how to grow them to the peak of perfection in their gardens and use them to landscape their homes and towns *in good taste?* And what if they knew at least the key trees of the forests and plants of the roadside and something of their natural succession? Such knowledge and the greater appreciation of nature that would come with it would be a worthy step in broadening the base of American culture.

The leadership and greatest impetus for the development of this phase of our cultural life is now coming from more than 500,000 members of Garden Clubs all over the U.S.A.—eager amateurs who are, in effect, trying to help America along the road to a pattern of maturity. If botanists could help to give leadership that would make possible the broad realization of such aims, they would be fulfilling a worthy mission in the "American way of life." The amateurs have long needed assistance, yet most of us who are professionals have neither taken advantage of their enthusiastic movement nor have we contributed to it. Now may well be the time to join forces with them and get under way with a definite plan for widespread education in horticulturally slanted botany.

While most university botany departments at present offer no training that will help supply personnel for popular education programs in botanic gardens and arboretums, there is every reason that they should do so. In some schools such training is given in departments of horticulture, but liberal arts colleges rarely offer horticulture in any form and students there can learn about plants only what traditionally slanted botany courses offer. Why not a course on species and varieties of cultivated plants—the outstanding ornamental plants of the world? And perhaps a course in landscape design? Linked with these might be other courses that would give further basic preparation for educational personnel in botanic gardens. Such instruction would by no means assure students of being fully qualified to take part in the popular education programs botanic gardens should be offering, but it would be a starter.

Some botanists will view such a program with jaundiced eye and regard it as departing too far from the teaching of "science." But why should botanists not face up to the responsibility of meeting the needs of students who might have an urge to make botany socially useful and widely interesting? Why limit the opportunity of the bachelor's-degree botanist either to going on for a higher degree in scientific work or to becoming a laboratory assistant with little or no opportunity for advancement? There are many students with outgoing personalities who would never find personal fulfillment in laboratory fact finding, nor are they attracted to it. Yet many are interested in plants and would work eagerly toward a socially slanted botanical goal. Why shouldn't these students have botanists' attention?

The botanic garden's opportunity lies in the fact that the training program suggested here cannot end with the college or university. A system of well-paid botanic-garden apprentice instructorships is needed, so that promising candidates can work with those who have set up and are now successfully operating programs of popular botanical education. There are only a few people in the entire country presently qualified to train students for this type of educational work. These people have learned from their predecessors, and frequently the hard way—from their own experience. It is they who must organize the apprentice-training programs for work in this field.

This seems to suggest that there are any number of educational opportunities in botanic gardens waiting for the persons so trained. Actually, such opportunities are at present limited, though at the Brooklyn Botanic Garden, for example, we could probably use ten promising college graduates in the next two years. But more important, *every botanic garden that now lacks a vital program in popular education should be eager to employ such people and get under way with a dynamic program.*

The suggestion here is simple enough. Botanic gardens and botany departments in the colleges should team up, with the avowed goal of making botanical education not only popular but available to everybody! The content of the short courses offered by the gardens must be matched to the current or potential interests of the people who take them. A wide range of courses should be tried out, and those that do not "take" quickly scrapped. Realistic guidance can be sought by asking amateur horticulturists what at first sight might seem to be naïve testimonials, such as "what plants have meant to me," or "what I am doing with plants," or "some of my finest experiences with plants." Geraldine Farrar [1] in "What My Garden Means to Me" has given interesting hints for those shaping a meaningful pattern for botanic gardens for the future.

CONCLUSION. We botanists have not even begun to live up to our responsibilities to contemporary society. We are molding potentially professional students after our own pattern, seemingly oblivious to the trends of our time. Why should we limit our thinking to the strictly traditional field of botany? Botanic gardens, like public libraries, are needed by the thousands if only they can have dynamic programs. We ought to be busy formulating the ways and means for making available a new socially slanted botany—for the education and enjoyment of all. Then we should hastily set about training personnel to accomplish this. Only with a timely and well-thought-out program can botanists hope to make a significant contribution to American culture.

[1] Published in *Horticulture* for October, 1952. Reprinted in *Plants & Gardens* 1952(4):304–305.

34

ARBORETA AND BOTANICAL GARDENS IN THE FIELD OF PLANT SCIENCES AND HUMAN WELFARE

R. J. Seibert

The botanic gardens and arboreta are a natural meeting ground for science, history, art, and culture in general; yet their basic importance to the broad field of plant sciences seems to have been overshadowed by a host of circumstances in recent years. Plant-science research in certain specific fields has been of a nature which demands that the scientist know more and more about fewer and fewer plants. More than ever before our plant scientist is delving into research on new plants. Through rumor, search of old literature, mass chemical analysis of plants, and ideas inspired by world-wide travel, the botanic garden is increasingly more called upon to supply basic information about plants for the general public, the hobbyist, the professional, the industrialist, the technical laboratory, the plant scientist, the home gardener, and the newspaper. Upon this point I would wish to say that the service of a botanical garden called on to give professional opinion, advice, information, and service as well as to answer the old questions, "what is the name of that plant," "where does it come from," and "how do you grow it," is usually given free of charge. At most, this service frequently goes along with the benefits of taking out a five- or ten-dollar annual membership, a contribution which scarcely pays for the member's servicing alone, much less for the time of some academically trained person to give a professional answer which may be the result of several hours' or days' research through the literature. May I merely pose the thought that if these services of the botanic garden and its recognized professional staff were paid for on the same basis that comparable professional advice, opinion, information, and service is given by the medical doctor, the lawyer, the engineering consulting company, the professional art appraiser, or the landscape architect, then perhaps the botanic garden, the botanist, and the plant taxonomist would be looked upon as a highly respected addition to the community. Furthermore, the botanic garden more than likely could afford to hire an extra gardener to make the garden more attractive to the visitor.

The economic plant which was formerly grown and studied at the botanical garden has now been turned over to the experiment station and the chemist, where again the hand of the highly specialized is in demand. The economic plant, as usually referred to, is one which produces food or medicine or other industrially usable product. We are all familiar with the fact that most of the economic plants were originally introduced and distributed to the other parts of the world through arboreta and botanic gardens. That is still going on today and no doubt will always continue to be an important function of theirs all over the world. I think, however, that we should revise our thoughts about economic plants. Statistics prove beyond doubt that the status of ornamental plants needs to be elevated to a position equal with that of "economic plants"—for that is what they are! Therefore, every arboretum and botanic garden is the potential source of new economic plants which eventually work their way into the trade and become that much more bread and butter to the nursery and cut-flower industry.

The floriculturist and the horticulturist have become concerned with bigger and better-grown, relatively few flowers and plants which can be mass-produced most economically for mass public consumption through high-pressure advertising. Far be it from me to say that the arboretum and botanic garden cannot find or produce and publicize new and highly desirable plants for the trade. It is being done every day and no doubt will always continue. I do think that with a few exceptions far too little credit has been given to the responsible gardens for the hundreds of plants which they have introduced into the trade and which today help to pay the income taxes of thousands of nurserymen and florists, horticulturists, and floriculturists.

The nurseryman has learned that it is easier and far more economical to mass-produce a relatively few plants than to deal in great quantities of species. The more progressive nurserymen of this country are working closely with the arboreta and botanical gardens and, I might say, do fully realize the value of these institutions. That value, I believe, centers around several theories about the future of ornamental horticulture: (*a*) Fads in flowers (and plants) are and can be as changeably exciting as fads in the clothing industry. (*b*) Although mass-produced plants of relatively monotonous variety will continue to form the bulk of the initial landscaping of newly constructed homes, the demands of the novice home gardener, as he becomes acquainted with the fascination of home gardening, become more those of the connoisseur and he wants something different from that in his neighbor's garden. (*c*) Home gardening is America's No. 1 hobby. Hobbies mean collections, and collections lead to the unusual and different. Therefore the nurseryman who can qualify with these plant materials will increasingly more be sought out by the gardening public. The nurseryman's best source of the unusual is the botanic garden.

The landscape architect, formerly a good gardener, has become involved with drawing-board design and mass-produced gardens to keep up with the building boom. Somewhere along the line he has settled on somewhat stereotyped planting materials. The landscape architect, if he is to hold up his end, must not only work on improved design and art appreciation but must keep up with his knowledge of plant materials and their every requirement and characteristic. I know of no better means for him to gain his knowledge firsthand than to spend a good deal of time in the botanical gardens exercising a combination of critical observation and creative imagination.

The botanist, taxonomist, and plant breeder have all been more or less forced to go into specialties, all too often of little significance to the botanical garden connected with the botanical institution to which they are attached. The botanist and/or taxonomist in some instances either has been placed on a shelf or has placed himself on a shelf in the herbarium to occupy his time solely on the plant or plants of his personal interest, giving too little thought to the wealth of plantings growing in the botanic garden and used in the landscaping of his community. I think it is the obligation of every botanical garden to retain on its staff a man of taxonomic inclination who will devote time to the ornamentals or cultivated plants with which he is surrounded. He is just as essential to the botanical garden as is the propagator and the gardener. Certainly, the plant breeder–geneticist is an integral part of this team, for through his efforts and frequently long-term breeding programs come the improved plants of the future by which the botanical gardens can build a worldwide recognition.

The true naturalist far too often has no advanced degree and is relegated to some field of outlet other than the botanic garden. The naturalist, as I like to see it, is that person who is well versed with the technical but has the patience and aptitude to translate the technical into lay language. He is the bridge between the "technical" and "popular." He or she is your public relations—the personal contact with the garden clubs, youth groups, service clubs, the press, plant lover, John Q. Public, and the home gardener. He or she may be a person or a part of the personality of some or all of the garden staff. Without this aspect represented at the garden, the situation is cold and the public is not interested.

By all means, no small part of this seeming calamity is due to "inflation" and higher wages without compensatory increases in income for most botanic gardens. "Inflations" and increased costs of salaries and operation have affected most of our public gardens, particularly those endowed many years ago and without adequate capital replacement reserves. These either have faced or will be forced to face methods of refinancing. Some of the newer ones have been quicker to refinance and probably have better financial security now than ever before. It would appear that where there is a will there is a way—if the proper way is used for the particular community in which the institution is located. The financial rejuvenation of a few arboreta and botanical gardens, both public and private, in widely separated sections of the country leads me to believe that in general the public approves of more and better public gardens, and therefore the positive approach must be assumed and refinancing must be faced, otherwise we must lose enthusiasm and ambition on the part of the younger generation to work toward botanical-garden careers. Just because a man or woman wishes to work in some capacity in a botanical garden is no reason to assume that he or she should not receive a salary comparable to "industry." Low and out-of-line salaries in this day and age only force the interested and qualified into second-choice better-paying fields of botanical sciences or completely away from plants entirely. The administrators of some of our gardens, facing economic ruin, must seek means of support which may sacrifice the appearance of their garden. The appearance of the arboretum or botanical garden and the quality of its plants and plantings must be kept first and foremost in the eyes of the administrators, employees, and the public just as the quality of food and appearance of the restaurant must be maintained at your favorite "eatery." Without that the first requirement for public and private support is lost.

Many of our public gardens, formerly surrounded by beautiful countryside or fine residential sections, now find themselves in the middle of the poorer section of town, off the beaten track, or in a pall of industrially polluted air so bad that only certain human beings continue to live there. Regardless of the location of any garden—if it is worthwhile seeing, people will come to see it. An arboretum or garden should be considered a permanent part of the community. Its surroundings will change from good to bad and perhaps eventually to good again. I think that a recent enlightening experience is worth relating. On the island of Jamaica there exists a small but charming garden called the Bath Botanical Garden in the town of Bath near the southeastern corner of the island. This botanical garden, the first on the island, was started in 1779. It is located in the center of a small crowded settlement of poor people and poorly maintained houses—yet, through the turmoil of life, events, generations, battle, hurricane, earthquake, and flood this garden shines out as a splendid example of the love, appreciation, and value of a botanic garden. Here, off the beaten track, in poor surroundings, and mellowed with age, it is clean, beautiful, and respected by the residents as a shining example for all botanic gardens. Furthermore, one sees the ornamental plants originally introduced to Jamaica through this garden being used around the homes of this community. The unattractive hovel has become a charming "native" hut through the use of attractive ornamentals.

Industrial and civic air pollution is a phase we are going through in rapidly growing industrial and population centers. Some of the best factual evidence that we have to prove the presence of air pollution may be found at the botanical gardens situated in such conditions. As we gather our evidence and the force of the public's opinion gathers weight, air pollution will become as bad an offense as polluting water and milk. Measures have been taken, can be taken, and will be taken to clean it up—the botanical garden can help a great deal by assisting our authorities in proving the damage caused to plants grown in the presence of polluted air and by further publicizing specific damage to specific plants to the gardening public.

Many gardens suffer the constant pressure of encroaching civilization and the march of the bulldozer preceding highways, subdivisions, and what not. The encroachment of civilization on the privacy and serenity of the botanical garden is one of our most serious problems. We all realize that we cannot prevent the advance of civilization—but by the same token there is no excuse for the planner to point his finger at the botanic garden with an "it's got to go" attitude. Public opinion is the best tool by which this attitude might give way to fair consideration. There is no way in which the valued specimens of many a threatened garden can be replaced, except by bodily moving many of the time-honored specimens to a new location. I'm sure that were the public authorities forced to dig up the funds for such operations, they too would look upon the value of a botanic garden or arboretum in a much different light. Arboreta and botanical gardens, in summary, are contributing their share to human welfare:

1. They are the basic source of plants and information about plants for that vast army of Americans who have made home gardening their No. 1 hobby.

2. They are the basic source of new information concerning plants which seeps into every level of education concerning the hundreds of thousands of plants known to science.

3. They serve as training grounds for our future plant scientists and gardeners.

4. More than a serene site of relaxation for "tired businessmen," they can always add to the facilities available for passive, educational, cultural, and meditative recreation.

5. It is to be observed that the trend of most of our park departments in this country is to make playgrounds out of more of our parks. The average person who formerly took a walk in a park because of the beautiful trees and other plants must now fear being hit by a baseball, run down by a charging herd of humanity, or finding some man-made structure where formerly stood a majestic tree. Our botanical gardens and arboreta must, in addition, serve a purpose for which much of the city park was originally designed.

GOLDEN JUBILEE SYMPOSIUM

PROGRESS AND OUTSTANDING ACHIEVEMENTS IN VARIOUS FIELDS OF BOTANY DURING THE PAST FIFTY YEARS

INTRODUCTION

James E. Canright

The six papers published here as a unit were presented in the Golden Jubilee Symposium of the Botanical Society of America during the AIBS meetings at the University of Connecticut, Storrs, Connecticut, on August 29, 1956.[1] The writer, in his capacity as chairman of the General Section of the Botanical Society of America, organized this symposium entitled "Progress and Outstanding Achievements in Various Fields of Botany during the Past Fifty Years" as part of the celebration of the fiftieth anniversary of the founding of the Society. The various sections of the Society, together with the American Bryological Society, American Fern Society, American Society of Plant Physiologists, American Society of Plant Taxonomists, Mycological Society of America, and Phycological Society of America cooperated fully in sponsoring this symposium. The following papers by the six participants were planned with the thought in mind that both current and future generations of botanists might now have available a single publication where it will be possible to read about the development of most of the principal fields of botany in the United States. These papers are all the more significant because of the fact that each of the participants has played a major role in the advancement of his particular field of botanical endeavor during the past fifty years. It is regrettable that, because of time limitations, *all* areas of botany could not have been represented in this symposium. The splendid cooperation of the six participants, the sponsoring societies, and the officials of the host institution is gratefully acknowledged.

[1] See *AIBS Bull.* 6(4):65, August, 1956.

35

PROGRESS AND OUTSTANDING ACHIEVEMENTS IN PHYCOLOGY DURING THE PAST FIFTY YEARS

George F. Papenfuss

The fiftieth birthday of our Society marks a period during which significant advances have been made in all branches of phycology. As it will be possible in this paper to point to only a few of the landmarks, I shall confine myself to important contributions to knowledge of the morphology of some of the major groups of algae and to the effects that this new knowledge has had on the classification of these plants. A fuller treatment of these topics, covering all the groups of algae and the period 1753–1953 was recently published (Papenfuss, 1955).

CHLOROPHYCOPHYTA

Hertwig in 1876, studying fertilization in a species of sea urchin, showed for the first time that a significant feature of sexual reproduction is the fusion of the gamete nuclei. A similar fusion of nuclei in plants was first observed by Schmitz (1879) in *Spirogyra,* and Berthold (1881) saw it in the brown alga *Ectocarpus,* shortly afterward.

Following the stimulating postulate of Weismann (1887) that the doubling of the chromatin mass at syngamy must be followed by a regulatory reducing process, many investigations were undertaken with the view of testing this hypothesis and of determining the place in the life history where the reduction may occur.

The first observations on meiosis in the green algae were made by Allen (1905) in *Coleochaete* during the time that he was working in Strasburger's laboratory. The life history of *Coleochaete* had previously been investigated by Pringsheim (1860), who showed that the zygospore divides into a number of cells, each of which produces a zoöspore. Pringsheim and others regarded this structure as the sporophyte of *Coleochaete.* Allen established, however, that meiosis occurs during the first two divisions of the nucleus of the germinating zygospore and that the multicellular structure produced by the zygote is haploid. Thus Allen eliminated the only green alga that up to that time was regarded as showing an alternation of generations. Cytological studies by a number of later investigators on diverse green algae confirmed the observation of Allen, and until 1925 it was generally believed that all green algae were haploid, with meiosis always occurring during the germination of the zygote.

In 1925 Williams showed that *Codium* is a diploid alga, and since that time our concepts of the life histories of the green algae and of their associated nuclear cycles have undergone a profound change. The evidence now at hand indicates that the Siphonocladales (Schechner-Fries, 1934; Schussnig, 1938), most of the Siphonales (Williams, 1925; Schussnig, 1930, 1932, 1939, 1950; Zinnecker, 1935), and the Dasycladales (Schulze, 1939) are diploid algae (at least those that have been studied cytologically) and that it is the diploid soma that in them functions as the gamete-producing generation.

The occurrence of an alternation of generations in the green algae was first observed by Hartmann (1929) and Føyn (1929, 1934a, 1934b), who established that members of the orders Cladophorales (*Cladophora, Chaetomorpha*) and Ulotrichales (*Enteromorpha, Ulva*) show an alternation of isomorphic generations. A similar cycle has since been reported by Singh (1945, 1947) for *Draparnaldiopsis* and *Fritschiella* (both Ulotrichales) and by Iyengar and Ramanathan (1940, 1941) for *Anadyomene* and *Microdictyon* (both Cladophorales).

Juller (1937) has demonstrated that *Stigeoclonium subspinosum* (Ulotrichales) possesses an alternation of heteromorphic generations, with the diploid sporophytic generation smaller than the haploid one, and Jorde (1933) has obtained fairly convincing evidence indicating that certain species of the unicellular *Codiolum* (a genus usually regarded as belonging to the Chlorococcales) represent the diploid sporophytic generation of species of the filamentous, septate *Urospora* (a genus usually placed in the Cladophorales). The observations of Jorde still require confirmation, but if they should be correct, we would have here an instance of two kinds of green algae, which for a long time have been regarded as phylogenetically very far apart, representing phases in the same life cycle.

Another apparent instance of this kind has been brought to light by Kornmann (1938) and Feldmann (1950). These authors have made observations which suggest with reasonable certainty that the vesicular *Halicystis* and the filamentous, nonseptate *Derbesia* constitute phases in the life history of one and the same alga, with *Halicystis* representing the gametophytic and *Derbesia* the sporophytic generation. These two genera have been regarded as the type representatives of two distinct families, Halicystidaceae and Derbesiaceae, in the order Siphonales. Inasmuch as *Derbesia* is the only genus of green algae outside the order Oedogoniales that is known to possess swarmers with a subterminal collar of flagella, the apparent existence of an intimate relationship between it and *Halicystis* (which forms terminally biflagellate gametes) is a matter of far-reaching significance. In fact, Feldmann (1954) recently removed *Derbesia* (and its gametophytic stage, *Halicystis*) from the Siphonales and erected for it the order Derbesiales.

Among the interesting discoveries of recent times are those showing that even the Volvocales include forms with two photosynthetic and alternating phases. Thus it has been shown by Strehlow (1929) and Behlau (1935) that the unicellular quadriflagellate *Chlorobrachis gracillima* is the diploid stage of the colonial *Pyrobotrys gracilis*. Behlau (1939) has also shown that *Carteria ovata* is the diploid stage of *Chlamydomonas variabilis*.

PHAEOPHYCOPHYTA

By 1906 the details of sexual reproduction had been studied in only six genera of brown algae: *Fucus, Zanardinia, Cutleria, Ectocarpus, Giffordia,* and *Dictyota. Fucus* had been shown by Strasburger (1897) to be diploid, and Yamanouchi in 1909a established that meiosis occurs during the first two divisions of the primary nucleus of the oögonium and antheridium. *Fucus* thus was shown to have a life history analogous to that of animals, and this appears to be true of all Fucales.

Reinke (1877, 1878) had obtained evidence indicating that *Zanardinia* shows an alternation of isomorphic generations, and he (1878) and Falkenberg (1879) were of the opinion that *Cutleria* showed an alternation of heteromorphic generations, with *Cutleria* representing the gametophytic generation and another brown alga, long known by the generic name *Aglaozonia,* representing the sporophytic generation. Yamanouchi (1909b, 1911, 1912, 1913) furnished cytological proof of the correctness of Reinke and Falkenberg's interpretations of the life histories of *Zanardinia* and *Cutleria.*

In consequence of the observations of Reinke (1877, 1878), Falkenberg (1879), Berthold (1881), Sauvageau (1896), and others concerning the gametic role of the zooids from the plurilocular reproductive organs of *Zanardinia, Cutleria, Ectocarpus,* and *Giffordia,* a firm conviction developed among botanists (and was adhered to for almost half a century) that the plurilocular organs of brown algae were always gametangia and the unilocular organs sporangia. Frequently it was observed that the zooids from the plurilocular organs germinated directly. To explain this asexual behavior it was assumed that the gametes had lost their sexual power and germinated parthenogenetically.

Studying *Pylaiella* and the related *Ectocarpus,* Knight (1923, 1929) showed that this explanation was incorrect. She demonstrated that brown algae have two kinds of plurilocular organs—some occurring on haploid plants and functioning as gametangia, and others on diploid plants and functioning as zoösporangia. The diploid plants frequently also form unilocular sporangia. Meiosis occurs in the unilocular sporangia, as had previously also been shown by Yamanouchi with reference to *Zanardinia* and *Cutleria* and by Kylin (1918) with reference to *Chorda*. No reduction divisions occur in the plurilocular sporangia of diploid plants, and the zooids produced in them germinate directly.

Knight (1923) showed that the life history of *Pylaiella* includes an alternation of isomorphic generations. She (1929) was unable, however, to demonstrate an alternation of generations in *Ectocarpus*. Contrary to the long-held belief that the zooids produced in the unilocular organs were zoöspores, she claimed that in British waters the zooids from the unilocular organs of *E. siliculosus* function as gametes. In this region there consequently existed only diploid plants. She repeated the observations of Berthold and others at Naples and established that in that area the plants were haploid and their plurilocular organs were gametangia.

Papenfuss (1933, 1935), studying *Ectocarpus siliculosus* in the region of Woods Hole, confirmed the observations of Knight that this species includes haploid plants which form only plurilocular organs and diploid plants which form both unilocular and plurilocular organs. He was unable, however, to confirm her observations regarding the gametic nature of the zooids from the unilocular structures. Instead, he found that *E. siliculosus* exhibits an alternation of isomorphic generations. Føyn (1934) has established the occurrence of a similar cycle in Norway.

Several other investigators have claimed a gametic role for the zooids from the unilocular organs of diverse brown algae. Although such behavior is theoretically possible, the evidence presented for the alleged instances of conjugation between these swarmers is not convincing. It would indeed be remarkable if gametes could be produced by the diploid as well as the haploid generation of a plant such as *Ectocarpus siliculosus*.

In 1915 Sauvageau made the epoch-making discovery that *Saccorhiza bulbosa*, a member of the Laminariales, possesses an alternation of heteromorphic generations comparable to that of ferns. The familiar macroscopic plant was shown to be the sporophyte. The zoöspores formed in its unilocular sporangia produce microscopic, filamentous gametophytes which are dioecious and form oögonia and antheridia.

This very significant discovery by Sauvageau, which was made on the basis of cultures, aroused a great deal of interest in the brown algae. It was evident that the cycle of development of many of these algae could not be ascertained unless they were grown in culture. It was also clear that rich rewards were in store for those who would follow his approach to problems relating to the life histories of the brown algae. We today know the broad outlines of the life history of a large number of brown algae. With the exception of the genera comprising the Fucales (and a number of genera which apparently have lost sexuality), the majority of forms show an alternation of generations. In some the two generations are morphologically similar, in others they are dissimilar.

The knowledge on the developmental and nuclear cycles and the anatomy of brown algae that has accumulated during the past fifty years has naturally had far-reaching effects on the classification of these algae. Ten of the eleven orders of brown algae currently accepted were erected between 1917 and 1926.

RHODOPHYCOPHYTA

By the turn of the century a good deal of information had accumulated about the anatomy and sexual reproduction of the red algae. It had been shown that in many of them the fertilized carpogonium establishes a connection with a neighboring cell, named the auxiliary cell by Schmitz in 1883, that the fertilized egg nucleus migrates into the auxiliary cell, and that the cystocarp develops from this cell.

The nuclear cycle, especially the place of meiosis in the life history, had as yet not been studied. Yamanouchi, about fifty years ago (1906a, b), first worked out the nuclear history and showed that in *Polysiphonia* the plants which bear tetrasporangia are diploid and that meiosis occurs in the tetrasporangium. The confirmatory cultural evidence was supplied by Lewis in 1912. Thus at last was determined the long-misunderstood role of the tetrasporangia in the life history of the red algae. As late as 1904 Oltmanns, in agreement with several earlier authors, had still regarded the tetrasporangia as accessory reproductive organs of the gametophytic generation.

Svedelius (1915), studying the development and cytology of *Scinaia*, a genus which was known to lack tetrasporangia, established that in it meiosis occurs soon after fertilization of the egg nucleus. Such species (the majority of Nemalionales) consequently lack free-living tetrasporophytes. It is now well established that the majority of red algae above the Nemalionales possess three generations: a haploid gametophyte (which is usually dioecious), a diploid carposporophyte which is permanently attached to and largely parasitic on the gametophyte, and a diploid free-living tetrasporophyte, whereas in the majority of Nemalionales the life history includes only two generations, a haploid gametophyte and a haploid carposporophyte.

We now also know that in a number of genera of red algae the life history deviates from the two general types outlined above. Of special interest is the condition that obtains in two genera of the Nemalionales. In four species of *Liagora* (Børgesen, 1927; Kylin, 1930; Yamada, 1938; Levring, 1941; Abbott, 1945) and in one of *Helminthocladia* (Feldmann, 1939) the carposporophyte forms tetrasporangia in the place of carposporangia. The cytology of these species has not yet been studied, but it is believed that in them meiosis, instead of occurring immediately after fertilization, has been delayed until the formation of carposporangia. This condition is of considerable phylogenetic interest, for it illustrates a probable intermediate step in the evolution of the triphasic type of life history characteristic of the bulk of the higher red algae. A further postponement of meiosis would of course result in diploid carpospores, which on germination and mitotic division of the nucleus would produce diploid free-living tetrasporophytes.

On the other hand, there are genera of higher red algae, such as *Phyllophora* (Rosenvinge, 1929; Claussen, 1929; Kylin, 1930) and *Gymnogongrus* (Chemin, 1933; Gregory, 1934; Doubt, 1935), which include species with a diphasic life history similar to that of the species of *Liagora* and *Helmintho-cladia* considered above. In these the diphasic condition clearly appears to be derived, having come about as the result of an advancement of meiosis to the time of carpospore formation and the consequent elimination of the free-living tetrasporophyte. Feldmann (1952) and others have expressed the opinion that all Florideophycidae that lack a free-living tetrasporophyte may be derived, but Svedelius (1956) has produced convincing evidence that this is not always so.

Attention should also be brought to the very interesting observations (made on the basis of cultures) by J. and G. Feldmann, Drew, Koch, Tseng and Chang, and others. J. and G. Feldmann (1942 and earlier papers) have obtained results which indicate that *Hymenoclonium serpens* and *Falkenbergia rufolanosa* represent filamentous tetrasporangial phases in the life histories of *Bonnemaisonia asparagoides* and *Asparagopsis armata*, respectively, and that *Trailliella intricata* probably represents a filamentous tetrasporangial stage in the life history of *Bonnemaisonia hamifera*. That a relationship actually exists between *T. intricata* and *B. hamifera* has recently been demonstrated by Koch (1950). *Bonnemaisonia* and *Asparagopsis* thus display a triphasic life history in which the free-living tetrasporophyte is morphologically very different from the gametophyte.

In the Bangiophycidae, in which to the best of our knowledge all the cells except the zygote are haploid (as in many Nemalionales of the Florideophycidae), Drew (1949, 1954b) and Tseng and Chang (1955) have shown that the filamentous, shell-inhabiting forms previously known as *Conchocelis rosea* are a stage in the life history of both the membranous *Porphyra* and the ribbon-like *Bangia*. The establishment of the existence of an intimate relationship between *Conchocelis* and these two genera is a matter not only of botanical significance but of considerable economic importance in those parts of the world where *Porphyra* is cultivated for food.

We are indebted to Kylin for the refinement of Schmitz's (1883) embryological system of classification of the main group of red algae, the Florideophycidae. In a long series of papers, especially the monographic works of 1923, 1928, 1930, and 1932, he immensely advanced our knowledge of the morphology and interrelationships of this large and diversified class. Despite certain shortcomings (cf. Papenfuss, 1951; Drew, 1954a) his system allows of a much more natural arrangement than had previously been possible.

In Kylin's (1932) system the orders are separated on whether a generative auxiliary cell is absent or present, its time of formation—before or after fertilization of the carpogonium—and its manner and place of formation. Whether or not the importance of this cell has been overemphasized in the creation of this system can only be determined from further work on the morphology of the many genera that await investigation. Since the generative auxiliary cell is the starting point of a generation, the carposporophyte, there at present appears to be ample justification for believing that the absence or presence of this cell and the characters associated with its formation are matters of the utmost importance in the establishment of major taxonomic categories.

CHRYSOPHYCOPHYTA

This phylum was erected by Pascher in 1914 (cf. also Pascher, 1921). It includes the three classes Xanthophyceae (known until 1930 as Heterokontae), Chrysophyceae, and Bacillariophyceae (commonly known as diatoms). Although the pigmented members of these three groups usually have yellow-green or golden-brown chromatophores and it has consequently been assumed that they possess similar pigment complexes, it is now known from the work of Strain (1951, p. 253) and others that there are significant differences. On the basis of pigment composition as well as structure of the cell and life history, the diatoms, at best, appear to be only distantly related to either the Xanthophyceae or the Chrysophyceae.

XANTHOPHYCEAE. The few Xanthophyceae that had become known previous to 1899 were regarded as green algae by botanists, and they were placed in widely separated families. Borzi in 1895 brought them together in an order Confervales, mainly on the basis of three characters: (1) they possessed discoid yellowish-green plastids; (2) they did not store starch; and (3) their zoöspores had only one flagellum (as he believed).

In the course of the next few years Bohlin (1897a, 1897b) and Luther (1899) produced evidence which showed that the characters whereby the Confervales differed from the green algae were of such magnitude that they could no longer be classified with them. It was established that they differ from green algae not only in pigment composition and storage products, but that the two overlapping pieces that form the lateral wall of the cells have a layered structure and that the wall is not composed of cellulose but of a pectic acid derivative. It was also shown that the motile cells are actually biflagellate, with the one flagellum much shorter than the other. Luther (1899) consequently erected for these algae a separate class, which he named Heterokontae. The currently accepted name Xanthophyceae was proposed by Allorge (1930).

Following the pioneering studies by Borzi, Bohlin, and Luther, many investigators of the present century, but especially Pascher, have made important contributions to our knowledge of the Xanthophyceae. The present system of classification of the group is essentially that of Pascher (1912, 1925, 1937–1939). In accordance with the morphology of the thallus, he established orders which parallel certain chlorophycean orders. He erected the order Heterochloridales to receive the flagellated genera, the Rhizochloridales for the amoeboid forms, the Heterocapsales for the palmelloid members, the Heterococcales for the coccoid types, the Heterotrichales for the filamentous representatives, and the Heterosiphonales (now known as Vaucheriales) for the siphonous taxa.

Significant observations favoring Pascher's belief in a relationship between the Xanthophyceae and Chrysophyceae were made by Vlk (1931, 1938). He showed that the biflagellate cells of the Xanthophyceae conform to those of the Chrysophyceae in that the long flagellum is of the tinsel type, being beset with two rows of delicate cilia, whereas the short flagellum lacks cilia.

A further character in support of such an alliance was brought into the foreground by Pascher in 1932. He pointed out that the bivalved cysts which he had discovered in certain Xanthophyceae were comparable to the bottle-like cysts (replete with bung) characteristic of the Chrysophyceae.

Blackman in 1900 brought attention to the fact that *Vaucheria* appeared to be the only "green" alga outside the Heterokontae which had chlorophyll possessing the same characters as in members of the Heterokontae. In 1901 Bohlin formally removed *Vaucheria* to the Heterokontae. He pointed out, among other things, that it had long ago been shown that the sperms of *Vaucheria* possess two flagella of unequal length. In general, botanists have preferred to retain *Vaucheria* in the Chlorophyceae, but recent work by Seybold, Egle, and Hülsbruch (1941) and Strain (1948) on the pigments and by Koch (1951) on the structure of the flagella of the sperm has shown that *Vaucheria* can no longer be classified with the green algae. This is inconvenient, for it has removed from the green algae the classical example of a siphonous and oögamous "green" alga and one that is readily obtained for classroom study.

CHRYSOPHYCEAE. With the exception of the genera *Hydrurus* and *Phaeothamnion*, which had been placed in the Phaeophyceae, the Chrysophyceae that became known during the last century were usually regarded as animals and were ignored by botanists. As was so often true during that period, Klebs was the first botanist to make a thorough study of some of these organisms. In 1892 he clearly recognized the salient features that characterize the group: (1) the golden-brown color of the organisms; (2) the characteristic storage products leucosin and oil in both the pigmented and the colorless members; (3) the three types of flagellation—one flagellum, two unequal flagella, or two more or less equal ones; and (4) the formation of endoplasmatic cysts of a unique type.

As is true of the Xanthophyceae, the bulk of our knowledge of the Chrysophyceae has been acquired during the past 40 years, mostly through the investigations of Pascher. At present the class is credited with some 10 orders and a large number of families. Work done during the last few decades has also demonstrated with reasonable certainty that two important groups of the phytoplankton of the sea, the coccolithophores and the silicoflagellates, are chrysophytes. As in the Xanthophyceae, the thalli of Chrysophyceae parallel those of certain orders of the green algae.

BACILLARIOPHYCEAE. Klebahn in 1896, working on *Rhopalodia gibba,* a member of the order Pennales, was the first to obtain cytological results suggesting that diatoms are diploid and that meiosis occurs during gametogenesis. Since that time various authors (Karsten, 1899, 1912; Geitler, 1927a, 1927b, 1928; Cholnoky, 1928, 1933a; Meyer, 1929; Subrahmanyan, 1947) have confirmed the fact that the Pennales are diploid and that meiosis precedes auxospore formation.

As a conjugation of cells was not known to occur during auxospore formation in the Centrales, it was believed for a number of years (cf. Oltmanns, 1922) that these forms, to the contrary, are haploid and that in them auxospore formation is an asexual process. Persidsky (1929, 1935) first showed that the Centrales are likewise diploid and that here auxospore formation is also a sexual process (autogamy). His observations have been confirmed by Cholnoky (1933b) and more particularly by Iyengar and Subrahmanyan (1942, 1944), Stosch (1951a), and Geitler (1952). The evidence at hand indicates, therefore, that the Centrales and Pennales are not as remote from each other as has been supposed.

In 1897 Murray observed in certain marine members of the order Centrales rounded protoplasmic bodies which he interpreted as reproductive cells. Later these so-called microspores were observed by a number of investigators in various marine and fresh-water Centrales. In some instances the microspores appeared to be provided with two lateral and in others with two terminal flagella of equal length. Stosch (1951a, 1954) observed with certainty only one flagellum. It was thought that these microspores may be gametes, but proof of this was not forthcoming until 1951 (a, b) when Stosch showed that in some species they actually are male gametes (see also Stosch, 1954; Geitler, 1952). The establishment of the occurrence of flagellated cells in the diatoms is a discovery of far-reaching significance.

PYRROPHYCOPHYTA

With few exceptions (e.g., *Pyrocystis*) the dinoflagellates that had become known to science previous to 1912 were flagellated forms. In that year Klebs published his significant discovery of several nonmotile unicellular organisms that at certain stages in their development clearly revealed their relationship to the dinoflagellates. Two years later Pascher (1914) announced the discovery of a number of additional nonmotile types and also proposed a far-reaching revision of the classification of the dinoflagellates. Some of the non-motile types have a palmelloid organization (Pascher's Dinocapsales), others have a coccoid organization (his Dinococcales), and the single representative of a third group has a filamentous organization (his Dinotrichales).

CONCLUSION

Fifty years ago botanists customarily recognized a phylum Thallophyta which received the algae and the fungi. Few, if any, mycologists and phycologists would today be willing to accept such a heterogeneous phylum.

Fifty years ago the algae were usually divided into about nine classes. On the basis of pigment composition, nature of food reserves, structure of the cell, type of flagellation, structure of the flagella, structure of the reproductive organs, and method of reproduction, the algae are today arranged in seven or more phyla and, in addition, several classes of uncertain systematic position.

In this paper reference has been made to only a few of the advances in knowledge that have led to this new classification—in fact, several of the major groups were entirely omitted from consideration. To the non-algologist it may appear that the present system of the algae has been made unduly complex by the recognition of an excessively large number of major taxa. It should be made clear that there is great unanimity among phycologists about this system. We may differ as to whether the cryptomonads and chloromonads should be regarded as classes of uncertain systematic position or as autonomous phyla, on whether the charophytes should be considered a class in the green algae or a separate phylum, on whether the blue-green algae should be placed together with the bacteria in a phylum Schizophyta or whether they constitute an independent phylum, and other such questions, but on the underlying principles of the system we show remarkable agreement.

LITERATURE CITED

ABBOTT, ISABELLA A. 1945. The genus *Liagora* (Rhodophyceae) in Hawaii. Bishop Mus. Hawaii Occasional Papers 18:145–169.

ALLEN, C. E. 1905. Die Keimung der Zygote bei *Coleochaete*. Ber. Deutsch. Bot. Ges. 23:285–292.

ALLORGE, P. 1930. Hétérocontes ou Xanthophycées? Rev. Algol. 5:230.

BEHLAU, J. 1935. Die Spondylomoraceen-Gattung *Chlamydobotrys*. Beitr. Biol. Pfl. 23:125–166.

————. 1939. Der Generationswechsel zwischen *Chlamydomonas variabilis* Dangeard und *Carteria ovata* Jacobsen. Beitr. Biol. Pfl. 26:221–249.

BERTHOLD, G. 1881. Die geschlechtliche Fortpflanzung der eigentlichen Phaeosporeen. Mitt. Zool. Stat. Neapel 2:401–413.

BLACKMAN, F. F. 1900. The primitive algae and the Flagellata. An account of modern work bearing on the evolution of the algae. Ann. Bot. 14:647–688.

BOHLIN, K. 1897a. Studier öfver några slägten af alggruppen Confervales Borzi. Bihang K. Sv. Vet.-Akad. Handl. 23, Afd. 3, No. 3. 56 pp.

————. 1897b. Zur Morphologie und Biologie einzelliger Algen. (Vorläufige Mitteilung.) Öfvers. K. Sv. Vet.-Akad. Förhandl. 1897:507–529.

————. 1901. Utkast till de gröna algernas och arkegoniaternas fylogeni. 43 + iv pp., 1 folding chart. Dissertation, Lund. (Publ. by the author.)

BØRGESEN, F. 1927. Marine algae from the Canary Islands . . . III. Rhodophyceae. Part 1. Bangiales and Nemalionales. K. Danske Vidensk. Selsk. Biol. Medd. 6(6):97 pp.

BORZI, A. 1895. Studi algologici . . . , fasc. 2. Pp. [i-vii], 121–378. Reber. Palermo.

CHEMIN, E. 1933. Sur le mode de reproduction de *Gymnogongrus griffithsiae* Mart. et de quelques espèces du même genre. Bull. Soc. Bot. Fr. 80:755–770.

CHOLNOKY, B. 1928. Über die Auxosporenbildung der *Anomoeoneis sculpta* E. Cl. Archiv Protistenk. 63:23–57.

————. 1933a. Beiträge zur Kenntnis der Karyologie der Diatomeen. Archiv Protistenk. 80:321–348.

————. 1933b. Die Kernteilung von *Melosira arenaria* nebst einigen Bemerkungen über ihre Auxosporenbildung. Zeitschr. Zellforsch. Mikr. Anat. 19:698–719.

CLAUSSEN, H. 1929. Zur Entwicklungsgeschichte von *Phyllophora brodiaei*. (Vorläufige Mitteilung.) Ber. Deutsch. Bot. Ges. 47:544–547.

DOUBT, DOROTHEA G. 1935. Notes on two species of *Gymnogongrus*. Amer. Jour. Bot. 22:294–310.

DREW, KATHLEEN M. 1949. *Conchocelis*-phase in the life-history of *Porphyra umbilicalis* (L.) Kütz. Nature 164:748–749.

————. 1954a. The organization and inter-relationships of the carposporophytes of living Florideae. Phytomorph. 4:55–69.

————. 1954b. Studies in the Bangioideae. III. The life-history of *Porphyra umbilicalis* (L.) Kütz. var. *laciniata* (Lightf.) J. Ag. Ann. Bot. N.S. 18:183–211.

FALKENBERG, P. 1879. Die Befruchtung und der Generationswechsel von *Cutleria*. Mitt. Zool. Stat. Neapel 1:420–447.

FELDMANN, J. 1939. Une Némalionale à carpotétraspores: *Helminthocladia hudsoni* (C. Ag.) J. Ag. Bull. Soc. Hist. Nat. Afr. Nord 30:87–97.

————. 1950. Sur l'existence d'une alternance de générations entre *l'Halicystis parvula* Schmitz et le *Derbesia tenuissima* (De Not.) Crn. C. R. Acad. Sci. [Paris] 230:322–323.

FELDMANN, J. 1952. Les cycles de reproduction des algues et leur rapports avec la phylogénie. Rev. Cytol. Biol. Vég. 13:1–49.

————. 1954. Sur la classification des Chlorophycées siphonées. VIII Congrès Internat. Bot. Rapp. Comm. Sect. 17. Pp. 96–98.

———— AND GENEVIÈVE FELDMANN. 1942. Recherches sur les Bonnemaisoniacées et leur alternance de générations. Ann. Sc. Nat. Bot. Sér. XI, 3:75–175.

FØYN, BIRGITHE R. 1934. Über den Lebenscyklus einiger Braunalgen. Vorläufige Mitteilung. Bergens Mus. Årbok 1934:1–9.

FØYN, BJÖRN. 1929. Untersuchungen über die Sexualität und Entwicklung von Algen. IV. Vorläufige Mitteilung über die Sexualität und den Generationswechsel von Cladophora und Ulva. Ber. Deutsch. Bot. Ges. 47:495–506.

————. 1934a. Lebenszyklus, Cytologie und Sexualität der Chlorophycee Cladophora suhriana Kützing. Archiv Protistenk. 83:1–56.

————. 1934b. Lebenszyklus und Sexualität der Chlorophycee Ulva lactuca L. Archiv Protistenk. 83:154–177.

GEITLER, L. 1927a. Die Reduktionsteilung und Copulation von Cymbella lanceolata. Archiv Protistenk. 58:465–507.

————. 1927b. Somatische Teilung, Reduktionsteilung, Copulation und Parthenogenese bei Cocconeis placentula. Archiv Protistenk. 59:506–549.

————. 1928. Copulation und Geschlechtsverteilung bei einer Nitzschia-Art. Archiv Protistenk. 61:419–442.

————. 1952. Oogamie, Mitose, Meiose und metagame Teilung bei der zentrischen Diatomee Clyclotella. Österr. Bot. Zeitschr. 99:506–520.

GREGORY, BERYL D. 1934. On the life-history of Gymnogongrus griffithsiae Mart. and Ahnfeltia plicata Fries. Jour. Linn. Soc. London Bot. 49:531–551.

HARTMANN, M. 1929. Untersuchungen über die Sexualität und Entwicklung von Algen. III. Über die Sexualität und den Generationswechsel von Chaetomorpha und Enteromorpha. Ber. Deutsch. Bot. Ges. 47:485–494.

HERTWIG, O. 1876. Beiträge zur Kenntniss der Bildung, Befruchtung und Theilung des thierischen Eies. Morph. Jahrb. 1:347–434.

IYENGAR, M. O. P., AND K. R. RAMANATHAN. 1940. On the reproduction of Anadyomene stellata (Wulf.) Ag. (Preliminary note.) Jour. Indian Bot. Soc. 19:175–176.

———— AND ————. 1941. On the life-history and cytology of Microdictyon tenuius (Ag.) Decsne. (Preliminary note.) Jour. Indian Bot. Soc. 20:157–159.

———— AND R. SUBRAHMANYAN. 1942. On reduction division and auxospore-formation in Cyclotella meneghiniana Kütz. (Preliminary note.) Jour. Indian Bot. Soc. 21:231–237.

———— AND ————. 1944. On reduction division and auxospore-formation in Cyclotella meneghiniana Kütz. Jour. Indian Bot. Soc. 23:125–152.

JORDE, INGERID. 1933. Untersuchungen über den Lebenszyklus von Urospora Aresch. und Codiolum A. Braun. Nyt. Mag. Naturvidensk. 73:1–19.

JULLER, E. 1937. Der Generations- und Phasenwechsel bei Stigeoclonium subspinosum. Archiv Protistenk. 89:55–93.

KARSTEN, G. 1899. Die Diatomeen der Kieler Bucht. Wiss. Meeresuntersuch. Abt. Kiel, N.F., 4:17–205.

KARSTEN, G. 1912. Über die Reduktionsteilung bei der Auxosporenbildung von *Surirella saxonica.* Zeitschr. Bot. 4:417–426.

KLEBAHN, H. 1896. Beiträge zur Kenntniss der Auxosporenbildung. I. *Rhopalodia gibba* (Ehrenb.) O. Müller. Jahrb. Wiss. Bot. 29:595–654.

KLEBS, G. 1892. Flagellatenstudien. I, II. Zeitschr. Wiss. Zool. 55:265–445.

———. 1912. Über Flagellaten- und Algen-ähnliche Peridineen. Verhandl. Naturhist.-Medizin. Ver. Heidelberg. N.F., 11:369–451.

KNIGHT, MARGERY. 1923. Studies in the Ectocarpaceae. I. The life-history and cytology of *Pylaiella litoralis* Kjellm. Trans. Roy. Soc. Edinburgh 53:343–360.

———. 1929. Studies in the Ectocarpaceae. II. The life-history and cytology of *Ectocarpus siliculosus* Dillw. Trans. Roy. Soc. Edinburgh 56:307–332.

KOCH, W. 1950. Entwicklungsgeschichtliche und physiologische Untersuchungen an Laboratoriumskulturen der Rotalge *Trailliella intricata* Batters (Bonnemaisoniaceae). Archiv Mikrobiol. 14:635–660.

KOCH, W. J. 1951. A study of the motile cells of *Vaucheria.* Jour. Elisha Mitchell Sci. Soc. 67:123–131.

KORNMANN, P. 1938. Zur Entwicklungsgeschichte von *Derbesia* und *Halicystis.* Planta 28:464–470.

KYLIN, H. 1918. Studien über die Entwicklungsgeschichte der Phaeophyceen. Sv. Bot. Tidskr. 12:1–64.

———. 1923. Studien über die Entwicklungsgeschichte der Florideen. K. Sv. Vet.-Akad. Handl. 63(11):139 pp.

———. 1928. Entwicklungsgeschichtliche Florideen-studien. Lunds Univ. Årsskr. N.F., Avd. 2, 24(4):127 pp.

———. 1930. Über die Entwicklungsgeschichte der Florideen. Lunds Univ. Årsskr. N.F., Avd. 2, 26(6):104 pp.

———. 1932. Die Florideenordnung Gigartinales. Lunds Univ. Årsskr. N.F., Avd. 2, 28(8):88 pp.

LEVRING, T. 1941. Die Meeresalgen der Juan Fernández-Inseln, *in* C. SKOTTSBERG, The natural history of Juan Fernández and Easter Island. Vol. 2. Pp. 601–670.

LEWIS, I. F. 1912. Alternation of generations in certain Florideae. Bot. Gaz. 53:236–242.

LUTHER, A. 1899. Ueber *Chlorosaccus* eine neue Gattung der Süsswasseralgen, nebst einigen Bermerkungen zur Systematik verwandter Algen. Bihang K. Sv. Vet.-Akad. Handl. 24, Afd. 3, No. 13. 22 pp.

MEYER, K. 1929. Über die Auxosporenbildung bei *Gomphonema geminatum.* Archiv Protistenk. 66:421–435.

MURRAY, G. 1897. On the reproduction of some marine diatoms. Proc. Roy. Soc. Edinburgh 21:207–219.

OLTMANNS, F. 1904. Morphologie und Biologie der Algen. Bd 1. vi + 733 pp. Gustav Fischer. Jena.

———. 1922. Morphologie und Biologie der Algen, 2d ed. Bd 1. Chrysophyceae–Chlorophyceae. vi + 459 pp. Gustav Fischer. Jena.

PAPENFUSS, G. F. 1933. Note on the life-cycle of *Ectocarpus siliculosus* Dillw. Science 77:390–391.

PAPENFUSS, G. F. 1935. Alternation of generations in *Ectocarpus siliculosus*. Bot. Gaz. 96:421–446.

———. 1951. Problems in the classification of the marine algae. Sv. Bot. Tidskr. 45:4–11.

———. 1955. Classification of the algae. Century Progr. Nat. Sci. 1853–1953. Pp. 115–224. Calif. Acad. Sci. San Francisco.

PASCHER, A. 1912. Zur Gliederung der Heterokonten. (Kleine Beiträge zur Kenntnis unserer Mikroflora 3.) Hedwigia 53:6–22.

———. 1914. Über Flagellaten und Algen. Ber. Deutsch. Bot. Ges. 32:136–160.

———. 1921. Über die Übereinstimmung den Diatomeen, Heterokonten und Chrysomonaden. Ber. Deutsch. Bot. Ges. 39:236–248.

———. 1925. Heterokontae, *in* PASCHER, Die Süsswasser-Flora Deutschlands, Österreichs und der Schweiz. Heft II. iv + 118 pp. Gustav Fischer, Jena.

———. 1932. Über die Verbreitung endogener bzw. endoplasmatisch gebildeter Sporen bei den Algen. Beih. Bot. Centralbl. 49:293–308.

———. 1937–1939. Heterokonten, *in* RABENHORST'S Kryptogamen-Flora von Deutschland, Österreich und der Schweiz. 2d ed. Bd II (issued by R. KOLKWITZ). x + ii + 1092 pp. Akademische Verlagsgesellschaft m.b.H. Leipzig.

PERSIDSKY, B. M. 1929. The development of the auxospores in the group of the Centricae (Bacillariaceae). 11 pp. Moscow. (Cited from the review by P. SCHMIDT in Zeitschr. Bot. 22:459–461, 1930.)

———. 1935. The sexual process in *Melosira varians*. Beih. Bot. Centralbl. 53(A): 122–132.

PRINGSHEIM, N. 1860. Beiträge zur Morphologie und Systematik der Algen. III. Die Coleochaeteen. Jahrb. Wiss. Bot. 2:1–38.

REINKE, J. 1877. Über das Wachsthum und die Fortpflanzung von *Zanardinia collaris* Crouan. (*Z. prototypus* Nardo.). Monatsber. K. Preuss. Akad. Wiss. Berlin 1876:565–578.

———. 1878. Entwicklungsgeschichtliche Untersuchungen über die Cutleriaceen des Golfs von Neapel. Nova Acta Ksl. Leop.-Carol. Deutsch. Akad. Naturforsch. 40(2):59–96.

ROSENVINGE, L. K. 1929. *Phyllophora brodiaei* and *Actinococcus subcutaneus*. K. Danske Vidensk. Selsk. Biol. Medd. 8(4):40 pp.

SAUVAGEAU, C. 1896. Observations relatives à la sexualité des Phéosporées. Jour. de Bot. 10:357–367, 388–398.

———. 1915. Sur la sexualité heterogamique d'une Laminaire (*Saccorhiza bulbosa*). C. R. Acad. Sci. [Paris] 161:796–799.

SCHECHNER-FRIES, MARGARETE. 1934. Der Phasenwechsel von *Valonia utricularis* (Roth) Ag. Öster. Bot. Zeitschr. 83:241–254.

SCHMITZ, C. J. F. 1879. Untersuchungen über die Zellkerne der Thallophyten. Sitzungsber. Niederrhein. Ges. Natur-u. Heilkunde Bonn 1878:345–376.

———. 1883. Untersuchungen über die Befruchtung der Florideen. Sitzungsber. K. Preuss. Akad. Wiss. Berlin 1883(1):215–258.

SCHULZE, K. L. 1939. Cytologische Untersuchungen an *Acetabularia mediterranea* und *Actetabularia wettsteinii*. Archiv Protistenk. 92:179–225.

SCHUSSNIG, B. 1930. Der Generations- und Phasenwechsel bei den Chlorophyceen. (Ein historicher Rückblick.) Öster. Bot. Zeitschr. 79:58–77.

————. 1932. Der Generations- und Phasenwechsel bei den Chlorophyceen III. Öster. Bot. Zeitschr. 81:296–298.

————. 1938. Der Kernphasenwechsel von *Valonia utricularis* (Roth) Ag. Planta 28:43–59.

————. 1939. Ein Beitrag zur Entwicklungsgeschichte von *Caulerpa prolifera*. Bot. Notiser 1939:75–96.

————. 1950. Die Gametogenese von *Codium decorticatum* (Woodw.) Howe. Sv. Bot. Tidskr. 44:55–71.

SEYBOLD, A., K. EGLE, AND W. HÜLSBRUCH. 1941. Chlorophyll- und Carotinoidbestimmungen von Süsswasseralgen. Bot. Archiv 42:239–253.

SINGH, R. N. 1945. Nuclear phases and alternation of generations in *Draparnaldiopsis indica* Bharadwaja. New Phytol. 44:118–129.

————. 1947. *Fritschiella tuberosa* Iyeng. Ann. Bot. N.S., 11:159–164.

STOSCH, H. A. 1951a. Entwicklungsgeschichtliche Untersuchungen an zentrischen Diatomeen. I. Die Auxosporenbildung von *Melosira varians*. Archiv Mikrobiol. 16:101–135.

————. 1951b. Zur Entwicklungsgeschichte zentrischer Meeresdiatomeen. Naturwiss. 38:191–192.

————. 1954. Die Oogamie von *Biddulphia mobiliensis* und die bisher bekannten Auxosporenbildungen bei den Centrales. Huit. Congrès Internat. Bot. Rapp. Comm. Sect. 17. Pp. 58–68.

STRAIN, H. H. 1948. Occurrence and properties of chloroplast pigments. Carnegie Inst. Wash. Year Book 47:97–100.

————. 1951. The pigments of algae, *in* G. M. SMITH (Ed.), Manual of phycology. . . . Pp. 243–262. Chronica Botanica Co. Waltham, Mass.

STRASBURGER, E. 1897. Kernteilung und Befruchtung bei *Fucus*. Jahrb. Wiss. Bot. 30:351–374.

STREHLOW, K. 1929. Über die Sexualität einiger Volvocales. Zeitschr. Bot. 21:625–692.

SUBRAHMANYAN, R. 1947. On somatic division, reduction division, auxospore-formation and sex-differentiation in *Navicula halophila* (Grun.) Cl. Iyengar Comm. Vol., Jour. Indian Bot. Soc. Pp. 239–266.

SVEDELIUS, N. 1915. Zytologisch-entwicklungsgeschichtliche Studien über *Scinaia furcellata* ein Beitrag zur Frage der Reduktionsteilung der nicht tetrasporenbildenden Florideen. Nova Acta Reg. Soc. Sc. Upsal. Ser. 4, 4(4):55 pp.

————. 1956. Are the haplobiontic Florideae to be considered reduced types? Sv. Bot. Tidskr. 50:1–24.

TSENG, C. K., AND T. J. CHANG. 1955. Studies on the life history of *Porphyra tenera* Kjellm. Scientia Sinica 4:375–398.

VLK, W. 1931. Über die Struktur der Heterokontengeisseln. Beih. Bot. Centralbl. 48:214–220.

————. 1938. Über den Bau der Geissel. Archiv Protistenk. 90:448–488.

WEISMANN, A. 1887. Ueber die Zahl der Richtungskörper und über ihre Bedeutung für die Vererbung. vii + 75 pp. Gustav Fischer. Jena.

WILLIAMS, MAY M. 1925. Contributions to the cytology and phylogeny of the siphonaceous algae. I. The cytology of the gametangia of *Codium tomentosum* (Stack.). Proc. Linn. Soc. New South Wales 50(2):98–111.

YAMADA, Y. 1938. The species of *Liagora* from Japan. Sci. Papers Inst. Alg. Res. Hokkaido Imp. Univ. 2:1–34.

YAMANOUCHI, S. 1906a. The life history of *Polysiphonia violacea*. Bot. Gaz. 41: 425–433.

———. 1906b. The life history of *Polysiphonia violacea*. Bot. Gaz. 42:401–449.

———. 1909a. Mitosis in *Fucus*. Bot. Gaz. 47:173–197.

———. 1909b. Cytology of *Cutleria* and *Aglaozonia*. (A preliminary paper.) Bot. Gaz. 48:380–386.

———. 1911. On the life history of *Zanardinia collaris* Crouan. (A preliminary note.) Bot. Mag. Tokyo 25:9–11.

———. 1912. The life history of *Cutleria*. Bot. Gaz. 54:441–502.

———. 1913. The life history of *Zanardinia*. Bot. Gaz. 56:1–35.

ZINNECKER, EMMI. 1935. Reduktionsteilung, Kernphasenwechsel und Geschlechtsbestimmung bei *Bryopsis plumosa* (Huds.) Ag. Öster. Bot. Zeitschr. 84:53–72.

36

MYCOLOGY DURING THE PAST FIFTY YEARS

William H. Weston

The opportunity to participate in this Symposium is particularly gratifying to me because, by a happy coincidence, it was just fifty years ago this summer that a growing awareness of the fungi as objects of interest developed into a dawning appreciation of their significance as material for botanical investigation. In subsequent years this admiration for the potentialities of the fungi has increased through continuing association with the wide range of their activities, and the significant progress in the fascinating field of mycology during this period has amply justified and rewarded that youthful enthusiasm. The contribution of the fungi to Botany and, indeed, to Biology during the last fifty years has been impressive, and it is from the point of view of this notable and significant service that the progress and the outstanding achievements in Mycology will be considered here.

The reason for the large part played by fungi in contributing to a half century of advances in Botany lies in their striking suitability as material for investigation, their notable advantages as objects of research. Some of the qualities which contribute to this advantageous suitability are the facility with which they may be manipulated in pure culture under controlled conditions, the rapidity with which they will develop and complete their cycles, the readiness with which they can be maintained for long-term investigation. Together with these is the diversity of physiological activity which characterizes them, and in this respect, among the eighty to ninety thousand species which may be recognized according to taxonomic prejudice, there is shown such versatility that from the array of readily available forms the investigator can with certainty select those especially suited to the requirements of the problem he wishes to study. Furthermore, their relative simplicity permits reducing the problem to comparatively simple terms divested of the complications imposed by the more complex and elaborated entities among the higher forms of plant life. In construction, they range from single-celled forms and simple aggregates and associations through ascending hierarchies to the highest architectural types involving the branching filamentous pattern which is their predominant structural feature. This pattern has marked advantages since it avoids the surface-volume-ratio problem which presents serious difficulties in the sphere and in the massive solid, gives tremendous effective surface for physiological and other activities, and affords notable facility in its growth. It provides also for continued growth which may outrun senescence, ever advancing centrifugally yet in an active condition with intercommunication between all its parts, and it permits the weaving, massing, aggregating, and growing together of these filaments into a great diversity of massive forms. Yet the filaments may readily break up into segments and cells which may serve as reproductive entities, or by simple modification may lead to the more specialized development of such in positions favorable for production and distribution. And finally, fusion between filaments, parts of filaments, and specialized developments therefrom can achieve the bringing together of different types of cells and nuclei, accomplishing the essential feature of sexual reproduction, while other developments provide suitable conditions and structures for the corollary event of meiosis with efficient provision for the production of vast numbers of propagative entities to ensure the expression of all possible combinations which may have evolutionary value.

Among investigators with the requisite scientific imagination, perceptive discernment, and experimental ingenuity, there has been a growing appreciation of the suitability of fungi as material for investigation, and the happy combination of the ingenuity of the investigator and the suitable potentialities of the fungi for investigation has yielded a striking amount of enlightening results on problems and questions of fundamental significance.

Progress in mycological work contributive to Botany has been in general a steady, continuing, step-by-step progress, with, in some instances, the rapid advances, the notable leaps forward, which are the exciting episodes in any branch of human endeavor. Continuing progress of the cumulative type has proceeded on all fronts as a result of the interest, devotion, and enthusiasm of the many productive workers in all the diverse areas which mycology comprises. The more striking and spectacular contributions, derived from the steady accumulation of results as their precursors, have often been initiated and quickened into rapid advance by special instigating factors. In some instances it was serendipitous observation which triggered a chain of events, as in the case of Fleming's recognition of the possible significance of the zone of inhibition around a contaminating fungus setting in motion the train of events that led to the startling developments of the field of antibiotics. In other instances, the advances were in response to the imperative challenge of demanding necessity, as in the case of the response of the research and development groups of the Quartermaster Corps and other agencies to the challenge of the losses and problems brought up by tropical deterioration. In still other instances the impetus was given by the effectiveness of new tools which could be applied to investigation, as, for example, the use of radiation in inducing mutations and other significant responses on the part of fungi or the use of materials tagged with radioactive materials such as C^{14} as a key to unlock some hitherto baffling phases of metabolism. Also, the application of microdissection apparatus of increasing precision to ever more delicate research procedures, or the use of the "smear and squash" cytological techniques and of phase microscopy for the effective interpretation of nuclear and other minute features led to notable advances, while electron microscopy applied to intricate submicroscopic structure in the fungi as in other groups revealed features hitherto unsuspected and of great significance. Similarly, the application of time-lapse motion-picture photography to the timing and careful study of developmental sequences of fundamental importance has instigated significant advances.

The progress has been so impressive and the quality and quantity of the significant results so notable that in the present survey of the advances and the outstanding achievements with which Mycology has contributed to Botany during the past half century, the problem is one of selecting the examples most fittingly representative, most justly evaluative, and most suitable for presentation here within the limits of time imposed by the program. Hence, in the following examples, if there is neglect of the areas you feel are more significant, attribute this to the limitations in time inherent in the program and the limitations in discrimination inherent in the speaker.

As examples of the steady progress shown by Mycology in its long-established areas, the following are representative. Taxonomy has made helpful progress, not only through the employment of the long-established means such as structural and reproductive features, but also through the utilization of more recent approaches such as the chromosome numbers in the wild species and crosses of *Allomyces*, the nuclear behavior in certain Mucorales and other Phycomycetes, the nature and activity of the flagellate motile apparatus in certain of the water molds, or the biochemical differences manifesting themselves in the pathogenicity of certain rusts of grain, in the metabolism of certain molds, and in the composition of the wall in certain aquatic fungi. The structure, development, and relationships of groups found in certain habitats previously only meagerly explored have been greatly extended and clarified by the work of Von Minden, Coker, Couch, Sparrow, Karling, and others on the submersed Phycomycetes; of Ingold, Ranzoni, and others on the Imperfect Fungi of fresh-water habitats, as well as by the work of Petersen, Sutherland, Linder, Barghoorn, Sparrow, and others on the unexpectedly diverse and fascinating fungus flora of the sea. Of ecological significance has been the extension in our understanding of the relation of the activities of the insect host to the positional location and to the host range of the Laboulbenialean parasites upon them, as shown by Benjamin, while the diverse and effective mechanisms of spore discharge in various fungi have been clarified by the work of Ingold and others and the fascinating chronicle of the diversity and efficiency of the adroit devices for the capture and utilization of amoebae, rhizopods, rotifers, and nematodes by certain molds in the soil has been recorded in detail by Drechsler.

Toward better understanding of the mechanisms operative in the fundamental activities of organisms, the utilization of fungi as experimental material has contributed significant and stimulating advances. In the category of response to environmental conditions, the investigation of reaction to light of different intensities and different wave lengths has found in fungi the advantages of comparable development in darkness and in light, with also a favorable lack of any of the complications involved in photosynthesis in green plants. As an example, *Phycomyces* has become for such investigation the classic material with which the work of Castle and others has yielded significant evidence as to the location of the zones of sensitivity, the range and limits of response, and the nature and extent of the resulting growth. Also in the problems involved in survival and in continuation of activity under severe and extreme conditions, the investigation of the molds concerned in the black spotting of cold stored meats, or active in retting of guayule, or in the heating of damp hay at thermophilic levels, or in the spoiling of canned fruits or other foodstuffs preserved in concentrated media of high osmotic tension has yielded results of considerable interest. In addition, the fungi have come to play an increasingly important part in the experimental exploration of the biochemical pathways of significant physiological mechanisms, cycles, and processes. They have been found useful as specialized and effective agents for the production of various essential enzymes, of important substances such as riboflavin, of rare organic acids, and of unusual pigments. They have rendered valuable services as prolific sources of vitamins of the B_{12} complex, as sensitive instruments for bioassay and for the detection of minute quantities of substances essential for growth. In all these capacities, the fungi have played an important part in the advances which have been made. Furthermore, they have rendered an important service as the agents for the exploration of the mechanism of degradation of complex organic substances such as cellulose, lignin, chitin, and keratin. The utilization of especially suitable and advantageous fungi in these fundamental lines of investigation has resulted in a notable extension of our knowledge of such features as the biochemical pathways by which degradation is accomplished, the sequence of the breakdown products which result, and the vulnerability of the structural linkages in these complex molecules. In contrast to the vulnerability of these natural substances is the relative invulnerability to fungus attack of man-made fibers of comparable complexity, such as nylon, dacron, and orlon. Considering the millions of years these natural substances have been available as substrata for the degrading activities of thousands of diverse and physiologically potent fungi, the probablility seems strong that in time some fungi will achieve the active degradation of man-made materials seemingly invulnerable at present.

Together with the general progress briefly and cursorily indicated above, some of the advances in Mycology have been more striking and spectacular in their contribution to various significant and productive areas of Biology. Of the many instances of such contributive service, the time available here may permit consideration of four examples especially representative and noteworthy. The first example is the contribution of Mycology to the field of morphogenesis, of organization, and the controls which govern size and form and development in organisms. In this area, during the early part of this fifty-year period, the use of zoological material dominated the field, and the botanists whose work was almost exclusively confined to higher plants, although contributing some highly significant results, were handicapped because the significant and critical early stages of development were enclosed within the complicated structure of the parent plant rather than freely accessible as in the egg, or blastula, or gastrula of certain animals. The situation shifted with dramatic suddenness, however, about twenty-five years ago, when K. B. Raper, stimulated by the potentialities implicit in the pioneer work of Olive and Harper and equipped with his increasingly expert knowledge of the simpler aggregating types of slime molds, began his illuminating studies of these especially advantageous organisms. Their advantages are inherent in the regular sequence of well-defined stages in the life cycle, as follows: from the germination of the spores and the feeding and multiplication of the amoeba-like swarmers to which they give rise, onward through the assembling of these in definite centers of aggregation with, in the case of some, a migration of the resulting pseudoplasmodium, to finally the ultimate phase of culmination, in which the originally totipotent swarmers differentiate into stalk cells and spores in the construction of a simple but effective fructification. The whole life cycle is thus a dedication to the objective of producing the numerous hardy spores in a position favorable for efficient distribution. Intensive and ingenious investigations, chiefly by K. B. Raper and John T. Bonner, have contributed materially toward our understanding of fundamental aspects of organization and the control of development in this cycle and have given these simple organisms a place of prominence in morphogenetic investigation. Also, they have channeled renewed research interest toward the myxobacteria and myxogastralean slime molds which achieve comparable fruiting bodies by constructional procedures different enough to promise still further information on the morphogenetic mechanisms involved.

As a second example, the contribution of Mycology to a broader understanding of some of the fundamental features of sex and sexuality may be considered. The pioneer work of Blakeslee fifty years ago gave recognition to the existence of two distinct and separate sexes in unisexual individuals of certain members of the bread-mold group. His discovery of this situation, unexpected but readily understandable and acceptable to human beings of similar pattern, had its stimulating impact on Botany and Biology. The realization of the potentialities of such simple, easily manipulatable material instigated a rapid extension of similar investigations. Continued studies by Blakeslee and his associates in this country and similar research in Europe by such workers as Burgeff and his associates yielded additional and significant results, but also brought out the fact that the suitability of this material was severely handicapped by the drawback of the multinucleate condition of the sporangial spores and of the zygospores. Therefore, while the impetus continued, the trend of investigation shifted to other groups as more suitable material.

In the case of other Phycomycetes, but of the biflagellate aquatic line, the pioneer work of Couch, followed later by the work of Bishop, showed that the separate-sexed condition occurred also in some members of this series, and the work of J. R. Raper revealed that this was in reality a condition of relative sexuality with a range showing pure male and pure female strains as the extremes between which occurred intermediate forms of mixed sexuality, with one sex predominantly expressed in various degrees, the other suppressed and latent but capable of expression in appropriate matings. Also, continued work by J. R. Raper convincingly demonstrated that here the four major steps in the sexual process were under the control of distinct, successively produced hormones, the first recognition of such a situation in any of the lower plants. Similarly, in the uni-flagellate series of the aquatic Phycomycetes, the pioneer work of Kniep, and especially the later and still continuing work of Emerson, together with some additional contributions by later investigators such as Harder, Sorgel, and others, established the now classic, full-cycle, diplobiontic alternation of generations in *Allomyces* and gave fitting prominence to this genus and related forms as highly favorable material for the investigation of such significant features as the variant life cycles, the parthenogenetic development of unfertilized female gametes, and the significant variations in sex expression.

In the case of the Ascomycetes, a similar sequence of investigations finally settled the long-continued controversy between Harper's contention that double fertilization occurred and Clausen's that a single fertilization took place, the evidence being preponderantly in favor of the latter interpretation. In this group also, the heterothallic, separate-sexed condition has been found to be a frequent occurrence, and the advantageous arrangement of the eight spores in the ascus has facilitated establishing in which of the three successive nuclear divisions the segregation of sex potentialities occurs, while in other forms has been reported the interesting condition of hermaphroditism simulating heterothallism through involving self-sterility and cross-fertility to compatible opposites.

In the case of the Basidiomycetes, a long and fruitful sequence of investigations from the pioneer work of Buller, Bensaude, Kniep, Vandendries, and others, to the more recent investigations of J. R. Raper and his associates, has revealed the interesting intricacies of the distinctive sexual reproduction in this group, especially the notable migration of nuclei to achieve an extension of diploidization, the frequency of occurrence of tetrapolar sexuality, and the significant complications of heterokaryosis. Even the Fungi Imperfecti, whose very status and existence as a classificational group implies the lack of sexual reproduction, have been revealed by the work of Pontecorvo, of Roper, and of K. B. Raper to possess the complicated mechanisms of heterokaryosis as a substitute for sex.

In general the fungi, with potentialities little suspected previously, have been found during the past fifty years to be highly advantageous material for the study of many significant aspects involved in the problems of sex and have revealed complexities of behavior beside which the human patterns reported by Kinsey, Havelock Ellis, Krafft-Ebing, Malinowski, and others show a limited and naïve simplicity.

The third example is inherent in the marked success with which the exploitation of mycological material has contributed to rapid and significant advances in Genetics. In the early years of this half century, there was in this field but little work with fungi. In the early 1920s, however, the pioneer work of B. O. Dodge discovered *Neurospora,* the ascomycetous perfect phase of the red bread molds, worked out the development and reproduction of the eight- and four-spored species of this genus and pointed out their exciting potentialities for genetic investigation. The geneticists, always ready to explore and to exploit the possibilities of advantageous material, took up the study of this easily manipulated mold and notable contributions such as those of Beadle and his associates, showed that in addition to the rapid life cycle, the ease of manipulation, the precision of the sequence of successive nuclear divisions which led to the definite positional alignment of the spores in the ascus, there were the additional advantageous features of hereditable and readily assayed biochemical differences in the resulting strains. Thus, in the case of this fungus, there was achieved a crossing over from Mycology to Genetics and a change in its position from a recessive obscurity to a dominant prominence. In a field which had been dominated by animals, by flitting fruit flies, and hovering *Habrobrachon,* redolent with rats, squeaking with mice, and twittering with guinea pigs, a field only sparsely garnished here and there with plant material, such as primroses or corn, this colorful and catalytic mold assumed a place of prominence. As a natural extension from this stimulus, interest was aroused in other fungi with features advantageous for such investigation and work such as that of Edgerton and his students on *Glomerella,* of Lindegren on yeasts, of Silver-Dowding and others on *Gelasinospora,* and of Keitt and his associates on *Venturia* showed clearly that the fungi were richly rewarding material for productive and significant work in the field of Genetics. So notable has been the progress that at the present time most research groups and laboratories feel they are not adequately equipped for competitive productivity unless an impressive array of mycological material is included in their extensive armament.

As a final example it is noteworthy that the advances in Mycology have served not only as the instigation, but even as the basic construction, for the development, in the long-established and ever-extending field of Medicine, of the new and important area of Medical Mycology. During this period, the field of medical mycology, at first regarded with some reserve, has gained acceptance as a reputable and significant area of medicine. This has been reflected in an increasing respect for mycologists through the growing realization that even though Ph.D.'s rather than M.D.'s, mycologists could render valuable service through their intimate knowledge of the nature and activities of the causal fungi. From the stimulating participation in this more effective working relationship has come significant productivity. Following the epoch-making volumes of the great pioneer Sabouraud and the early work of Castellani, Brumpt, and others in Europe, there have appeared in this country such medically and mycologically helpful books as those by Lewis and Hopper, by Conant and his associates, by Schwartz and others, together with books with more specialized utility such as the encyclopedic compendium of C. W. Dodge, the small but helpful identification handbook of Hazen and Reed, and the useful volume assembled under the editorship of Nickerson, with its discussion of the physiological and biological aspects of the causal fungi by contributing specialists. Similarly, in Europe the literature has been strengthened by contributions of Langeron and others in France, of Nannizzi and of Redaelli and Ciferri and their associates in Italy.

In this area then, there has been steady progress reflected in a notable increase in the effective working literature, both in the textbooks and working manuals in the clinical, epidemiological, and other aspects of medical mycology as such and in the more specialized literature of a more strictly mycological nature and fundamental character on the identity, relationship, behavior, physiology, and biochemistry of the fungi concerned. There has developed also an increasing awareness on the part of mycologists of pertinent publications in the more strictly medical journals and on the part of medical men of the valuable papers appearing in the more technical journals of Mycology.

In particular, there have been numerous notable advances, some of which, because of their especial interest and importance, may merit mention here as representative examples. Notably, there has been a growing understanding of the fundamental biochemical mechanisms involved in the lack of acquired immunity common in the case of most human diseases of fungus origin, with growing evidence as to the fundamental mechanisms involved in the notable exceptions which show acquired immunity, such as *Histoplasma* and *Coccidioides,* the two most striking examples subjected to study by Salvin and others. Progress has been made also on the subtle and previously obscure conditions which, in the case of most of the deep-seated mycoses, control the expression of two dimorphic types of growth, the one developing in the human tissue being decidedly different from that developing in culture even on media designed to simulate as closely as possible the characteristics of the tissue invaded. Encouraging also has been the extension and improvement of the methods of treatment of the mycoses. There has been advance in the application of more effective, newly developed chemical compounds beyond the standard medicaments of even a decade ago, while of the antibiotics, formerly thought of chiefly in relation to diseases of bacterial origin, some have been found to have notable potentialities against diseases of fungus origin as well.

One of the most striking advances has been in the area of epidemiology, where intensive investigation has yielded valuable information concerning the sources and the natural reservoirs of infection of some of the more destructive fungus diseases of man. For example, in one of these cases, the sources of the *Sporotrichum* responsible for severe outbreaks of sporotrichosis among the native workers in the deep mines in Witwatersraand in South Africa, was traced by Weintroub and associates to the timber with which the mine tunnels were braced and shored, thus adding to the list of natural sources of infection of this serious pathogenic fungus already known to occur as a saprophyte in plant material and in the rich soil of gardens and greenhouses. In the case of *Coccidioides,* the fungus responsible for the tuberculosis-simulating "valley fever" and for the deadly systemic "coccidioidal granuloma," work pioneered by Emmons has revealed that the natural reservoirs of infection are the ground rodents native to the regions of the Southwest where these diseases are endemic and thence carried from the soil in dust to man. More recently, the work of Ajello and his associates, in the southern United States, has shown the potential sources of histoplasmosis to lie in the occurrence of *Histoplasma* in the dirt of chicken houses and chicken runs heavily enriched with fowl droppings as well as in the dust from the air of such regions, while Bridges and associates have shown the occurrence of this fungus in the sludge of the sewage-disposal plants in Ohio. Even more recently, in the mycological programs of these very meetings is the report by Morrow and associates of the occurrence in airborne dust in Texas of *Allescheria,* the fungus causing the disfiguring maduromycosis.

Corollary to the advances in our knowledge of the fungi as causes of disease in man has developed an increasing body of information on the spores of fungi in the air as the causative agents of the inhalant allergies included under the general heading of asthma and hayfever. Active in this investigation have been not only mycologists together with the sneeze, wheeze, and itch associates of the medical profession, but also various state boards of health and the research staffs of some of the larger companies in the pharmaceutical industry. From the early pioneer investigations showing that the heavy load of spores of smuts and rusts of cereals released into the air from the thrashing operation on these grains could cause allergic reactions on the part of some people, the work has extended to implicate a considerable number of fungi as responsible exciting agents and has brought out some interesting differences such as the generalized reaction to species of *Alternaria* and the strikingly specific response to species of *Cladosporium*. Also, these agents have been found to be active not only outdoors but also inside the home, where the sources of the excitant spores have been traced in some cases to the filling of mattresses and pillows and in others to damp cellars.

Finally, the advances in Mycology during the past half century have in many cases found expression in the applied fields. In Plant Pathology, where the threat of some newly recognized and highly destructive fungus disease can always be counted upon to arise opportunely with stimulating effect, the menace of chestnut blight, of the Dutch elm disease, and more recently of the oak wilt have aroused renewed and eager activity and yielded helpful mycological information on the nature, origin, distribution, and activities of the fungi concerned. The stimulating contest between the development of new pathogenic strains by such fungi as the smuts and rusts and wilts on the one side and the plant breeder and plant pathologist on the other has yielded not only strains of crop plants, hardier and more resistant to these diseases, but also fundamental mycological information on the action of fungus parasites and the mechanisms of susceptibility, tolerance, and immunity. Continued employment of the indispensable services of spores and other fungus material as the means for testing the efficacy of fungicides and for determining the mechanisms by which they function has yielded helpful information as to the effect on fungus cells of chelating compounds, of cell toxicants, and of enzyme inhibitors.

Also, there have been advances contributive to progress in the field of mildew-proofing and the protection of textiles, of foodstuffs, of electronic apparatus, and of other important materials and equipment against the inroads of destructive fungi. In the research and development laboratories of the Quartermaster Corps and of other branches of the Armed Forces, as well as in similar laboratories of pertinent industries, there has been productive continuation of the investigations stimulated and instigated by the imperative urgency of the severe losses occasioned by the destructive activity of fungi under drastic tropical conditions during the last war. The original programs set up to determine what organisms were concerned in this deterioration, how they operated and how they might be controlled, have led to two lines of development. They have set in motion fundamental studies on the breakdown of cellulose and other raw materials, as already noted previously. Also, in their practical applications, they have led to more effective measures of prevention and control through the use of inert and immune materials where possible, through the increasingly effective application of more efficient and more persistent fungicides, and through alteration of the essential material to render it less vulnerable, as in the case of the acetate and butyrate modification of cellulose and the impregnation of vulnerable materials with invulnerable melamine and urea-formaldehyde resins.

In the case of antibiotics, a field essentially mycological, stemming from Fleming's perceptive recognition of this previously unappreciated aspect of fungus activity, the development of higher-yielding strains of *Penicillium*, the improvements in the production of penicillin and the extension of its applications, have marked notable advances. Also, although penicillin still retains its paramount importance, there have been other valued additions to the therapeutic armament of the medical profession, derived not only from the more typical and well-defined filamentous fungi, but also from the Actinomycetes of less sure taxonomic position. There also has been an interesting and promising extension from the application of antibiotics in the control of the diseases of human beings to their application in the control of diseases of crop plants. An additional application, of interesting potentialities but only recently developed and still in its experimental stages, has been the use of antibiotics in the feed of chickens, livestock, and other domestic animals.

Even from the foregoing brief, condensed, and abridged review, it is clear that this association of man and microbes, this exploitation by mycologists of the powers and potentialities of the fungi, this combination of the imagination, resourcefulness, and ingenuity of man with the diversity, versatility, and cooperation of the fungi has been a contributive and productive association yielding results of value to Botany and to Biology in the last half century.

The evidence extrapolates to the prospect and the probability that during the next fifty years this will continue and will develop into ever-extending areas in fruitful fields as yet unknown.

Yet it should be remembered that if man does not control the chaos he has contrived and fails to direct the course of his destiny; if man, through unheeding employment to destructive ends of the tremendous, superhuman powers he has discovered and developed, should finally destroy himself; then the fungi unhindered and unheeding will continue their many activities undisturbed and will remove the fragments of man's failure, the debris of his disaster and destruction, the remains and the wreckage of his recklessness, until they obliterate all traces of man himself.

The responsibility rests with us, not with the fungi, and whether we continue in our successful utilization of their potentialities or whether we fail and are ourselves removed by them depends on us.

37

PLANT TAXONOMY IN AN AGE OF EXPERIMENT

Lincoln Constance

Because taxonomy was, by some centuries, the first aspect of plant science to emerge as botany, there is a regrettable tendency to think of it as old, antiquated, and even obsolete. In the lexicon of our modern world, "new" is ordinarily equated with "good," "old" with "bad," or at least "obsolescent." Emphasis in botany has shifted strongly in the past half century toward the more novel, and particularly the experimental disciplines, with a marked recent emphasis on the biochemical.

The thesis I should like to develop during the few minutes at my disposal is that, while every branch of natural science must have a preliminary stage of sorting out and appropriately designating the objects with which it has to deal, the role of taxonomy has been by no means completed when this initial organizational impulse exhausts itself. In the plant and animal kingdoms even the pioneer stage of systematics is not within sight of successful completion. It is a moot question whether one group of men will succeed in recording the remaining unclassified organisms before other men succeed in inadvertently destroying them.

But even if this sorting and naming activity had been completed, the possible uses of a taxonomic system would be only in their infancy. Too often, perhaps, we visualize a taxonomic system as resembling a brick wall, each brick a taxon, and each taxon firmly cemented in its place. Of course, someone periodically pulls down and rebuilds the wall, employing some of the original bricks (properly cleaned) and adding new ones where appropriate. Other walls are so poorly fabricated that they may fall of their own weight even when no one touches them, and occasionally they fall on their builder.

Instead of visualizing a taxonomic system as a wall, we might better consider it to be something like a system of library shelves, with the bricks substituted for by pamphlet or file boxes. The pamphlet boxes would have obvious advantages over bricks because, first, they would be readily movable from any given position to a more logical and advantageous one. Secondly, each pamphlet box could be a repository for every scrap of information contributed by workers in diverse fields. Thirdly, the system could easily be made three-dimensional when this seemed desirable. Hence, by our analogy, we achieve an open, growing, vital taxonomic system in place of the closed, static, and dormant one that we are sometimes accused of cherishing. You will note that I have succeeded in substituting three "good" words for three "bad" ones!

If the concept of an open, information-thirsty taxonomy has any merit, let us note the different kinds of data it has been absorbing since 1906 and what effect these accretions have had upon the current status of plant taxonomy.

Obviously, the first increment of data in our file boxes, as well as the prime factor governing their initial arrangement in the bookcases, was contributed by morphology. Because structure was the first basis for any real classification, it is usually indissolubly linked with taxonomy in the minds even of taxonomists. Likewise, because it was highly developed before evolutionary theory came into the picture in any significant way, it is sometimes viewed, like taxonomy, as essentially descriptive, only semi-scientific, and even as exerting a drag on progress in systematics. The taxonomist, having no suitable substitute for laying out the warp and woof of his various arrangements, has perhaps been preoccupied with form, even to the extent of feeling that other criteria are non-essential, or at least of distinctly inferior merit. The fact that recorded observations on morphology have been sufficiently numerous and extensive to provide some systematic purview of this aspect has made it of unique importance to classifiers. My colleague, Professor Mason, has wisely noted (1950) that abundant, systematized, comparative data are essential in any field before such information can be employed satisfactorily for purposes of classification.

Comparative morphological evidence has been accumulating at least since the time of Theophrastus, the Herbalists made extensive contributions, and all systems with which I am familiar are primarily morphological in basic content. I should venture the guess, also, that they will continue to be for the foreseeable future. In his excellent monograph on the genus *Crepis* (1947) Babcock clearly indicated the dependence of the cytologist and geneticist upon morphological taxonomy for the organization and interpretation of their data. In recent decades, however, the central if not exclusive preoccupation with flower and fruit in classification has yielded to a growing recognition of the taxonomic importance of other organs and structures, as well.

The morphology accepted and employed for his classifications by the systematist, as you are aware, was *classical* morphology, with its emphasis on the existence of discrete fundamental organs and their presumably unalterable relationships. These once generally accepted canons have been under nearly continuous attack for several decades by students of ontogeny, physiology, paleobotany, and evolution, shaking the whole tenuous framework of systematics. If I read the record correctly, however, pre-evolutionary morphology has proved to be rather more durable and resilient than might have been anticipated and modification rather than abandonment of the bases of our laboriously contrived classifications seems to be called for. Telomic and cauline floral organs and stachysporic sporangia appear to be concepts of doubtful validity, at least in the angiosperms, and are certainly of less use to us than the more conservative interpretation of floral structures as basically foliar. The frequent association of primitively simple secondary xylem with sporophyll-like carpels and sporophyll-like stamens appears to have been firmly established.

We might regard as special branches of morphology other sources which have furnished data of taxonomic utility, notably descriptive anatomy, embryology, and cytology and paleobotany.

Anatomy, the first of these in time, beginning with the work of Malpighi and Grew in the 17th Century, advanced rapidly and had assembled a well-organized body of systematic data by the end of the 19th Century. The uses of systematic anatomy by such workers as Radkofer and Van Tieghem in the past century are too well known and appreciated to require emphasis. The authors of *Die Pflanzenfamilien* were perhaps the first to apply anatomical characteristics to over-all classification on the grand scale. In this country, the contributions of Jeffrey and his distinguished students—Bailey, Eames, and Sinnott—and *their* students, and their *students'* students, to systematic anatomy are of conspicuous importance. It would perhaps not be an exaggeration to state that the pattern has been laid for an over-all classification of vascular plants on morphological-anatomical grounds that may ultimately replace all prior ones. At the same time we should not forget that even the rich treasuries of anatomical information, represented by the masterly compilations of Solereder and Metcalfe and Chalk, deal mostly with selected plant structures and that a very large number of plants are not represented either in whole or in part.

The findings of Irving Bailey and his associates with regard to the development, form, and sequence of vessels and vessel types in vascular plants have shed a clear, cold light on the relationships of gymnosperms with angiosperms and of monocotyledons with dicotyledons. The analysis of floral vascularization by Eames and his students has done much to unravel the trends and permutations of floral evolution and to enable us to discriminate between primitively simple and secondarily simplified modes of organization. By application of such information, the so-called "Amentiferae" have been neatly deprived at once of both their supposed unity and the basal position among dicotyledons accorded them by Engler, Rendle, and Wettstein. Cheadle's application of similar criteria to monocotyledons indicates the necessity of major alterations of all proposed systematizations of this group and threatens to destroy the generally accepted Alismataceae-Ranunculaceae bond with dicotyledons. These are typical of the corrective discipline comparative anatomy can apply to phylogenetic taxonomy.

The rise of developmental and experimental morphology promises to tell us many new and interesting things, and perhaps the solution to the age-old problems of growth, differentiation, and maturation. The welcome burgeoning of this experimental field should not, however, have the effect of labeling as static and antiquated the systematic analysis and description of mature tissues. Before we can determine how all mature tissues develop so marvelously and intricately from the fertilized egg, we must know what and where these adult tissues are. Although as a good biologist he has an intense interest in the outcome of developmental approaches, the taxonomist must build his classifications on systematically assembled information. Another of my biological colleagues, this one not a botanist, recently remarked that there are probably two kinds of biologists: those who are interested primarily in the origin of life, and those who are interested in its various manifestations. Neither he nor I were able to see why one group should claim superiority over the other, nor deny importance to its scientific efforts.

Comparative embryology, which has served systematic zoology so well, has just come into its own in botany and is in its infancy of application to problems of botanical classification. By embryology I mean to indicate all the gametophytic stages of vascular plants, including especially nature and mode of development of microspores and megaspores and the embryonic and early juvenile stages of the sporophyte. As you know, there has been an impressive growth in analytical and comparative data on the embryo sac by Schnarf, Maheshwari, Fagerlind, and Battaglia, among others. The recent books of Johansen (1950) and Maheshwari (1950) indicate the marked progress in this field. These data have been utilized to attempt clarification of relationships between angiosperms and certain groups of gymnosperms, although with somewhat conflicting conclusions. Certain families and genera have been tested for degree of affinity on embryo-sac characteristics, with interesting results. But numerous families remain untouched, and the distribution of embryo-sac types does not yet present a clearly phylogenetic picture. The study of microspores has expanded rapidly, stimulated by the employment of microfossils as a tool for dating in various aspects of science and by recognition that knowledge of pollens is important medically. Systematic ordering of information from this area, as illustrated by the publications of Wodehouse and Erdtman, to name only two, promises much of utility for plant taxonomy. Already, the interrelations of gymnosperms and the two great classes of angiosperms have been notably clarified by this means.

Descriptive cytology is a child largely of the 20th Century and has enjoyed a vigorous infancy and adolescence. Although chromosome number and morphology have not proven to be the general panacea that some of their early sponsors predicted, they have provided exceedingly useful classificatory data, and the inclusion of information on karyotype has become a common-place in taxonomic papers. Chromosome number has been particularly help-ful in flagging anomalous situations and pointing up problems of polyploidy, supernumerary chromosomes, and the like. Intensive investigation of such cases by experimental means has not infrequently revealed a good deal about the nature of natural populations and the origin and establishment of new taxa. As the body of cytological information grows—witness the compendia of Tischler (1950), Delay (1951), and Darlington (1945, 1955)—the more readily can it be applied to taxonomic ends. The taxonomist should always be aware, however, that such cytological information may be worthless or even misleading when it is not properly documented by voucher specimens. The comparative study of such cell types as trichomes, stomatal members, and sclereids also holds considerable promise.

It has always been assumed that if we had before us the whole fossil record of vascular plants, we should be able to reconstruct a complete phylogeny of their living descendants. Lam, for instance, says dogmatically that phylogeny *is* paleobotany and all else is at best pseudo-phylogeny. Almost from the time it was decided that fossil impressions were not works of the Devil to delude True Believers, but had some natural reference to previous life on the Earth, paleobotany has been coloring our ideas about relationships of organisms and contributing to our essays at phylogenetic reconstruction. The main difficulty is always that the material preserved is so sparse, so fragmentary, and so lack-ing in critically diagnostic characters that much of it is subject to radically divergent interpretations. Fossils often seem to be lacking just where we could use them most profitably to show the branching of phyletic lines and to link together now discrete and anomalous groups. It is also possible, of course, that we are frequently searching for certain kinds of things that never existed either on land or sea! The application of an ecological approach to paleobotany, despite its dangerous assumption of long-term genetical and physiological stability, has served as a wholesome corrective to a purely gross morphological approach to fossil identification. Recent advances in the study of fossil microspores, epidermis, and wood suggest that it is far too early to conclude that all the evidence is now in and that the past is a permanently closed book.

If there is a measure of justification in the complaint of some workers that it is basically unsound to interpret the structures of living and extinct lower vascular plants in terms of those of living angiosperms, it would seem equally tenuous to try to derive angiosperm features solely from those of Devonian cryptogams—the origin of the magical "telome." A recent article in the journal *Evolution* (LeClercq, 1956) points to the existence of a body of Silurian and Cambrian vascular plants that were by no means psilophytalean, and yet greatly antedate *Rhynia* and *Hornea* and *Asteroxylon,* which thereby forfeit their unique basal position. Systematic paleobotany would appear to set some limits to our phylogenetic thinking, but we should be wary in over-rating what has been found as well as in overanticipating what may ultimately be discovered. Meanwhile, I see no reason why we should not go as far as possible with other kinds of information. The true essence of Science is the continuous re-examination and testing of tentative conclusions. Paleobotanical investigation should continue to provide us with important data for such re-evaluation.

No phase of biological advance has so drastically affected taxonomy in the past half century as genetics and those cytological matters associated with inheritance. I approach this portion of my résumé with considerable trepidation. The body of available information is tremendous, its applications to systematics are currently filling and overflowing books and journals, and there has grown up a mass of neo-orthodox doctrine which one dares to question at his peril. Moreover, I cannot claim any mastery of the subject—yet I wish to demonstrate that no taxonomist can afford to ignore it.

The application of genetical information to taxonomy is sometimes based upon the assumption that breeding behavior can establish the Truth about relationships of organisms and that evidence gained in this way is entitled to supersede all other indications of affinity. In the view of many, existence of genetical compatibility establishes close phylogenetical relationship; incompatibility precludes it. Species and subordinate taxa can be defined on the basis of fertility, sterility, and associated cytological behavior. Morphological-anatomical criteria, not being "experimental," are of lesser moment and cannot be allowed to gainsay genetical truth. A genetical system of classification for at least the smaller taxonomic units can eventually be developed, with a fine disregard of all other considerations, that will be "true." Evidence from experimental crossing can at once tell us what has happened and what is going to happen, and all else is irrelevant or permitted only probationary status until it can be tested cytogenetically. Moreover, genetical evidence can explain origins, migrations, and distributions and has already demonstrated the essential correctness of the Wegnerian Hypothesis of wandering continents. In view of these impressive attainments of our experimental colleagues, it is small wonder that practitioners of descriptive botany are sometimes regarded as hopelessly antiquated.

Probably very few individuals would support all the propositions I have just mentioned, but all have been advanced in one form or another in recent decades. One will recognize in them, I think, the aura of enthusiasm and missionary zeal which often accompanies new advances in any line of thought or endeavor. We should not allow irritation at overstatement and intolerance to blind us to the very real contributions that genetics and cytogenetics have made to taxonomy. We have gained some knowledge of the methods by which characters are combined, separated, and recombined in nature and how new types of individuals and populations may arise. Artificial production of polyploids has given us clues as to the nature and origin of polyploid systems in nature, although their present genetical behavior may be very different from what we must assume it once to have been. We can no longer escape the conclusion that hybridization is rife under at least semi-natural conditions and that it must be reckoned with seriously by the systematist. At the lower taxonomic levels we can obtain invaluable evidence from genetics and cytology to correct, supplement, or even replace our tentative conclusions from other kinds of observation.

It remains that genetical evidence is one more kind of evidence, that it has no unique monopoly on Truth, and that a system of classification built on genetical data alone is artificial and special and lacks general utility. Nevertheless, the taxonomist cannot afford to omit genetical tools and viewpoints from his professional equipment.

Turesson's neglected term "genecology" seems to me the preferable one to designate the observation and comparison of the behavior of organisms of known cytogenetical constitution under identical or contrasted environments. Its basic accomplishments have been to show that physiological capacity is inherited just like other features of the individual, and thus to provide another set of characters for taxonomic evaluation. We have gained a fascinating new vista of the biological complexity and geobotanical fractioning of natural populations under field conditions. I am inclined to think, however, that the attempt to equate genecological categories with taxonomic ones, or to substitute the former for the latter, was overhasty and ill-advised. Each has validity within its own frame of reference and very little outside it. The taxonomic system is best employed as a repository for the totality of all kinds of evidence and should recognize no favored kinds of truth. Certainly, our appreciation of the intricacies of relationship among individuals of a population has been wonderfully enhanced by the endeavors of Turesson and Clausen, Keck, and Hiesey and their disciples, and much remains to be done.

The application of biochemical data to the taxonomy of vascular plants is perhaps the next great advance to be anticipated. Very little of unquestionable merit and applicability has been done thus far; much may lie ahead. Most of us speak hopefully but vaguely of serum diagnosis, but few seem to have explored the abundant German literature on the subject to assure themselves of the scientific objectivity of its embattled "schools." It is gratifying to note that this field has recently shown signs of rejuvenation along sounder lines. Botanists have long been aware of the presence of characteristic colors, odors, tastes, essential oils, latex, alkaloids, glandular exudations, and the like, in setting up empirical relationships. It is only logical to assume that these features have an ascertainable and classifiable biochemical basis. Attempts to establish classification on such features in higher plants have been few and can be as yet of little more than prophetic interest. We may have to await the establishment of adequate classifications of biochemical substances and processes before we can hope to utilize them freely in systematic botany, but we should not forget their great potentialities.

In terms of formal schematization, the device by which taxonomists attempt to record their over-all advances and mark the ground gained, the past fifty years have seen the complete recasting of the organization of the vascular cryptogams, with the breaking up of the "Pteridophyta" into smaller and more unified groupings on the basis of paleobotanical, morphological, anatomical, and embryological evidence. The gymnosperms have been and are being drastically re-evaluated and reorganized as their extinct members have come under intensive scrutiny, their embryology has been re-examined, and they have been studied extensively in the field, by such workers as Buchholz, Sahni, and Florin.

Proposed classifications of angiosperms, however, have been scarcely revolutionary during this period. Rendle, Wettstein, Janchen, Pulle, Skottsberg, and Lam have pursued elaboration and modification, on various grounds, of the basic Englerian sequence. Bessey, in 1915, re-enunciated his earlier-proposed arrangement along Candollean-Bentham and Hooker lines; Hallier and Lotsy and Gunderson, to name a few, have expressed varying but rather similar ideas. Hutchinson has produced a new and ostensibly phylogenetic classification after the Bentham and Hooker model, but notable for the subdivision of dicotyledons into woody versus herbaceous phyla, the large number of small orders, and a complete and useful reorganization of monocotyledons. Hayata, for one, has framed an arrangement for flowering plants that is founded on abandonment of the hope that there is any one phylogenetic solution to the mysteries of angiosperm evolution. Others have scoffed at the ideal of a phylogenetic classification, in favor of some kind of utilitarian device. It seems clear that no system constructed in the past half century has fully capitalized on the accumulations of data referred to above. It is encouraging to note that papers given at these meetings are attempting to remedy this lack. However, there seems to be rather general agreement that sufficient evidence to formulate a really new, thoroughgoing, and generally satisfactory phylogenetic arrangement of flowering plants is not yet available.

In summary, systematic botany is healthy but in a state of profound transition. Significant new textbooks, those of Lawrence (1951, 1955) and Core (1955), are attempting to broaden the subject of plant taxonomy at the undergraduate level and to show that it can be more than concern with a limited local flora, the mechanics of nomenclature, and dry and formal terminology. The past fifty years have seen substantial accretions of data of taxonomic significance from all the older sources of such evidence and from quite new sources. We may confidently expect that information will continue to flow in at an ever-increasing tempo, and we should be prepared to receive and apply it wisely toward the furtherance of our goals. Perhaps our chief problem is to make ourselves and our students fully aware of the potential complexity and richness of our subject and to train ourselves and them to master the essential tools to pursue it most productively.

Plant taxonomy has not outlived its usefulness: it is just getting under way on an attractively infinite task.

LITERATURE CITED

BABCOCK, E. B. 1947. The genus *Crepis*. Univ. California Publ. Bot. 21:1–197; 22:1–1030.

CONSTANCE, L. 1951. The versatile taxonomist. Brittonia 7:225–231.

———. 1953. The role of plant ecology in biosystematics. Ecology 34:642–649.

———. 1955. The systematics of the angiosperms. A century of progress in the natural sciences, 1853–1953. Pp. 405–483. California Academy of Sciences. San Francisco.

CORE, E. L. 1955. Plant taxonomy. xiv + 459 pp. Prentice-Hall. Englewood Cliffs, N.J.

DARLINGTON, C. D., AND E. K. JANAKI AMMAL. 1945. Chromosome atlas of cultivated plants. 397 pp. Allen & Unwin. London.

——— AND A. P. WYLIE. 1955. Chromosome atlas of flowering plants. xix + 519 pp. Allen & Unwin. London.

DELAY, CÉCILE. 1951. Nombres chromosomiques chez les phanérogames. Rev. Cytol. et Biol. Végét. Paris 12:1–368.

JOHANSEN, D. A. 1950. Plant embryology: embryogeny of the Spermatophyta. xvi + 305 pp. Chronica Botanica Co. Waltham, Mass.

LAWRENCE, G. H. M. 1951. Taxonomy of vascular plants. xii + 823 pp. Macmillan. New York.

———. 1955. An introduction to plant taxonomy. vii + 179 pp. Macmillan. New York.

LECLERCQ, S. 1956. Evolution of vascular plants in the Cambrian. Evolution 10: 109–114.

MAHESHWARI, P. 1950. An introduction to the embryology of the angiosperms. x + 453 pp. McGraw-Hill. New York.

MASON, H. L. 1950. Taxonomy, systematic botany, and biosystematics. Madroño 10:193–208.

TISCHLER, G. 1950. Die Chromosomenzahlen der Gefässpflanzen Mitteleuropas. 263 pp. W. Junk. 'S-Gravenhage.

38

FIFTY YEARS OF PALEOBOTANY
1906-1956

Theodor Just [1]

Although fossil plants have been known and recognized as such since the days of antiquity, their scientific study began less than 150 years ago. This comparatively short span of time can be divided into three roughly equal periods. The first of these was the formative period during which the classic works of Sternberg, Schlotheim, Brongniart, Witham, Corda, Unger, and others appeared. The second period may be called the period of exploration—at least as far as the United States is concerned—during which Dawson, Lesquereux, Newberry, Macbride, and Ward did their pioneer work. The third period coincides approximately with the life of the Botanical Society of America. The outstanding events in paleobotany in 1906 were the publication of the first volume of *American Fossil Cycads* by Wieland and the establishment by the Federal Government of the Petrified Forest National Monument in Arizona. A few years before, at the turn of the century, the seed ferns were recognized as such and described in great detail. Since then paleobotanical research has greatly expanded in scope and now encompasses the whole world, ranging from studies on permafrost in arctic North America to the petrified forests of Patagonia, and from the coal fields of Korea to the Karroo beds of South Africa, over the whole plant kingdom and all fossiliferous horizons of the geological column. New or improved techniques (providing 50–100 serial sections in place of a single thin section and enabling us to see the other side of the fence) and new or revitalized interest in paleobotany in many countries outside of Europe have greatly aided this progress and expansion.

[1] The author is greatly indebted to the late Dr. J. H. Hoskins, University of Cincinnati, Dr. W. Spackman, Jr., Pennsylvania State University, and Dr. A. Traverse, Shell Development Company, Houston, Texas, for reading the manuscript and offering helpful criticisms.

In short, the last fifty years in paleobotany have been the most productive and influential, as definite outward signs attest.

The first and oldest organization of paleobotanists is represented by the Paleobotanical Section of the Botanical Society of America. Membership in this Section does not depend upon membership in the parental society. During the Eighth International Botanical Congress in Paris in 1954 an international paleobotanical organization was formed and affiliated with the International Association for Plant Taxonomy. An institute devoted solely to paleobotanical research was founded by the late Professor Birbal Sahni in Lucknow, India. The Palynological Laboratories, Pennsylvania State University, will soon occupy a separate building. Two scientific journals carrying only paleobotanical contributions are currently being published, *Palaeontographica* (Section B) and *The Palaeobotanist*. More universities and colleges in this country and abroad offer courses in paleobotany than ever before. More paleobotanists are gainfully employed in academic positions, in government service, and in industry. More and better paleobotanical collections are being built up. Fossil plants are gaining increased recognition and wider use as index fossils. More financial aid, both private and governmental, is available in support of paleobotanical research. In the United States alone we have two national monuments and one state park in localities where fossil plants were found or are still to be seen, namely, the Petrified Forest National Monument in Arizona, the Fossil Cycad National Monument [2] in South Dakota, and the Ginkgo Petrified Forest State Park in Washington. Thus the influence of paleobotanical research has certainly transgressed far beyond its own borders.

In paleobotanical studies structurally preserved material is always most desired as it furnishes the detailed information needed to appraise the nature and character of the fossil being studied. In fact, some fossil plants described during the last fifty years are anatomically far better known than many living plants. The chronological sequence of appearance of all fundamental tissues has also been worked out. Remarkable details such as nuclei, gametophytes, and parasitic fungi have been demonstrated and illustrated. Although assimilatory tissue in Cordaitean leaves has long been known, spectroscopic proof of the presence of chlorophyll during Ordovician times has now been furnished (*fide* Mägdefrau, 1953). Practically all major groups of the plant kingdom are now represented in the fossil record, and the known age for many is constantly being extended, notably that of the vascular plants from the Silurian to the Cambrian and that of the angiosperms from the Jurassic to the Paleozoic. The groups that have been studied most intensively are the fossil representatives of the pteridophytes and gymnosperms. As a result, our ideas regarding

[2] According to a news release dated August 29, 1956, issued by the Department of the Interior, this monument was to be abolished effective September 1, 1957, and the area then administered as a public domain.

them have changed drastically and various far-reaching proposals for their dismemberment and realignment have been made. Of necessity all new systems of classification proposed for these groups now include both living and fossil members.

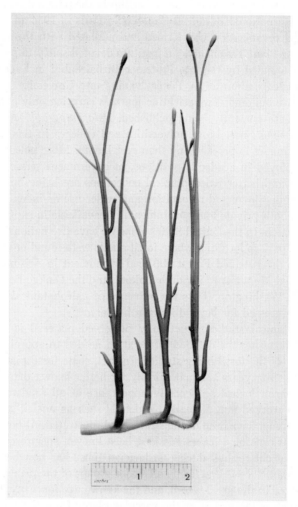

Fig. 1. Reconstruction of *Rhynia Gwynne-Vaughani* Kidston and Lang. Life-size glass model on exhibit in Chicago Natural History Museum, ×½.

The following examples of outstanding structural work on fossil plants must suffice. Although the first psilophytes were described from Canadian deposits almost one hundred years ago, their great morphological and phylogenetic importance was not recognized until the discovery in 1913 of beautifully preserved Old Red Sandstone plants of middle Devonian age found in Rhynie chert beds, Aberdeenshire, Scotland. Three genera of petrified plants, *Rhynia*, *Horneophyton*, and *Asteroxylon*, as well as algal and fungous remains, were described by Kidston and Lang (1917–1921). Soon other genera were found and described from western Germany in a series of classic studies by Kräusel and Weyland, as well as from Belgium, England, Spitzbergen (Crofts, Høeg, Leclercq, Stockmans), and the United States (Arnold, Banks, Dorf, Goldring). In 1935, true vascular plants, the lycopod *Baragwanathia* and the psilophyte

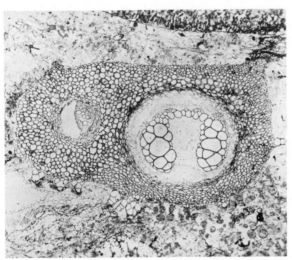

FIG. 2. *Anachoropteris clavata* Graham, a coenopterid fern found in coal balls collected near Berryville, Illinois. Cross section of a primary petiole with departing stem trace. Enlarged, ×19.5. (*Courtesy Wilson N. Stewart. For details see Am. J. Botany* 41:192–198, 1954.)

Yarravia, were described from middle Silurian strata in Australia by Lang and Cookson.

Most famous among petrified materials are coal balls, known from the Coal Measures (Upper Carboniferous) of England and Pennsylvanian strata in the United States. Although British paleobotanists have been working on these floras for some time, coal balls were first reported in the United States in 1922 and sectioned by Hoskins in the laboratory of the late Professor Noé at the University of Chicago. To date American coal balls have yielded over 150 species of fossil plants, many of them in beautiful state of preservation and described in excellent monographs.

Carbonized remains, if studied by special methods, also yield spectacular results, particularly in regard to the structure of the cuticle and epidermis. Studies of the cuticles and epidermis of all groups of gymnosperms, living and fossil, have completely altered our concepts of that group. The earlier work of Nathorst, Thomas, and Bancroft was climaxed by that of Harris and Florin. The latter has applied this technique to all groups of gymnosperms and clarified numerous problems of classification.

The success story of the application of this technique is the reconstruction by Florin of the oldest known fossil cycad (Triassic), *Bjuvia simplex,* from two frequently associated organs, a leaf (*Taeniopteris*) and a megasporophyll (*Palaeocycas*). Beyond that, the elaborate studies of the cuticular characters of gymnosperms have disclosed that this group is no longer tenable for reasons other than convenience, but that it includes widely separate taxa. This is especially true of the cycads and the "fossil cycads" (cycadeoids). The resemblances between these two groups are largely external and not indicative of close relationship. Using cuticular characters, much doubtful cycadophyte material could be definitely assigned either to one or the other group. Thus the true cycads, long considered relatively unimportant in the fossil record, have been re-instated as an important group of fossils, even though they can no longer be regarded as "fossil cycads." On the other hand, wholly new and striking types of cycadeoids have been described from other localities, notably from Austria by Kräusel, that resemble small sunflower heads more than they do other cycadeoids.

Another famous case of reconstruction is that of the pteridosperm *Calymmatotheca hoeninghausi* (*Lyginopteris oldhamia*) by Jongmans (1930), who found various organs in organic connection. Such cases are rare, indeed, but prove that the possibility always exists. The achievement as such is greater than the temporary inconvenience of trying to work out which of the organ genera should be redefined to include the others ard then be applied to the whole plant.

Although Zimmermann's *Phylogenie der Pflanzen* (1930) was never written as a textbook of paleobotany, it has had a far-reaching effect on paleobotanical as well as neobotanical research. His telome theory, as proposed in this work, has been widely applied in the interpretation of complex structures, especially that of conifer cones by Florin and that of the angiosperm stamen by Wilson. Since then Zimmermann has formulated several basic morphological principles traceable throughout the evolution of the plant kingdom. Lam followed Zimmermann and Sahni in applying certain morphological concepts, notably stachyospory and phyllospory, to the classification of vascular plants and proposed various categories which are roughly indicative of the time sequence as well as increasing morphological complexity, namely, *Palaeostelocormophyta, Mesostelocormophyta,* and *Neostelocormophyta* (gymnosperms in part and angiosperms). Similarly, new classifications of lower plants have been proposed. The last of several proposals of this kind, advocating the adoption of more than two kingdoms, came from a paleontologist, Raymond C. Moore, who wishes to re-instate Haeckel's Protista (1866), in an effort to broaden the contents of the proposed *Treatise on Invertebrate Paleontology* by including fossil diatoms, charophytes, and other groups of lower plants.

Many paleobotanical studies are more floristic, systematic, and ecological in character. Outstanding among them are Dorf's study of Devonian floras of Wyoming, Read's preliminary description of the New Albany Shale flora (basal Mississippian) of Kentucky, White's Flora of the Hermit Shale, Arizona, Daugherty's monograph on the Petrified Forest in Arizona, Berry's numerous studies of late Mesozoic and Tertiary floras of the southeastern United States, Central and South America, the corresponding studies of Western American fossil floras by Chaney and his students, MacGinitie's Flora of the Florissant Beds, Colorado, Hollick's Tertiary floras of Alaska, and Wieland's well-known accounts of the Cerro Cuadrado Petrified Forest in Patagonia and the Liassic flora of the Mixteca Alta in Mexico. Significant contributions of this kind have come from other parts of the world, among them Høeg's study of the Downtonian and Devonian flora of Spitzbergen, Halle's studies of the Paleozoic floras of eastern Asia, Corsin's monographs of French Carboniferous plants, Harris' exemplary studies of the Rhaetic floras of eastern Greenland and of the Jurassic flora of the Yorkshire coast of England, Reid and Chandler's flora of the London Clay, and many others. The evolution and distribution of fossil floras are recorded in Seward's *Plant Life through the Ages* (1931), one of the most readable scientific books of our times, and more compactly so in Kräusel's *Versunkene Floren* (1950) as well as in Edwards' "The Geographical Distribution of Past Floras" (1955).

Work of this kind is obviously time-consuming and difficult to evaluate. A Danish botanist, H. M. Hansen, has just published some startling figures. In order to assess the value of Raunkiaer's life forms as age indicators, Hansen surveyed the entire paleobotanical literature (5,000 papers) published since Schimper's Treatise (1869–1874). He counted 21,000 described species belonging to 3,300 genera of higher plants ranging from Late Cretaceous to the beginning of the Pleistocene. As the number of species described from older strata is likely to be smaller, the grand total of known fossil plants may exceed 30,000 and may even be closer to 40,000. Figures of this kind are, however, tentative at best. For instance, the number of fossil cycadophytes has been estimated in the tens of thousands but has never been shown to be that high. Conservative estimates are certainly more probable, as no group of vascular plants has ever been as successful in conquering available land areas as have the angiosperms. Also, the number of fossil angiosperms described and likely to be described is bound to be smaller than that of living angiosperms.

Palynology is a fairly recent, collective designation for a very active segment of paleobotanical research, dealing with fossil spores (sporomorphs) and pollen. These organs are often found in adequate numbers and well-preserved condition. Detailed studies based on these microfossils have yielded some remarkable results. The synopsis of fossil spores published by Schopf, Wilson, and Bentall (1944) marks the beginning of organized research in this group of microfossils, pioneered in Europe by Potonié, Raistrick, and Zerndt a decade before. The finest practical application of the use of fossil spores was made by Kosanke (1950) in his study of Illinois coal beds as correlated by spores. Fossil pollen studies are also increasing in number and content, but as yet no generally acceptable synopsis has appeared. This fairly new field of morphological, systematic, ecological, and stratigraphic research is bound to develop immensely in the next decade or so. Increased knowledge of this kind will affect greatly our ideas of fossil floras, their composition, and ecology, as well as stratigraphic sequence. Unless fossil spores and pollen are found *in situ,* they cannot be referred to the biological species to which they belong and must temporarily be placed in artificial categories. If found in place, they can be transferred to the plant to which they really belong, as were the microspores and megaspores, with their own names to the new species *Selaginellites crassicinctus* by Hoskins and Abbott (1956).

In addition to the development of new techniques used in the study of fossil plants, other significant tools have been made available to paleobotanists. For the first time specific rules and recommendations pertaining to fossil plants are included in the new International Code of Botanical Nomenclature, and others will no doubt be proposed before the next International Botanical Congress in Montreal in 1959. Various fundamental reference works such as Andrews' *Index of Generic Names of Fossil Plants, 1820–1950,* Knowlton's *Catalogue of Mesozoic and Cenozoic Plants of North America* and LaMotte's *Supplement* to it, LaMotte's *Catalogue of the Cenozoic Plants of North America through 1950, Fossilium Catalogus, Plantae* by Jongmans and collaborators, Hirmer's and Mägdefrau's annual reviews in *Fortschritte der Botanik,* Selling's *Report on European Paleobotany, Reports of the Committee of British Paleobotanists,* Sahni's reports on *Paleobotany in India, Pollen and Spore Circular,* and the *Paleobotanical Reports* published since 1929 under the auspices of the National Research Council have brought considerable organization and stability to the field.

As the study of evolution has in recent years taken on a wholly new approach and outlook, paleobotanical data provide many suitable examples of evolutionary rates, migrations, and distribution patterns as well as of the origins of major and minor categories (Stebbins, 1950). Certainly the old phylogenetic trees can now be cut down, as they no longer express correctly our ideas of known or suspected relationships. This wholesale eradication of phylogenetic trees automatically disposes of many old controversies and thereby opens the door for new facts and interpretations.

Probably no discovery of a fossil plant ever received as much public attention as that of the genus *Metasequoia,* the so-called dawn redwood. It is the last and perhaps best-known example of genera with a relic distribution in eastern Asia to be described. Chaney's *Revision of Fossil Sequoia and Taxo-*

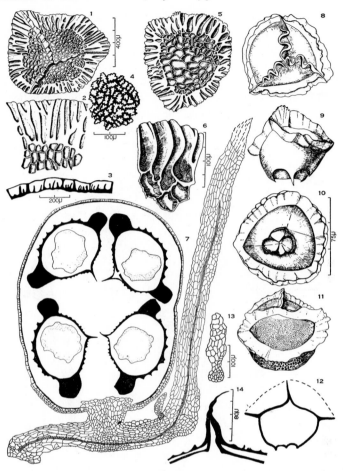

FIG. 3. *Selaginellites crassicinctus* Hoskins and Abbott.—1. Megaspore of *S. crassicinctus*, proximal surface.—2. Detail of flange and adjacent wall of megaspore.—3. Transverse section of sporangium wall showing the numerous buttresses which may easily be mistaken for cell walls.—4. Tangential section of sporangium wall. The cells are irregular polygons and possess numerous buttresses on radial and inner tangential walls.—5. Megaspore, distal surface.—6. Detail of flange and adjacent wall of megaspore.—7. Semi-diagrammatic drawing of a megasporophyll and sporangium; megaspores are shown in axial section.—8–12. Microspores of *S. crassicinctus*.—8. Proximal surface.—9. Axial view.—10. Distal surface with "cloverleaf" depressions.—11. Axial view showing flange, lips, and wall ornamentation of both proximal and distal surfaces.—12. Outline of axial section showing relative size and position of flange and lips.—13. Ligule (not that shown in 7).—14. Apical portion of megaspore in which the flange, lips, and reticulations of both proximal and distal surfaces have separated as a unit from the remainder of the exospore. (This is best seen in spores freed by maceration.) (*For details see Am. J. Botany* 43:36–46, 1956.)

*dium in Western North America Based on the Recent Discovery of Metase-
quoia* (1951) records the entire story. The confusion surrounding the fossils
now assignable to three genera dates back nearly one hundred years. The
convincingly documented story of this long and unbroken series of mistakes is
a remarkable example of the perpetuation of scientific errors. The meticulous
and unhesitating exposure of these errors, committed by a number of early
and living paleobotanists, including the author himself, provides reading at

Fig. 4. *Metasequoia glyptostroboides* Hu and Cheng.—1. Fruiting branch showing
leaves and young strobiles ($\times \frac{1}{2}$).—2. Two mature strobiles ($\times \frac{1}{2}$).—3. Male
flowering branch showing the arrangement of male flowers ($\times \frac{1}{2}$).—4. Male flower,
enlarged.—5–6. Two scales of male flowers showing ventral and dorsal faces, respectively, with stamens attached at the base ($\times 8$).—7. Seed ($\times 2.5$). (*Adapted
from Bull. Fan Mem. Inst. Biol. Vol. 1, plate 1, p. 158, 1948.*)

least as dramatic as the report of the "discovery" of the living dawn red-wood. If we designated the last fifty years of paleobotany as the period of *Metasequoia*, such simplification would have great popular appeal but would misrepresent the accomplishments of all other paleobotanists. As Andrews pointed out, the same sequence of events that led to the discovery of *Metasequoia* could have happened in regard to a number of other genera.

Once living plants of *Metasequoia* had been found, paleobotanists did not have to attempt a restoration of it as is customarily done with other fossil plants. Jongmans and Kräusel have traced the evolution of our concepts of fossil plants from their earliest restorations to our present-day museum exhibits. These restorations reflect indeed the knowledge of a particular generation of paleobotanists in regard to the periods or plants shown. In this respect restorations and exhibits play an important role in clarifying our concepts and indicating levels of our changing knowledge. The great popular appeal of these visual aids testifies to their immense educational value.

Despite the vast progress made in paleobotany during the last fifty years, we are far from having solved all problems confronting us. As yet we know all too little of the origin of life, the earliest living beings, and only the general sequence of major groups throughout the geological time scale. The geological column is still essentially zoological despite Gothan's efforts to establish paleobotanically more suitable divisions, namely, the paleophytic, mesophytic, and cenophytic eras. These and many minor problems will eventually be resolved in a manner similar to that by which the seed ferns were worked out. And in regard to the origin of angiosperms, that "abominable mystery," as Darwin called it, we now have at least one more suggestion of a possible ancestral group, one never before considered in this context. Bisexual fructifications found attached to several species of the famous leaf genus *Glossopteris*, the dominant member of the Gondwana flora of the Southern Hemisphere generally referred to the seed ferns, have recently been described as two new genera from South African material. In Mrs. Plumstead's considered opinion (1956), these plants "may well be Permian forerunners of Angiosperms." Whether these fossils represent the actual forerunners of angiosperms or not, "the accumulating mass of evidence suggests that we may soon have to reverse Darwin's wonderment and enquire how it was that the angiosperms took so long to spread and multiply" (Edwards, 1955).

LITERATURE CITED

ANDREWS, H. N., JR. 1947. Ancient plants and the world they lived in. Comstock. Ithaca, N.Y.

———. 1948. *Metasequoia* and the living fossils. Missouri Bot. Gard. Bull. 36:79–85.

———. 1948. Some evolutionary trends in the pteridosperms. Bot. Gaz. 110:13–31.

———. 1951. American coal-ball floras. Bot. Rev. 17:430–469.

ANDREWS, H. N., JR. 1955. Index of generic names of fossil plants, 1820–1950. Geol. Survey Bull. 1013. 262 pp.

———— AND S. H. MAMAY. 1955. Some recent advances in morphological palaeobotany. Phytomorphology 5(2/3):372–393.

ARNOLD, C. A. 1938–1948. Paleozoic seeds. Bot. Rev. 4(5):205–234; 14(7):450–472.

————. 1947. An introduction to paleobotany. McGraw-Hill. New York.

————. 1948. Classification of gymnosperms from the viewpoint of paleobotany. Bot. Gaz. 110:2–12.

————. 1949. Fossil flora of the Michigan coal basin. Contr. Mus. Pal. Univ. Michigan 7(9):131–269. 34 pls.

————. 1953. Origin and relationships of the cycads. Phytomorphology 3(1/2):51–65.

AXELROD, D. I. 1950. Studies in Late Tertiary paleobotany. Carnegie Inst. Wash. Publ. 590.

————. 1952. A theory of angiosperm evolution. Evolution 6(1):29–60.

BANKS, H. P. 1944. A new Devonian lycopod genus from southeastern New York. Amer. Jour. Bot. 31:649–659.

BARGHOORN, E. S. 1951. Age and environment: A survey of North American Tertiary floras in relation to paleoecology. Jour. Paleont. 25:736–744.

————. 1953. Evidence of climate change in the geologic record of plant life. Pp. 235–248 in H. SHAPLEY, Climatic change: evidence, causes, and effects. Harvard Univ. Press. Cambridge, Mass.

———— AND W. SPACKMAN. 1950. Geological and botanical study of the Brandon lignite and its significance in coal petrology. Econ. Geol. 45(4):344–357.

BERRY, E. W. 1920. Paleobotany: a sketch of the origin and evolution of floras. Smithson. Inst. Ann. Report 1918:289–407 (Publ. 2563).

————. 1923. Tree ancestors. Williams & Wilkins. Baltimore.

————. 1937. Tertiary floras of eastern North America. Bot. Rev. 3:31–46.

————. 1942. Mesozoic and Cenozoic plants of South America, Central America, and the Antilles. Proc. 8th Amer. Sci. Congress 4:365–373.

————. 1945. The origin of land plants and four other papers. Johns Hopkins Univ. Studies Geol. 14.

BERTRAND, PAUL. 1947. Les végétaux vasculaires. Masson et Cie. Paris.

———— AND P. CORSIN. 1950. Reconstitutions de payages fossiles. Ann. Paléont. 36:125–139.

BOUREAU, E., AND G. DEPAPE. 1953. Revue de paléobotanique. Bull. Soc. Bot. France 100:207–246.

BRAUN, E. L. 1950. Deciduous forests of eastern North America. Blakiston. New York.

BROWN, R. W. 1939. Fossil leaves, fruits, and seeds of Cercidiphyllum. Jour. Paleont. 13:485–499.

————. 1943. Some prehistoric trees of the United States. Jour. Forestry 41:861–868.

CHANEY, R. W. 1936. The succession and distribution of Cenozoic floras around the northern Pacific basin. In Essays in geobotany in honor of W. A. Setchell, pp. 55–85. Berkeley, Calif.

CHANEY, R. W. 1947. Tertiary centers and migration routes. Ecol. Monographs 17: 159–183.

——. 1948. The bearing of the living *Metasequoia* on problems of Tertiary paleobotany. Proc. National Acad. Sci. (U.S.) 34:503–515.

——. 1951. A revision of fossil *Sequoia* and *Taxodium* in western North America based on the recent discovery of *Metasequoia*. Trans. Amer. Philos. Soc. N.S. 40(1950):171–263. 12 pls.

CORSIN, PAUL. 1951. Bassin houiller de la Sarre et de la Lorraine. I. Flore fossile. 4me fasc. Pécoptéridées. 2 vols. Loos-Nord.

CROOKALL, R. 1929. Coal measure plants. Edward Arnold. London.

DARRAH, W. C. 1937. American Carboniferous floras. Compt. Rend. 2. Congr. Avanc. Etud. Stratigr. Carbonifère Heerlen (1935)1:109–129.

DAUGHERTY, L. H. 1941. The Upper Triassic flora of Arizona. Carnegie Inst. Wash. Publ. 526.

DORF, E. 1933. A new occurrence of the oldest known terrestrial vegetation from Beartooth Butte, Wyoming. Bot. Gaz. 95:240–257.

——. 1934. Lower Devonian flora from Beartooth Butte, Wyoming. Bull. Geol. Soc. Amer. 45:425–440.

——. 1955. Plants and the geologic time scale. *In* ARIE POLDERVAART (Ed.), The crust of the earth. Geol. Soc. Amer. Spec. Paper 62:575–592.

EAMES, A. J. 1952. Relationships of the Ephedrales. Phytomorphology 2(1):79–100.

EDWARDS, W. N. 1955. The geographical distribution of past floras. Advancement of Sci. 46:1–12.

ELIAS, M. K. 1942. Tertiary prairie grasses and other herbs from the high plains. Geol. Soc. Amer. Spec. Paper 41:1–176. 16 pls.

EMBERGER, L. 1944. Les plantes fossiles dans leurs rapports avec les végétaux vivants. Masson et Cie. Paris.

FLORIN, R. 1931. Untersuchungen zur Stammesgeschichte der Coniferales und Cordaitales. I. Morphologie und Epidermisstrucktur der Assimilationsorgane bei den rezenten Coniferen. K. Svenska Vetensk.-Akad. Handl., 3. ser., 10:1–588. 58 pls. 111 figs.

——. 1933. Studien über die Cycadales des Mesozoikums, nebst Erörterungen über die Spaltöffnungsapparate der Bennettitales. K. Svenska Vetensk.-Akad. Handl., 3. ser., 12(5):1–134. 16 pls. 40 figs.

——. 1936. Die fossilen Ginkgophyten von Franz-Joseph-Land nebst Erörterungen über vermeintliche Cordaitales mesozoischen Alters. Palaeontographica 81B (3–6):71–173. 20 figs. pls. 11–42. 82B(1–4):1–72. 8 figs. pls. 1–6.

——. 1948. On the morphology and relationships of the Taxaceae. Bot. Gaz. 110: 31–39.

——. 1950. Upper Carboniferous and Lower Permian conifers. Bot. Rev. 16:258–282.

——. 1951. Evolution in *Cordaites* and conifers. Acta Hort. Berg. 15:285–388.

——. 1952. On *Metasequoia*, living and fossil. Bot. Notiser 1952:1–29.

——. 1955. The systematics of the gymnosperms. *In* A century of progress in the natural sciences, 1853–1953. Pp. 323–403. California Academy of Sciences. San Francisco.

FRENGUELLI, J. 1952. The Lower Gondwana in Argentina. Paleobotanist 1:183–188.

GOLDRING, W. 1927. The oldest known petrified forest. Sci. Monthly 24:514–529.

GOTHAN, W. 1924. Paläobiologische Betrachtungen über die Pflanzenwelt. Fortschr. Geol. und Paläont. 8. 178 pp.

———. 1948. Die Probleme der Paläobotanik und ihre geschichtliche Entwicklung: Probleme der Wissenschaft in Vergangenheit und Gegenwart, vol. 10. G. Kropp. Berlin.

——— AND H. WEYLAND. 1954. Lehrbuch der Paläobotanik. Akademie-Verlag. Berlin.

HALLE, T. G. 1933. The structure of certain fossil spore-bearing organs believed to belong to pteridosperms. K. Svenska Vetensk.-Akad. Handl. 3 ser., 12:1–103.

———. 1937. The relation between the Late Palaeozoic floras of eastern and northern Asia. Compt. Rend. 2. Congr. Avanc. Etud. Stratig. Carbonifère Heerlen 1:237–248.

———. 1938–1940. De utdöda växterna. In SKOTTSBERG, CARL. Växternas liv. 4:449–667, 5:1–136. Nordisk Familjeboks Förlags A. B. Stockholm.

HANSEN, H. M. 1956. Life forms as age indicators. A. Rasmussens Bogtrykkeri Ringkjbing.

HARRIS, T. M. 1931–1937. The fossil flora of Scoresby Sound, East Greenland. Parts 1–5. Meddelelser om Grønland 85 (2, 3, 5); 112 (1, 2): 941 pp. 186 figs.

———. 1938. The British Rhaetic flora. British Museum (Natural History). 84 pp. London.

———. 1941. Cones of extinct Cycadales from the Jurassic rocks of Yorkshire. Philos. Trans. Roy. Soc. London Ser. B, 231:75–98.

———. 1949. Recent developments in palaeobotany. Science Prog. 37:219–231.

———. 1951. The fructification of Czekanowskia and its allies. Phil. Trans. Roy. Soc. London 235B:483–508.

———. 1951. The relationships of the Caytoniales. Phytomorphology 1(1/2):29–39.

HEIM, R., ET AL. 1952. Evolution et phylogénie chez les végétaux. 320 pp. Colloques Internationaux du Centre National de la Recherche Scientifique 41. Paris.

HIRMER, M. 1927. Handbuch der Paläobotanik. Vol. 1. R. Oldenbourg. Munich.

———. 1942. Die Forschungsergebnisse der Paläobotanik auf dem Gebiet der Känophytischen Floren. Ein Sammelbericht über die Erscheinungen der Jahre 1936–1941. Engler's Bot. Jahrb. 72(3/4):347–563. pls. 8–20.

HOFFMEISTER, W. S., F. L. STAPLIN, AND R. E. MALLOY. 1955. Geologic range of Paleozoic plant spores in North America. Micropaleontology 1(1):9–27. pls. 1–4, charts 1–4.

HOFMANN, E. 1934. Paläohistologie der Pflanze. Julius Springer. Vienna.

HØEG, O. A. 1937. The Devonian floras and their bearing upon the origin of vascular plants. Bot. Rev. 3:563–592.

———. 1942. The Downtonian and Devonian flora of Spitzbergen. Norg. Svalbardog Ishavs-Undersøkelser 83:1–283.

HOLLICK, A. 1936. Tertiary floras of Alaska. U.S. Geol. Survey Prof. Paper 182. 185 pp.

HOSKINS, J. H., AND A. T. CROSS. 1951. Paleobotany of the Devonian-Mississippian black shales. Jour. Paleont. 25:713–728.

——— AND M. L. ABBOTT. 1956. Selaginellites crassicinctus, a new species from the Desmoinesian Series of Kansas. Amer. Jour. Bot. 43:36–46.

JEFFREY, E. C. 1917. The anatomy of woody plants. Univ. Chicago Press. Chicago.

——. 1924. The origin and organization of coal. Mem. Amer. Acad. Arts and Sciences 15:1–52.

JOHNSON, J. H. 1954. An introduction to the study of rock building algae and algal limestones. Colorado School Min. Quart. 49:1–117.

JONGMANS, W. J. 1930. On the fructification of *Sphenopteris hoeninghausi* and its relations with *Lyginodendron oldhamium* and *Crossotheca schatzlarensis.* Geol. Bur. voor het Neder. Mijn. te Heerlen Jaarver. over 1929:77–81.

——. 1949. Het Wisselend aspect van het bos in de ouders geologische formaties. Pp. 1–165 *in* W. B. BEEKMAN, Hout in alle Tijden, Part 1. Deventer, The Netherlands.

—— ET AL. 1913 to date. Fossilium catalogus. II. Plantae. The Hague.

JUST, T. 1947. Geology and plant distribution. Ecol. Monographs 17(2):127–137.

——. 1948. Gymnosperms and the origin of angiosperms. Bot. Gaz. 110:91–137.

——. 1949. The nomenclature of fossil plants. Amer. Jour. Bot. 36:28–32.

——. 1951. Mesozoic plant microfossils and their geological significance. Jour. Paleont. 25(6):729–735.

——. 1952. Origine et évolution de la fleur. Ann. Biol. 28(5/6):135–143.

——. 1952. Fossil floras of the Southern Hemisphere and their phytogeographical significance. Bull. Amer. Mus. Natur. Hist. 99(3):189–203.

—— ET AL. 1946. Symposium on paleobotanical taxonomy. Amer. Midl. Natur. 36(2):257–380.

KIDSTON, R. 1924. Fossil plants of the Carboniferous rocks of Great Britain. Mem. Geol. Survey Gr. Britain 2:377–522.

—— AND W. H. LANG. 1917–1921. On Old Red Sandstone plants showing structure, from the Rhynie chert bed, Aberdeenshire. Trans. Roy. Soc. Edinburgh 51:761–784, 52:603–627, 643–680, 831–854, 855–902, 52 pls.

KNOWLTON, F. H. 1919. Catalogue of the Mesozoic and Cenozoic plants of North America. Geol. Survey Bull. 696.

——. 1927. Plants of the past. Princeton Univ. Press. Princeton, N.J.

KOSANKE, R. M. 1950. Pennsylvanian spores of Illinois and their use in correlation. Illinois Geol. Survey Bull. 74.

KRÄUSEL, R. 1949. Vom Wesen des Steinkohlen-Waldes: Ein Kapitel aus der Geschichte der paläobotanischen Forschung. Natur und Volk 79(3/4):54–63.

——. 1950. Versunkene Floren: Eine Einführung in die Paläobotanik. Waldemar Kramer. Frankfurt am Main.

—— H. WEYLAND. 1930–1949. Pflanzenreste aus dem Devon. Parts 1–14. Senckenbergiana vols. 12–17.

KREMP, G. O. W. 1955. The most important results of microflora investigations in Tertiary and Mesozoic strata of Europe, especially of Germany. Mimeographed. 26 pp.

KRYSHTOFOVICH, A. N. 1929. Evolution of the Tertiary Flora in Asia. New Phytol. 28:303–312.

LAM, H. J. 1955. Comments on two charts relative to the phylogeny of the Cormophyta, with some remarks of a general nature. Acta Bot. Néerlandica 4(3): 410–428.

LaMotte, R. S. 1944. Supplement to catalogue of Mesozoic and Cenozoic Plants of North America 1919–1937. Geol. Survey Bull. 924.

——. 1952. Catalogue of the Cenozoic plants of North America through 1950. Geol. Soc. Amer. Memoir 51.

Lang, W. H., and I. Cookson. 1935. On a flora including vascular plants associated with *Monograptus*, in rocks of Silurian age, from Victoria, Australia. Phil. Trans. Roy. Soc. London 224B:421–449.

Leclercq, S. 1940. Contribution à l'étude de la flore du Dévonien de Belgique. Acad. Roy. Belgique, Classe Sci., Mém. II sér., 12(3):66 pp. 12 pls.

——. 1951. Étude morphologique et anatomique d'une fougère du Dévonien superieur, le *Rhacophyton zygopteroides* n. sp. Ann. soc. géol. de Belgique 9:1–62. pls. 1–12.

——. 1954. Are the psilophytes a starting or a resulting point? Svensk Bot. Tidskr. 48:301–315.

——. 1956. Evidence of vascular plants in the Cambrian. Evolution 10(2):109–114.

MacGinitie, H. D. 1953. Fossil plants of the Florissant beds, Colorado. Carnegie Inst. Wash. Publ. 599.

Mägdefrau, K. 1952. Vegetationsbilder der Vorzeit. 2d ed. Gustav Fischer. Jena.

——. 1953. Paläobiologie der Pflanzen. 2d ed. Gustav Fischer. Jena.

Mason, H. L. 1947. Evolution of certain floristic associations in western North America. Ecol. Monographs 17:201–210.

Moore, R. C. 1954. Kingdom of organisms named Protista. Jour. Paleont. 28(5):588–598.

Peck, R. E. 1953. Fossil Charophytes. Bot. Rev. 19(4):209–227.

Plumstead, E. P. 1956. Bisexual fructifications borne on *Glossopteris* leaves from South Africa. Palaeontographica Abt. B, 100(1–3):1–25. pls. 1–14, 5 figs.

Radforth, N. W. 1946. The taxonomic treatment of the fern-pteridosperm complex. Amer. Midl. Natur. 36(2):325–330.

Read, C. B. 1947. Pennsylvania floral zones and floral provinces. Jour. Geol. 55(3, pt. 2):271–279.

—— and G. Campbell. 1939. Preliminary account of the New Albany shale flora. Amer. Midl. Natur. 21(2):435–453.

Reid, E., and M. Chandler. 1933. The London Clay flora. British Museum. London.

Sahni, B. 1920. On the structure and affinities of *Acmopyle pancheri* Pilger. Phil. Trans. Roy. Soc. London 210B:253–310.

——. 1927. The southern floras: a study in plant geography of the past. Proc. 13th Indian Sci. Congress. Pp. 229–254.

——. 1948. The Pentoxyleae: a new group of Jurassic gymnosperms from the Rajmahal Hills of India. Bot. Gaz. 110:47–80.

Schopf, J. M. 1948. Pteridosperm male fructifications: American species of *Dolerotheca*, with notes regarding certain allied forms. Jour. Paleont. 22:681–724.

——, L. R. Wilson, and R. Bentall. 1944. An annotated synopsis of Paleozoic fossil spores and the definition of generic groups. Illinois Geol. Survey, Report of Investigations No. 91.

Scott, D. H. 1920–1923. Studies in fossil botany. 2 vols. 3d ed. Black. London.

——. 1924. Extinct plants and problems of evolution. Black. London.

Scott, R. A. 1956. Evolution of some endocarpal features in the tribe Tinosporae (Menispermaceae). Evolution 10(1):74–81.

Selling, O. H. 1948. Report on European paleobotany 1939–1947. Naturhist. Riksmuseum. Stockholm. Mimeographed.

———. 1950. Report on European paleobotany 1948–1949. Naturhist. Riksmuseum. Stockholm.

Sen, J. 1956. Fine structure of degraded, ancient and buried wood, and other fossilized plant derivatives. Bot. Rev. 22(6):343–374.

Seward, A. C. 1898–1919. Fossil plants. Vols. 1–4. Cambridge Univ. Press. Cambridge.

———. 1931. Plant life through the ages. Cambridge Univ. Press. Cambridge.

Stebbins, G. L., Jr. 1950. Variation and evolution in plants. Columbia Univ. Press. New York.

Steere, W. C. 1946. Cenozoic and Mesozoic bryophytes of North America. Amer. Midl. Natur. 36(2):298–324.

Stewart, W. N., and T. Delevoryas. 1956. The medullosan pteridosperms. Bot. Rev. 22(1):45–80.

Stockmans, F. 1948. Végétaux du Dévonien superieur de la Belgique. Mém. Mus. Roy. Hist. Nat. Belgique 10:83 pp. 14 pls.

Thomas, H. H. 1936. Paleobotany and the origin of angiosperms. Bot. Rev. 2: 397–418.

———. 1946. The history of plant form. Advancement of Sci. 4:243–254.

———. 1955. Mesozoic pteridosperms. Phytomorphology 5(2/3):177–185.

Traverse, A. 1955. Pollen analysis of Brandon lignite of Vermont. Bureau of Mines, Report of Investigations 5151. 107 pp.

Walton, John. 1953. An introduction to the study of fossil plants. 2d ed. A. & C. Black. London.

White, D. 1929. Flora of the Hermit Shale, Grand Canyon, Arizona. Carnegie Inst. Wash. Publ. 405.

Wieland, G. R. 1906–1916. American Fossil Cycads. Vol. 1–2. Carnegie Inst. Wash. Publ. 34.

———. 1916. La flora Liássica de la Mixteca Alta. Bol. Inst. Geol. México 31.

———. 1934. Fossil cycads, with special reference to the *Raumeria Reichenbachiana* Goeppert sp. of the Zwinger of Dresden. Palaeontographica 79:86–130.

———. 1935. The Cerro Cuadrado petrified forest. Carnegie Inst. Wash. Publ. 405.

———. 1936. Twenty-five years of paleobotany, 1910–1935. Brooklyn Bot. Garden Memoirs 4:87–95. 2 pls.

Williams, E. G. 1949–1950. Ancient Plants. Part I. Proc. Liverpool Geol. Soc. 20(2):69–85; Part II, *Ibid.* 20(3):123–136.

Wilson, C. L. 1953. The telome theory. Bot. Rev. 19(7):417–437.

Wilson, L. R. 1944. Spores and pollen as microfossils. Bot. Rev. 10(8):499–523.

———. 1956. Composite micropaleontology and its application to Tertiary and near-Recent stratigraphy. Micropaleontology 2(1):1–6. Table.

Wodehouse, R. P. 1935. Pollen grains. McGraw-Hill. New York.

Zimmermann, W. 1930. Die Phylogenie der Pflanzen. Gustav Fischer. Jena.

———. 1949. Geschichte der Pflanzen. G. Thieme. Stuttgart.

39

SOME ASPECTS OF PROGRESS IN PLANT MORPHOLOGY DURING THE PAST FIFTY YEARS

Arthur J. Eames

Fifty years ago as an undergraduate, I was learning about vascular crypto-gams and seed plants and how the herbaceous stem becomes the woody stem. In secondary schools, pupils were studying about "exogens" and "endo-gens" and how to identify the wild flowers. Morphology in this country—as illustrated by the general textbooks of that day—consisted almost entirely of the descriptions of plants and their life histories. Classification was based largely on single characters. Internal structure was seldom mentioned. Com-parative morphology was only beginning to receive attention.

Progress in the morphological field has been remarkable, even extraordinary, as we look back and try to outline it. Advance has followed many lines: first, the acquisition of much factual material, necessary as a foundation for com-parative interpretations and for the testing of earlier theories and the proposal of new ones; secondly, the development of emphasis on the comparative viewpoint—the use of the more abundant descriptive material for the de-termination of evolutionary progress in form, and thus for the establishment of probable natural relationships.

The development of comparative study produced new bases for interpreta-tion: the recognition that sound morphology must deal with the entire plant body, with vegetative as well as reproductive parts, with internal as well as external structure; the recognition that simplicity may represent reduction from complexity as well as primitiveness; that parallel and convergent evolu-tion have played an important part in evolutionary modification; that evidence of these changes is as often hidden as obvious and must be obtained from as many fields of research as possible—not from morphology alone, but from taxonomy, cytology, genetics, geography, paleobotany, serology, and other fields. In the light of the broader viewpoint of today, the morphology of the beginning of the century seems almost archaic.

Because of the limited time available, I am restricting this discussion to a narrow field, to what is called "classical morphology" and to vascular plants, especially the angiosperms.

Looking broadly, first, over this field: the study of the *entire* plant body rose rapidly to prominence; it soon became unnecessary to announce a course in morphology as "comparative"—as was customary in the earlier decades of the century. All morphological study was soon accepted as both descriptive and comparative (comparative in the sense of evolutionary modification).

Comparative study of the plant as a whole brought great changes in the classification of the major taxa of vascular plants and the drastic modification of the pretty evolutionary tree, so long dear to the teacher's heart. The change was far-reaching because it involved the discard of the seed as the basis for delimitation of major taxa and the breakup of the seed plants as the taxon representing the highest attainment in the plant world. The seed had come to be accepted as the ultimate step in reproductive methods, and the fact that the seed might have developed independently more than once did not enter the picture. Study of the entire plant body has shown that other characters are at least as important as the seed. The union of the seed plants with the ferns in the new taxon, Pteropsida, seemed to many botanists an unholy one, so deepseated had the value of the seed as a distinguishing character become. Almost as difficult to accept was the separation of the ferns from the horsetails and club mosses, so long their close "allies." The separation, a little later, of the horsetails from the club mosses, as unrelated taxa, came more easily.

The Phanerogams—the seed plants of the early nineteen hundreds—have similarly seen extensive changes in classification, and the new treatment, a dissection into isolated groups, receives continuing support from evidence in many fields. In place of the direct-line, tree-trunk relationship—cycads, conifers, Gnetales, angiosperms—we now see at least two lines: the Cycadophyte and the Coniferophyte, with the Gnetales and angiosperms as lines with attachment to the ancestral system still uncertain (the Gnetales are probably isolated end products of more than one ancestral line).

As we understand the gymnosperms today, they are a highly unnatural taxon, consisting of at least two clearly distinct lines, with the ancient pteridosperms a possible third, ancestral to some or to all of the others. The term Gymnospermae is no longer useful in a natural classification.

Protests arise now and then that morphology is becoming phylogeny; that it is no longer a "pure" science. But the study of morphology is, above all, the study of evolutionary modification of form. And theories of the basis of change in form can be interpreted only in the light of its relationship to natural classification; morphology must go hand in hand with other fields in the establishment of phylogenetic relationships.

Another outstanding feature of advance in the morphology of the past fifty years is the rise of anatomy to a position of prominence in the interpretation of form and in the support of theories of phylogenetic relations. In descriptive morphology, anatomy played only a minor part in the elementary textbooks of the early decades of this century—except in discussions of "inside" versus "outside" growers and the origin of the woody stem from the herbaceous with illustrations from—of all plants—the woody vines, *Aristolochia* and *Clematis*. Unfortunately, even today, the dissected stele (frequently illustrated by *Ranunculus*) is often described as characteristic of herbs, although such a stele is rare in herbs. A casual study in New York State showed the dissected stele present in less than 5 per cent of herbs. Fifty years ago the herbaceous habit was generally accepted as primitive; today no one questions its advanced nature.

In the last few decades, the importance of critical studies of internal structure, both descriptive and comparative, has been recognized. Contributions in the field of anatomy have been many and have greatly affected classification and opinions of natural relationships. Note the evidence shown by stelar structure in the breakup of the old Pteridophyta; the evidence shown by histological structure of the xylem in the classification of the conifers and the primitive dicotyledons; and the evidence of reduction provided by the vascular vestiges of lost organs.

Since simple plants clearly gave rise to complex ones, the apparently simple forms in any taxon have long been accepted as the more primitive members. Note the Amentiferae in the angiosperms. And some will remember when aquatic monocotyledons were considered the most primitive angiosperms because of their resemblance to *Isoetes*. (The monocotyledons were then believed to be more primitive than the dicotyledons.) Now, we question simplicity: is it primitive or the result of reduction? And we are using more than one character as evidence of simplicity. We look at the plant as a whole, at *all* structure, external and internal. Comparison with related taxa shows series in modification, series that often can be read in both directions. Here, internal structure, with vestiges of lost parts, is critically important. And we must always, in reading series, consider evidence from other fields as well as morphology.

The recognition that simplicity often represents reduced complexity has made great changes in our interpretation of the morphology of organs and the classification of major and minor taxa. The flowers of the Amentiferae are not simple; their unisexuality, small numbers of sporophylls, and apetaly represent reduction. Reduction is also represented in angiosperms as a whole by such structures as the solitary stamen, the basal ovule, the solitary microspore. The naked flower may be primitive or advanced. The answer to the question of primitive or advanced status of simple structure lies often in comparison with related taxa, sometimes in ontogeny, often in the presence of vestigial vascular supply. For example, comparison with related taxa shows the simple leaf of some legumes to be a surviving leaflet of a compound leaf, as in *Cercis* and *Crotalaria;* that of other legumes, the result of the fusion of two leaflets, as in *Bauhinia* and related genera. Vascular stubs in the receptacle of the flowers of some Scrophulariaceae support the taxonomist's interpretation made from comparison with other scrophulariaceous genera, that stamen number has been reduced in the family from five to four, two, and even one.

Simplicity may be the result not only of reduction and loss but also of fusion. External, and even internal, evidence of the fusion may be absent, for the vascular system may be involved in the fusion. And ontogeny may be of no help, because the fusion may have become fixed in phylogeny—may be congenital. In 1910, in this country, the morphological significance of congenital fusion was not, or only rarely, recognized; today, morphologists, with rare exceptions, recognize the importance of both ontogenetic and phylogenetic fusion.

A combination of fusion and reduction has brought about such morphological complexities as the orchid flower—first correctly interpreted by Darwin, with the aid of anatomy, nearly one hundred years ago. Today, though we recognize the nature of the orchid column as the result of congenital adnation and reduction, there is often refusal to accept the downward continuation of this modification into the ovary.

Parallel and convergent evolution were rarely mentioned at the beginning of the century. Today, we recognize that parallel and convergent development of morphological similarity of structure occur frequently. These similarities may occur in any part of the plant; for example, a single leaflet surviving from a compound leaf; one stamen representing an entire flower; the inferior ovary; the basal ovule; the vessel. We recognize that parallel and convergent evolution must be taken into account in interpreting all basic form and natural relationships.

Beginning as early as thirty years ago, morphologists urged that conclusions as to natural relationships should be based on evidence from as many fields as possible. Let me repeat: morphology and taxonomy alone are not in themselves sufficient for phylogenetic interpretation. Moreover, within the field of morphology itself, evidence must come from internal as well as external form, from skeletal form and structure, both gross and detailed—from stele, xylem, phloem, and vestigial tissues.

The acceptance of characters of diverse origin in the determination of relationship has been steady though slow. A recent example, based on evidence from vascular anatomy, cytology, and ontogeny, is the removal of *Paeonia* from the Ranunculaceae and the establishment of the family Paeoniaceae, in the Dilleniales, far from the Ranales. The Ranunculaceae have commonly been called a natural family, but the removal of *Paeonia* has been followed by that of *Hydrastis* and *Glaucidium* as other genera out of place. Even twenty-five years ago, a breakup of the Ranunculaceae would have been no more acceptable than that of the seed plants and vascular crypto-gams, but that we accept the change now with little objection is a sign of progress to broader concepts. The Ranales provide another example of the use of characters from several fields; even the woody families have been shown to be a heterogeneous assemblage of small families which seem to represent at least three independent lines: the Winteraceae, the Magnoliaceae, and four probably related families—the Degeneriaceae, Annonaceae, Eupomatiaceae, and Himantandraceae.

Fifty years ago, the angiosperms were considered too large and diverse a taxon for sound interpretation. Today, we still have too little information about them; but we recognize even more clearly the vast numbers, the great diversity of structure, and the possible importance of families and genera yet little known, or still unknown. (Note the major changes made in our recog-nition of the primitive members of the angiosperms by the recent critical studies of the woody Ranales.)

Fifty years ago, the evolutionary line of vascular plants led from the lower gymnosperms through the Gnetales to the angiosperms. Today, we have tested and discarded three possible ancestral lines. The cycadophyte line was long and strongly supported—and still is by some morphologists—but it must be set aside. This line cannot be ancestral to the angiosperms because of major differences not only in body structure—huge pith, thin vascular cyclinder, thick cortex, and even number of encircling leaf traces—but also in structure of xylem, in sporophyll type, and in microsporangium position and structure. The coniferophyte line—never seriously considered in this respect—has re-cently been urged as showing connection with the Amentiferae. This con-nection has been considered to be from *Juniperus* to the Amentiferae because of similarity in cone and flower structure. Here, also, general body type and detailed vascular structure show the impossibility of any such close relation. The similarities are those of simplicity in form of reproductive structure—similarities that in both taxa are the result of reduction. The Gnetales have, until recently, been seen as the obvious step from the simpler gymnosperms to the flowering plants, largely because of the presence of vessels. We now know a great deal more about the vessel and recognize it as a product of high specialization in xylem—a structure developed independently several times even within the angiosperms. The presence of vessels is clearly without value as support for the Gnetalean origin of the angiosperms.

A new ancestral group for the angiosperms has recently been proposed—the Prephanerogamae. In a contribution from the so-called "New Morphol-ogy," *Casuarina* is removed from the angiosperms and added to the Gnetales to constitute this new taxon. Superficial resemblance to *Ephedra* is part of the evidence. But *Casuarina* is an angiosperm in every detail of structure—

stamen, carpel, gametophytes, vascular tissue—and its wood structure is that of an advanced angiosperm. *Casuarina* is a highly specialized and reduced angiosperm; its simplicity is that of reduction, not of primitiveness. The maintenance, therefore, of the Prephanerogamae as a valid taxon is absurd.

Our opinion of the nature of the primitive flower has changed completely in recent years. Formerly, the simplest flower was considered the most primitive, and the flowers of the Amentiferae and those of some of the lower aquatic monocotyledons—unisexual, with few sporophylls, and naked—were accepted as primitive. Now, the bisexual flower with numerous sporophylls, with an elementary perianth—well demonstrated by the woody Ranales—is generally accepted. The claim that the primitive flower was unisexual with few sporophylls is, however, still maintained by some botanists.

Our understanding of the stamen has perhaps changed more than that of any other floral organ. The stamen has long been considered a simple organ as compared with the carpel, but that concept must be changed. We now know that it is fundamentally a laminar organ, very like the carpel, as we might expect from comparison with the micro- and megasporophylls of the other major taxa. In these primitive laminar sporophylls, the two pairs of wall-less microsporangia are deeply sunken near the center of the sporophyll. The angiosperm microsporangia have long been interpreted as typically superficial, with heavy walls, each pair marginal on a slender axis. We now see that it is the pairs, not the individual sporangia, that appear marginal. Reduction of the ancestral lamina by narrowing of the blade has so displaced one member of each pair that, commonly, these two sporangia stand on the sporophyll surface opposite that on which they were ancestrally borne. The genus *Eupomatia* shows anatomical evidence that, in some taxa at least, more than a displacement of two of the sporangia has occurred; the sporophyll has been folded, as has the carpel, and complete evidence is present in anatomical structure. The theory that the stamen is a folded organ like the carpel was proposed more than one hundred years ago, but soon forgotten. The anther-sac wall, which is commonly considered the sporangium wall, represents the reduced blade of the broad ancestral sporophyll. The embedded, wall-less character of the microsporangium is probably of great importance in our search for the ancestors of the angiosperms.

The carpel is usually considered a tightly closed structure, but the primitive carpel is a loosely closed, or still open, laminar organ, without style or stigma, receptive to pollen along the entire ventral margin. Placentation was originally laminar; the ovules, like the microsporangia, are not primitively marginal or submarginal. Nor, when all evidence is considered, are the ovules of any angiosperm taxon borne morphologically on the receptacle, as formerly generally believed.

On the new evidence of primitiveness, the most primitive dicotyledons are not the Amentiferae (a heterogeneous lot at best) but the woody Ranales and some of the Ranunculaceae; the primitive monocotyledons are some of the Helobiales and the primitive Liliales. The simplicity that ranked the Amentiferae as the most primitive angiosperms is the simplicity of reduction. In place of the Amentiferae, we have three or more lines of woody Ranales forming a new group of basal branches on the angiosperm evolutionary tree which now looks very shrub-like. We see, as yet, in these primitive Ranalean plants no single stock but a group of taxa, isolated end products of an ancient stock, perhaps itself complex.

What of the age of the angiosperms? Fifty years ago, we looked upon the angiosperms as the climax of evolutionary progress among plants, as the taxon not merely highest in morphological structure but most recent geologically. Now we are seriously questioning their apparent youth. Paleobotany gives evidence of their presence in the Jurassic and, with little doubt, in the Triassic. The study of fossil pollen is going to help greatly in finding the earliest records of the angiosperms. Associated with our growing doubts as to the youth of the angiosperms is the theory that the angiosperms sprang, Minerva-like, from some stock in the Lower Cretaceous—presumably Cycadophyte—and then evolved "explosively." This theory is based on too little fossil evidence; it fits too well into the picture of the typical evolutionary tree. Apparently, no other major taxon, plant or animal, has so evolved. The diversification in Mid- and Upper Cretaceous indeed appears rapid, but no more so than that of the Tertiary.

Now that we recognize the simple, unisexual, wind-pollinated flower as advanced and look at the Lower Cretaceous flora—at such genera as *Populus, Sassafras, Platanus*—we see these genera as samples of unrelated lines, each highly specialized in several characters. And when we consider the structure of the flowers, inflorescences, and wood of the families to which these genera belong, we cannot accept them as other than relatively well-advanced types, much more specialized than the woody Ranales.

Then consider these woody Ranales themselves. Each taxon has, along with its many primitive characters of flower, node, and wood structure, some advanced character: unisexuality, perigyny, solitary carpel, petaloid corolla. Such diversity of structure—marked advance along different lines in these otherwise so generally primitive taxa—can only mean that these, also, are not the earliest angiosperms.

Support for great age of the angiosperms has recently come from plant geography and floristic taxonomy. Analysis of the flora of Australia shows that this isolated and supposedly quite different flora is not fundamentally different from that of the other continents; the basic angiosperm families— from which has evolved this apparently strange, but by no means primitive, flora—are the same as those of the rest of the world. These families have not entered Australia since Cretaceous times; the angiosperms were apparently basically alike the world over in the Cretaceous. A long period of diversification must have preceded this world-wide Cretaceous distribution of basic families.

Recently I have been assessing morphological variation broadly throughout angiosperms in respect to as many characters as possible, and the variety, extent, and degree of specialization have compelled me to consider great age as the only answer; I see no evidence of "explosive" evolution.

In the light of such great diversity of form among the more primitive families (compare the woody Ranales, the Ranunculaceae, the Helobiales, the Liliales), must we consider a possible polyphyletic origin for the angiosperms? We hear this suggestion more and more frequently. I have lived through the period when any suggestion of polyphyletic origin for the angiosperms was met by the statement that it is inconceivable that so remarkable a structure as the 8-nucleate gametophyte could have arisen more than once. Yet, today, we accept not only embryo sacs of greatly different structure, but those of such extreme morphological origin as derivation from one, two, or four spores.

Fifty years ago, we could hardly have accepted the breakup of the vascular cryptogams into unrelated taxa, that is, polyphyletic origin. Even recently, we at first considered the breakup of the Ranales a doubtful step, but now we see even the woody Ranales as an unnatural group. We have insufficient evidence yet to come to any well-substantiated decision about a multiple origin for the angiosperms, but there seem to be at least three apparently unrelated primitive lines in the angiosperms as we know them today: the woody Ranales, the primitive Liliales, and the Helobiales. These may, of course, represent extreme diversification in a very old monophyletic line.

What can we say today of the origin of the angiosperms? Darwin's "abominable mystery" is still unsolved, but we are making progress by the process of elimination. Discarding both the coniferophyte and the cycadophyte lines, there remain among known seed-plant lines only the ancient pteridosperms—a great and diverse group almost unknown fifty years ago. This we are rapidly learning to know. The angiosperms resemble the pteridosperms in many fern-like characters of both body type and anatomy. We know little yet about the Permian and early Mesozoic members of this great taxon. Perhaps these forms will shed more light on the origin of the angiosperms.

Walking with Professor A. C. Seward in his garden during the International Congress at Cambridge in 1930, I asked him what he thought of the possibility of finding fossil evidence of the origin of the angiosperms. He replied, "How shall we recognize them when we find them? Perhaps we already know them." This seems prophetic today when we realize that few, if any, of the characters long used to distinguish the angiosperms can be looked for in their ancestors. We have progressed a long way in our study of the morphology of the angiosperms when we acknowledge this—a long way from the narrow view of single-character classification, of simplicity as always indicative of primitiveness, to the broader view that, in outlining morphological change, we must look upon—expect—simplicity in higher groups as at least as likely to be the result of reduction as of the retention of ancient form, that simplicity may be the result of parallel development. We must realize that resemblances may have little morphological significance unless evidence is derived from several fields of botanical study. I am reminded of a remark made by an assistant in one of my morphology courses, "This course should be called 'Things are not always what they seem.'"

40

FIFTY YEARS OF PLANT PHYSIOLOGY IN THE U.S.A.

F. W. Went

Plant physiology as a separate branch of botany is just 100 years old; its beginning can be traced back to the start of the career of Julius Sachs. Here in the United States it can properly be said that plant physiology is just about 50 years old, and many of the botanists who started their careers in the early nineteen hundreds by studying the life processes of the plant are still with us today. A really authentic history could have been presented if Allard, Duggar, Kraus, MacDougal, Osterhout, Shantz, Shive, or Shull had been asked to do so, but these men have earned their emeritate and should not be called upon to perform still further tasks which we younger men can do by looking up the records of their performances. I hope, however, that they will be willing to provide footnotes and add to what I can only inadequately present in half an hour. For most of you of the old guard the trip to Storrs may have become too strenuous. We, who have seen you so often at our yearly meetings, and the younger ones who have not had that privilege, we all salute you, and we rededicate ourselves to furthering botany in the next 50 years, as you did in the previous half century.

History can be approached in many different ways. But since we are dealing with such recent history, it seems better not to stress personalities who actually made this history. A proper evaluation of the contributions of each plant physiologist in the United States during the last 50 years is utterly impossible at present. In so many cases the stimulation coming from research, teaching, critical evaluation, or organization in the past 50 years cannot be judged until the next 50 years have elapsed. Toward the end of this talk I will try to give you shortly my own personal evaluation of specific events and investigations, but to begin with I would like to apply the physiological method to the history of plant physiology. Or, to put it more accurately, I would like to analyze the forces which seem to have molded our science into what it is today, to trace causal relationships between our sister sciences and ourselves, to enquire into the role government, private enterprise, social conditions, organization, education, publication policies, and professional organizations have played in our development.

The experimental method, which lies at the basis of plant physiology, had its real inception in the 17th century, but it started to come into its own in biology about a century ago. The world in general owes America a debt of gratitude when it led in the 1870s with the introduction of the experimental method into agriculture with the establishment of government-supported Agricultural Experiment Stations. Except as far as plant nutrition was concerned, plant physiology did not have its own place in these experiment stations, but it became an important subject in connection with investigations in plant pathology, horticulture, agriculture, and recently in forestry, so that at present more than half of all plant physiological work is carried out in experiment stations and college and university departments of applied botany. This clearly points out that with the present structure of society, large-scale financial support of research is possible only when such research has a demonstrable practical implication.

Admitting that the experimental method now is thoroughly entrenched in most branches of science, and was so in plant physiology long before it started to blossom in the United States, we now should see to what extent other sciences have contributed to the advances in plant physiology, especially in the last half century. The invention of printing and the development of the microscope, those two most important factors in the growth of botany as a science, sufficiently antedated the inception of plant physiology as not to be factors in its development. We might almost say that the opposite is true. For not enough plant physiology is carried out on the cellular level.

After Stephen Hales' famous *Vegetable Staticks* almost any advance in chemistry was soon followed by a comparable advance in botany. The discovery of photosynthesis was almost simultaneous with the discovery of oxygen; elementary analysis led de Saussure to his biochemical analysis of respiration; and the chemical isolation of hormones and vitamins gave rise to their application in the control of plant development. In some cases physiology even spearheaded advances in other sciences, such as Dutrochet's work on osmosis. Pfeffer's quantitative measurement of osmotic pressure formed the basis for van't Hoff's theory of this phenomenon, while de Vries' isotonic coefficients provided strong evidence for the dissociation theory of electrolytes. Biochemistry had its inception as a joint effort by physiologists, microbiologists, and chemists, to which all contributed simultaneously and equally.

The direct impact of mathematics on plant physiology has not been very great. There is a natural tendency among biologists to express their facts and fancies in as precise terms as possible, which naturally leads to the symbolism

WILLIAM CROCKER, 1876–1950

OTIS F. CURTIS, 1888–1949

BENJAMIN M. DUGGAR, 1872–1956

WIGHTMAN W. GARNER, 1875–1956

of mathematical formulae, but their further development did not require more than the standard methods of calculus. It is possible that the new electronic computers will in the future contribute significantly to the development of biology, where the highly complex interrelationships between constituent parts, whole organisms, and environment require equally complex mathematical treatment.

It would not be correct to mention the increased use of statistics as an example of the impact of mathematics on biology. It is rather the other way around. Biometricians, such as Galton and Pearson, developed statistics; Johansen applied it to genetics; and in agriculture the great variability in field experiments required special methods to evaluate results. This led a number of mathematicians to develop the theory of probabilities further until now it is an important tool in all biological research where for one or another reason one is dealing with variable material. During the last quarter century statistics has been used increasingly in plant physiology, almost to the point where it has become a fad, and a number of cases can be cited where the statistical treatment of the experiment has taken precedence over consideration of the physiological significance of the data.

In physics the quantum theory, now just 50 years old, has overshadowed probably all other developments in theoretical significance and has caused the rapid development of many new branches of physics as well as of chemistry. As such it also has influenced biology in a secondary manner. However, the first direct applications of quantum theory to photosynthesis by Warburg touched off a whole new development in this field, particularly here in America. Now, using these energy considerations as a basis, physicists like Franck, chemists like Calvin, and plant physiologists like Emerson, French, and Arnon are on common ground in their attack on the most important single reaction on earth: the photoreduction of carbon dioxide.

Other developments in physics of basic significance, such as the theory of relativity and the problem of elementary particles, have had no direct applications in biology, except inasmuch as they led to new techniques. Electronics has brought us a new era of measuring and of instruments, which in the hands of technicians produce wonders of accuracy. For the new generation of plant physiologists it is hard to imagine what a pH measurement or spectral determination involved 30 years ago. Fortunately the budgets of plant physiologists have increased so that they can take at least partial advantage of the availability of commercial meters and recorders. We should not lose sight, however, of the dangers involved in fancy instruments. They all have been designed for specific purposes, and thus one may not be measuring what one wants but rather what the instrument can. Thus the investigator is exposed to the risk of becoming a slave of his instrument instead of the instrument being the slave of the investigator. Even such universal instruments as the Warburg manometer are not free of this evil, and I cannot escape the feeling that the universality of investigations of O_2 and CO_2 exchange, to the exclusion of most other gases, is due to the limitations of the Warburg technique. It is to be hoped that the development of gas chromatography will bring as healthy a re-evaluation of the general problem of gas exchange as column and paper chromatography has achieved in the general field of metabolism.

Special mention should be made of the advances in the field of electron diffraction, which produced the electron microscope. This instrument has opened completely new possibilities in correlating structure and function, because it brings visibility down almost to the molecular level. The problem of cell growth has been revived by electron microscope studies of the cell wall, and it seems certain that in the next few years the function of cytoplasm, plastids, and nucleus will become much better understood with the help of the electron microscope. It is hard to believe now that in the 1920s it was generally accepted that no further improvements in microscopic observation could be expected. This shows how one simple conclusion of Dirac, that particle streams could have wave properties, has opened completely new horizons in biology.

As a plant physiologist one must regret that other branches of physics have not kept pace with the development of nuclear physics. It is certain that any new light which could be shed on the properties of water, on ion and electron transfer in solid and liquid phases, or on diffusion phenomena would be eagerly welcomed by physiologists and very likely would lead to important theoretical and practical advances in water-relation problems and cellular metabolism. A historical analysis like the foregoing practically proves this.

The relationships between physical chemistry and chemistry, on the one hand, and plant physiology, on the other hand, have traditionally been very close, and if possible have become still closer in the 20th century. Here again excesses have occurred, and applications have sometimes assumed fad-like proportions. In the 1920s pH measurements became a panacea for solving physiological problems, and at present many persons seem to labor under the misapprehension that plant physiology is identical with biochemistry. I would like to emphasize my personal conviction that physiology is the analysis and synthesis of life phenomena in terms of individual reactions or processes. Once such a reaction or process is isolated from the behavior of the organism as a whole, the biochemist or biophysicist can further identify the individual process. Without a proper physiological analysis, however, biochemical studies are meaningless. By diligent grinding of different plants a whole number of auxin-destroying and auxin-synthesizing enzymes have been discovered. Since the necessary physiological studies have not preceded—or even followed—the biochemical work, the significance of these enzymes in the life of the plant is a complete mystery, and thus this biochemical evidence has no obvious relation to our understanding of the functioning of the plant.

Among the most important advances in chemistry, which have had immediate significance for plant physiology, are in the first place Pregl's contributions to micro-chemistry. These opened the road toward the chemical identification of biologically active substances which usually are obtainable only in minute quantities. The identification of auxins *a* and *b* and of indoleacetic acid as plant-growth hormones by Kögl and Haagen Smit, or the analysis of traumatic acid as a plant-wound hormone by Bonner, English, and Haagen Smit, would have been impossible without such micro-methods. A more thorough study would have to take into account the separate contributions of analytical and synthetic chemistry, both so strongly influenced by the development of micro-chemistry, to plant physiology.

Of equal importance is the development of chromatography. Its foundation was laid by a plant physiologist, Tswett, who in 1906 separated the leaf pigments with an adsorption column. Chemists, such as Zechmeister, perfected this technique and made it applicable to an untold number of analytical chemical problems. It was especially when the adsorption-column chromatography was complemented with paper chromatography that it became fully effective in biological research. In conjunction with radio-active tracer technique, not only numerous metabolic products, but also metabolic pathways, can be identified. Much of the recent advance in our knowledge of photosynthesis is due to the application of these techniques, in the first place by Calvin and coworkers.

Radio-chemistry, based on the new nuclear physics, is the third in the triumvirate of new chemical techniques which are revolutionizing plant physiology. Not only have tracer elements become indispensable for biochemistry, but they are of equal importance in studies of translocation of organic and inorganic compounds inside the plant, of salt uptake, of root distribution in the soil, and of many other problems.

It is utterly impossible for me to be complete in the listing of new developments in chemistry which have contributed significantly to plant physiology. I could mention studies on the nature of the chemical bond, in thermodynamics, leading to a better understanding of the dynamics of chemical reactions inside the plant; the magnificent advances in spectroscopy; and many others; but I would be much amiss if I did not specifically enumerate high-polymer chemistry. It was again a plant physiologist, Sponsler, who opened the door to this field by his interpretation of the X-ray-diffraction pattern of cellulose. The more we come to know about the living system, the more we come to the conclusion that life is intimately linked with high polymers and macro-molecules: proteins, nucleic acids as functional units, cellulose and pectin as structural units, starch and inulin as energy storage.

It is not only the basic sciences which have furthered plant physiology. Cell physiological studies carried out mainly by zoologists have provided a basis for understanding of the plant cell as well. Plant pathology has provided plant physiologists with a magnificent experimental material, the crown gall.

RODNEY B. HARVEY, 1890–1945   DENNIS R. HOAGLAND, 1884–1949

FRANCIS E. LLOYD, 1868–1947   DANIEL T. MacDOUGAL, 1865–1958

Erwin Smith recognized the importance of crown gall in the study of normal and abnormal growth, and Braun, Riker, and many others have fully taken advantage of its excellence as experimental material. Microbiology has provided an inordinately great amount of stimulation to plant physiology, partly in connection with the biochemical reactions of the higher plant, and partly through the masterful studies of Van Niel on the photosynthetic bacteria, showing that H_2S or organic compounds perform the same function in the green and purple sulfur bacteria as water performs in higher plant photosynthesis, namely, that of a hydrogen donor.

Prompt and complete publication is an important prerequisite for the development of science. Throughout the 50 years under consideration the *Botanical Gazette* has nobly performed the function of an outlet for plant physiological papers. From 1914 on it was assisted by the *American Journal of Botany,* and 9 years later the establishment of *Plant Physiology* as the official publication of the American Society of Plant Physiologists provided a further outlet for publication. Whereas during the first years of their coexistence there was a keen sense of competition between the two botanical societies, at present there is complete cooperation between the Physiological Section of the Botanical Society of America and the American Society of Plant Physiologists, as evidenced by their joint programs at local and national meetings and the overlapping membership. In spite of the gradually expanding publication facilities for plant physiology in the U.S.A., the whole publication system is due for a thorough overhaul. Restrictive editorial policies are forcing an increasing number of American investigators to publish in foreign journals. If we are in a position to support research, we also should be able to support its publication.

Another aspect of publication is of paramount importance in the development of a science: textbooks. During the first quarter of this century translated textbooks such as those of Maximow or Palladin provided plant physiological information to students, whereas the big textbook of Pfeffer gave more details. The first extensive textbook of plant physiology published in America was that of Miller. Its emphasis on nutritional plant physiology reflected the significance of this branch in the U.S.A., but it was severely lacking in information about the responses of plants to their surroundings. Meyer and Anderson in 1939 provided a well-balanced text, which has done American plant physiology a signal service. But there is obviously the need for a more extensive and more detailed handbook.

The enormous growth of plant physiology during the last 50 years has been paralleled by the growth of research facilities. In most places plant physiology is housed in the buildings of the Botany or Biology departments, but there are also special laboratories for plant physiology. To mention just a few: the University of Iowa has a well-appointed laboratory built under the guidance of Dr. Loehwing. At the University of Chicago the Barnes Laboratory houses primarily plant physiologists, and at the California Institute of Technology the Dolk, Clark, and Earhart Laboratories provide unsurpassed facilities for plant physiological work. However, in general it would seem better to house plant physiologists together with other botanists and bio-chemists to stress the essential unity between these sciences.

Although it is true that a good scientist can always think up more research projects than he can get money for, financial support of plant physiological work in general can be considered adequate at present. It is only in regard to basic research that there are difficulties, in spite of the generous help from the Rockefeller Foundation, the Office of Naval Research, the Carnegie In-stitution of Washington, and the National Science Foundation. For instance, most of the money allotted for work on plant-growth regulators goes for prac-tical testing, leaving us still in the dark about the basic reactions which causes 2,4-D, for example, to be so toxic to plants.

During the 50 years of plant physiology here in the United States the proportion of work carried out in private universities and institutions has probably remained about the same. The greater amount of basic research still seems to emerge from privately financed institutions, although during the last 20 years the government has supported basic research in photo-periodism and plant-growth regulators on a very modest scale in Beltsville.

In spite of the fact that science is international in every aspect, it still is possible to discern special national traits in the work carried out in the United States. There is in general a greater emphasis on the problems which have practical implications. This is due to several factors. In the first place a greater proportion of the work is carried out in experiment stations, in contradistinc-tion to Europe where the proportion of contributions by the universities is greater. And in the second place there is usually more money available for practical problems. In the third place the American mind is more focused on problems which have a practical implication. This explains why during the first 10 years of plant-hormone research most of it was carried out in European universities. Seven years after I had carried out my experiments on auxin in the *Avena* coleoptile, I was asked pityingly by a group of young physiologists in one of our great universities whether I actually believed in plant hormones. This attitude changed completely when we could show that auxins not only regulated cell elongation but also controlled root formation and bud inhibition. Then later fruit set, weed control, and other functions of auxins made them practically so important that now America leads research in plant-growth regulators. For the same reason plant nutrition is leading other research sub-jects in the States. On the other hand, work on tropisms is definitely lagging here.

Teamwork has been developed more in the United States than in Europe, where the individualistic attitude of the scientist is more pronounced. The "Herr Professor" attitude of department heads is unthinkable here. Having a whole range of positions from Assistant to Instructor, Assistant Professor to full Professor does not make the latter stand out as a sort of half-god.

In discussing special problems in plant physiology during the last 50 years it is possible to use the book by Weevers, written to cover this same period, but not restricted to America.

In conclusion I want to mention some of the most outstanding achievements of plant physiology in the U.S.A. during the last 50 years. As mentioned earlier, plant nutrition was one of the subjects receiving early attention, largely because of its practical significance. But the contributions to this field by American physiologists soon surpassed the merely practical aspects. Probably most significant was the group of investigators which Hoagland organized in the College of Agriculture of the University of California in Berkeley. There the uptake of ions by the plant was studied from all possible angles, and for the last quarter century much of the progress in the field of plant nutrition was spearheaded by Hoagland's group, among whom I would like to mention Davis, Arnon, Stout, Barker, Jenny, Hassid, Broyer, and Ulrich, with F. C. Steward and others as visiting scientists. The recognition of zinc, molybdenum, and chlorine as essential elements in the nutrition of plants was due to teamwork, possible through the American genius of organization embodied in Hoagland, which leaves full room for personal expression yet integrates the individual efforts into something greater than the arithmetical sum of the contributions. Other laboratories have also contributed significantly to the problem of plant nutrition, such as the Rutgers group under Shive and the U.S. Salinity Laboratory in Riverside.

Problems of ion uptake by cells were studied in other directions also, e.g., by Osterhout and Blinks in connection with bioelectric potentials, by Brooks and Jacobs using the animal cell as a starting point, and by Thimann and Bonner and coworkers, employing the effects of auxins on water and ion uptake, and by F. C. Steward in connection with protein synthesis.

Another problem which received much attention in the early days of American plant physiology was that of water relations of plants. The investigations of Briggs and Shantz in this field are fundamental in determining the wilting percentage of soils in relation to crop plants and in measuring total water loss. From this work stemmed the development of the lysimeter. Livingston's name will always remain connected with his atmometer, providing a physical measurement of evaporative power, which can be directly compared with plant transpiration. Books like those by Crafts and Currier and by Kramer testify to the continued interest in these problems in the U.S.A.

Seed physiology was studied in the early days by Crocker and Shull, at the University of Chicago, and from this work the predilection of American physiologists for the lowly cocklebur (*Xanthium*) stems. When Crocker organized the Boyce Thompson Institute for Plant Research, germination problems remained among the favorite research problems which are sum-

JAMES B. OVERTON, 1869–1937

HOWARD S. REED, 1876–1950

HERMAN A. SPOEHR, 1885–1954

O. L. SPONSLER, 1879–1953

marized in Crocker and Barton's book. As in the rest of the world, the numerous seed-testing laboratories have contributed very little to our theoretical insight of germination problems. An exception to this general rule should be made for the investigations of both the Tooles at the U.S. Department of Agriculture, now joined by Hendricks and Borthwick in connection with the light sensitivity of germination of lettuce.

Fruit physiology, being of commercial importance in relation to shipping conditions and storage, has received much attention, as indicated by the studies of Harvey in Minnesota, Smock at Cornell, and most recently Biale at U.C.L.A., who has investigated especially the respiration behavior of fruits in connection with ripening: establishing the so-called climacteric in lemons, avocados, and a few other fruits.

Probably no other problem can claim such a high degree of American stimulation as that of flower induction. In their classical paper in 1920, Garner and Allard demonstrated that the length of daily illumination controlled the flowering behavior of a large number of plants, particularly annuals. From a theoretical point of view this discovery was of the greatest importance, because a morphogenetic process could thus be controlled experimentally. It is gratifying that the U.S.D.A., in whose laboratories this work was started, has continued its investigation in Beltsville under the direction of Borthwick, Parker, and Hendricks. But now everywhere in the United States and the rest of the world, photoperiodism is one of the most important research subjects. And there is hardly a Department of Horticulture where the flowering of flower crops is not being controlled by photoperiodic treatments.

In the same year, 1920, another important paper appeared on control of plant development, namely, one by Coville, in which he showed that dormancy of leaf and flower buds in deciduous plants could be broken by keeping the plants in the cold for several months. Soon afterward it was found that this chilling treatment can also induce flowering in many plants, such as sugar beets. Now chilling of seeds or plants (sometimes called vernalization) provides an experimental tool for research in plant development of equal importance to day-length treatments.

The pioneer investigators in the field of plant hormones and growth substances in this country were Dolk and Thimann at Cal Tech. When it became clear to what extent plant development could be controlled by chemical means, using auxins and chemically related compounds, suddenly from 1935 studies on plant-growth substances became very popular research subjects; and when it turned out that chemically related compounds were highly effective weed killers, all stops were pulled. To enumerate the principal investigators in the plant-growth-substance field would lead to a roster of American plant physiologists. Very active groups in this field are at the California Institute of Technology, the Boyce Thompson Institute of Plant Research, the U.S.D.A. Agricultural Research Center in Beltsville, the Army Chemical Corps, the

University of Wisconsin, a number of big chemical companies, and practically all agricultural experiment stations. Most of this work is directed toward application of chemical compounds, so that we do not have a good general theory explaining the action of these compounds. A more theoretical approach to the problem of the action of growth regulators is definitely the most important desideratum in this field.

As already mentioned earlier, photosynthesis has been investigated in a very active fashion, especially during the last quarter century. The approaches followed are the biophysics and biochemistry of CO_2 reduction, with little emphasis on the physiology of the process. Spoehr through his work on the photosynthesis of succulents started the work now carried out at the Stanford Laboratory of the Carnegie Institution of Washington by French, Smith, and coworkers. At the Universities of California, Utah, Wisconsin, Minnesota, Illinois, and Chicago, with Calvin, Arnon, Spikes, Stauffer, Brown, Rabinowitsch, Emerson, Franck, and Gaffron and coworkers much work is going on, whereas Van Niel at the Hopkins Marine Station advanced our knowledge about photosynthesis in general by studying this process in bacteria.

Especially during the last 10 years a most active group of investigators has dedicated itself to the study of plant biochemistry, with Vickery, Goddard, Bonner, Thimann, Hassid, Skoog, Steward, and hundreds of others working on the metabolism of the plant cell, following the pathways of respiration, protein and carbohydrate metabolism, the action of plant hormones, and many other subjects. Being such a young branch of plant physiology, it is hardly surprising that much of the work is still a checking of the extent to which the findings with animal materials can be applied to plants, but in the near future we can expect a real autochthonous Plant Biochemistry to emerge.

The subject of organ and tissue cultures is a typically American one, and P. White's name will always remain connected with plant-tissue cultures. He first succeeded in the unlimited culture of excised roots in a synthetic medium containing some yeast extract, and later made tissue cultures as well. This work is now carried on in many laboratories, where the yeast extract was found to be replaceable by Vitamins B_1 and B_6 and niacin for the growth of excised roots and by auxins for callus cultures.

Problems of radiation, apart from photoperiodism and photosynthesis, have found surprisingly little interest among American plant physiologists, with the Withrows as exceptions. In connection with the use of atomic energy a little work is carried out on plants. But subjects like phototropism are almost in abeyance in spite of the stimulation given to the subject by Galston.

A subject studied somewhat spasmodically here is the problem of translocation of organic and inorganic substances, and the names of Curtis, Crafts, Bennett, and Biddulph come to mind.

The problem of plant growth apart from its chemical control has received some attention by investigators such as MacDougal, Reed, and Kraus, and now the Earhart Plant Research Laboratory is reviving this interest. This is also the ideal place to study development of the plant in relation to its environment, or experimental Ecology. Men like Clements, Hall, Hiesey, Olmsted, and Weaver have been active in this field.

Many names of important plant physiologists have not been mentioned, either because they moved in so many different fields or because their significance lay especially in teaching. Let me mention, however, Barnes, True, Lloyd, Gustafson, Fuller, Robbins, Loomis, and Loehwing.

Thus, in the short span of 50 years, plant physiology has grown in the United States from a small beginning, when it received most of its inspiration from Europe, to a fully autonomous science, strongly supported because of its significance as a basic science for so many of the applied botanical fields. Being myself from the West Coast, I probably have overstressed the importance of contributions from there, but even an impartial evaluation will show that a remarkably high percentage of superior contributions come from there.

For the future let us look forward to a further period of steady growth of plant physiology, for the sake of gaining a better understanding of the world around us, and to help the applied botanical disciplines in making plants serve us better. To this end we should cooperate to the fullest extent with each other and with our colleagues in the applied fields and obtain further cooperation from the sciences which are basic to ours. But perhaps even more than doing more and better research, we should pay much attention to the teaching of plant physiology so that we will see our ranks swelled with eager young colleagues, not only fully trained, but also full of enthusiasm and imagination. To this end our individual efforts are not enough; strong botanical societies are needed for coordination of our efforts.

Index